Maura H.

Illustrations Credits

All illustrations © K12 Inc. unless otherwise noted

Elephant. © Photodisc/Getty Images
Water buffalo. © Dynamic Graphics/Jupiterimages
Elk. © Photos.com/Jupiterimages
Moose. © Dmark3/Dreamstime
Bison. © Jupiterimages
Polar bear. © Warren Jacobi/Corbis
Black bear. © Photodisc/Getty Images
Giraffe. © Photos.com/Jupiterimages

About K12 Inc.

K12 Inc., a technology-based education company, is the nation's leading provider of proprietary curriculum and online education programs to students in grades K–12. K^{12} provides its curriculum and academic services to online schools, traditional classrooms, blended school programs, and directly to families. K12 Inc. also operates the K^{12} International Academy, an accredited, diploma-granting online private school serving students worldwide. K^{12}'s mission is to provide any child the curriculum and tools to maximize success in life, regardless of geographic, financial, or demographic circumstances. K12 Inc. is accredited by CITA. More information can be found at www.K12.com.

ISBN: 1-60153-084-6
Printed by RR Donnelley, Shenzhen, China, March 2011, Lot 032011

Contents

Whole Number Multiplication Sense

Whole Number Multiplication

Whole Number Division Sense

Whole Number Division

Semester Review and Checkpoint

Whole Numbers and Multiple Operations

Geometry

Decimals and Money

Fractions and Probability

Measurement: Length and Time

Measurement: Capacity and Weight

Mathematical Reasoning

Perimeter, Area, and Volume

Semester Review and Checkpoint

Glossary

Program Overview

Lesson Overview

The table at the beginning of each lesson tells you what activities are in the lesson and whether students are on the computer (**ONLINE**) or at a table or desk (**OFFLINE**). The expected time for each activity is given.

Objectives and Prerequisite Skills

Each lesson teaches the Lesson Objectives. The lesson assumes that students know the Prerequisite Skills from their previous math experience. The Get Ready activity is designed to remind students of the prerequisite skills, and to prepare them for the lesson.

Content Background

The Content Background tells you what students will learn in the lesson, and it explains any complex math concepts, putting the lesson into perspective with wider math knowledge.

Advance Preparation

Some lessons require preparation that extends beyond gathering materials. In these cases, the lesson includes an Advance Preparation section.

Materials

This box tells you what materials students will need in the lesson. More information about the materials is included on page x.

Understand Multiplication

Lesson Overview

GET READY Model Multiplication	10 minutes	OFFLINE
LEARN Effect of Multiplication	15 minutes	OFFLINE
LEARN Multiplication Patterns	15 minutes	OFFLINE
TRY IT Multiplication Results	10 minutes	OFFLINE
CHECKPOINT	10 minutes	ONLINE

▶ Lesson Objectives
Demonstrate an understanding of how multiplication affects whole numbers.

▶ Prerequisite Skills
Use objects or sketches to solve a multiplication problem.

▶ Content Background
Students may already have a basic knowledge of multiplication and understand how to model and solve multiplication problems. In this lesson, they will learn how multiplication affects whole numbers, gaining an understanding that with multiplication, the product is usually greater than the factors. They will explore multiplying by 1 and zero and the effects of those numbers on the product. They will identify patterns of multiples. (For example, multiples of 2 are even numbers; multiples of 5 end in the digit 5 or zero; and multiples of 10 end in the digit zero.) Seeing these general patterns will help students develop a broader understanding of mathematics. Students will be introduced to the term *multiples* and will learn that when they skip count by 10s, starting at zero, they are saying the multiples of 10.

▶ Common Errors and Misconceptions
Students might not understand that the two factors in a multiplication expression have different meanings. For example, 3 sets of 6 dots is written as 3 × 6, not 6 × 3. However, the product of each expression is 18.

▶ Advance Preparation
Print the Hundred Chart, and use the Number Line Creator Tool to print a page with four number lines from 0 to 20.

DIRECTIONS FOR USING THE NUMBER LINE CREATOR TOOL
To create number lines from 0 to 20:

1. Set Range:	2. Select Options:	3. Print Number Line:
• Start Number Line at: 0	• Tick Marks: ones	• Page Orientation: landscape
• End Number Line at: 20	• Labels: ones	• Number Lines per Sheet: 4

Materials to Gather

SUPPLIED
number lines from the Number Line Creator Tool
base-10 blocks
Hundred Chart (printout)
Multiplication Results activity page

124 WHOLE NUMBER MULTIPLICATION SENSE

Common Errors and Misconceptions

Research shows that students might misunderstand certain concepts, which then leads to misunderstanding of more advanced concepts. When certain research applies to a lesson, the lesson has a Common Errors and Misconceptions section.

Materials

K[12] supplies math materials, including this Lesson Guide and the Activity Book, the student book.

The **block set** includes various counters as well as 2-D and 3-D shapes. Note that the blocks are labeled with letters. The materials lists in each lesson refer to these blocks by their letter (for instance, B blocks or BB blocks or C blocks). The O blocks refer to the cubes. These blocks aren't labeled with the letter O, but the hole in each block resembles this letter. Within the lesson, you might see a more descriptive term, such as "circles" for the B blocks. A set of base-10 blocks contains blocks representing ones, tens, and hundreds.

Printouts, Plastic Sheet Cover, and Dry-Erase Markers

A lesson may ask you to print a document showing a number line, place-value chart, or other math tool. These documents will be reused throughout the course. We recommend that you obtain a plastic sheet cover and dry-erase markers so students can place the sheet over the printout and write answers on the sheet. They can then erase the answers and reuse the printout multiple times.

Important: Some printouts, including graded Checkpoints, require students to measure shapes or angles. By default, many printers scale documents to fit to a printable area. Be sure to turn off page scaling so that documents print at 100% of their intended size.

Number and Symbol Cards

Index cards labeled with numbers or symbols are frequently called for in the lessons. We recommend that you create a set of index cards numbered 0–100, and use them throughout the course. You can also create the symbols that will be used most frequently: − (minus), + (plus), = (equals), > (greater than), < (less than).

Math Notebook, Paper, and Pencil

Obtain a binder or spiral notebook to serve as the Math Notebook in which students will work problems, make sketches, and write answers to the problems in the Activity Book. Students should always have notebook paper and a pencil handy. These materials are not listed in each lesson.

Also Needed

Other common items are called for in lessons, designated in the materials list as "Also Needed." Gather or purchase these materials, such as a ruler, scissors, and index cards.

Working Through a Lesson

When you go online with students to do a math lesson, you will see a list of the activities that are included in the lesson. Some lessons begin with a Skills Update. Skills Updates are online activities that focus on previously learned math skills or addition, subtraction, multiplication, or division facts. *Required* Skills Updates are noted in the Lesson Guide. *Optional* Skills Updates appear online only. Students should complete Skills Updates independently.

The Lesson Guide gives an overview of the remaining lesson activities. Instructions for online activities are online. Students may complete these activities independently, or you may sit at the computer with them, reading text to them as necessary. The Lesson Guide may include a teaching tip or other information. In some cases, such as when an open-ended Learning Tool is used, there will be instructions to follow in the Lesson Guide. The online screen will guide you to follow these instructions.

Instructions for offline activities are in the Lesson Guide. These activities may use supplied or common materials, and some include pages from the Activity Book.

Types of Activities

Skills Update   Short problem set covering topics taught in previous units or game to build fluency, or speed, with math facts. Skills Updates are online and may be required or optional. Required Skills Updates are listed in the Lesson Guide.

Get Ready   Review of previous math knowledge that will be needed for this lesson. The Get Ready activities can be online or offline.

Learn   Presentation of math concepts, or guided practice. The Learn activities can be online or offline.

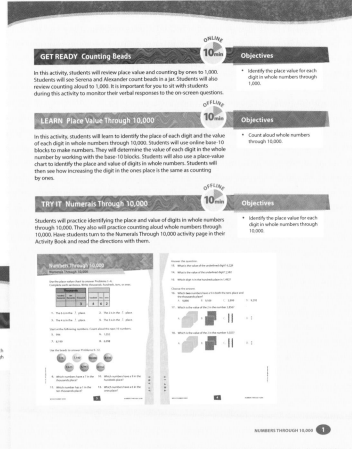

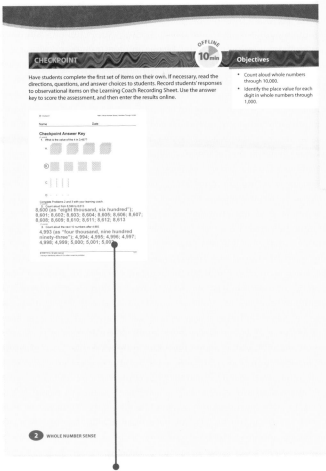

The Lesson Guide includes the answers, shown in magenta, to the Activity Book pages and offline Checkpoints.

Try It   Practice problems on the concepts taught in the lesson. Students should complete these problems independently. The Try It activities can be online or in the Activity Book.

Checkpoint   Assessments of whether students have learned the objectives taught in the lesson or lessons. Not every lesson has a Checkpoint. In some Checkpoints, students show or explain their answers, and you record their performance.

In addition to the regular Checkpoints, **Unit Reviews** and **Unit Checkpoints** are lessons at the end of each unit. Each semester ends with a **Semester Review** and **Semester Checkpoint**.

Online Activities

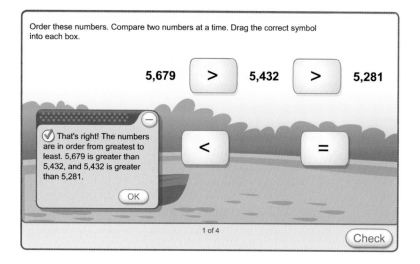

Online activities will show whether students answered correctly.

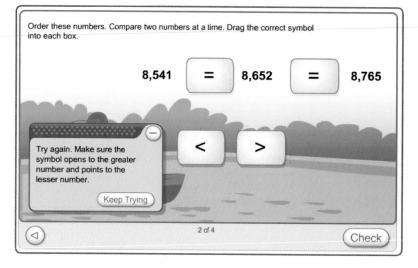

If students answer incorrectly, they will see feedback. They should click Keep Trying to try again. If they answer incorrectly a second time, they can click Show Me to see the correct answer.

Learning Tools are online activities that you set up to give students math exercises that will apply to what they are learning in a specific lesson.

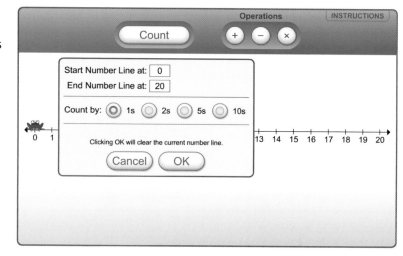

Whole Number Sense

$876 = $ 8 hundreds $+$ 7 tens $+$ 6 ones

- Identify the place value for each digit in whole numbers through 10,000.
- Count aloud whole numbers through 10,000.
- Identify odd and even numbers and describe their characteristics.
- Read whole numbers through 10,000.
- Write numerals through 10,000.
- Write number words through 10,000.
- Use expanded form to represent numbers through 10,000.
- Demonstrate understanding of place vales as cumulative multiples of 10.
- Compare whole numbers through 10,000.
- Order three or more whole numbers through 10,000.
- Round numbers through 10,000.

▶ Big Ideas

Place-value notation makes it easier to write and operate on large numbers.

▶ Unit Introduction

In this unit, students will continue their journey through numbers all the way up to 10,000. They will start with place value and counting and then will look at odd and even numbers and their characteristics. Students will read and write numbers and number words, including writing numbers in expanded form. Students will also learn to see place values as "cumulative multiples of 10." They will round out this unit with rounding! Students will learn how to round numbers to the nearest ten, hundred, and thousand.

▶ Keywords

boundary number	greater-than symbol ($>$)	place-value chart
compare	less-than symbol ($<$)	place-value mat
digit	multiple	place-value period
divide	odd numbers	round (v.)
even numbers	place value	standard form
expanded form		

Numbers Through 10,000

Lesson Overview

GET READY Counting Beads	10 minutes	ONLINE
LEARN Place Value Through 10,000	20 minutes	ONLINE
LEARN Count to 10,000	10 minutes	OFFLINE
TRY IT Numerals Through 10,000	10 minutes	OFFLINE
CHECKPOINT	10 minutes	OFFLINE

▶ Lesson Objectives
- Identify the place value for each digit in whole numbers through 10,000.
- Count aloud whole numbers through 10,000.

▶ Prerequisite Skills
- Identify the place value for each digit in whole numbers through 1,000.
- Count aloud whole numbers through 1,000.

▶ Content Background

Students will learn to identify the place and value of digits in numbers through 10,000. Students will also learn to count aloud numbers through 10,000, starting at any number less than 10,000.

The smallest base-10 block is a ones cube. It has a value of 1. Ten ones cubes combine to make a tens rod. It has a value of 10. Ten tens rods combine to make a hundreds flat. It has a value of 100. Ten hundreds flats combine to make a thousands cube. It has a value of 1,000. Students can use these blocks to model and represent numbers.

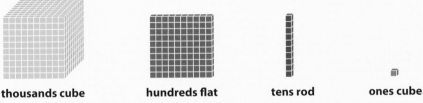

thousands cube   **hundreds flat**   **tens rod**   **ones cube**

Students often struggle to understand the value of each digit in a number. They may incorrectly say that the greatest digit in a number has the greatest value. First, students must understand that the numbers 0 through 9 are called *digits*. The digits 0 through 9 can be used to write any number in the base-10 system. The math term *digit* refers to a specific number within another number.

Example: In the number 591, there are three digits: 5, 9, and 1.

Materials to Gather

SUPPLIED

Count to 10,000 activity page
Numerals Through 10,000 activity page
Checkpoint (printout)
place-value mat
base-10 blocks

Thousands				hundreds	tens	ones
hundred thousands	ten thousands	thousands				
		3	,	4	6	2

The place where a digit is located is its *place value*. Once students are able to identify the place value of each digit in whole numbers to 10,000, they can then use the place value to determine the digit's value. For example, in the number 254, the 2 is in the hundreds place and has a value of 200.

Starting from right to left, each group of three digits (or place-value positions) in a whole number is called a *place-value period*. Commas separate each period and are useful when reading greater whole numbers correctly.

▶ Common Errors and Misconceptions

- Students might not realize that a digit's place-value position determines its value. For example, students might think the digits in 14 have values of 1 and 4, not 10 and 4.

- Students might not think of numbers as groups of tens, hundreds, and so forth. For example, students might think of 24 only as 24 single units, not 2 tens and 4 ones.

- Students might have difficulty thinking of numbers as groups of tens, hundreds, and so forth because some English number words do not emphasize place value. For example, the number word *twelve* does not suggest 1 ten and 2 ones.

- Students might have difficulty thinking of numbers as groups of tens, hundreds, and so forth because the teaching of place-value concepts often moves too quickly to the use of abstract symbols.

▶ Safety

Be sure students have ample space to work with the base-10 blocks.

GET READY Counting Beads

ONLINE
10min

Objectives

- Identify the place value for each digit in whole numbers through 1,000.

- Count aloud whole numbers through 1,000.

Students will review counting by ones to 1,000. They will see Serena and Alexander count beads in a jar. As the beads appear, have students count aloud. First students will start at 1 and count forward to 10. Then they'll jump to 297 and count forward to 300. After that, they'll go to 995 and count forward to 1,000. Students will then review place value and see why 3 and 300 are so different. Finally they will identify the place value of the digits in a three-digit number.

It is important for you to sit with students during this activity to monitor their counting and responses to on-screen questions.

If students are having difficulty counting numbers in the hundreds, have them practice counting 2-digit numbers. Remind students that counting by ones follows a pattern. The digit in the ones place increases by one each time you count forward.

LEARN Place Value Through 10,000

Objectives

- Identify the place value for each digit in whole numbers through 10,000.

Students will learn to identify the place and value of each digit in whole numbers through 10,000. They will use online base-10 blocks to make numbers. They will determine the value of each digit in the whole number by working with the base-10 blocks. Students will also use a place-value chart to identify the place and value of digits in whole numbers. They will then see how increasing the digit in the ones place is the same as counting by ones.

Tips Emphasize the importance and use of the comma in 4- and 5-digit numbers to separate the thousands period. Knowing how to place the comma will help students work with reading and writing greater numbers in future lessons.

LEARN Count to 10,000

Objectives

- Count aloud whole numbers through 10,000.

Students will learn to count whole numbers through 10,000. They will use base-10 blocks and a place-value chart to model numbers and show counting by ones.
  Gather the base-10 blocks and place-value mat.

1. Begin by practicing counting aloud by ones from 0 to 50. Explain the pattern for counting by ones.

   Say: The digit in the ones place increases by one for 0 through 9. Then we regroup the ones to make a 10, and the digit in the ones place becomes 0.

   Emphasize that counting by ones will always produce this pattern, even when counting greater numbers.

2. Have students use base-10 blocks to model the number 1,836 on their place-value mat. Tell students the number is one thousand, eight hundred thirty-six.

3. Ask students to identify the ones place and the digit in the ones place. Tell students that when we count by ones, the digit in the ones place increases by one.

4. Have students add ones cubes, one at a time, to the ones place. Count aloud with students each time a ones cube is added to the place-value mat. Continue counting forward to 1,850. Remember to regroup 10 ones to make 1 ten each time there are 10 ones in the ones place.

5. Next make the number 1,996, using base-10 blocks, on the place-value mat. Continue counting forward to 2,012, adding ones cubes to the place-value mat and regrouping when needed. Have students use 10 of their hundreds flats to make a second thousands cube.

6. When students are comfortable using the base-10 blocks to count by ones, practice counting aloud without the blocks. Start at the following numbers: 5,000; 5,384; 9,500; 9,750; and 9,987. Count forward 15 to 20 numbers each time. Students should identify when they go across place values.

7. Have students turn to the Count to 10,000 activity page in their Activity Book and read the directions with them. Students should copy the problems from the Activity Book into their Math Notebook as necessary and solve them there.

Tips

If students are having difficulty counting greater numbers, have them practice counting 2- and 3-digit numbers by ones. Recognizing the pattern in the ones place when counting by ones is an important skill. Students can continue to model numbers using a place-value mat and base-10 blocks until they understand and can explain the pattern.

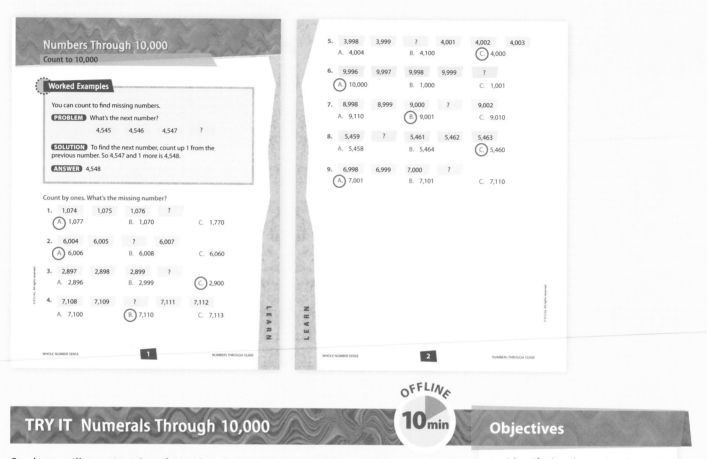

Numbers Through 10,000
Count to 10,000

Worked Examples

You can count to find missing numbers.

PROBLEM What's the next number?

| 4,545 | 4,546 | 4,547 | ? |

SOLUTION To find the next number, count up 1 from the previous number. So 4,547 and 1 more is 4,548.

ANSWER 4,548

Count by ones. What's the missing number?

1. 1,074 1,075 1,076 ?
   (A) 1,077   B. 1,070   C. 1,770

2. 6,004 6,005 ? 6,007
   (A) 6,006   B. 6,008   C. 6,060

3. 2,897 2,898 2,899 ?
   A. 2,896   B. 2,999   (C) 2,900

4. 7,108 7,109 ? 7,111 7,112
   A. 7,100   (B.) 7,110   C. 7,113

5. 3,998 3,999 ? 4,001 4,002 4,003
   A. 4,004   B. 4,100   (C) 4,000

6. 9,996 9,997 9,998 9,999 ?
   (A) 10,000   B. 1,000   C. 1,001

7. 8,998 8,999 9,000 ? 9,002
   A. 9,110   (B.) 9,001   C. 9,010

8. 5,459 ? 5,461 5,462 5,463
   A. 5,458   B. 5,464   (C) 5,460

9. 6,998 6,999 7,000 ?
   (A) 7,001   B. 7,101   C. 7,110

LEARN

LEARN

OFFLINE
10 min

TRY IT Numerals Through 10,000

Objectives

Students will practice identifying the place and value of digits in whole numbers through 10,000. They also will practice counting aloud whole numbers through 10,000. Have students turn to the Numerals Through 10,000 activity page in their Activity Book and read the directions with them.

Students should copy the problems from the Activity Book into their Math Notebook as necessary and solve them there.

- Identify the place value for each digit in whole numbers through 10,000.
- Count aloud whole numbers through 10,000.

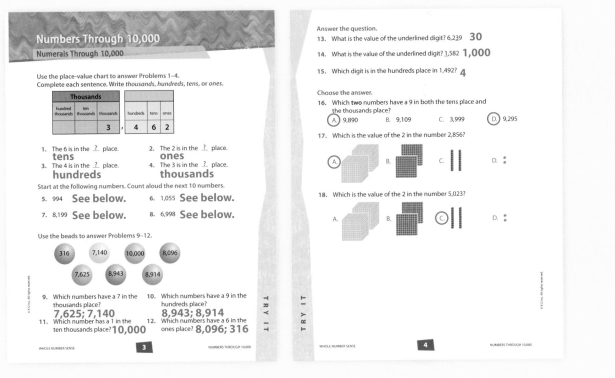

Numbers Through 10,000
Numerals Through 10,000

Use the place-value chart to answer Problems 1–4.
Complete each sentence. Write *thousands, hundreds, tens,* or *ones.*

Thousands					
hundred thousands	ten thousands	thousands	hundreds	tens	ones
		3	4	6	2

1. The 6 is in the ? place. **tens**
2. The 2 is in the ? place. **ones**
3. The 4 is in the ? place. **hundreds**
4. The 3 is in the ? place. **thousands**

Start at the following numbers. Count aloud the next 10 numbers.

5. 994 **See below.**
6. 1,055 **See below.**
7. 8,199 **See below.**
8. 6,998 **See below.**

Use the beads to answer Problems 9–12.

316　7,140　10,000　8,096
7,625　8,943　8,914

9. Which numbers have a 7 in the thousands place? **7,625; 7,140**
10. Which numbers have a 9 in the hundreds place? **8,943; 8,914**
11. Which number has a 1 in the ten thousands place? **10,000**
12. Which numbers have a 6 in the ones place? **8,096; 316**

WHOLE NUMBER SENSE　　3　　NUMBERS THROUGH 10,000

TRY IT

Answer the question.

13. What is the value of the underlined digit? 6,2<u>3</u>9　**30**
14. What is the value of the underlined digit? <u>1</u>,582　**1,000**
15. Which digit is in the hundreds place in 1,492?　**4**

Choose the answer.

16. Which **two** numbers have a 9 in both the tens place and the thousands place?
    - (A.) 9,890
    - B. 9,109
    - C. 3,999
    - (D.) 9,295

17. Which is the value of the 2 in the number 2,856?
    - (A)
    - B.
    - C.
    - D.

18. Which is the value of the 2 in the number 5,023?
    - A.
    - B.
    - (C)
    - D.

WHOLE NUMBER SENSE　　4　　NUMBERS THROUGH 10,000

TRY IT

Additional Answers

5. 995; 996; 997; 998; 999; 1,000; 1,001; 1,002; 1,003; 1,004

6. 1,056; 1,057; 1,058; 1,059; 1,060; 1,061; 1,062; 1,063; 1,064; 1,065

7. 8,200; 8,201; 8,202; 8,203; 8,204; 8,205; 8,206; 8,207; 8,208; 8,209

8. 6,999; 7,000; 7,001; 7,002; 7,003; 7,004; 7,005; 7,006; 7,007; 7,008

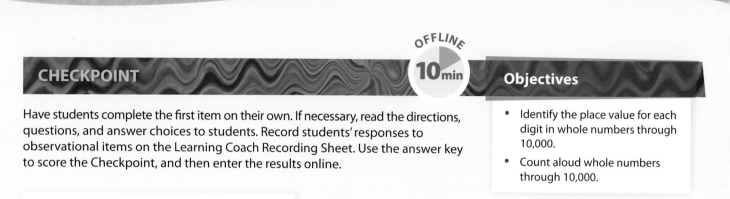

CHECKPOINT

OFFLINE 10 min

Objectives

- Identify the place value for each digit in whole numbers through 10,000.
- Count aloud whole numbers through 10,000.

Have students complete the first item on their own. If necessary, read the directions, questions, and answer choices to students. Record students' responses to observational items on the Learning Coach Recording Sheet. Use the answer key to score the Checkpoint, and then enter the results online.

✪ Checkpoint   Math | Whole Number Sense | Numbers Through 10,000

Name _____ Date _____

Checkpoint Answer Key

(1 point)
1. What is the value of the 4 in 3,457?

A.

Ⓑ

C.

D.

Complete Problems 2 and 3 with your learning coach.
(1 point)
2. Count aloud from 8,599 to 8,613.

8,600 (as "eight thousand, six hundred");
8,601; 8,602; 8,603; 8,604; 8,605; 8,606; 8,607;
8,608; 8,609; 8,610; 8,611; 8,612; 8,613

(1 point)
3. Count aloud the next 10 numbers after 4,992.

4,993 (as "four thousand, nine hundred
ninety-three"); 4,994; 4,995; 4,996; 4,997;
4,998; 4,999; 5,000; 5,001; 5,002

1 of 1

Odd and Even Numbers

Lesson Overview		
Skills Update	5 minutes	ONLINE
GET READY Numbers to 100	5 minutes	ONLINE
LEARN Sort Odd and Even Numbers	15 minutes	ONLINE
LEARN Sums of Odd and Even Numbers	15 minutes	OFFLINE
TRY IT Odd or Even?	10 minutes	OFFLINE
CHECKPOINT	10 minutes	ONLINE

▶ Lesson Objectives

Identify odd and even numbers and describe their characteristics.

▶ Prerequisite Skills

Count by 2s though 100.

▶ Content Background

Students will learn to identify numbers as odd or even by looking at the last digit in the number. They will also use B blocks to see that even numbers can be divided evenly into two groups while odd numbers cannot. Students will make conclusions about the sums and differences of even and odd numbers.

Recognizing patterns in the number system, such as odd and even numbers, helps students solve a variety of problems more easily. An even number of objects can be divided into two equal groups. An even number always ends with one of the even digits: 0, 2, 4, 6, or 8. An odd number of objects cannot be divided into two equal groups. There will always be one object left over. An odd number always ends with one of the odd digits: 1, 3, 5, 7, or 9.

▶ Advance Preparation

Label index cards with the following numbers, one per card: 5, 6, 6, 8, 9, 9. Label 5 more index cards **even** and 4 cards **odd**.

Materials to Gather

SUPPLIED

blocks – B (all colors)

Odd or Even? activity page

ALSO NEEDED

index cards – 15, labeled

GET READY Numbers to 100

ONLINE 5min

Objectives

- Count by 2s through 100.

Students will use the Number Line Learning Tool to review skip counting odd and even numbers. The learning tool has audio for numbers being counted.

DIRECTIONS FOR USING THE NUMBER LINE LEARNING TOOL

1. Click Count and choose the following:
   - Start Number Line at: 0
   - End Number Line at: 30
   - Count by: 2s

   Click OK.

2. Students should click each number to count by 2s. As they click each number, the frog will hop to the number and it will be said aloud. The number line will slide over automatically when necessary to display more numbers. When they reach 30, students should click Count Again and repeat.

3. Repeat Steps 1 and 2 with the following selections. (Students will count by 2s again, but this time they'll count by odd numbers for two of the number lines.) Click Count to change the number line.
   - 1–21
   - 74–100
   - 51–75

LEARN Sort Odd and Even Numbers

ONLINE 15min

Objectives

- Identify odd and even numbers and describe their characteristics.

Tips

Students can also use the Hundred Chart printout to color odd and even numbers.

Students will explore odd and even numbers. They will use the online Hundred Chart Learning Tool. By shading odd and even numbers on a hundred chart, they will begin to recognize that for even numbers the digit in the ones place is alway 0, 2, 4, 6, or 8, and for odd numbers the digit in the ones place is always 1, 3, 5, 7, or 9. Students will then do an activity in which they will try to make even groups of objects. They'll see that an even number of objects can always be separated into two equal groups, but an odd number of objects can never be separated into equal groups. They'll learn that if you try to show an odd number of objects in two equal groups, there is always one left over.

DIRECTIONS FOR USING THE HUNDRED CHART LEARNING TOOL

1. First, have students identify the even numbers on the chart. Have them click the pink paint choice and count by 2s on the chart, starting at 0 and clicking every other number as they count aloud. When they click, the number will be highlighted in pink and will be said aloud. If an incorrect number is clicked, simply have them click it again to remove the color. When they marked all the even numbers, have them click the speaker icon to hear the numbers counted aloud.

2. Next, have students identify the odd numbers on the chart. Have them click the blue paint choice and count by 2s on the chart, starting with 1. Have them count aloud as they click every second number. When they have marked all the odd numbers, have them click the speaker icon to hear the numbers counted aloud.

3. Have students look for patterns on the chart.
   Examples: the numbers appear in columns on the chart; even numbers end in 0, 2, 4, 6, or 8 and odd numbers end in 1, 3, 5, 7, or 9

LEARN Sums of Odd and Even Numbers

Students will continue to explore even and odd numbers. They have seen that you can separate an even number of objects into two equal groups, but if you try to separate an odd number of objects into two equal groups, there is always one left over. Students will use circle blocks to recognize the following:

- If two even numbers are added, the sum is even.
- If two odd numbers are added, the sum is even.
- If an even number and an odd number are added, the sum is odd.

Gather the circle blocks and the index cards you prepared.

ADDING EVEN NUMBERS

1. Tell students they will explore the sums of even and odd numbers. Remind them that a sum is the answer to an addition problem and is found by combining two groups.

2. Place the 6 card on a desk or table. Ask students if this number even or odd, then place an even card to the right, leaving room for the circles.

   Have student show that 6 is even by counting 6 yellow circles and placing them in pairs as shown.

   Remind students that even numbers can be shown in two equal groups. Ask students to point out the two equal groups. (Each column is a group.)

3. Place the index card with the 8 on the desk or table as shown. Ask students if 8 is even or odd. Have students place an even card across from the 8. Have students count 8 yellow circles and place them in pairs to show 8 as two equal groups.

4. Ask students to look at the circles. Explain that if you combine the 6 circles and the 8 circles, they form a total that can be shown as two equal groups. (Slide the circles closer to each other.) This shows the total must be an even number. Point out that you don't have to count how many there are to see that it's an even amount because you can see two equal groups.

5. Have students count the total to verify that it is an even number. 14
   Tell students we know that any time you combine two even numbers, you get an even number, because the two columns always form two equal groups.

6. Test the rule that whenever you add two even numbers, you get an even number. Choose numbers that are easy to add with mental arithmetic and see if the sum is always an even number. Try $10 + 8$, $20 + 30$, and $100 + 44$. Students should become convinced that whenever two even numbers are added, the sum is even.

Objectives

- Identify odd and even numbers and describe their characteristics.

Tips

You can extend this activity by allowing students to add greater numbers. Ask students to find the sum of $34 + 38$, $51 + 29$, and $42 + 37$ and predict whether the sum will be even or odd.

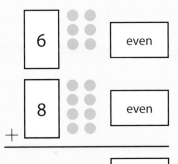

ADDING ODD NUMBERS

7. Repeat Steps 2 and 3 with two odd numbers, 5 and 9, as shown. Place the 5 card and ask if it is even or odd. Have students place the appropriate cards.

   Have students place 5 blue circles, arranging them in pairs. The fifth circle will not be part of a matching pair. This unmatched circle is what makes the number odd. Replace that fifth circle with a red circle, placing it as shown.

8. Place the 9 card and have students count out 9 blue circles, arranging them in pairs. The ninth circle will not have a match. Have students replace the ninth circle with a red circle, placing it as shown.

9. Have students observe what happens when you combine the two odd numbers. Slide the circles from the two numbers closer so that the unmatched circles for each number come together to form a pair. Tell students that the total forms two equal groups and is therefore an even number. This is true whenever two odd numbers are added together.

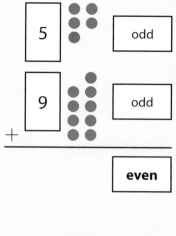

ADDING AN EVEN NUMBER AND AN ODD NUMBER

10. Repeat Steps 2 and 3 with an even number, 6, and an odd number, 9. Work through the problem as before. Have students notice that when they combine the two sets of circles, the total will have a circle with no match. This makes the sum odd.

11. Have students repeat Step 10 using other pairs of even and odd numbers. Pick numbers that are easy to add with mental arithmetic. Students should recognize that if an even number and an odd number are shown with circles, there will always be one circle without a match. So the sum will always be odd.

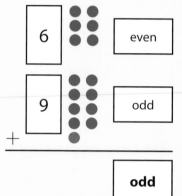

TRY IT Odd or Even?

OFFLINE
10min

Students will practice identifying numbers and sums as odd or even. Have students turn to the Odd or Even? activity page in their Activity Book and read the directions with them.

Students should copy the problems from the Activity Book into their Math Notebook as necessary and solve them there.

Objectives

- Identify odd and even numbers and describe their characteristics.

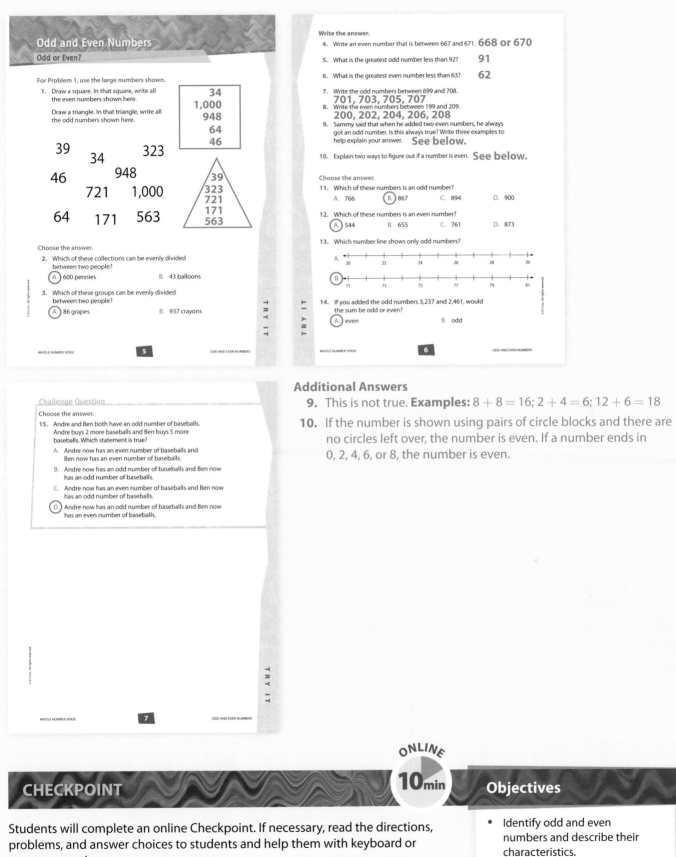

Odd and Even Numbers
Odd or Even?

For Problem 1, use the large numbers shown.

1. Draw a square. In that square, write all the even numbers shown here.

   Draw a triangle. In that triangle, write all the odd numbers shown here.

39   34   323
46   948
721   1,000
64   171   563

34
1,000
948
64
46

39
323
721
171
563

Choose the answer.

2. Which of these collections can be evenly divided between two people?

   A. 600 pennies   B. 43 balloons

3. Which of these groups can be evenly divided between two people?

   A. 86 grapes   B. 937 crayons

WHOLE NUMBER SENSE   **5**   ODD AND EVEN NUMBERS

TRY IT

Write the answer.

4. Write an even number that is between 667 and 671. **668 or 670**

5. What is the greatest odd number less than 92?   **91**

6. What is the greatest even number less than 63?   **62**

7. Write the odd numbers between 699 and 708.
   701, 703, 705, 707

8. Write the even numbers between 199 and 209.
   200, 202, 204, 206, 208

9. Sammy said that when he added two even numbers, he always got an odd number. Is this always true? Write three examples to help explain your answer.   **See below.**

10. Explain two ways to figure out if a number is even.   **See below.**

Choose the answer.

11. Which of these numbers is an odd number?

    A. 766   B. 867   C. 894   D. 900

12. Which of these numbers is an even number?

    A. 544   B. 655   C. 761   D. 873

13. Which number line shows only odd numbers?

    A.   20 22 24 26 28 30

    B.   71 73 75 77 79 81

14. If you added the odd numbers 3,237 and 2,461, would the sum be odd or even?

    A. even   B. odd

WHOLE NUMBER SENSE   **6**   ODD AND EVEN NUMBERS

TRY IT

Challenge Question

Choose the answer.

15. Andre and Ben both have an odd number of baseballs. Andre buys 2 more baseballs and Ben buys 5 more baseballs. Which statement is true?

    A. Andre now has an even number of baseballs and Ben now has an even number of baseballs.

    B. Andre now has an odd number of baseballs and Ben now has an odd number of baseballs.

    C. Andre now has an even number of baseballs and Ben now has an odd number of baseballs.

    D. Andre now has an odd number of baseballs and Ben now has an even number of baseballs.

WHOLE NUMBER SENSE   **7**   ODD AND EVEN NUMBERS

TRY IT

Additional Answers

9. This is not true. **Examples:** $8 + 8 = 16$; $2 + 4 = 6$; $12 + 6 = 18$

10. If the number is shown using pairs of circle blocks and there are no circles left over, the number is even. If a number ends in 0, 2, 4, 6, or 8, the number is even.

CHECKPOINT

ONLINE
10 min

Students will complete an online Checkpoint. If necessary, read the directions, problems, and answer choices to students and help them with keyboard or mouse operations.

Objectives

- Identify odd and even numbers and describe their characteristics.

Read and Write Numerals Through 10,000

Lesson Overview

Skills Update	5 minutes	ONLINE
GET READY Read Numbers Through 1,000	5 minutes	ONLINE
LEARN Read Numbers Through 10,000	15 minutes	ONLINE
LEARN Write Numerals Through 10,000	20 minutes	OFFLINE
TRY IT Write and Read Numerals	15 minutes	OFFLINE

▶ Lesson Objectives

- Read whole numbers through 10,000.
- Write numerals through 10,000.

Materials to Gather

SUPPLIED

Write and Read Numerals activity page

▶ Prerequisite Skills

- Read whole numbers through 1,000.
- Write numerals through 1,000.
- Identify the place value for each digit in whole numbers through 10,000.

▶ Content Background

Students will learn how to read and write numerals through 10,000.

In mathematics, a *number* represents a quantity and a *numeral* is a symbol we use to describe the quantity. Therefore, a number, such as 1, or 32, or 546, is a symbol that represents a number. In everyday language, we use *number* to describe both the symbol and the quantity. As you speak with students, you may use *number*. In this lesson, *numeral* is used to convey correct mathematical terminology.

Students will learn to write numerals with commas between each period, or group of three digits. In this course, numbers with four or more digits include commas. For example, *nine thousand, two hundred twenty* will be shown as 9,220.

You should encourage students to use commas when they enter numeric answers to questions online. The computer, however, will still score a question as correct if students omit the commas.

It is important for you to sit with students throughout the lesson to be sure they are reading the numerals correctly.

ONLINE
5 min

GET READY Read Numbers Through 1,000

Students will read numbers through 1,000. It is important to sit with students during this activity to listen to their responses. If students read a number incorrectly, pause the activity and point out how to say the number correctly.

Objectives

- Read whole numbers through 1,000.

LEARN Read Numbers Through 10,000

Students will learn how to read numbers through 10,000. They will read numbers shown on a place-value chart. When students say numbers greater than 1,000, have them think of the comma when they say the word *thousand*. This should help them remember always to use the comma when they write numbers that are 1,000 or greater.

When students see 9,999 turn into 10,000 by adding 1, remind them that each place value is 10 times the value of the place to the right. Be sure they don't insert the word *and* when saying numbers. For example, when saying 6,803, students should say "six thousand, eight hundred three," not "six thousand, eight hundred and three."

Objectives

• Read whole numbers through 10,000.

Tips

Have students use number cards to build 4-digit numbers and read the number shown.

LEARN Write Numerals Through 10,000

Students will learn how to write numbers through 10,000. First, have students create a place-value chart in their Math Notebook. They may use abbreviations for the column heads: TTh (ten thousands), Th (thousands), H (hundreds), T (tens), and O (ones). For this activity, students can write several numbers in the same set of boxes, one under the other.

After writing numbers in the place-value chart, students will write numbers without a place-value chart, placing each digit and the comma in its appropriate place.

Objectives

• Write numerals through 10,000.

Tips

Provide a place-value chart for struggling students to use throughout the lesson.

TTh	Th	,	H	T	O

WRITE NUMBERS WITH A PLACE-VALUE CHART

1. **Say:** Suppose you collected five thousand, seven hundred forty-three cans. You can write the number in a place-value chart. Listen to the number again to decide where to write each digit.

2. Repeat the number. Explain how to write each digit in the number in a place-value chart. Students should write 5 in the thousands place to show five thousand. They should write a comma, to separate the thousands. They should write 7 in the hundreds place to show seven hundred. They should write 4 in the tens place and 3 in the ones place to show forty-three.

3. **Say:** Now let's try another number. Write six thousand, eight hundred four. Write the number in the place-value chart.

4. Say each part of the number again. Since there are no tens in the number, students should have a 0 in the tens place in the place-value chart.

5. Explain that when students do not hear a place, they should write a 0 to show that there is no other digit in that place. Guide students to write a 0 in the tens place.

6. Say the following numbers and guide students to write each number in the place-value chart:

   • nine thousand, seventy-one 9,071

   • ten thousand 10,000

   • three thousand, nine hundred twelve 3,912

WRITE NUMBERS WITHOUT A PLACE-VALUE CHART

7. Tell students they will now write numbers without the place-value chart. Remind students to use a comma when writing numbers greater than one thousand. The only time they don't need a comma is when writing a year. Ask students to write the year two thousand nine. Ask them to write the year two thousand fifteen. 2009; 2015

8. Say the following numbers and guide students to write each number. Remind student to write zeros when there is no digit in a place-value position.

- one thousand, two hundred three 1,203
- four thousand, one hundred sixty-one 4,161
- six thousand 6,000
- two thousand, three-hundred forty-four 2,344
- five thousand, six hundred two 5,602
- ten thousand 10,000
- seven thousand, four hundred thirty-seven 7,437
- three thousand, seven hundred fifteen 3,715
- nine thousand, fifty-six 9,056
- four thousand, five hundred ninety 4,590
- eight thousand, nine hundred twenty-nine 8,929
- one thousand eight 1,008

TRY IT Write and Read Numerals

OFFLINE 15 min

Objectives

- Read whole numbers through 10,000.
- Write numerals through 10,000.

Students will practice writing numerals through 10,000 and then practice reading numbers through 10,000. This Try It has two parts. In the first part, you will read number words aloud to students and they will write the number. In the second part, students will read aloud numbers, write numbers, and answer multiple-choice questions.

PART 1

Say each of the following numbers. Have students write each number. Tell students to check that they wrote a comma after the thousands place.

1. five thousand, seven hundred nine 5,709

2. eight thousand, two hundred thirteen 8,213

3. four thousand, six hundred seventy-two 4,672

4. three thousand, forty-five 3,045

5. ten thousand 10,000

6. one thousand, five hundred three 1,503

7. six thousand, ninety-eight 6,098

8. two thousand, one hundred sixty-five 2,165

9. seven thousand, nine hundred forty 7,940

10. nine thousand, two hundred eighteen 9,218

PART 2

Have students turn to the Write and Read Numerals page in their Activity Book. Read the directions. Listen as students read aloud each number. Check that students do not insert the word *and* when saying numbers. For example, when saying 5,709, students should say "five thousand, seven hundred nine," not "five thousand, seven hundred and nine."

Have students complete Problems 16–20 on their own.

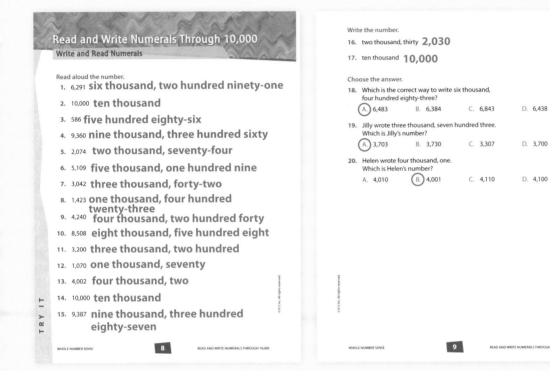

Read and Write Numerals Through 10,000
Write and Read Numerals

Read aloud the number.

1. 6,291 **six thousand, two hundred ninety-one**

2. 10,000 **ten thousand**

3. 586 **five hundred eighty-six**

4. 9,360 **nine thousand, three hundred sixty**

5. 2,074 **two thousand, seventy-four**

6. 5,109 **five thousand, one hundred nine**

7. 3,042 **three thousand, forty-two**

8. 1,423 **one thousand, four hundred twenty-three**

9. 4,240 **four thousand, two hundred forty**

10. 8,508 **eight thousand, five hundred eight**

11. 3,200 **three thousand, two hundred**

12. 1,070 **one thousand, seventy**

13. 4,002 **four thousand, two**

14. 10,000 **ten thousand**

15. 9,387 **nine thousand, three hundred eighty-seven**

WHOLE NUMBER SENSE | 8 | READ AND WRITE NUMERALS THROUGH 10,000

Write the number.

16. two thousand, thirty **2,030**

17. ten thousand **10,000**

Choose the answer.

18. Which is the correct way to write six thousand, four hundred eighty-three?
   A. 6,483   B. 6,384   C. 6,843   D. 6,438

19. Jilly wrote three thousand, seven hundred three. Which is Jilly's number?
   A. 3,703   B. 3,730   C. 3,307   D. 3,700

20. Helen wrote four thousand, one. Which is Helen's number?
   A. 4,010   B. 4,001   C. 4,110   D. 4,100

WHOLE NUMBER SENSE | 9 | READ AND WRITE NUMERALS THROUGH 10,000

Write Number Words Through 10,000

Lesson Overview

GET READY Number Words Through 1,000	5 minutes	ONLINE
LEARN Number Words Through 10,000	30 minutes	OFFLINE
TRY IT Write Number Words	15 minutes	OFFLINE
CHECKPOINT	10 minutes	OFFLINE

▶ Lesson Objectives

Write number words through 10,000.

▶ Prerequisite Skills

- Write number words through 1,000.
- Identify the place value for each digit in whole numbers through 10,000.

▶ Content Background

Students will continue learning about numbers through 10,000. They will learn how to write the number words through 10,000. First, students will create 4-digit numerals with number cards and show numerals on a place-value chart. Then students will learn how to write numerals through 10,000 by using number words and the correct punctuation. Students will use the place-value chart to help them write number words. Then students will write number words without the assistance of the place-value chart.

Students will learn to write number words with commas between each period, or group of three digits. For example, they will learn to write 3,013 as "three thousand, thirteen." In everyday life, people often omit the commas. For example, when writing a check for $1,050, most people would write "one thousand fifty dollars." In this course, students will primarily see number words written with commas.

▶ Common Errors and Misconceptions

Students might have difficulty writing multidigit numbers because numerals do not correspond exactly to English number words. For example, students might write twenty-five as 205 (20 and 5) instead of 25.

▶ Advance Preparation

- Print the Place-Value Chart Through Ten Thousands and the Index of Number Words.
- For the Learn: Number Words Through 10,000 activity, cut 6 index cards into fourths. Number two sets of cards 0 through 9. Label two other cards 0. Make a very small card with a big comma on it.

Materials to Gather

SUPPLIED

Place-Value Chart Through Ten Thousands (printout)

Index of Number Words (printout)

Write Number Words activity page

Checkpoint (printout)

ALSO NEEDED

index cards – 6

household objects – paper bag

GET READY Number Words Through 1,000

Students will match number words with numerals through 1,000. They also will read number words and type the corresponding numbers.

Objectives

- Write number words through 1,000.

LEARN Number Words Through 10,000

Students will learn how to write number words through 10,000.
 Gather the Place-Value Chart Through Ten Thousands printout, the Index of Number Words printout, and the number cards you prepared.

Objectives

- Write number words through 10,000.

1. Select number cards for 2, 3, 6, and 5. Arrange the cards in the place-value chart to show the number 2,365. Put the 2 in the thousands place, the 3 in the hundreds place, the 6 in the tens place, and the 5 in the ones place.

2. Have students tell you what number is shown.

3. Tell students that they can use number words to show that number. Write *two thousand, three hundred sixty-five*. Point out that it is important to use a comma and hyphen correctly when writing number words. Highlight or circle the comma and hyphen to emphasize them.

4. Tell students that, just as they wrote a comma after the thousands place when writing a numeral, they should write a comma after the thousands place when writing number words.

5. Point out the hyphen. Tell students that they should use hyphens when writing numbers between 20 and 99, except when writing *twenty*, *thirty*, *forty*, *fifty*, and so on.

6. Have students show the numeral 4,811 with number cards on the place-value chart. Have them use their little comma card to show where the comma goes.

7. Display the Index of Number Words. Explain that students should use it to help spell the number words.

8. Point to the numeral 4,811 and have students say it. Ask students which words should be written first. Guide them to see that the 4 is first and in the thousands place. Point out the words *four* and *thousand* on the Index of Number Words and have students write those words. Remind them to use a comma after the word *thousand*.

9. Have students tell which words should be written next. Have them write the words. Guide them to make connections between the numerals and the place value as well as the spoken number. They should write *eight hundred*.

10. Help students locate the word *eleven* on the Index of Number Words. Discuss that a hyphen is not needed because 11 is less than 20. Have them write the word.

11. Have students point to the numeral 4,811 and say it. Then have them point to the number words. They should check to see that their number words are correct.

12. Show the numeral 9,072 with number cards on the place-value chart. Have students tell you the number. Explain that just as they don't say "zero" when they say the number, they don't write *zero* in the written words for the number. Guide students in writing *nine thousand, seventy-two*.

Tips

Students may use the place-value chart at first, but encourage them to move away from using the chart. Students may also continue to use the Index of Number Words to help with spelling.

13. Move the cards from the chart onto a flat surface such as a desk or table. Switch the cards around to show 9,702. Have students say the number and guide them in writing *nine thousand, seven hundred two*. Point out that the hyphen is not needed in this number word.

14. Switch the cards around to show 9,720. Have students say the number and write it. Point out the need for the comma but not the hyphen.

15. Show the number 10,000 with cards. Have students read the number aloud and write the number words.

16. Place the number cards in a paper bag. Have students choose 3 or 4 cards and arrange them to form a number. Then have students write the numeral and its number words. Point out that a comma is not used for number words describing a 3-digit number. Repeat this step with different number cards, as time allows. As time permits, include the number 10,000.

OFFLINE
15min

TRY IT Write Number Words

Objectives

- Write number words through 10,000.

Students will practice writing number words through 10,000. They will see numerals that give the weight of animals at a zoo and will write the number words. Have students turn to the Write Number Words activity page. Allow them to use the Index of Number Words printout if needed.

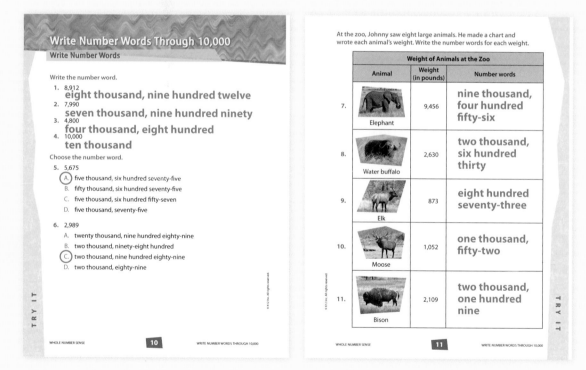

Write Number Words Through 10,000
Write Number Words

Write the number word.

1. 8,912
   eight thousand, nine hundred twelve
2. 7,990
   seven thousand, nine hundred ninety
3. 4,800
   four thousand, eight hundred
4. 10,000
   ten thousand

Choose the number word.

5. 5,675
   (A) five thousand, six hundred seventy-five
   B. fifty thousand, six hundred seventy-five
   C. five thousand, six hundred fifty-seven
   D. five thousand, seventy-five

6. 2,989
   A. twenty thousand, nine hundred eighty-nine
   B. two thousand, ninety-eight hundred
   (C) two thousand, nine hundred eighty-nine
   D. two thousand, eighty-nine

At the zoo, Johnny saw eight large animals. He made a chart and wrote each animal's weight. Write the number words for each weight.

	Weight of Animals at the Zoo		
	Animal	Weight (in pounds)	Number words
7.	Elephant	9,456	nine thousand, four hundred fifty-six
8.	Water buffalo	2,630	two thousand, six hundred thirty
9.	Elk	873	eight hundred seventy-three
10.	Moose	1,052	one thousand, fifty-two
11.	Bison	2,109	two thousand, one hundred nine

TRY IT

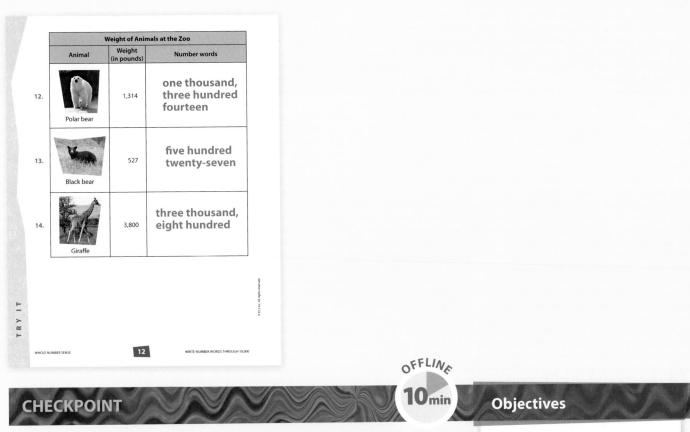

Weight of Animals at the Zoo

	Animal	Weight (in pounds)	Number words
12.	Polar bear	1,314	one thousand, three hundred fourteen
13.	Black bear	527	five hundred twenty-seven
14.	Giraffe	3,800	three thousand, eight hundred

TRY IT

WHOLE NUMBER SENSE 12 WRITE NUMBER WORDS THROUGH 10,000

OFFLINE

10 min

CHECKPOINT

Have students complete the first set of items on their own. If necessary, read the directions, problems, and answer choices to students. Record students' responses to observational items on the Learning Coach Recording Sheet. Use the answer key to score the Checkpoint, and then enter the results online.

Objectives

- Read whole numbers through 10,000.
- Write numerals through 10,000.
- Write number words through 10,000.

☼ Checkpoint   Math | Whole Number Sense | Write Number Words Through 10,000

Name _____ Date _____

Checkpoint Answer Key

Write the number in numerals.
(1 point)
1. Three thousand, six hundred twenty-two   **3,622**

(1 point)
2. One thousand, one hundred forty-four.   **1,144**

Write the number words.
(1 point)
3. Write 9,101 in words.
   nine thousand, one hundred one

Choose the answer.
(1 point)
4. Which shows 1,234 written using number words?
   A. ten thousand, two hundred thirty-four
   (B) one thousand, two hundred thirty-four
   C. one thousand, two hundred four
   D. two hundred thirty-four

(1 point)
5. Which of the following shows 6,220 written in words?
   (A) six thousand, two hundred twenty
   B. six thousand, two hundred, two
   C. six thousand, twenty-two
   D. sixty thousand, two hundred twenty

1 of 2

☼ Checkpoint   Math | Whole Number Sense | Write Number Words Through 10,000

Name _____ Date _____

(1 point)
6. Which shows 8,091 written in words?
   A. eight thousand, nine hundred, one
   (B) eight thousand, ninety-one
   C. eight hundred, ninety-one
   D. eight thousand, nineteen

(1 point)
7. Which shows 2,001 written using words?
   A. two thousand, one hundred
   (B) two thousand, one
   C. twenty-one hundred
   D. two thousand, ten

(1 point)
8. Which of the following shows nine thousand, twenty-seven?
   A. 9,702   B. 9,072   C. 9,270   (D) 9,027

9. Which of the following shows two thousand, one hundred forty-seven?
   A. 2,471   B. 2,174   (C) 2,147   D. 2,741

Complete Problems 10–14 with your learning coach.
(1 point)
10. Say this number aloud: 3,355.

(1 point)
11. Say this number aloud: 2,220.

(1 point)
12. Say this number aloud: 7,501.

(1 point)
13. Say this number aloud: 8,091.

(1 point)
14. Say this number aloud: 5,600.

2 of 2

Numbers in Expanded Form

▶ Lesson Objectives

Use expanded form to represent numbers through 10,000.

▶ Prerequisite Skills

Use expanded forms to represent numbers through 1,000, such as 754 = 7 hundreds + 5 tens + 4 ones.

Materials to Gather

SUPPLIED

Expanded Form and Standard Form activity page

▶ Content Background

In this lesson, students will learn to represent numbers through 10,000 in expanded form. They will begin by reviewing expanded form for numbers through 1,000 and progress to numbers through 10,000. Students will see models that show two ways to write numbers in expanded form: (1) with numbers and (2) with words and numbers. Students will then be asked to identify and write a number or its expanded form.

Expanded form is a way to write numbers to show the value of each digit in the number. The number 365 can be written in expanded form as 300 + 60 + 5 or 3 hundreds + 6 tens + 5 ones. Students must have a strong understanding of place value to write numbers in expanded form. When numbers are written in the conventional way, such as 365, they are said to be written in standard form.

GET READY Numbers to 1,000

ONLINE 10 min

Objectives

In this activity, students will review how to represent numbers less than 1,000 in expanded form.

Some students may benefit from using a place-value chart to record a given number. The chart will help students identify the value of each digit in a given number.

- Use expanded forms to represent numbers through 1,000, such as 754 = 7 hundreds + 5 tens + 4 ones.

LEARN Numbers to 10,000

Objectives

- Use expanded form to represent numbers through 10,000.

Students will use two ways to show numbers through 10,000 in expanded form. They use (1) only numbers and (2) numbers and words together. They also will play a hidden picture game to practice expanded form.

Tips Review values of digits in multidigit numbers. Remind students to use the value of each digit to write numbers in expanded form.

TRY IT Expanded Form and Standard Form

Objectives

- Use expanded form to represent numbers through 10,000.

Students will identify and write numbers in expanded form. Have students turn to the Expanded Form and Standard Form activity page in their Activity Book and read the directions with them. Students should copy the problems from the Activity Book into their Math Notebook as necessary and solve them there.

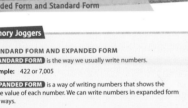

Numbers in Expanded Form
Expanded Form and Standard Form

Memory Joggers

STANDARD FORM AND EXPANDED FORM
STANDARD FORM is the way we usually write numbers.

Example: 422 or 7,005

EXPANDED FORM is a way of writing numbers that shows the place value of each number. We can write numbers in expanded form two ways.

❶ With numbers and words: $422 = 4$ hundreds $+ 2$ tens $+ 2$ ones
❷ With numbers only: $422 = 400 + 20 + 2$

When a number has a zero in one or more places, those places are not shown in the expanded form.

Example: $7,005 = 7$ thousands $+ 5$ ones
$7,005 = 7,000 + 5$

Write the number in expanded form with numbers only.

1. 2,964 **See below.**
2. 7,419 **See below.**
3. 3,620 **See below.**
4. 8,904 **See below.**
5. 5,046 **See below.**
6. 9,007 **See below.**

Choose the answer.

7. Which shows 6,430 written in expanded form?
   - (A.) $6,000 + 400 + 30$
   - B. $6 + 4 + 3$
   - C. $6,000 + 40 + 3$
   - D. $600 + 40 + 30$

WHOLE NUMBER SENSE **13** NUMBERS IN EXPANDED FORM

8. Which means the same as 4,602?
   - (A) 4 thousands + 6 hundreds + 2 ones
   - B. 4 hundreds + 6 thousands + 2 ones
   - C. 4 thousands + 6 ones + 2 hundreds
   - D. 4 thousands + 6 tens + 2 ones

9. Jim counted the number of jelly beans in a container. He counted 4,000 black, 30 pink, 900 purple, and 1 red. How many jelly beans are in the container?
   - (A.) 4,931
   - B. 4,391
   - C. 4,193
   - D. 4,139

Complete the table. Write the missing standard form or expanded form of the number.

	Standard form	Expanded form with numbers only	Expanded form with numbers and words
10.	9,394	$9,000 + 300 + 90 + 4$	**See below.**
11.	203	$200 + 3$	**See below.**
12.	5,043	$5,000 + 40 + 3$	**See below.**
13.	1,124	**See below.**	1 thousand + 1 hundred + 2 tens + 4 ones
14.	6,599	**See below.**	6 thousands + 5 hundreds + 9 tens + 9 ones
15.	2,207	**See below.**	2 thousands + 2 hundreds + 7 ones
16.	**1,077**	$1,000 + 70 + 7$	1 thousand + 7 tens + 7 ones
17.	**507**	$500 + 7$	5 hundreds + 7 ones

WHOLE NUMBER SENSE **14** NUMBERS IN EXPANDED FORM

TRY IT

Additional Answers

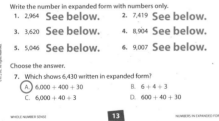

1. $2,000 + 900 + 60 + 4$
2. $7,000 + 400 + 10 + 9$
3. $3,000 + 600 + 20$
4. $8,000 + 900 + 4$
5. $5,000 + 40 + 6$
6. $9,000 + 7$
10. 9 thousands + 3 hundreds + 9 tens + 4 ones

11. 2 hundreds + 3 ones
12. 5 thousands + 4 tens + 3 ones
13. $1,000 + 100 + 20 + 4$
14. $6,000 + 500 + 90 + 9$
15. $2,000 + 200 + 7$

Construct Numbers to 10,000 (A)

Lesson Overview

Skills Update	5 minutes	ONLINE
GET READY Place Value to 1,000	5 minutes	ONLINE
LEARN Place Value as Multiples of 10	40 minutes	OFFLINE
TRY IT Working with Place Value	10 minutes	OFFLINE

▶ Lesson Objectives

Demonstrate understanding of place values as cumulative multiples of 10.

▶ Prerequisite Skills

Demonstrate that multidigit numbers represent groups of 100s, 10s, and ones.

▶ Content Background

Students normally see numbers in standard form, which is our usual way of writing numbers. The number 365 is written in standard form. Students learn the meaning of numbers when they break numbers apart. When students recognize that the digits in the number 365 represent 3 hundreds, 6 tens, and 5 ones, they show an understanding of place value. In this lesson, students will take a closer look at place value. They will make numbers with base-10 blocks and use the idea that 10 blocks in any place-value position can be regrouped to make 1 block in the place-value position to the left. Using this idea, students will see that 365 can also be made using 2 hundreds, 16 tens, and 5 ones, or 1 hundred, 26 tens, and 5 ones. The number 365 can also be made with just 365 ones. Students will see that these are only a few of the ways to represent 365. The ability to represent numbers in different ways helps students develop greater fluency with the base-10 number system.

Materials to Gather

SUPPLIED

Place Value as Multiples of 10 activity page

Working with Place Value activity page

base-10 blocks

place-value mat

GET READY Place Value to 1,000

ONLINE 5 min

Students will use on-screen base-10 blocks to show numbers as groups of hundreds, tens, and ones. Review place-value positions to thousands. Have students look at a place-value chart. Ask them to identify ones, tens, hundreds, and thousands.

Objectives

- Demonstrate that multidigit numbers represent groups of 100s, 10s, and ones.

LEARN Place Value as Multiples of 10

Objectives

- Demonstrate understanding of place values as cumulative multiples of 10.

Students will use their understanding of place value and regrouping to show that numbers can be represented in a variety of ways.

Gather the base-10 blocks and place-value mat. Have students turn to the Place Value as Multiples of 10 page in their Activity Book.

1. Review with students the place-value positions: ones, tens, hundreds, thousands, and ten thousands.

   Say: When you have 10 in any place-value position, you can regroup it to get 1 in the next position to the left. So 10 ones equal 1 ten, 10 tens equal 1 hundred, 10 hundreds equal 1 thousand, and 10 thousands equal 1 ten thousand. We can use this information to show numbers in many different ways.

SHOWING NUMBERS MANY WAYS

2. Have students look at the first worked example on the activity page. Tell students that the problem asks for different ways to show 325 with base-10 blocks. Point out that there are many correct ways to show 325. The ways given are just examples.

3. Go through the worked example with students. Tell students that 325 is made with 3 hundreds, 2 tens, and 5 ones. Point out that this combination of blocks is recorded in the chart as 3 in the hundreds column, 2 in the tens column, and 5 in the ones column.

4. Have students look at the solution.

   Say: In Step 1, the number is still 325 but 1 hundreds flat has been regrouped to make 10 tens rods. In this step, 325 is shown with 2 hundreds, 12 tens, and 5 ones. Notice how hundreds, tens, and ones are recorded in the chart.

5. Have students look at Step 2 of the worked example.

   Say: Notice that in this step, one of the tens rods from Step 1 has been regrouped into 10 ones. In this step, 325 is shown with 2 hundreds, 11 tens, and 15 ones.

6. Have students look at Step 3.

   Say: Notice that 3 hundreds have been regrouped to make 30 tens, and 2 tens were regrouped to make 20 ones. So there are 30 tens and 25 ones altogether.

   Ask: What is the total value of 30 tens and 25 ones? 325

7. Point to Step 4.

   Say: If all the blocks were regrouped to make ones cubes, we could show the number with 325 ones cubes.

   Have students look at the completed chart in the answer. Explain that these are all different ways to make 325.

8. Have students look at Problem 1. Give students the base-10 blocks and have them make 453 with 4 hundreds, 5 tens, and 3 ones. Have students make a chart for the number 453 and record the hundreds, tens, and ones they used to make the number.

   As in the worked example, have students regroup a hundreds flat or a tens rod to make the number a different way. Remind students that sometimes they will come up with combinations that require more of one kind of block than they have. In these cases, students can still write the combinations in the chart.

Tips

As students make numbers in different ways, they may at times want to go back and regroup. For example, if they make 1,532 with 15 hundreds and 32 ones, they may want to regroup to see the 15 hundreds as 1 thousand and 5 hundreds, or regroup to see the 32 ones as 3 tens and 2 ones. Going between standard form (1,532) and other forms will reinforce the idea that numbers can be broken up in many ways.

325		
hundreds	tens	ones
3	2	5
2	12	5
2	11	15
	30	25
		325

9. Have students look at Problem 2. The problem shows one way to make the number 1,546. Have students create a chart in their Math Notebook and work through this problem in a similar fashion to the worked example. Let students decide which place values they want to regroup. Guide students in finding three more ways to make 1,546 and recording the combinations of blocks in the chart.

10. Direct students' attention to Problem 3. Have students copy the chart in their Math Notebook and read the problem. This problem is about the number 10,000. Mention to students that if we had a base-10 block for 10,000, it would be a giant rod made up of 10 thousands cubes in a long line. If we regrouped this giant rod, we could exchange it for 10 thousands cubes.

    Say: We can show the number 10,000 with 9 thousands cubes and 10 hundreds flats. What would happen if we regrouped all the thousands cubes and made our number with hundreds flats? How many hundreds flats would we have? Record your answer. We would have 100 hundreds flats.

    What would happen if we regrouped all those hundreds flats and made our number with only tens rods? Record your answer. We would have 1,000 tens rods.

    And if we regrouped all those tens rods and made our number with only ones cubes? Record your answer. We would have 10,000 ones cubes.

GETTING BACK TO STANDARD FORM

11. **Say:** You can also figure out a number if you're given a combination of base-10 blocks.

12. Have students look at the second worked example in the Activity Book. This example shows how to go from a combination of base-10 blocks back to the number in standard form.

    Show students 23 tens rods and 5 ones cubes.

    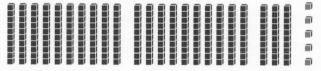

    Say: Standard form is the way numbers are usually written. What is the standard form of the number we can make with these tens rods and ones cubes?

    Count the base-10 blocks: 10, 20, 30, and so on to show that their value is 235. Explain that showing 23 tens and 5 ones is another way to show 235. Have students solve Problems 4–7.

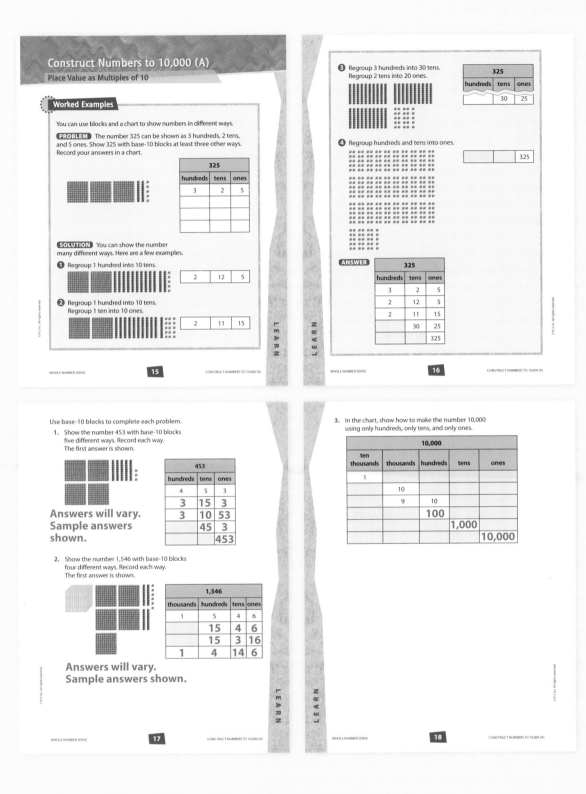

Construct Numbers to 10,000 (A)
Place Value as Multiples of 10

Worked Examples

You can use blocks and a chart to show numbers in different ways.

PROBLEM The number 325 can be shown as 3 hundreds, 2 tens, and 5 ones. Show 325 with base-10 blocks at least three other ways. Record your answers in a chart.

325		
hundreds	tens	ones
3	2	5

SOLUTION You can show the number many different ways. Here are a few examples.

1 Regroup 1 hundred into 10 tens.

2	12	5

2 Regroup 1 hundred into 10 tens. Regroup 1 ten into 10 ones.

2	11	15

3 Regroup 3 hundreds into 30 tens. Regroup 2 tens into 20 ones.

325		
hundreds	tens	ones
	30	25

4 Regroup hundreds and tens into ones.

		325

ANSWER

325		
hundreds	tens	ones
3	2	5
2	12	5
2	11	15
	30	25
		325

Use base-10 blocks to complete each problem.

1. Show the number 453 with base-10 blocks five different ways. Record each way. The first answer is shown.

Answers will vary. Sample answers shown.

453		
hundreds	tens	ones
4	5	3
3	15	3
3	10	53
	45	3
		453

2. Show the number 1,546 with base-10 blocks four different ways. Record each way. The first answer is shown.

Answers will vary. Sample answers shown.

1,546			
thousands	hundreds	tens	ones
1	5	4	6
	15	4	6
	15	3	16
1	4	14	6

3. In the chart, show how to make the number 10,000 using only hundreds, only tens, and only ones.

10,000				
ten thousands	thousands	hundreds	tens	ones
1				
	10			
		9	10	
			100	
				1,000
				10,000

LEARN

Worked Examples

You can write a number in standard form for any combination of base-10 blocks. (Reminder: Standard form is the way we normally write numbers.)

PROBLEM What is the standard form of the number we can make with 23 tens rods and 5 ones cubes?

SOLUTION

❶ Look at how many ones and tens there are.

❷ If there are more than 10 of any kind of block, regroup to make one or more blocks of the next greater place value.

❸ There are 23 tens rods and 5 ones cubes.
Regroup 20 tens so there are 2 hundreds, 3 tens and 5 ones.

❹ Write the answer in standard form—235.

ANSWER 235

Write the standard form for each number.

4. 40 tens and 8 ones **408**

5. 27 tens **270**

6. 12 hundreds and 25 ones **1,225**

7. 3 thousands, 15 hundreds, 1 ten, and 32 ones **4,542**

L E A R N

TRY IT Working with Place Value

OFFLINE 10 min

Objectives

- Demonstrate understanding of place values as cumulative multiples of 10.

Students will use base-10 blocks to show place value and numbers in different ways. Gather the base-10 blocks and the place-value mat. Have students turn to the Working with Place Value activity page in their Activity Book and read the directions with them.

Students should copy the problems from the Activity Book into their Math Notebook as necessary and solve them there.

Additional Answers

7. **Example:** Susan could take the 5 paper clips and the 16 paper clips and
   make 2 groups of 10 and 1 single. She could then take the 9 groups of 10
   and the 1 group of 10 and make 1 group of 100. She would then have
   3 groups of 100, 1 group of 10, and 1 single.

8. Answers may vary. **Sample answers:** 15 tens rods, 9 ones cubes;
   14 tens rods 19 ones cubes

Construct Numbers to 10,000 (B)

Lesson Overview

Skills Update	5 minutes	ONLINE
LEARN Numbers to 10,000	35 minutes	ONLINE
TRY IT Constructing Numbers to 10,000	10 minutes	OFFLINE
CHECKPOINT	10 minutes	ONLINE

▶ Lesson Objectives

Demonstrate understanding of place values as cumulative multiples of 10.

▶ Prerequisite Skills

Demonstrate that multidigit numbers represent groups of 100s, 10s, and ones.

▶ Content Background

Students will use base-10 blocks to construct numbers in different ways. They will use a specified number of hundreds, tens, and ones to create numbers by dragging online base-10 blocks. Students will also make numbers by using the fewest base-10 blocks possible. Students should demonstrate that there is more than one way to represent a number.

Students normally see numbers in standard form, which is our usual way of writing numbers. The number 365 is written in standard form. Students learn the meaning of numbers when they break numbers apart. When students recognize that the digits in the number 365 represent 3 hundreds, 6 tens, and 5 ones, they show an understanding of place value. In this lesson, students will take a closer look at place value. They will make numbers with base-10 blocks and use the idea that 10 blocks in any place-value position can be regrouped to make 1 block in the place-value position to the left. Using this idea, students will see that 365 can also be made using 2 hundreds, 16 tens, and 5 ones, or 1 hundred, 26 tens, and 5 ones. The number 365 can also be made with just 365 ones. Students will see that these are only a few of the ways to represent 365. The ability to represent numbers in different ways helps students develop greater fluency with the base-10 number system.

Materials to Gather

SUPPLIED

Constructing Numbers to 10,000 activity page

base-10 blocks

place-value mat

LEARN Numbers to 10,000

ONLINE
35min

Objectives

- Demonstrate understanding of place values as cumulative multiples of 10.

Students will use online base-10 blocks to show different ways to represent a number. They will also construct numbers by using a specified number of base-10 blocks in a particular place-value position. Help students focus on the idea that 10 in any place-value position is equal to 1 in the place-value position to the left. For example, students will make the number 5,000 in such a way that there are 10 ones cubes in the ones place by creating 5,000 as 4 thousands, 9 hundreds, 9 tens, and 10 ones.

TRY IT Constructing Numbers to 10,000

Objectives

- Demonstrate understanding of place values as cumulative multiples of 10.

Students will use base-10 blocks to show numbers in different ways. Gather the base-10 blocks and place-value mat. Have students turn to the Constructing Numbers to 10,000 activity page in their Activity Book and read the directions with them.

Students should copy the problems from the Activity Book into their Math Notebook as necessary and solve them there. They should answer Problems 5 and 6 aloud. Listen to their answers and check them with the answer key.

Construct Numbers to 10,000 (B)
Constructing Numbers to 10,000

Use base-10 blocks for Problems 1–3. Record how many of each block you use.

1. Show the number 923 three different ways. **See right.**

2. Matt shows the number 258. He uses 24 tens. Show how many ones he will need. **See right.**

3. Ashley shows the number 593. She uses 23 ones. Show how many hundreds and tens she will need. **See right.**

You may use base-10 blocks to help you answer Problems 4–6.

4. Write 6 hundreds, 12 tens, and 14 ones in standard form. Explain the trades needed to write the number in standard form. **See right.**

5. Explain why 573 is the same as 4 hundreds, 17 tens, and 3 ones. **See right.**

6. Explain why 304 is the same as 2 hundreds, 8 tens, and 24 ones.

When 10 is in any place, it is the same as 1 in the place to the left. Therefore, 24 ones are the same as 2 tens and 4 ones. Two more tens added to 8 tens gives you 10 tens, which is now the same as 1 hundred. So you now have 3 hundreds and 4 ones. Therefore, 304 is the same as 2 hundreds, 8 tens, and 24 ones.

WHOLE NUMBER SENSE 22 CONSTRUCT NUMBERS TO 10,000 (B)

Additional Answers

1. Answers may vary.
   Examples: 9 hundreds, 2 tens, and 3 ones; 8 hundreds, 12 tens, and 3 ones; 7 hundreds, 21 tens, and 13 ones

2. 18 ones

3. Answers may vary.
   Examples: 5 hundreds and 7 tens; 4 hundreds 17 tens

4. The standard form is 734. Twelve tens are the same as 1 hundred and 2 tens, and 14 ones are the same as 1 ten and 4 ones. Add 6 hundreds and 1 hundred. Add 2 tens and 1 ten. The 4 remains in the ones place.

5. When 10 is in any place, it is the same as 1 in the place to the left. Therefore, 17 tens are the same as 100 with 7 tens. That 100 increases the 4 hundreds to 5 hundreds. So 573 is the same as 4 hundreds, 17 tens, and 3 ones.

CHECKPOINT

Objectives

- Demonstrate understanding of place values as cumulative multiples of 10.

Students will complete an online Checkpoint. If necessary, read the directions, problems, and answer choices to students and help them with keyboard or mouse operations.

Compare and Order Numbers Through 10,000

Lesson Overview		
Skills Update	5 minutes	ONLINE
GET READY Compare Numbers Through 1,000	5 minutes	ONLINE
LEARN Compare Numbers Through 10,000	15 minutes	ONLINE
LEARN Order Numbers Through 10,000	15 minutes	ONLINE
TRY IT Compare and Order Numbers	10 minutes	ONLINE
CHECKPOINT	10 minutes	ONLINE

▶ Lesson Objectives

- Compare whole numbers through 10,000.
- Order three or more whole numbers through 10,000.

▶ Prerequisite Skills

Compare whole numbers through 1,000 by using the symbols $<, =, >$.

▶ Content Background

The terms *sign* and *symbol* are often used interchangeably. Although *sign* may be used to refer to greater than ($>$), less than ($<$), and equals ($=$), *symbol* will be used in this lesson as it is a more accurate mathematical term. In math, *sign* specifically refers to the positive signs and negative signs of numbers.

▶ Common Errors and Misconceptions

- Students might compare numbers based on the ones digits as opposed to the digits in the greatest place-value position. For example, students might think 69 is greater than 71 because 9 is greater than 1.
- Students might have more difficulty using the word *less* to compare numbers than using the word *more*.
- Students might misinterpret the equals symbol ($=$) as a signal they should "do" something. For example, in the number sentence $5 + 3 = \underline{\quad}$, students might think the equals symbol means "adds up to" or "produces." So they might view $8 = 5 + 3$ or $8 = 8$ as unacceptable or wrong because they believe the equals symbol must be followed by the answer to a problem.

Materials to Gather

SUPPLIED

base-10 blocks (optional)

place-value mat (optional)

GET READY Compare Numbers Through 1,000

ONLINE 5 min

Students will use $<$, $>$, and $=$ to compare two numbers through 1,000. As students complete the activity, ask the following questions:

- Which is the greater number?
- Which is the lesser number?
- How can you say the comparison a different way? (Note: One set of numbers is equal. The comparison for those numbers cannot be said a different way.)

Objectives

- Compare whole numbers through 1,000 by using the symbols $<$, $=$, $>$.

Tips

Students can build the numbers in each pair with base-10 blocks, then compare the blocks.

LEARN Compare Numbers Through 10,000

ONLINE 15 min

Students will use $<$, $>$, and $=$ to compare whole numbers through 10,000. First, students will identify the place-value position that is used to compare two numbers. For instance, if the numbers were 643 and 651, students would see that the digits in the hundreds places were the same. They would then look at the digits in the tens places. They would determine that 643 is less than ($<$) 651.

Then students will identify the symbol that correctly compares two numbers. Finally, students will order the digits in 4-digit numbers to make the greatest numbers possible. They'll use the numbers they ordered in comparison statements.

Objectives

- Compare whole numbers through 10,000.

Tips

Students can write numbers in place-value charts to help make comparisons.

LEARN Order Numbers Through 10,000

ONLINE 15 min

Students will use the $<$, $>$, and $=$ symbols to order three or more numbers through 10,000 from greatest to least or least to greatest. As students complete the activity, ask the following questions:

- Which is the greatest number?
- Which is the least number?
- How can you order the numbers a different way? (Note: One set of numbers is equal. Those numbers cannot be ordered in a different way.)

Objectives

- Order three or more whole numbers through 10,000.

Tips

Students can use a number line to help order numbers from greatest to least or least to greatest.

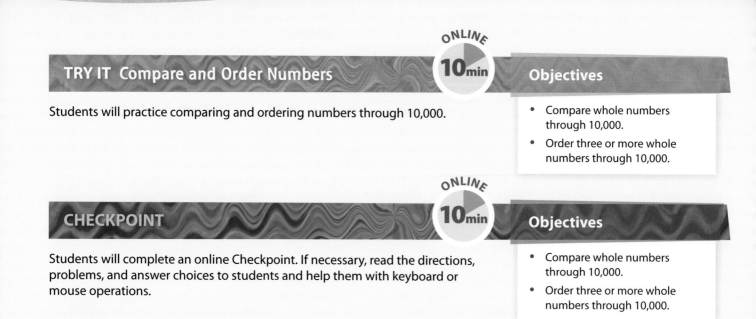

TRY IT Compare and Order Numbers

ONLINE 10 min

Students will practice comparing and ordering numbers through 10,000.

Objectives

- Compare whole numbers through 10,000.
- Order three or more whole numbers through 10,000.

CHECKPOINT

ONLINE 10 min

Students will complete an online Checkpoint. If necessary, read the directions, problems, and answer choices to students and help them with keyboard or mouse operations.

Objectives

- Compare whole numbers through 10,000.
- Order three or more whole numbers through 10,000.

Round Numbers Through 10,000

Lesson Overview

Skills Update	5 minutes	ONLINE
GET READY Comparing Numbers	5 minutes	ONLINE
LEARN Round to the Nearest Ten or Hundred	15 minutes	ONLINE
LEARN Round to the Nearest Hundred or Thousand	15 minutes	OFFLINE
TRY IT Round to Tens, Hundreds, and Thousands	10 minutes	OFFLINE
CHECKPOINT	10 minutes	ONLINE

▶ Lesson Objectives

Round numbers through 10,000.

▶ Prerequisite Skills

- Identify the place value for each digit in whole numbers through 10,000.
- Compare whole numbers through 10,000.

▶ Content Background

Students will learn how to round whole numbers through 10,000. They will use a number line to visualize the position of a target number between two boundary numbers. Boundary numbers are the numbers less than and greater than the target number. For example, if the target number 845 is to be rounded to the nearest hundred, the boundary numbers are 800 and 900. Students decide whether 845 is closer to 800 or to 900. The answer is that 845 rounded to the nearest hundred is 800. The selection of boundary numbers depends on whether the problem asks for rounding to the nearest ten, hundred, or thousand. Then students identify the boundary number that is closest to the target number.

This lesson provides students with their first experience rounding numbers. Numbers are rounded to the nearest ten, hundred, or thousand.

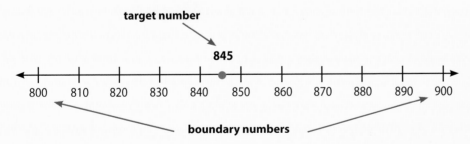

▶ Advance Preparation

Print the Round to the Nearest Hundred or Thousand.

> **Materials to Gather**
>
> **SUPPLIED**
>
> Round to the Nearest Hundred or Thousand (printout)
>
> Round to Tens, Hundreds, and Thousands activity page

ROUND TO THE NEAREST *THOUSAND*

Explain that when they round to the nearest thousand, they look for the thousand that the target number is closer to.

6. Point to the number line to 10,000 on the printout. Have students count by thousands.

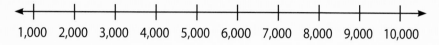

7. Mark a dot on the number line where 4,681 would go, and label it **4,681**.

8. **Ask:** Look at the number line, and underline the two boundary numbers for rounding 4,861 to the nearest thousand. 4,000 and 5,000

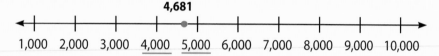

9. **Ask:** Is 4,681 closer to 4,000 or 5,000? Circle the closer number. 5,000

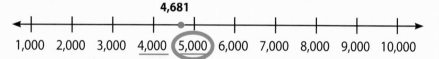

Repeat Steps 7–9 for the following numbers, rounding to the nearest thousand:

- 4,500
- 3,279
- 5,802

Have students write the boundary numbers in their Math Notebook and circle the boundary number that the target number is closer to.

Target number	Boundary numbers
4,500	4,000 (5,000)
3,279	(3,000) 4,000
5,802	5,000 (6,000)

OFFLINE

TRY IT Round to Tens, Hundreds, and Thousands **10 min**

Students will practice rounding numbers through 10,000. Have students turn to the Round to Tens, Hundreds, and Thousands activity page in their Activity Book and read the directions with them.

Students should copy the problems from the Activity Book into their Math Notebook as necessary and solve them there.

Objectives

- Round numbers through 10,000.

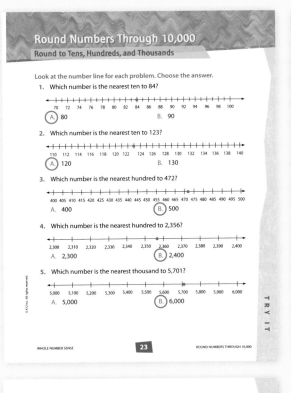

Round Numbers Through 10,000
Round to Tens, Hundreds, and Thousands

Look at the number line for each problem. Choose the answer.

1. Which number is the nearest ten to 84?

70 72 74 76 78 80 82 84 86 88 90 92 94 96 98 100

(A.) 80   B. 90

2. Which number is the nearest ten to 123?

110 112 114 116 118 120 122 124 126 128 130 132 134 136 138 140

(A.) 120   B. 130

3. Which number is the nearest hundred to 472?

400 405 410 415 420 425 430 435 440 445 450 455 460 465 470 475 480 485 490 495 500

A. 400   (B.) 500

4. Which number is the nearest hundred to 2,356?

2,300 2,310 2,320 2,330 2,340 2,350 2,360 2,370 2,380 2,390 2,400

A. 2,300   (B.) 2,400

5. Which number is the nearest thousand to 5,701?

5,000 5,100 5,200 5,300 5,400 5,500 5,600 5,700 5,800 5,900 6,000

A. 5,000   (B.) 6,000

WHOLE NUMBER SENSE | 23 | ROUND NUMBERS THROUGH 10,000

TRY IT

Write the answer.

6. If you want to round 3,483 to the nearest thousand, what are the boundary numbers? **3,000 and 4,000**

2,000 — 3,483 — 3,000 — 4,000 — 5,000

7. Round 3,483 to the nearest thousand. **3,000**

8. Round 4,654 to the nearest hundred. **4,700**

Choose the answer.

9. Michael wants to round 809 to the nearest hundred. Which boundary numbers should he use?
   A. 800 and 810   (B.) 800 and 900
   C. 800 and 1,000   D. 700 and 800

10. Dawn says 14 rounded to the nearest ten is 10. Eddie says 14 rounded to the nearest ten is 0. Who is correct? Why?
    (A.) Dawn is correct because the ten nearest to 14 is 10.
    B. Eddie is correct because 14 is closer to 0 than to 20.

11. Which shows 4,008 rounded to the nearest thousand?
    A. 4,010   B. 4,100   (C.) 4,000   D. 5,000

12. Which shows 2,132 rounded to the nearest ten?
    A. 2,100   (B.) 2,130   C. 2,140   D. 2,200

13. Which shows 6,781 rounded to the nearest hundred?
    A. 6,500   B. 6,700   (C.) 6,800   D. 6,900

14. Which shows 7,651 rounded to the nearest thousand?
    A. 7,000   B. 7,600   C. 7,700   (D.) 8,000

WHOLE NUMBER SENSE | 24 | ROUND NUMBERS THROUGH 10,000

TRY IT

Write the answer.

15. Gina wants to round 6,726 to the nearest ten. Explain how she should do it. **See right.**

16. Explain how to round 4,522 to the nearest thousand. **See right.**

17. Lila says that 3,772 rounded to the nearest hundred is 3,700. Is Lila correct? Explain why or why not. **See right.**

18. Calvin rounded the number 2,345 to the nearest hundred. He said the answer was 2,400. Calvin explained that he figured out that 2,345 was closer to 2,350. Then he said 2,350 was closer to 2,400 than 2,300. Did Calvin correctly round 2,345 to the nearest hundred?

No. Sample explanation: When rounding 2,345 to the nearest hundred, decide only if it is closer to 2,300 than to 2,400. Don't round to the nearest ten first.

WHOLE NUMBER SENSE | 25 | ROUND NUMBERS THROUGH 10,000

TRY IT

Additional Answers

15. 6,730. Answers will vary.
Sample explanation: 6,726 is closer to 6,730 than to 6,720.

16. 5,000. Answers will vary.
Sample explanation: 4,522 is closer to 5,000 than to 4,000.

17. No.
Sample explanation: 3,772 rounded to the nearest hundred is 3,800, and not 3,700. 3,772 is closer to 3,800 than it is to 3,700.

ONLINE

10min

CHECKPOINT

Objectives

• Round numbers through 10,000.

Students will complete an online Checkpoint. If necessary, read the directions, problems, and answer choices to students and help them with keyboard or mouse operations.

Unit Review

▶ Unit Objectives

This lesson reviews the following objectives:

- Identify the place value for each digit in whole numbers through 10,000.
- Count aloud whole numbers through 10,000.
- Identify odd and even numbers and describe their characteristics.
- Read whole numbers through 10,000.
- Write numerals through 10,000.
- Write number words through 10,000.
- Use expanded form to represent numbers through 10,000.
- Demonstrate understanding of place values as cumulative multiples of 10.
- Compare whole numbers through 10,000.
- Order three or more whole numbers through 10,000.
- Round numbers through 10,000.

Materials to Gather

There are no materials to gather for this lesson.

▶ Advance Preparation

In this lesson, students will have an opportunity to review previous activities in the Whole Number Sense unit. Look at the suggested activities in Unit Review: Prepare for the Checkpoint online and gather any needed materials.

UNIT REVIEW Look Back

ONLINE 10min

Students will review key concepts from the unit to prepare for the Unit Checkpoint.

Objectives

- Review unit objectives.

UNIT REVIEW Checkpoint Practice

ONLINE 50min

Students will complete an online Checkpoint Practice to prepare for the Unit Checkpoint. If necessary, read the directions, problems, and answer choices to students. Have students answer the problems on their own. Review any missed problems with students.

Objectives

- Review unit objectives.

⏩ UNIT REVIEW Prepare for the Checkpoint

What you do next depends on how students performed in the previous activity, Unit Review: Checkpoint Practice. If students had difficulty with any of the problems, complete the appropriate review activity listed in the table online.

Unit Checkpoint

UNIT CHECKPOINT Online	30 minutes	**ONLINE**
UNIT CHECKPOINT Offline	30 minutes	**OFFLINE**

▶ Unit Objectives

This lesson assesses the following objectives:

- Identify the place value for each digit in whole numbers through 10,000.
- Count aloud whole numbers through 10,000.
- Identify odd and even numbers and describe their characteristics.
- Read whole numbers through 10,000.
- Write numerals through 10,000.
- Write number words through 10,000.
- Use expanded form to represent numbers through 10,000.
- Demonstrate understanding of place values as cumulative multiples of 10.
- Compare whole numbers through 10,000.
- Order three or more whole numbers through 10,000.
- Round numbers through 10,000.

Materials to Gather

SUPPLIED

Unit Checkpoint (printout)

UNIT CHECKPOINT Online

Objectives

- Assess unit objectives.

Students will complete this part of the Unit Checkpoint online. Read the directions, problems, and answer choices to students. If necessary, help students with keyboard or mouse operations.

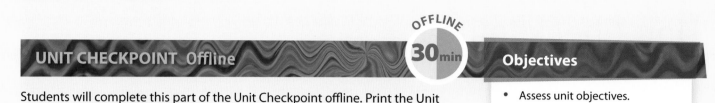
Objectives

- Assess unit objectives.

Students will complete this part of the Unit Checkpoint offline. Print the Unit Checkpoint. Read the directions, problems, and answer choices to students, if necessary. Use the answer key to score the Unit Checkpoint. Use the Learning Coach Recording Sheet to keep track of answers to observational questions. Then enter the results online.

○ Checkpoint   Math | Whole Number Sense | Unit Checkpoint

Name _____ Date _____

Unit Checkpoint Answer Key

Perform the task described in each item.
(1 point)
1. Write the number 2,020 using words.
   two thousand, twenty
(1 point)
2. Write the number five thousand, ninety. **5,090**

Complete Problems 3–8 with your learning coach.
(1 point)
3. Say this number aloud: 4,029. **four thousand, twenty-nine**
(1 point)
4. Say this number aloud: 8,030. **eight thousand, thirty**
(1 point)
5. Say this number aloud: 5,005. **five thousand, five**
(1 point)
6. Say this number aloud: 6,387. **six thousand, three hundred, eighty-seven**
(1 point)
7. Count aloud from 1,592 to 1,609.
   1,593 (as "one thousand, five hundred ninety-three"); 1,594; 1,595; 1,596; 1,597; 1,598; 1,599; 1,600; 1,601; 1,602; 1,603; 1,604; 1,605; 1,606; 1,607; 1,608; 1,609
(1 point)
8. Count aloud from 4,992 to 5,002.
   4,993 (as "four thousand, nine hundred ninety-three"); 4,994; 4,995; 4,996; 4,997; 4,998; 4,999; 5,000; 5,001; 5,002

Whole Number Addition and Subtraction

▶ Unit Objectives

- Demonstrate an understanding of how addition and subtraction affect whole numbers.

- Determine the sum or difference of two whole numbers.

- Recognize and solve a story problem in which two quantities are combined.

- Recognize and solve a story problem in which a quantity changes by addition or subtraction.

- Recognize and solve a story problem in which two quantities are compared by the use of addition or subtraction.

- Recognize and solve a story problem in which one quantity must be changed to equal another quantity.

▶ Big Ideas

- Inverses undo each other. Addition and subtraction are inverse operations, and multiplication and division are inverse operations.

- The use of letters, numbers, and mathematical symbols makes possible the translation of complex situations or long word statements into concise mathematical sentences or expressions.

▶ Unit Introduction

In this unit, students will review and extend their understanding of addition and subtraction. They will look at addition and subtraction in a general way to notice the effects that adding and subtracting have on whole numbers. For instance, when whole numbers greater than zero are added the sum is greater than either of the numbers being added. This and other insights about addition and subtraction will help students' basic understanding of how our number system works. Students will also add numbers with sums through 10,000 and they will subtract from numbers through 10,000. They will use place value to understand how addition and subtraction work, and they will review and expand their skill with the traditional algorithm (the traditional steps for adding or subtracting greater numbers). Students will then put their skills to work in context, solving a variety of story problems in which quantities are combined, or one quantity is changed by addition or subtraction, or quantities are compared, or one quantity is made equal to another. By the end of this unit, students will have greater skill with addition and subtraction calculations as well as story problems.

▶ Keywords

addends	difference	sum
algorithm	regrouping	whole numbers

Effects of Addition and Subtraction

Lesson Overview

GET READY Add and Subtract Through 1,000	5 minutes	OFFLINE
LEARN Number Relationships	15 minutes	OFFLINE
LEARN Answers on a Number Line	15 minutes	ONLINE
TRY IT Addition and Subtraction Answers	15 minutes	ONLINE
CHECKPOINT	10 minutes	ONLINE

▶ Lesson Objectives

Demonstrate an understanding of how addition and subtraction affect whole numbers.

▶ Prerequisite Skills

Find the sum or difference of two whole numbers with sums and minuends up through 1,000.

▶ Content Background

Students will explore what happens when they add and subtract whole numbers. The sum of two or more whole numbers is greater than each addend, or number being added. The difference between a greater whole number and lesser whole number is less than the greater number.

Zero is an exception to those rules. Even though zero is a whole number, adding or subtracting it has no effect on the sum or difference of two whole numbers. (Whole numbers are 0, 1, 2, 3, 4, and so on.)

Remember, the rules are true only for whole numbers (except 0). The effects of addition and subtraction are different when negative numbers are used.

Materials to Gather

SUPPLIED

blocks – B (15 of any color)

Number Line (0–50) (printout, optional)

Place-Value Chart Through Ten Thousands (printout, optional)

base-10 blocks (optional)

GET READY Add and Subtract Through 1,000

OFFLINE 5 min

Objectives

- Find the sum or difference of two whole numbers with sums and minuends up through 1,000.

Students will discuss what they know about the answers to addition and subtraction problems before they actually solve the problems.

1. Tell students that they know information about the answers to addition and subtraction problems even before they solve the problems.

2. Write $405 + 510 = ?$ on paper.

3. Point to the $+$ symbol and ask students what it means. Students should note that a plus symbol means to add, or combine amounts.

4. Ask students if the answer, or sum, can be less than 405. Then ask if the answer can be less than 510. Discuss with students that when they add whole numbers, the sum will be greater than either number. Therefore, the sum will be greater than 510. Have students solve the problem mentally.

5. Write $915 - 405 = ?$

6. Point to the $-$ symbol and ask students what it means. Students should note that a minus symbol means to subtract, take away, or separate amounts.

7. Ask students if the answer can be greater than 915. Discuss with students that when they subtract whole numbers, the answer will be less than the greater number. Therefore, the answer will be less than 915. Have students find the difference.

8. Write $300 + 400 = ?$, then have students tell what they know about the answer. They should note that the answer will be greater than 400.

9. Write $999 - 600 = ?$, then have students tell what they know about the answer. They should note that the answer will be less than 999.

LEARN Number Relationships

OFFLINE 15 min

Objectives

- Demonstrate an understanding of how addition and subtraction affect whole numbers.

Tips

Have students use counters or base-10 blocks to model combining and separating groups.

Students will explore the relationships between the numbers in addition and subtraction problems. They will learn that when whole numbers are added, the sum is greater than any of the addends. They will learn that subtraction is the opposite of addition— it undoes addition. Then they will learn that when whole numbers are subtracted, the difference is less than the greater number. Gather the blocks.

1. Display the B circles. Ask students to use the circles to show the problem $7 + 8 = ?$ Student should make two separate piles.

2. Slide the two piles close together but slightly separated. Ask students whether the two groups combined will have a total greater than 7. Ask them if the total will be greater than 8. Ask them whether, regardless of the size of the piles, the total will always be greater than either pile by itself. They should see that the sum of two numbers is always greater than either number.

3. Remind students that the piles showed $7 + 8$. Ask students if the same piles could be used to show $8 + 7$, and if so why. Yes. You can add numbers in any order.

   Ask: Would the same answer be true for subtraction? Can you subtract numbers in any order? Would $5 - 3$ be the same as $3 - 5$?
   No. You cannot subtract numbers in any order.

4. Have students tell you how many circles are in the two piles combined. 15 Then take away 7 and ask how many are left. 8

5. Explain to students that subtraction undoes addition.

   Say: We had $8 + 7 = 15$ (slide the piles near each other) and now we have $15 - 7 = 8$. (Slide the pile of 7 off to the side.)

6. Slide the piles close again and ask students to show another subtraction problem that can be made with these same piles. $15 - 8 = 7$

7. Ask students to write the four related number sentences. See if students know what they are. If not, help them write the following:

   - $8 + 7 = 15$
   - $7 + 8 = 15$
   - $15 - 7 = 8$
   - $15 - 8 = 7$

8. Highlight the addition sentences and remind students that when they combined two numbers, the sum was always more than either number.

   Say: There are 15 circles altogether here. If I take some away, the difference will always be less than the amount I started with. (Have students use the piles to show $15 - 7$ and then $15 - 8$.) When you subtract whole numbers, the difference is always less than the greater number.

9. Try a problem with greater numbers. Write $450 + 350 = ?$ Have students tell you what numbers the sum will be greater than. The sum will be greater than 450 and it will be greater than 350. Students might notice that they can simply say it will be greater than 450, which is correct.

   Have students find the sum. 800

10. Have students write the related subtraction problems. $800 - 450 = 350$ and $800 - 350 = 450$.

    Have them notice that the answer in both subtraction problems is less than the 800 they were subtracting from.

11. Ask students to consider what happens when they add 0 to a number. Consider $280 + 0 = ?$ Is it still true that the sum of the two numbers is greater than either number? The sum is the same as the number that isn't zero.

    Ask about subtracting 0. Consider $280 - 0 = ?$ Is the difference less than the greater number? The difference is the same as the nonzero number.

12. Summarize by reminding students that when they add numbers, the sum is greater than any of the numbers added, and when they subtract one number from another, the difference is less than the number subtracted from. And, finally, adding or subtracting zero has no effect.

LEARN Answers on a Number Line

ONLINE 15 min

Students will visualize sums and differences on a number line. A sum is greater than either addend, which means the sum will be to the right of the addends on the number line. A difference is less than the greater number (the minuend) in a subtraction problem, which means the difference will be to the left of the minuend on the number line. Students will then use their understanding of sums and differences to identify which of three answers could be correct when portions of an addition or subtraction problem are hidden.

Objectives

- Demonstrate an understanding of how addition and subtraction affect whole numbers.

Tips

Allow students to use the Number Line (0–50) printout or Place-Value Chart Through Ten Thousands to help determine which answer is most reasonable.

TRY IT Addition and Subtraction Answers

ONLINE 15 min

Students will answer questions online to solve a range of problems. They will use the following ideas:

- The sum of whole numbers greater than zero is always greater than any of the addends.
- The difference between whole numbers greater than zero is always less than the greater number.
- Adding zero to a number or subtracting it from a number has no effect on the number.

Objectives

- Demonstrate an understanding of how addition and subtraction affect whole numbers.

CHECKPOINT

ONLINE 10 min

Students will complete an online Checkpoint. If necessary, read the directions, problems, and answer choices to students and help them with keyboard or mouse operations.

Objectives

- Demonstrate an understanding of how addition and subtraction affect whole numbers.

Addition and Subtraction Answers

Lesson Overview

Skills Update	5 minutes	ONLINE
GET READY Add Numbers Through 1,000	5 minutes	ONLINE
LEARN Addition to 10,000	10 minutes	ONLINE
TRY IT Add Numbers Through 10,000	15 minutes	OFFLINE
LEARN Subtraction to 10,000	10 minutes	ONLINE
TRY IT Subtract Numbers Through 10,000	15 minutes	OFFLINE

▶ **Lesson Objectives**

Determine the sum or difference of two whole numbers.

▶ **Prerequisite Skills**

Find the sum or difference of two whole numbers with sums and minuends up through 1,000.

▶ **Content Background**

Addition is combining, or putting together, groups of objects. The total number of objects is the sum. Subtraction is taking a lesser amount away from a greater amount. The amount left over is the difference. Students should be able to use the terms *addends*, *sum*, and *difference* within the context of addition and subtraction.

Algorithm is a mathematical term for a repeated step-by-step mathematical procedure, such as adding or subtracting numbers. Regrouping is a critical component of the traditional addition and subtraction algorithms. The term *regrouping* has replaced the old terms *carrying* and *borrowing*. Many algorithms exist for performing any given operation.

Students will see the step-by-step process of the algorithm on the screen. They will do problems first with on-screen base-10 blocks and then with numbers in a place-value chart. This should help students move from concrete to abstract representations.

Materials to Gather

SUPPLIED

Add Numbers Through 10,000 activity page

Subtract Numbers Through 10,000 activity page

Place-Value Chart Through Ten Thousands (printout, optional)

base-10 blocks (optional)

GET READY Add Numbers Through 1,000

ONLINE
5min

Students will solve online addition problems by using the Place-Value Addition Learning Tool.

DIRECTIONS FOR USING THE PLACE-VALUE ADDITION LEARNING TOOL

1. Click Begin Setup and choose the following:
   - Present addition problems with SUMS up to: 999
   - Allow REGROUPING in problems: YES
2. Have students complete the problems given. Continue as time allows.

   Students can reset a problem by clicking the Menu button, then clicking Restart. They can click Cancel if they decide they no longer want to change the problem.

Objectives

- Find the sum or difference of two whole numbers with sums and minuends up through 1,000.

LEARN Addition to 10,000

Students will see a 4-digit addition problem solved using the traditional step-by-step procedures. The problem will be shown in a place-value chart to help students see that they are adding ones, tens, hundreds, and thousands and regrouping as they move to each place-value position.

Objectives

- Determine the sum or difference of two whole numbers.

TRY IT Add Numbers Through 10,000

Students will add two or more numbers with and without regrouping. Have students turn to the Add Numbers Through 10,000 activity page in their Activity Book and read the directions with them.

Students should copy the problems from the Activity Book into their Math Notebook as necessary and solve them there.

Objectives

- Determine the sum or difference of two whole numbers.

Tips

Allow students to use base-10 blocks or the Place-Value Chart Through Ten Thousands to solve the problems.

Addition and Subtraction Answers
Add Numbers Through 10,000

Add.

1. 3,291
    + 5,947
    9,238

2. 2,117
    3,123
    + 3,852
    9,092

3. 2,664
    + 7,336
    10,000

4. 1,553
    + 8,447
    10,000

5. 7,825
    + 1,287
    9,112

6. 4,696 + 3,754 = ?
    8,450

7. 2,809 + 3,476 = ?
    6,285

8. ? = 5,869 + 4,131
    10,000

Choose the answer.

9. 3,892
    + 5,708

    A. 8,500
    B. 8,590
    C. 9,500
    (D.) 9,600

10. 4,816 + 1,794 = ?

    A. 3,022
    B. 3,182
    C. 5,610
    (D.) 6,610

TRY IT

WHOLE NUMBER ADDITION AND SUBTRACTION   26   ADDITION AND SUBTRACTION ANSWERS

LEARN Subtraction to 10,000

Students will solve subtraction problems with on-screen base-10 blocks by using the Place-Value Subtraction Learning Tool. They will then see a 4-digit subtraction problem solved using the traditional step-by-step procedures. The problem will be shown in a place-value chart to help students see that they are subtracting ones, tens, hundreds, and thousands and regrouping as necessary to solve the problem.

Objectives

- Determine the sum or difference of two whole numbers.

DIRECTIONS FOR USING THE PLACE-VALUE SUBTRACTION LEARNING TOOL

1. Click Begin Setup and choose the following:
   - Present subtraction problems with MINUENDS up to: 999
   - Allow REGROUPING in problems: YES
2. Have students complete the problems given. Continue as time allows. Students can reset a problem by clicking the Menu button, then clicking Restart. They can click Cancel if they decide they no longer want to change the problem.

TRY IT Subtract Numbers Through 10,000

Students will subtract greater numbers. Have students turn to the Subtract Numbers Through 10,000 activity page in their Activity Book and read the directions with them.

Students should copy the problems from the Activity Book into their Math Notebook as necessary and solve them there.

Objectives

- Determine the sum or difference of two whole numbers.

Tips

Allow students to use base-10 blocks or the Place-Value Chart Through Ten Thousands to solve the problems.

Addition and Subtraction Answers
Subtract Numbers Through 10,000

Subtract.

1. $\begin{array}{r} 9,714 \\ -\ 2,337 \\ \hline \mathbf{7,377} \end{array}$

2. $\begin{array}{r} 5,025 \\ -\ 4,261 \\ \hline \mathbf{764} \end{array}$

3. $\begin{array}{r} 10,000 \\ -\ 7,836 \\ \hline \mathbf{2,164} \end{array}$

4. $\begin{array}{r} 10,000 \\ -\ 3,561 \\ \hline \mathbf{6,439} \end{array}$

5. $\begin{array}{r} 1,044 \\ -\ 88 \\ \hline \mathbf{956} \end{array}$

6. $6,599 - 1,570 =\ ?\ \mathbf{5,029}$

7. $5,281 - 3,004 =\ ?\ \mathbf{2,277}$

8. $9,925 - 1,475 =\ ?\ \mathbf{8,450}$

Choose the answer.

9. $7,562 - 1,516 =\ ?$
    - (A.) 6,046
    - B. 6,054
    - C. 8,078
    - D. 9,078

10. $\begin{array}{r} 4,563 \\ -\ 856 \end{array}$
    - A. 3,507
    - (B.) 3,707
    - C. 4,419
    - D. 5,419

TRY IT

Combine and Change Problems

Lesson Overview

GET READY Combine and Change to 1,000	5 minutes	ONLINE
LEARN Combine Problems	10 minutes	ONLINE
TRY IT Solve Combine Problems	10 minutes	ONLINE
LEARN Change Problems	15 minutes	ONLINE
TRY IT Solve Change Problems	10 minutes	ONLINE
CHECKPOINT	10 minutes	ONLINE

▶ Lesson Objectives

- Recognize and solve a story problem in which two quantities are combined.
- Recognize and solve a story problem in which a quantity changes by addition or subtraction.

Materials to Gather

There are no materials to gather for this lesson.

▶ Prerequisite Skills

- Recognize and solve word problems involving sums up through 1,000 in which two quantities are combined.
- Recognize and solve word problems involving sums or minuends up through 1,000 in which one quantity changes by addition or subtraction.

▶ Content Background

Researchers have classified addition and subtraction story problems into different categories.

Many addition problems are categorized as *combine problems*. In these problems, students combine two or more groups to get a sum or total. In some combine problems, they need to find the sum. In others, they need to find one of the addends. Students can write an addition number sentence with a missing addend, such as $3 + ? = 7$. They can use subtraction to find the missing addend or they can ask themselves, "3 plus what number equals 7?" When students encounter combine problems, they may find that using a part-part-total chart will help them understand how to find the missing quantity and write the number sentence that represents the problem. The chart can also help students understand the opposite or *inverse* relationship between addition and subtraction.

Some story problems are categorized as *change problems* because they describe situations in which a starting quantity changes by having more added to it or having some taken away. When students encounter change problems, they may find that using a start-change-result chart will help them understand how to write the number sentence that represents the problem. The start-change-result chart is very similar to the part-part-total chart. While these charts can be used interchangeably in story problems involving a change of an amount, the start-change-result chart suggests the action of a change problem more clearly. Therefore, this chart helps students more easily recognize a problem involving change versus one where two parts are simply combined.

Students do not need to memorize the types of problems. Instead, they should gain the experience and confidence necessary to read a problem, create a mental image, and figure out which quantities within the problem to add or subtract to find the solution.

GET READY Combine and Change to 1,000

ONLINE 5 min

Objectives

Students will match number sentences to stories. The problems illustrate two kinds of story problems—combine problems (in which amounts are combined using addition) and change problems (in which an amount changes because something is added to or taken away from it).

Tips — Encourage students to make a sketch to model the problems.

- Recognize and solve word problems involving sums up through 1,000 in which two quantities are combined.
- Recognize and solve word problems involving sums or minuends up through 1,000 in which one quantity changes by addition or subtraction.

LEARN Combine Problems

ONLINE 10 min

Objectives

Students will learn about combine problems, or story problems where two quantities are combined.

- Recognize and solve a story problem in which two quantities are combined.

In combine story problems, students will be finding the sum or total.
Example: $30 + 70 = ?$
Other times students will be finding one of the numbers being added (a missing addend).
Example: $30 + ? = 100$ or $? + 70 = 100$
Combine problems can be put in a part-part-total chart to see the relationship of the numbers. Whenever you combine two numbers, each number is part of the total. The problem $30 + 70 = ?$ can be shown like this. Students add $30 + 70$ to get the total.

The key to the chart is that once you put numbers in it, you can see four relationships. It shows the sum in two ways, and it shows that the total minus a part equals the other part.

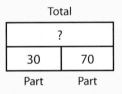

Total	
?	
30	70
Part	Part

Total	
100	
30	70
Part	Part

$30 + 70 = 100$
$70 + 30 = 100$
$100 - 30 = 70$
$100 - 70 = 30$

When students encounter combine story problem, they can put the numbers in a part-part-total chart to help them write the number sentence. When there is a missing addend, students often count up to find the missing number. However, if the numbers are difficult, it's easiest to find the missing part by subtracting the part that's known. The following charts show the three kinds of problems that can be solved with the chart previously filled in.

Combine Problems	Missing Total	Missing Addend	Missing Addend
	Total	**Total**	**Total**
	?	100	100
	30 | 70	? | 70	30 | ?
	Part Part	Part Part	Part Part
Number Sentence	$30 + 70 = ?$	$? + 70 = 100$	$30 + ? = 100$
Solution	$30 + 70 = 100$	$100 - 70 = 30$	$100 - 30 = 70$

As students do the problems in this lesson, have them make a part-part-total chart for any problem they find difficult.

TRY IT Solve Combine Problems

ONLINE 10 min

Objectives

Students will practice solving story problems where two quantities are combined. They will identify the number sentence that can be used to solve a problem and then find the solution.

- Recognize and solve a story problem in which two quantities are combined.

Tips   Students may wish to use a part-part-total chart to determine whether they need to find a part or a total to solve the problem.

LEARN Change Problems

ONLINE 15 min

Objectives

Students will learn how to solve change problems, or story problems where one quantity changes by addition or subtraction. They will use a start-change-result chart to help them solve the problems. Let's say that students are asked to solve the following change problem:

- Recognize and solve a story problem in which one quantity changes by addition or subtraction.

- Bror had 30 apples. He picked 60 more. How many apples does he have altogether?

Students can use a start-change-result chart to help them solve this problem. Bror started with one amount, 30. Students should put 30 in the start section of the chart. Then Bror's amount changed, because he picked 60 more apples. Since Bror got more apples, students should put a plus symbol (+) after the 30 in the chart. Next they should put 60 in the change section of the chart to show how much Bror's amount changed. They can then solve the problem by adding the amounts. Students would put the answer, 90, in the result box.

Start	+ or −	Change	=	Result
30	+	60	=	?

Students would use the chart to solve.

$30 + 60 = 90$

Some problems, however, are not as straightforward. Look at this one.

- Bror had 45 apples. He picked some more apples. He then had 120 apples. How many apples did he pick?

This is a missing-addend problem. Some students will count up from 45 to 120, but they should also know that they can subtract 120 − 45 to get 75.

Start	+ or −	Change	=	Result
45	+	?	=	120

Students would use the chart to solve.

$$45 + ? = 120$$
$$120 - 45 = 75$$

Sometimes story problems are worded in such a way that they begin with the result. In problems like this, it may help to rearrange the boxes in the chart, as follows:

- At the end of the day, Bror had 120 apples. He started with a wagon full of apples in the morning and then picked 75 more. How many were in the wagon when he started?

If students put the result box first, their chart might look like the one that follows. Students would solve this problem using subtraction.

Result	=	Start	+ or −	Change
120	=	?	+	75

As students do problems in this online activity, have them make start-change-result charts. Ask them to think about the change and choose either addition or subtraction depending on whether the change increases the start number or decreases it.

TRY IT Solve Change Problems

 ONLINE 10min

Objectives

- Recognize and solve a story problem in which one quantity changes by addition or subtraction.

Students will answer questions online to solve story problems where one quantity changes by addition or subtraction. They will identify the number sentence that can be used to solve a problem and then solve some problems.

Be sure that students have paper and pencil available to find solutions.

Tips Encourage students to put the numbers from the story problems into start-change-result charts to help them determine the number sentence.

CHECKPOINT

ONLINE 10min

Objectives

- Recognize and solve a story problem in which two quantities are combined.
- Recognize and solve a story problem in which one quantity changes by addition or subtraction.

Students will complete an online Checkpoint. If necessary, read the directions, problems, and answer choices to students and help them with keyboard or mouse operations.

Compare and Equalize Story Problems

Lesson Overview

Skills Update	5 minutes	ONLINE
GET READY Compare Numbers to 1,000	5 minutes	ONLINE
LEARN Compare Problems	10 minutes	ONLINE
TRY IT Compare and Solve	10 minutes	OFFLINE
LEARN Equalize Problems	10 minutes	ONLINE
TRY IT Make Equal Amounts	10 minutes	OFFLINE
CHECKPOINT	10 minutes	ONLINE

▶ Lesson Objectives

- Recognize and solve a story problem in which two quantities are compared by the use of addition or subtraction.
- Recognize and solve a story problem in which one quantity must be changed to equal another quantity.

▶ Prerequisite Skills

- Recognize and solve word problems involving numbers up to 1,000 in which two quantities are compared by the use of addition or subtraction.
- Recognize and solve word problems involving numbers up to 1,000 in which one quantity must be changed to equal another quantity.

▶ Content Background

Students will solve *compare problems* and *equalize problems*. They will write number sentences in which two quantities are compared or one quantity is changed to match another.

Compare problems are story problems in which two quantities are compared. In compare problems, students must compare two groups to find how many more or fewer are in one group. Here's a compare problem:

- Ron has 12 marbles. Alex has 18. How many more marbles does Alex have than Ron?

To solve this problem, students can make a row of 12 objects and a row of 18 objects. Using one-to-one correspondence, they can count how many objects do not have a match to find the difference.

As students move to greater numbers where counting isn't practical, they can model the problems with a diagram showing bars for each number.

- Andre collected 1,120 pennies and Kelly collected 920 pennies. How many more pennies did Andre collect than Kelly? (or: How many fewer pennies did Kelly collect than Andre?)

Materials to Gather

SUPPLIED

Compare and Solve activity page

Make Equal Amounts activity page

blocks – B (19 of any color, optional)

1,120	
920	?

The bars of the diagram help students see the relationship between the numbers. They should recognize that they can subtract to find the difference.

Equalize problems are story problems that require students to compare two quantities or make two quantities equal. Here's an example of an equalize problem:

- Andre collected 1,120 pennies and Kelly collected 920 pennies. How many more pennies must Kelly collect to have the same number of pennies as Andre?

Students should come to realize that *how many more one quantity is than another* is the same as *how many fewer the second quantity is than the first.*

Once they understand this concept, they will be ready to learn how to *equalize* quantities, or determine how many more should be added to one quantity to make it equal to another quantity. As they practice solving equalize problems, students should make the connection that the difference between two amounts is the same as the number needed to make the two amounts equal.

ONLINE 5 min

GET READY Compare Numbers to 1,000

Students will complete online story problems in which two quantities are compared to find the difference.

Objectives

- Find the sum or difference of two whole numbers with sums and minuends up through 1,000.

Tips If students have trouble with the idea of comparing numbers, have them use B blocks to compare 7 and 12. Have them make a row of 7 circles and a row of 12 circles and match up pairs of circles in the two rows. Circles that do not have a match represent the difference between the two numbers.

ONLINE 10 min

LEARN Compare Problems

Students will solve story problems in which they compare two amounts by adding or subtracting. Have paper and pencil available for them to use to solve the problems. Encourage students to draw comparison bars to compare the numbers concretely.

Objectives

- Recognize and solve a story problem in which two quantities are compared by the use of addition or subtraction.

TRY IT Compare and Solve

Students will practice solving story problems in which two quantities are compared. They will identify the number sentence that can be used to solve a problem and then find the solution. Have students turn to the Compare and Solve activity page in their Activity Book and read the directions with them.

Students should copy the problems from the Activity Book into their Math Notebook as necessary and solve them there. Encourage them to draw a diagram to compare the numbers.

- Recognize and solve a story problem in which two quantities are compared by the use of addition or subtraction.

Compare and Equalize Story Problems
Compare and Solve

Read the problem. Answer the question.

1. 2,043 people drove to the football game. 3,102 people took a bus or a train to the game. How many more people took a bus or train to the game?

3,102	
2,043	**1,059**

Write the number sentence you can use to solve the problem, and then solve.

2. The soccer stadium has 5,645 seats. It has 3,425 fewer seats than the football stadium. How many seats does the football stadium have?
$$5,645 + 3,425 = 9,070$$

Choose the number sentence that could be used to solve the problem.

3. Ella collected 2,345 pennies. Linda has 234 more pennies than Ella. How many pennies does Linda have?

  A. $2,345 - 234 = \square$ (B.) $2,345 + 234 = \square$ C. $234 - 2,345 = \square$

TRY IT

LEARN Equalize Problems

Students will solve story problems in which they will compare amounts and then add or subtract to make one amount equal to the other. Encourage students to draw a diagram with bars to compare the amounts.

- Recognize and solve a story problem in which one quantity must be changed to equal another quantity.

TRY IT Make Equal Amounts

OFFLINE 10 min

Objectives

- Recognize and solve a story problem in which one quantity must be changed to equal another quantity.

Students will practice solving story problems where one quantity changes to equal another quantity. They will identify the number sentence that can be used to solve a problem and then find the solution. Have students turn to the Make Equal Amounts activity page in their Activity Book and read the directions with them.

Students should copy the problems from the Activity Book into their Math Notebook as necessary and solve them there. Students may want to draw a diagram to help them solve the problem.

Compare and Equalize Story Problems
Make Equal Amounts

Read the problem. Write the number sentence and the solution to the problem.

1. There are 1,923 pumpkin seeds. There are 3,997 watermelon seeds. How many more pumpkin seeds do you need if you want to have the same amount as the watermelon seeds?

   Number sentence: ? **1,923 + ? = 3,997**

   Solution: ? **2,074 pumpkin seeds**

2. Farmer Li has 2,457 pounds of green beans. He has 1,032 pounds of peas. How many pounds of green beans would he have to sell to have the same amount of green beans and peas?

   Number sentence: ? **2,457 − ? = 1,032**

   Solution: ? **1,425 pounds of green beans**

Choose the number sentence that could be used to solve this problem.

3. The City Art Gallery has 3,458 paintings in its collection. If it buys 1,257 more paintings, it will have as many paintings as the National Art Gallery. How many paintings does the National Art Gallery have?

   A. 1,257 − 3,458 = ☐

   B. 3,458 − 1,257 = ☐

   C. 3,458 + 1,257 = ☐

T R Y   I T

CHECKPOINT

ONLINE 10 min

Objectives

- Recognize and solve a story problem in which two quantities are compared by the use of addition or subtraction.
- Recognize and solve a story problem in which one quantity must be changed to equal another quantity.

Students will complete an online Checkpoint. If necessary, read the directions, problems, and answer choices to students and help them with keyboard or mouse operations.

Unit Review

Lesson Overview

UNIT REVIEW Look Back	10 minutes	**ONLINE**
UNIT REVIEW Checkpoint Practice	50 minutes	**ONLINE**
▶ **UNIT REVIEW** Prepare for the Checkpoint		

▶ Unit Objectives

This lesson reviews the following objectives:

- Demonstrate an understanding of the effects of addition and subtraction on whole numbers.
- Determine the sum or difference of two whole numbers.
- Recognize and solve a story problem in which two quantities are combined.
- Recognize and solve a story problem in which a quantity changes by addition or subtraction.
- Recognize and solve a story problem in which two quantities are compared by the use of addition or subtraction.
- Recognize and solve a story problem in which one quantity must be changed to equal another quantity.

▶ Advance Preparation

In this lesson, students will have an opportunity to review previous activities in the Whole Number Addition and Subtraction unit. Look at the suggested activities in Unit Review: Prepare for the Checkpoint online and gather any needed materials.

Materials to Gather

There are no materials to gather for this lesson.

UNIT REVIEW Look Back   ONLINE 10min

Students will review key concepts from the unit to prepare for the Unit Checkpoint.

Objectives
- Review unit objectives.

UNIT REVIEW Checkpoint Practice   ONLINE 50min

Students will complete an online Checkpoint Practice to prepare for the Unit Checkpoint. If necessary, read the directions, problems, and answer choices to students. Have students answer the problems on their own. Review any missed problems with students.

Objectives
- Review unit objectives.

➡ UNIT REVIEW Prepare for the Checkpoint

What you do next depends on how students performed in the previous activity, Unit Review: Checkpoint Practice. If students had difficulty with any of the problems, complete the appropriate review activity listed in the table online.

Unit Checkpoint

UNIT CHECKPOINT Online   60 minutes **ONLINE**

▶ Unit Objectives

This lesson assesses the following objectives:

- Demonstrate an understanding of how addition and subtraction affect whole numbers.
- Determine the sum or difference of two whole numbers.
- Recognize and solve a story problem in which two quantities are combined.
- Recognize and solve a story problem in which a quantity changes by addition or subtraction.
- Recognize and solve a story problem in which two quantities are compared by the use of addition or subtraction.
- Recognize and solve a story problem in which one quantity must be changed to equal another quantity.

Materials to Gather

There are no materials to gather for this lesson.

ONLINE 60min

UNIT CHECKPOINT Online

Objectives

- Assess unit objectives.

Students will complete the Unit Checkpoint online. If necessary, read the directions, problems, and answer choices to students and help them with keyboard or mouse operations.

Algebra Thinking

▶ Unit Objectives

- Use a mathematical expression to represent a relationship between quantities.
- Use an equation to represent a relationship between quantities.
- Use an inequality to represent a relationship between quantities.
- Select the appropriate symbol to show an operation or a relationship that makes a number sentence true.
- Determine a missing number in an equation or an inequality.
- Extend a linear pattern, such as stating what number comes next in a series.
- Recognize and describe a linear pattern, such as counting by 5s or multiplying 5 times a number to reach 100, by its rule.
- Solve a simple story problem that involves a function.

▶ Big Ideas

- Addition, subtraction, multiplication, and division can be represented by models and by using math symbols.
- The equals symbol denotes an equivalent relationship.
- An expression represents a value that can be a number, a variable, or a group of numbers, variables, and operation symbols. Some examples of expressions are $10 - 4 + 1$, $3 + x$, $5y + 2$, b, and 5.
- Rules can be used to generate number patterns.

▶ Unit Introduction

In this unit, students will begin thinking *algebraically*. Algebra is a branch of mathematics focused on representing real-world relationships as equations, or number sentences, and then solving for unknowns in these number sentences.

Students will learn that expressions show quantities (for example, $9 + 2$) and that number sentences show the relationship between quantities (for example, $9 + 2 = 11$ or $9 + 2 < 15$). They will learn that the same expression can be shown in many ways: $8 + 2$, 10, and $6 + 4$ are equal expressions. Building on the idea of equal and unequal expressions, students will compare quantities using the symbols $<$, $>$, and $=$. They will learn that number sentences are like balances. For example, if a number sentence uses the equals symbol, the expressions on either side of the symbol must be balanced, or equal.

Students will also learn about patterns in which the same number is added to or subtracted from each term. They will find the next term in patterns, solve story problems with patterns, and determine rules for patterns.

▶ Keywords

array	function	linear pattern
equals symbol ($=$)	greater-than symbol ($>$)	number sentence
expression	less-than symbol ($<$)	simplify

Mathematical Expressions

Lesson Overview

GET READY Problem Solving Through 1,000	5 minutes	ONLINE
LEARN Match Expressions	20 minutes	ONLINE
LEARN Story Expressions	20 minutes	OFFLINE
TRY IT Identify and Write Expressions	15 minutes	OFFLINE

▶ Lesson Objectives

Use a mathematical expression to represent a relationship between quantities.

▶ Prerequisite Skills

Write and solve addition or subtraction number sentences to represent problem-solving situations with sums and minuends up through 1,000.

▶ Content Background

A mathematical *expression* is a combination of numbers and symbols that represents a given value. For example, $2 + 3$ and $4 - 3$ are expressions. An expression can also be a single number. The number 5 alone is an expression.

An expression does not include the symbols $=$, $<$, and $>$. When two or more expressions are put together with an equals symbol ($=$), this creates an *equation*. For example, $2 + 3$ is an expression, but $2 + 3 = 5$ is an equation.

When two or more expressions are put together with a less-than ($<$), greater-than ($>$), or not-equal-to ($\neq$) symbol, this creates an *inequality*. While $2 + 3$ and 6 are each expressions, $2 + 3 < 6$ is an inequality. (We will not introduce the terms *equation* and *inequality* to students at this level; we will refer to both as *number sentences*.)

In this lesson, students will learn about expressions. They will see that many word phrases can be written as expressions. For instance, *3 more than 4* can be written as $3 + 4$. And *3 less than 7* can be written as $7 - 3$.

Materials to Gather

SUPPLIED

Story Expressions activity page

Identify and Write Expressions activity page

GET READY Problem Solving Through 1,000

Students will read addition and subtraction story problems and choose the correct expression that matches the problem. They will determine the correct sum or difference to solve the problem. Point out to students that expressions are used to make number sentences, but expressions do not include an equals symbol.

Objectives

- Write and solve addition or subtraction number sentences to represent problem-solving situations with sums and minuends up through 1,000.

LEARN Match Expressions

Objectives

- Use a mathematical expression to represent a relationship between quantities.

Students will learn that math expressions are numbers or numbers and operation symbols ($+, -, \times, \div$) combined to show a value. An expression can even be a missing value, such as the question mark in $? = 2 + 3$. Students will also learn that expressions make up number sentences but are not themselves number sentences. Expressions never have an equals symbol ($=$).

In this activity, students will learn that number phrases (for example, 3 more than 4) can be written as expressions. Here are a few examples:

- 3 more than 4 $4 + 3$
- 3 less than 7 $7 - 3$
- twice as many as 5 5×2
- 8 divided into 2 equal groups $8 \div 2$

LEARN Story Expressions

Objectives

- Use a mathematical expression to represent a relationship between quantities.

In this activity, students will create mathematical expressions to match stories.

Have students turn to the Story Expressions activity page in their Activity Book. Students should copy the problems from the Activity Book into their Math Notebook as necessary and solve them there.

Tips

If students have difficulty, have them act out the story situations using B blocks for the objects.

1. Before working on the activity page, introduce the idea that when students write number sentences to solve story problems, they use expressions on each side of the equals symbol. (Be careful not to use *number sentence* and *expression* interchangeably.)

2. Remind students that an expression can be just a number, such as 5, or a missing value shown by just a question mark. And it can have operation symbols, such as $+, -, \times, \div$. These are all expressions: $5 + 3$, $8 - ?$, 14, $? \div 2$, and even just ? by itself. But expressions never have an equals symbol. Only number sentences, which are made up of expressions, have an equals symbol. These are number sentences: $? + 5 = 10$, $10 - ? = 5$, $8 \div ? = 4$.

3. Tell students they will create expressions to match stories from the Activity Book.

4. Go over the Worked Examples and the sample problems. Guide students to do Problems 1–8.

5. Direct students' attention to Problem 9.

   Say: Sara has 24 tickets. Then she buys or sells 6 more. Which word—*buys* or *sells*—completes the story so that it matches the expression shown?

   Students should realize that since 6 is added to 24, Sara buys more tickets. When she buys more tickets, she is adding to the amount she already has.

6. Have students complete the rest of the activity page in their Math Notebook.

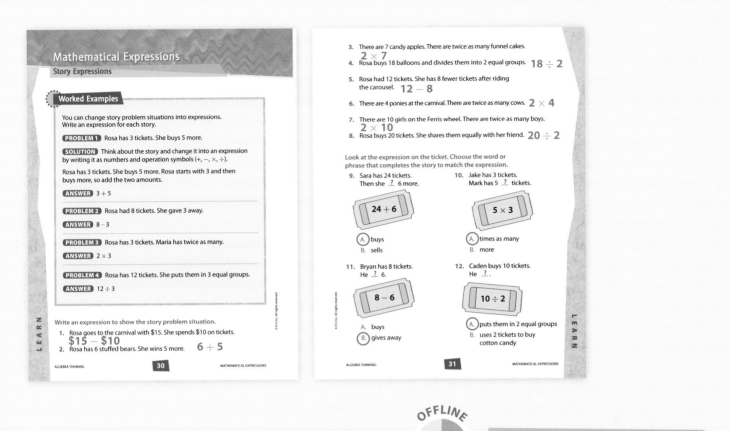

Mathematical Expressions
Story Expressions

Worked Examples

You can change story problem situations into expressions. Write an expression for each story.

PROBLEM 1 Rosa has 3 tickets. She buys 5 more.

SOLUTION Think about the story and change it into an expression by writing it as numbers and operation symbols ($+$, $-$, $\times$, $\div$).

Rosa has 3 tickets. She buys 5 more. Rosa starts with 3 and then buys more, so add the two amounts.

ANSWER $3 + 5$

PROBLEM 2 Rosa had 8 tickets. She gave 3 away.

ANSWER $8 - 3$

PROBLEM 3 Rosa has 3 tickets. Maria has twice as many.

ANSWER 2×3

PROBLEM 4 Rosa has 12 tickets. She puts them in 3 equal groups.

ANSWER $12 \div 3$

Write an expression to show the story problem situation.

1. Rosa goes to the carnival with $15. She spends $10 on tickets.
   $\$15 - \$10$
2. Rosa has 6 stuffed bears. She wins 5 more. $6 + 5$

3. There are 7 candy apples. There are twice as many funnel cakes.
   2×7
4. Rosa buys 18 balloons and divides them into 2 equal groups. $18 \div 2$
5. Rosa had 12 tickets. She has 8 fewer tickets after riding the carousel. $12 - 8$
6. There are 4 ponies at the carnival. There are twice as many cows. 2×4
7. There are 10 girls on the Ferris wheel. There are twice as many boys.
   2×10
8. Rosa buys 20 tickets. She shares them equally with her friend. $20 \div 2$

Look at the expression on the ticket. Choose the word or phrase that completes the story to match the expression.

9. Sara has 24 tickets. Then she _?_ 6 more.

   $24 + 6$

   A. buys
   B. sells

10. Jake has 3 tickets. Mark has 5 _?_ tickets.

    5×3

    A. times as many
    B. more

11. Bryan has 8 tickets. He _?_ 6.

    $8 - 6$

    A. buys
    B. gives away

12. Caden buys 10 tickets. He _?_.

    $10 \div 2$

    A. puts them in 2 equal groups
    B. uses 2 tickets to buy cotton candy

OFFLINE 15 min

TRY IT   Identify and Write Expressions

Objectives

Students will practice identifying and writing expressions that match given values and stories. Have students turn to the Identify and Write Expressions activity page in their Activity Book and read the directions with them.

Students should copy the problems from the Activity Book into their Math Notebook as necessary and solve them there.

- Use a mathematical expression to represent a relationship between quantities.

Mathematical Expressions
Identify and Write Expressions

Choose the answer.

1. Which expression shows 5 more than 15?
   A. $15 + 5$ B. 15×5
   C. $5 - 5$ D. $15 \div 5$

2. Which expression shows 10 divided into 2 equal groups?
   A. $10 + 2$ B. 10×2
   C. $10 - 2$ D. $10 \div 2$

3. Which expression shows 4 less than 9?
   A. $9 + 4$ B. 9×4
   C. $9 - 4$ D. $9 \div 4$

4. Which expression shows twice as many as 3?
   A. $2 + 3$ B. 2×3
   C. $2 - 3$ D. $2 \div 3$

5. Tom washed 8 cars and then he washed 14 more. Which expression shows how many cars he washed in all?
   A. $8 + 14$ B. $14 \div 8$ C. 8×14 D. $8 - 14$

Write the expression.

6. 7 more than 15
   $15 + 7$
7. 8 less than 21 $21 - 8$
8. 10 times 4 10×4
9. Gavin has 13 toy trucks. He buys 5 more. $13 + 5$
10. Jane planted 25 tulips. She picks 15 of the tulips.
    $25 - 15$
11. Will had $18. He spent $3. $\$18 - \$3$
12. Valeria has 7 boxes. Each box has 2 shoes.
    7×2
13. Dina has 20 bananas. She divides them equally among 10 friends.
    $20 \div 10$

Expressions and Number Sentences (A)

Lesson Overview

GET READY Expression Matchup	10 minutes	ONLINE
LEARN Is It Equal?	20 minutes	ONLINE
LEARN Same Value	15 minutes	OFFLINE
TRY IT Equal Expressions	15 minutes	OFFLINE

▶ Lesson Objectives

Use an equation to represent a relationship between quantities.

▶ Prerequisite Skills

Write and solve addition or subtraction number sentences to represent problem-solving situations with sums and minuends up through 1,000.

▶ Content Background

A mathematical *expression* is a combination of numbers and symbols that represents a given value. For example, $2 + 3$ and $4 - 3$ are expressions. An expression can also be a single number. The number 5 alone is an expression.

An expression does not include the symbols $=$, $<$, and $>$. When two or more expressions are put together with an equals symbol ($=$), this creates an *equation*. For example, $2 + 3$ is an expression, but $2 + 3 = 5$ is an equation.

When two or more expressions are put together with a less-than ($<$), greater-than ($>$), or not-equal-to ($\neq$) symbol, this creates an *inequality*. While $2 + 3$ and 6 are each expressions, $2 + 3 < 6$ is an inequality. (We will not introduce the terms *equation* and *inequality* to students at this level; we will refer to both as *number sentences*.)

In this lesson, students will learn about number sentences that have an equals symbol (equations). The equals symbol shows that two expressions have the same value. It is important that students begin to view the equals symbol as a way to show a relationship and not as a symbol that tells one to find the answer.

▶ Advance Preparation

Label 2 sets of index cards with numbers 0 through 9. Label 4 other cards with the $+$, $-$, $\times$, and $\div$ symbols. On 5 additional cards, write one each of the following expressions:

- $8 + 2$
- $15 - 3$
- $7 + 0$
- 5×1
- $4 + 4$

Materials to Gather

SUPPLIED

Equal Expressions activity page

ALSO NEEDED

index cards – numbered 0 through 9 (two sets)

index cards – labeled with $+$, $-$, $\times$, $\div$ symbols

index cards – labeled with expressions

GET READY Expression Matchup

Students will read addition and subtraction story problems and choose the correct expression that represents the problem. They will then determine the correct sum or difference to solve the problem.

Objectives

- Write and solve addition or subtraction number sentences to represent problem-solving situations with sums and minuends up through 1,000.

LEARN Is It Equal?

Students will explore the equals symbol and learn that number sentences show two equal expressions. They will see that a number sentence is like a balance where expressions on both sides have the same value. Students will practice finding different expressions with the same value. Understanding that the equals symbol is used to show a relationship between two expressions is emphasized throughout the activity.

Objectives

- Use an equation to represent a relationship between quantities.

LEARN Same Value

Students will learn about the equals symbol ($=$) and writing number sentences. An equals symbol shows that two expressions have the same value. A number sentence can show that two expressions are equal. Here are some examples of number sentences:

$$4 + 1 = 5 \qquad 6 = 6 \qquad 9 = 10 - 1 \qquad 3 + 4 = 9 - 2$$

Understanding that the equals symbol is used to show a relationship between two expressions is emphasized throughout the activity. Gather the labeled index cards.

1. Show students the $8 + 2$ expression card. Have students record the expression in their Math Notebook and determine its value. 10

2. Ask students to use the number cards and symbol cards to make an expression that is equal to the expression on the $8 + 2$ card. (For example, $8 + 2$ has the same value as $6 + 4$.) Have students record this expression and several others. **Sample answers:** $5 + 5, 2 \times 5, 1 + 9, 12 - 2, 90 - 80$

3. Have students continue to find other expressions that are equal. Ask them to use more than one operation symbol in each expression. Have students record their expression. **Sample answer:** $3 + 5 + 2$

4. Discuss with students the number of different expressions that have the same value as the expression on the card. Guide students to see that there is an endless number of expressions with the same value.

5. Place the other expression cards face down in front of students. Ask students to select an expression card and use the number cards and symbol cards to create an expression that's equal to the expression on the card they chose. Have students write the two expressions (the one they selected and the one they came up with) as a number sentence. Repeat this step.

6. Repeat Step 5 two or three times, using different expression cards.

Objectives

- Use an equation to represent a relationship between quantities.

Tips

Point out that when students solve a story problem, they write a number sentence with an expression on each side of an equals symbol. Present a few simple story problems, and have students write the number sentence. Example: Sam has 16 flowers. He gives 4 flowers to his sister. How many flowers does he have left? Number sentence: $16 - 4 = 12$.

7. Place the equals symbol card in front of students. Ask students to explain what the symbol means and how it is used. Remind students that the equals symbol is used in number sentences and shows that two expressions have the same value or are equal.

8. Have students look at their lists of number sentences.

Ask: Where did you place the equals symbol? between two equal expressions
Ask: How do you know that you wrote a number sentence? I have two expressions that have the same value separated by an equals symbol.

9. Have students read their number sentences aloud. **Sample answer:** $8 + 2 = 10 - 0$ is read "Eight plus two is equal to ten minus zero."

OFFLINE
15 min

TRY IT Equal Expressions

Objectives

- Use an equation to represent a relationship between quantities.

Students will practice writing equal expressions and number sentences. For Problem 1, they will write five expressions equal to the given expression. Encourage them to use different operations and even more than one operation in an expression. Remember that the number of equivalent expressions is limitless. For Problems 2–6, students will match equal expressions and then place an equals symbol between the expressions to form a number sentence. Check students' placement of the equals symbol.

Have students turn to the Equal Expressions activity page in their Activity Book and read the directions with them. Students should copy the problems into their Math Notebook as necessary and solve them there.

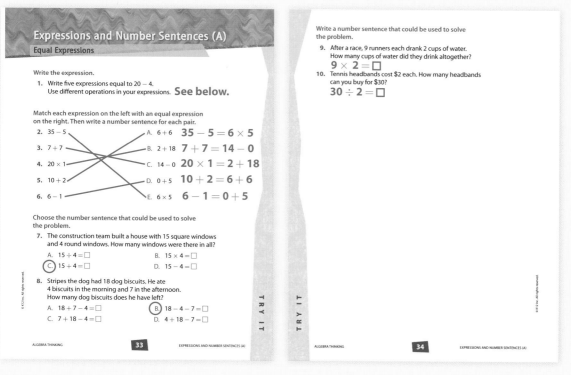

Expressions and Number Sentences (A)
Equal Expressions

Write the expression.

1. Write five expressions equal to $20 - 4$.
   Use different operations in your expressions. **See below.**

Match each expression on the left with an equal expression on the right. Then write a number sentence for each pair.

2. $35 - 5$ A. $6 + 6$ $35 - 5 = 6 \times 5$
3. $7 + 7$ B. $2 + 18$ $7 + 7 = 14 - 0$
4. 20×1 C. $14 - 0$ $20 \times 1 = 2 + 18$
5. $10 + 2$ D. $0 + 5$ $10 + 2 = 6 + 6$
6. $6 - 1$ E. 6×5 $6 - 1 = 0 + 5$

Choose the number sentence that could be used to solve the problem.

7. The construction team built a house with 15 square windows and 4 round windows. How many windows were there in all?
   A. $15 \div 4 = \square$ B. $15 \times 4 = \square$
   C. $15 + 4 = \square$ D. $15 - 4 = \square$

8. Stripes the dog had 18 dog biscuits. He ate 4 biscuits in the morning and 7 in the afternoon. How many dog biscuits does he have left?
   A. $18 + 7 - 4 = \square$ B. $18 - 4 - 7 = \square$
   C. $7 + 18 - 4 = \square$ D. $4 + 18 - 7 = \square$

Write a number sentence that could be used to solve the problem.

9. After a race, 9 runners each drank 2 cups of water. How many cups of water did they drink altogether?
   $9 \times 2 = \square$
10. Tennis headbands cost $2 each. How many headbands can you buy for $30?
   $30 \div 2 = \square$

TRY IT

Additional Answer

1. Answers will vary. **Sample answers:** $8 + 8$; 2×8; $12 + 4$; $32 \div 2$; $4 + 4 + 4 + 4$; $16 - 0$

Expressions and Number Sentences (B)

Lesson Overview

Skills Update	5 minutes	ONLINE
LEARN Carnival Game	30 minutes	ONLINE
TRY IT Choose the Number Sentence	15 minutes	OFFLINE
CHECKPOINT	10 minutes	ONLINE

▶ Lesson Objectives

Use an equation to represent a relationship between quantities.

▶ Prerequisite Skills

Write and solve addition or subtraction number sentences to represent problem-solving situations with sums and minuends up through 1,000.

▶ Content Background

A mathematical *expression* is a combination of numbers and symbols that represents a given value. For example, $2 + 3$ and $4 - 3$ are expressions. An expression can also be a single number. The number 5 alone is an expression.

An expression does not include the symbols $=$, $<$, and $>$. When two or more expressions are put together with an equals symbol ($=$), this creates an *equation*. For example, $2 + 3$ is an expression, but $2 + 3 = 5$ is an equation.

When two or more expressions are put together with a less-than ($<$), greater-than ($>$), or not-equal-to ($\neq$) symbol, this creates an *inequality*. While $2 + 3$ and 6 are each expressions, $2 + 3 < 6$ is an inequality. (We will not introduce the terms *equation* and *inequality* to students at this level; we will refer to both as *number sentences*.)

In this lesson, students will continue to learn about number sentences that have an equals symbol (equations). The equals symbol shows that two expressions have the same value. It is important that students begin to view the equals symbol as a way to show a relationship and not as a symbol that tells one to find the answer.

Materials to Gather

SUPPLIED

Choose the Number Sentence activity page

LEARN Carnival Game

ONLINE
30min

Students will review the meaning and use of multiplication and division. Then they will explore choosing a number sentence that matches a story problem. Remind students that number sentences are made up of expressions. The equals symbol in a number sentence shows that the expressions on each side have the same value.

Also remind students that multiplication is a way of adding equal groups quickly and that division is taking a number of objects and dividing those objects into equal groups.

Objectives

- Use an equation to represent a relationship between quantities.

Tips

If students have difficulty with a problem, have them model it with B blocks or other objects.

TRY IT Choose the Number Sentence

Students will choose the number sentence that matches a given story problem. They will then write number sentences to match story problems. They do not need to solve the story problems; rather, they should stay focused on practicing turning the words into number sentences.

Have students turn to the Choose the Number Sentence activity page from their Activity Book and read the directions with them. Students should copy the problems from the Activity Book into their Math Notebook as necessary and solve them there.

Expressions and Number Sentences (B)
Choose the Number Sentence

Choose the number sentence that represents the problem.

1. Candy Apple Café sells candy apples at the carnival. On Friday, 120 candy apples were sold. On Saturday, 60 candy apples were sold. How many total candy apples were sold on those two days?
   A. $\square = 120 + 60$
   B. $\square = 120 - 60$
   C. $120 \div 60 = \square$

2. The clowns are putting on a show at the carnival. There are 50 people watching the show. Before the show is over, 12 people leave and 9 people arrive. How many people are now watching the show?
   A. $\square = 50 + 12 + 9$
   B. $\square = 50 - 12 - 9$
   C. $\square = 50 - 12 + 9$

3. Candy apples cost $4 each. Jerome and his friends want to buy 8 candy apples. How much money do they need?
   A. $\square = 4 + 8$
   B. $\square = 4 \times 8$
   C. $\square = 8 \div 4$

4. There are 20 people riding the roller coaster. They are in 5 cars, and an equal number of people are in each car. How many people are in each car?
   A. $20 \div 5 = \square$
   B. $20 \times 5 = \square$
   C. $20 + 5 = \square$
   D. $20 - 5 = \square$

5. Paula read 5 pages of her book each hour for 3 hours. How many pages did she read in all?
   A. $5 + 3 = \square$
   B. $5 \times 3 = \square$
   C. $5 \div 3 = \square$
   D. $5 - 3 = \square$

6. Dario had $30. He spent $12 at the toy store and $10 at the paper store. How much money does he have left?
   A. $\$30 + \$12 + \$10 = \square$
   B. $\$30 + \$12 - \$10 = \square$
   C. $\$12 + \$30 - \$10 = \square$
   D. $\$30 - \$12 - \$10 = \square$

7. Sasha had 43 table tennis balls. She lost 22 of them and then found 12. How many balls does she have now?
   A. $43 + 22 + 12 = \square$
   B. $43 - 22 - 12 = \square$
   C. $43 + 22 - 12 = \square$
   D. $43 - 22 + 12 = \square$

Write a number sentence that could be used to solve the problem.

8. Kelly read 250 pages on Saturday and 50 pages on Sunday. How many pages did Kelly read on these two days?
   $250 + 50 = \square$

9. The bakery baked 35 loaves of bread. Of the loaves, 18 were white. The rest were wheat. How many loaves were wheat?
   $35 - 18 = \square$ or $35 = 18 + \square$

10. The gazelle spends 12 hours a day grazing for food. How many hours would the gazelle spend grazing in 5 days?
   $5 \times 12 = \square$ or $12 \times 5 = \square$

TRY IT

CHECKPOINT

Students will complete an online Checkpoint. If necessary, read the directions, problems, and answer choices to students and help them with keyboard or mouse operations.

Expression Comparison (A)

Lesson Overview

GET READY Compare Numbers and Expressions	15 minutes	ONLINE
LEARN Show Expressions	15 minutes	ONLINE
LEARN Compare Expressions	20 minutes	OFFLINE
TRY IT Represent Situations	10 minutes	OFFLINE

▶ Lesson Objectives

Use an inequality to represent a relationship between quantities.

▶ Prerequisite Skills

- Use an equation to represent a relationship between quantities.
- Compare whole numbers through 10,000.

▶ Content Background

Students will use the greater-than (>) and less-than (<) symbols to compare expressions. The greater-than symbol points to the right, and the less-than symbol points to the left. However, it is easier for students to remember that these two comparison symbols point to the lesser number and open to the greater number.

The terms *sign* and *symbol* are often used interchangeably. Although *sign* may be used to refer to greater than (>), less than (<), and equals (=), the term *symbol* will be used in this lesson because it is a more accurate mathematical term. In math, *sign* specifically refers to the positive signs and negative signs of numbers.

▶ Advance Preparation

Label 3 index cards with words and symbols for **greater than (>)**, **less than (<)**, and **equals (=)**. On 10 index cards, write one each of the following math expressions:

- 3×5
- 9×2
- 2×5
- 6×2
- 3×6
- $9 + 6$
- $5 + 5$
- $4 + 12$
- $8 + 8$
- $9 + 3$

Materials to Gather

SUPPLIED

Represent Situations activity page

ALSO NEEDED

index cards – labeled with words and symbols

index cards – labeled with expressions

GET READY Compare Numbers and Expressions

ONLINE 15min

Students will use a greater-than symbol (>) or a less-than symbol (<) to compare numbers and expressions.

Objectives

- Use an equation to represent a relationship between quantities.
- Compare whole numbers through 10,000.

LEARN Show Expressions

ONLINE 15min

Students will match expressions to story problem situations. This is an important skill in learning to solve story problems. Remind students that expressions by themselves do not include an equals symbol. However, numbers sentences, which compare expressions, can include a less-than, greater-than, or equals symbol.

Objectives

- Use an inequality to represent a relationship between quantities.

LEARN Compare Expressions

OFFLINE 20min

Students will use an equals symbol to show equivalent expressions. Then they will use greater-than and less-than symbols to compare expressions. Gather the labeled index cards.

1. Display the 10 prepared number-expression cards. Set the 3 symbol cards aside.

2. Choose an expression, such as $9 + 6$, and display the equals symbol (=) card after it. Read the expression displayed: nine plus six equals. Point out that the equals symbol is read as "equals" in a number sentence. Ask students to name the sum. 15

3. Tell students they need to identify another expression that has a value of 15 to make a true number sentence. 3×5

   Have students read the completed number sentence, emphasizing the equivalent quantities.

4. Return the expressions to the group of number expression cards.

5. Repeat Steps 2–4 three more times.

6. Put the equals symbol aside and display the greater-than (>) and less-than (<) symbols.

7. Choose two expressions that are not equal, such as $4 + 12$ and 6×2. Explain to students that when expressions are not equal, they should use the greater-than or less-than symbol to make a number sentence.

8. Ask students which symbol should be placed between the two expressions to make a true number sentence. Remind students that the symbol points to the lesser quantity and opens to the greater quantity.

9. Have students read the number sentence and check that it is true. Have them say the product or sum of each expression.

10. Repeat Steps 7–9 three more times.

Objectives

- Use an inequality to represent a relationship between quantities.

Tips

Have students write the sum or product on the back of each number-expression card. Then have them flip over the cards to check their number sentences.

TRY IT Represent Situations

- Use an inequality to represent a relationship between quantities.

Students will practice using the greater-than ($>$), less-than ($<$), and equals ($=$) symbols to compare expressions. Then they will practice choosing an expression that matches a given situation. Have students turn to the Represent Situations activity page in their Activity Book and read the directions with them.

Students should copy the problems from their Activity Book into their Math Notebook as necessary and solve them there.

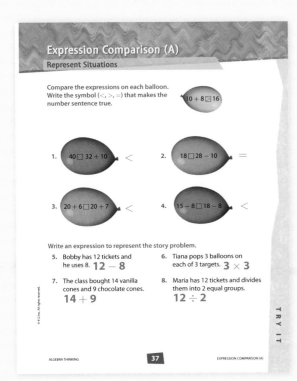

Expression Comparison (B)

▶ Lesson Objectives

Use an inequality to represent a relationship between quantities.

▶ Prerequisite Skills

- Use an equation to represent a relationship between quantities.
- Compare whole numbers through 10,000.

▶ Content Background

Students will continue to use the greater-than ($>$) and less-than ($<$) symbols to compare expressions. The greater-than symbol points to the right, and the less-than symbol points to the left. However, it is easier for students to remember that these two comparison symbols point to the lesser number and open to the greater number.

The terms *sign* and *symbol* are often used interchangeably. Although *sign* may be used to refer to greater than ($>$), less than ($<$), and equals ($=$), the term *symbol* will be used in this lesson because it is a more accurate mathematical term. In math, *sign* specifically refers to the positive signs and negative signs of numbers.

Materials to Gather

SUPPLIED

Compare Quantities activity page

Write Expressions activity page

LEARN Situation Expressions

ONLINE 15 min

Students will match math expressions with everyday situations. Then they will learn how to break apart a situation and write the two expressions as a comparison number sentence. Allow them to calculate problems with paper and pencil.

Objectives

- Use an inequality to represent a relationship between quantities.

LEARN Compare Quantities

Students will use a greater-than or less-than symbol to write a number sentence that compares quantities in a practical situation.

Have students turn to the Compare Quantities activity page in their Activity Book. Students should copy the problems from the Activity Book into their Math Notebook as necessary and solve them there.

1. Discuss the Worked Examples with students. Tell students that there are two expressions in this situation.

2. Have students identify the two different expressions. Remind students that an expression can be a number, such as 8.

3. Ask students what math operation shows 4 racks with 3 pretzels on each rack. Guide students to see that equal groups, with the same number in each group, indicate multiplication.

4. Have students compare the two expressions. Guide students to think of 4×3 as 12. Tell students that thinking of each expression as a number makes it easier to compare.

5. Remind students that the comparison symbol points to the lesser quantity and opens to the greater quantity. Tell students that because 12 is greater than 8, 4×3 is greater than 8.

6. Guide students to complete each section of Problems 1 and 2.

7. Have students write a number sentence for each situation in Problems 3–8. Remind them that the expressions should match the situations and the symbols should compare the quantities.

Objectives

- Use an inequality to represent a relationship between quantities.

Tips

Have students use different-colored highlighters to identify each part of the situation.

Expression Comparison (B)
Compare Quantities

Worked Examples

You can use the $<$, $>$, or $=$ symbol to write a number sentence that compares quantities in story problems.

PROBLEM There are 4 racks with 3 pretzels on each rack. There is a bag of 8 pretzels.

SOLUTION

❶ Break the situation into parts that can be written as expressions.

❷ Decide if the first expression is less than, greater than, or equal to the second expression.

❸ Compare the expressions with $<$, $>$, or $=$.

Expression 1:
4 racks with 3 pretzels on each rack
4×3

THINK:
$4 \times 3 = 12$

Expression 2:
bag of 8 pretzels
8

ANSWER

Number sentence:
$4 \times 3 > 8$

ALGEBRA THINKING   **38**   EXPRESSION COMPARISON (B)

Write an expression to match the situation. Then write a number sentence to compare the numbers that are in the expression.

1. Mr. Weaver has 25 peanuts and gives the same number of peanuts to each of his 5 children. Mrs. Mead has 4 peanuts.

   Expression 1:
   25 peanuts to each of 5 children
   $25 \square 5 \div$

   Think:
   $25 \square 5 = 5 \div$

   Expression 2:
   _?_ peanuts **4 peanuts**
   _?_ **4**

   Number sentence:
   _?_ $25 \div 5 > 4$

2. Lola has 10 rings. Kari has 2 rings on each of 5 fingers.

   Expression 1:
   _?_ rings **10**

   Expression 2:   **5**
   _2_ _?_ rings on each of _?_ fingers

   Think:
   _?_ $2 \times 5 = 10$

   Number sentence:
   _?_ $10 = 2 \times 5$

Write a number sentence to compare the numbers that are in the situation.

3. There are 45 children in the red line and 23 in the blue line for the roller coaster. There are 62 children in line for the fun house. $45 + 23 > 62$

4. There are 72 prizes at the duck booth, and 49 prizes are given away. There are 56 prizes at the bottle booth. $72 - 49 < 56$

5. There are 3 riders on the swings. On the cars there are 30 riders separated equally into 5 groups. $3 < 30 \div 5$

6. Each of 5 children tosses 3 rings. Mike tosses 8 rings. $5 \times 3 > 8$

7. There are 22 candy apples, and 18 are eaten. Seven children buy drinks. $22 - 18 < 7$

8. Naomi plays games for 45 minutes. Allie plays skee ball for 10 minutes and ring toss for 20 minutes. $45 > 10 + 20$

ALGEBRA THINKING   **39**   EXPRESSION COMPARISON (B)

TRY IT Write Expressions

Objectives

- Use an inequality to represent a relationship between quantities.

Students will practice writing expressions and number sentences to describe quantities in a given situation. Have students turn to the Write Expressions page in their Activity Book and read the directions with them.

Students should copy the problems from the Activity Book into their Math Notebook as necessary and solve them there.

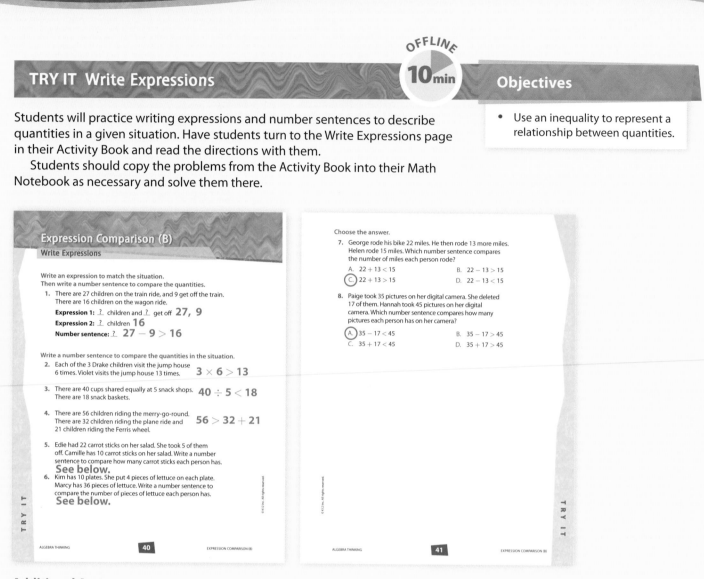

Expression Comparison (B)
Write Expressions

Write an expression to match the situation.
Then write a number sentence to compare the quantities.

1. There are 27 children on the train ride, and 9 get off the train. There are 16 children on the wagon ride.

   Expression 1: ? children and ? get off **27, 9**
   Expression 2: ? children **16**
   Number sentence: ? $27 - 9 > 16$

Write a number sentence to compare the quantities in the situation.

2. Each of the 3 Drake children visit the jump house 6 times. Violet visits the jump house 13 times. $3 \times 6 > 13$

3. There are 40 cups shared equally at 5 snack shops. There are 18 snack baskets. $40 \div 5 < 18$

4. There are 56 children riding the merry-go-round. There are 32 children riding the plane ride and 21 children riding the Ferris wheel. $56 > 32 + 21$

5. Edie had 22 carrot sticks on her salad. She took 5 of them off. Camille has 10 carrot sticks on her salad. Write a number sentence to compare how many carrot sticks each person has.
   See below.

6. Kim has 10 plates. She put 4 pieces of lettuce on each plate. Marcy has 36 pieces of lettuce. Write a number sentence to compare the number of pieces of lettuce each person has.
   See below.

ALGEBRA THINKING   40   EXPRESSION COMPARISON (B)

Choose the answer.

7. George rode his bike 22 miles. He then rode 13 more miles. Helen rode 15 miles. Which number sentence compares the number of miles each person rode?

   A. $22 + 13 < 15$ B. $22 - 13 > 15$
   C. $22 + 13 > 15$ D. $22 - 13 < 15$

8. Paige took 35 pictures on her digital camera. She deleted 17 of them. Hannah took 45 pictures on her digital camera. Which number sentence compares how many pictures each person has on her camera?

   A. $35 - 17 < 45$ B. $35 - 17 > 45$
   C. $35 + 17 < 45$ D. $35 + 17 > 45$

ALGEBRA THINKING   41   EXPRESSION COMPARISON (B)

Additional Answers

5. **Example:** $22 - 5 > 10$; Other correct answers are acceptable.

6. **Example:** $10 \times 4 > 36$; Other correct answers are acceptable.

CHECKPOINT

Objectives

- Use an inequality to represent a relationship between quantities.

Students will complete an online Checkpoint. If necessary, read the directions, problems, and answer choices to students and help them with keyboard or mouse operations.

Missing Symbols

GET READY Number Sentences	10 minutes	ONLINE
LEARN Missing Operation Symbols	15 minutes	ONLINE
LEARN Find the Symbol	15 minutes	OFFLINE
TRY IT Make It True	10 minutes	OFFLINE
CHECKPOINT	10 minutes	ONLINE

▶ Lesson Objectives

Select the appropriate symbol to show an operation or a relationship that makes a number sentence true.

▶ Prerequisite Skills

- Write and solve addition or subtraction number sentences to represent problem-solving situations with sums and minuends up through 1,000.
- Use an equation to represent a relationship between quantities.
- Use an inequality to represent a relationship between quantities.

▶ Content Background

An *expression* is a combination of numbers and symbols that represents a given value. For example, $2 + 3$ and $4 - 3 + ?$ are expressions. Also, a number alone, such as 5, is an expression. An expression does not include relational symbols, such as $=$, $<$, and $>$, in the way number sentences do.

Operation symbols ($+$, $-$, $\times$, $\div$) and relation symbols ($<$, $>$, $=$) make number sentences true. Operation symbols show an action to be performed with numbers, while relation symbols show the relationship between numbers and quantities. When working with students, avoid the term *relation symbols*. Instead, refer to them as *comparison symbols* or *symbols that compare expressions* to show whether two expressions are equal or one is greater than or less than the other. It is important that students focus on the meaning of operation symbols and relation or comparison symbols to be sure that number sentences show true relationships between quantities.

▶ Advance Preparation

Place a piece of clear tape on 3 yellow E blocks. Write a comparison symbol ($<$, $>$, $=$) on each.

Materials to Gather

SUPPLIED
Make It True activity page
blocks – E (3 yellow)

ALSO NEEDED
clear tape
marker

GET READY Number Sentences

ONLINE 10 min

Objectives

Students will review the meaning and use of operation symbols $(+, -, \times, \div)$ and comparison symbols $(<, >, =)$. The operation symbols tell students which operation to do. The comparison symbols compare the expressions to indicate whether they are equal or whether one is greater than or less than another. Students will also review how to represent a story problem with a number sentence, and they will solve a story problem.

- Write and solve addition or subtraction number sentences to represent problem-solving situations with sums and minuends up through 1,000.
- Use an equation to represent a relationship between quantities.
- Use an inequality to represent a relationship between quantities.

LEARN Missing Operation Symbols

ONLINE 15 min

Objectives

Students will use their knowledge of operation symbols $(+, -, \times, \div)$ to determine which operation symbol can be used to make a number sentence true. Remind students that when they see an expression on one side of a number sentence, they should find its value. For example, if they see the number sentence $5 + 5 = 2 \underset{?}{} 8$, they should first find the value of $5 + 5$. Then they should figure out the correct operation symbol for the other side of the number sentence. In this example, they should be able to fill in the correct operation symbol to show that $5 + 5 = 2 + 8$.

- Select the appropriate symbol to show an operation or a relationship that makes a number sentence true.

LEARN Find the Symbol

OFFLINE 15 min

Objectives

Students will put the correct comparison symbol in number sentences to make the number sentences true.

Gather the labeled blocks. During the activity, students should write the number sentences in their Math Notebook.

- Select the appropriate symbol to show an operation or a relationship that makes a number sentence true.

1. Show students the comparison symbols $(<, >, =)$ on the yellow blocks. Explain that comparison symbols tell whether an expression is less than, greater than, or equal to another expression.

2. Write $10 + 10 \underset{?}{} 20$ large enough so that students can place a labeled block on the number sentence for the answer.

3. Have students look at both sides and decide whether they are equal or not.

   Ask: What is the value of $10 + 10$? Is it the same as 20? If not, is it greater than 20 or less than 20?

   Say: Place the correct symbol between the $10 + 10$ and the 20.
   Correct symbol: $=$

4. Repeat with the following number sentences:
   - $10 - 10 \underset{?}{} 20$ Correct symbol: $<$
   - $10 \times 10 \underset{?}{} 20$ Correct symbol: $>$

   Review the greater-than and less-than symbols. Demonstrate that each symbol opens toward the greater number and points at the lesser number. Ask students to think of ways to remember this fact.

Tips

Ask students to write their own true number sentences by using at least one operation symbol and one comparison symbol.

5. Explain that sometimes the comparison symbol is on the left in the number sentence. Write these problems. Have students fill in the correct comparison symbol to make the number sentence true.

- $30 \underline{\ ?\ } 20 + 20$ Correct symbol: $<$
- $30 \underline{\ ?\ } 30 - 0$ Correct symbol: $=$
- $30 \underline{\ ?\ } 25 - 25$ Correct symbol: $>$
- $30 \underline{\ ?\ } 25 + 3$ Correct symbol: $>$

6. Challenge students to place the correct comparison symbol into number sentences with two operation symbols, such as the following:

- $5 + 4 \underline{\ ?\ } 10 - 2$ Correct answer: $>$
- $8 - 3 \underline{\ ?\ } 4 + 1$ Correct answer: $=$

OFFLINE
10 min

TRY IT Make It True

Objectives

- Select the appropriate symbol to show an operation or a relationship that makes a number sentence true.

Students will decide which operation or comparison symbol is needed to make a true number sentence. Have students turn to the Make It True activity page in their Activity Book and read the directions with them.

Students should copy the problems from the Activity Book into their Math Notebook as necessary and solve them there.

Missing Symbols
Make It True

Memory Jogger

When solving for a missing operation or comparison symbol, find the value of expressions first.

Example:
Write the comparison symbol ($<$, $>$, $=$) to make the number sentence true.
$$\overset{12}{5 + 7} \leq 13$$

Example:
Write the operation symbol ($+$, $-$, $\times$, $\div$) to make the number sentence true.
$$\overset{17}{7 + 10} = 20 \,\underline{-}\, 3$$

Write the operation symbol ($+$, $-$, $\times$, $\div$) that makes the number sentence true.

1. $15 \square 3 = 18$ $+$
2. $30 = 10 \square 3$ $\times$
3. $20 \square 4 = 16$ $-$
4. $8 = 16 \square 2$ $\div$
5. $6 + 7 = 21 \square 8$ $-$
6. $5 \square 4 = 9 + 11$ $\times$
7. $15 \square 5 = 8 - 5$ $\div$
8. $3 \times 10 = 24 \square 6$ $+$

Write the comparison symbol ($<$, $>$, $=$) that makes the number sentence true.

9. $16 + 7 \square 24$ $<$
10. $9 \square 14 - 5$ $=$
11. $55 \square 5 \times 10$ $>$
12. $47 - 13 \square 30$ $>$
13. $0 + 5 \square 3 \times 10$ $<$
14. $12 \square 4 \times 3$ $=$
15. $7 - 7 \square 7 - 0$ $<$
16. $28 + 12 \square 38$ $>$

TRY IT

ALGEBRA THINKING   **42**   MISSING SYMBOLS
ALGEBRA THINKING   **43**   MISSING SYMBOLS

ONLINE
10 min

CHECKPOINT

Objectives

- Select the appropriate symbol to show an operation or a relationship that makes a number sentence true.

Students will complete an online Checkpoint. If necessary, read the directions, problems, and answer choices to students and help them with keyboard or mouse operations.

Missing Values (A)

GET READY Choose the Sentence	10 minutes	**ONLINE**
LEARN Choose the Symbol	15 minutes	**ONLINE**
LEARN True Statements	25 minutes	**OFFLINE**
TRY IT What's Missing?	10 minutes	**OFFLINE**

▶ Lesson Objectives

Determine a missing number in an equation or an inequality.

▶ Prerequisite Skills

- Write and solve addition or subtraction number sentences to represent problem-solving situations with sums and minuends up through 1,000.
- Use an equation to represent a relationship between quantities.
- Use an inequality to represent a relationship between quantities.

▶ Content Background

Students will use their understanding of operation symbols ($+$, $-$, $\times$, $\div$), relation symbols ($<$, $>$, $=$), and inverse operations to find a missing value that will make a number sentence true. Students will see problems such as the following:

- $30 = 25 + \square$
- $10 + 20 = 3 \times \square$
- $17 > 9 + \square$

Students will learn that number sentences with an equals symbol and one missing value, such as the first two examples, have only one correct answer. They will learn that a number sentence with a greater-than or less-than symbol (an inequality), such as the last example, can be true with a range of different values in the blank space. As students complete these types of problems, they will become more fluent with expressions, number sentences, and the type of thinking that will be useful for algebra in the future.

▶ Advance Preparation

Label a set of small sticky notes with numbers 0 through 9. They should be small enough that students can stick them on the page.

Materials to Gather

SUPPLIED

True Statements activity page

What's Missing? activity page

ALSO NEEDED

sticky notes, small – labeled 0–9

GET READY Choose the Sentence

Students will review the use of number sentences to represent a relationship between quantities. First they will decide which number sentence can be used to solve a story problem. Then they will decide which number sentence compares two expressions. Finally students will solve a story problem.

Objectives

- Write and solve addition or subtraction number sentences to represent problem-solving situations with sums and minuends up through 1,000.
- Use an equation to represent a relationship between quantities.
- Use an inequality to represent a relationship between quantities.

LEARN Choose the Symbol

Students will identify the two expressions that make up a number sentence. Remind students that expressions have numbers and operation symbols, while number sentences are made up of expressions with a comparison symbol between them, showing whether the expressions are equal or one expression is greater than or less than the other. After identifying the expressions in a number sentence, students will decide which comparison symbol will make the number sentence true.

Objectives

- Determine a missing number in an equation or an inequality.

Tips

Mention that when reading the greater-than and less-than symbols, students can read the symbols left to right. If the left side is the greater opening ($>$), students read "greater than." If the left side is the smaller point ($<$), students read "less than."

LEARN True Statements

Students will create expressions to make number sentences true. Then they will use a set of numbered sticky notes to fill in missing values and make true number sentences. Finally, they will write missing values in number sentences.

Have students turn to the True Statements activity page in their Activity Book. Students should copy the problems from the Activity Book into their Math Notebook as necessary and solve them there. Set aside the sticky notes until later in the activity.

1. Discuss the Worked Examples with students.
2. Have students look at Problem 1. Ask them to identify the expression on the left side of the equals symbol and to simplify the expression by finding its value. $5 + 7; 12$
3. Point to the right side of the number sentence. Ask students what two numbers added together have the same value as $5 + 7$, or 12. Encourage students to name numbers other than 5 and 7 that have a sum of 12, such as $6 + 6$ or $8 + 4$.
4. Explain that the numbers 8 and 4 make the number sentence true because the quantity on each side of the equals symbol is the same. Tell students that the numbers 9 and 4 would make the number sentence false because the value of 9 and 4 is 13, not 12.

Objectives

- Determine a missing number in an equation or an inequality.

Tips

You may wish to have students place a clear plastic sheet over the activity page and use an erasable marker for exercises that don't require the sticky notes. If you have numbered counters or tiles, you can use them instead of sticky notes.

5. Have students complete Problems 2–6. They should find the value of the given expression and then identify numbers that have a sum or difference of the same value. Check students' work.

6. Have students look at Problems 7 and 8. Point out that these problems use the less-than and greater-than symbols rather than the equals symbol. Explain that the best strategy is to solve them as though there is an equals symbol and then adjust the numbers so that one expression is greater than or less than the other. In Problem 7, have students simplify the expression on the right first to find that its value is 4 (because $8 - 4 = 4$). Explain that they need to create an expression with a difference less than 4. Any expression with a value less than 4 will work. Use the same strategy to solve Problem 8.

7. Display the sticky notes numbered 0–9. Tell students they will use the sticky notes to complete Problems 9–15. Explain that they have 10 notes and there are 10 empty boxes. Emphasize that each note will be used only once to complete the problems. Students should place the notes in the boxes on the activity page to make each number sentence true.

8. Guide students to complete the problems with only one box first and then use the remaining notes to complete the problems with two boxes. Note that some problems would normally have more than one possible answer; however, because each note can be used only one time, there is only one correct way to place the 10 notes so that each number sentence is true.

9. As students complete the problems, ask questions such as the following, using their answers from the activity page:

- What number subtracted from 5 equals 4? 1
- What two numbers added together equal 5? 2, 3
- What number added to 4 equals 4? 0

10. Direct students' attention to Problems 16–21. Tell students they will use the sticky notes again to make these number sentences true. Ask students what differences they see in Problems 16–21. Explain that generally with less-than and greater-than symbols, there is more than one possible answer. Remind students that since each note can be used only once, there is only one correct way to place the 10 notes so every number sentence is true. Be sure students complete the problems in order so possible solutions are narrowed down with each subsequent problem.

11. As students complete the problems, ask questions such as the following, using their answers from the activity page:

- What numbers added together have a value less than 2? 0, 1
- What numbers added together have a value less than 6? 2, 3
- What number added to 6 has a sum less than 11? 4

12. Have students set aside the sticky notes and look at Problems 22–27. Explain that some of these missing numbers are greater than 9 and some have more than one possible solution. Ask questions such as the following:

- What number added to 9 equals 17? 8
- What number added to 9 is greater than 17? any number greater than 8
- What number is greater than the sum of 8 and 9? any number greater than 17

Tips

Remind students that some exercises have more than one correct answer.

Worked Examples

You can create an expression to make a number sentence true.

PROBLEM 1 Create an expression to make the number sentence true.

$$8 + 7 = \square + \square$$

SOLUTION Find the value of the expression you know: $8 + 7 = 15$.
Look at the operation in the unknown expression (addition).
Find numbers that add up to 15.

$$8 \overset{15}{+} 7 = \boxed{10} + \boxed{5}$$

ANSWER The answer can be any numbers with a sum of 15, such as $15 + 0$, $14 + 1$, or $13 + 2$.

PROBLEM 2 Create an expression to make the number sentence true.

$$\square - \square < 9 - 2$$

SOLUTION Find the value of the expression you know: $9 - 2 = 7$.

$$\square - \square < 9 \overset{7}{-} 2$$

Look at the comparison symbol (less than) and find a number less than 7 (such as 6). Find two numbers whose difference is 6 or less than 6.

$$\square \overset{6}{-} \square < 9 - 2$$

ANSWER $\boxed{9} - \boxed{3} < 9 - 2$

The answer can be any numbers whose difference is less than 7 such as $7 - 1$, $10 - 9$, or $100 - 95$.

Create an expression to make the number sentence true.
Some problems have several correct answers.

1. $5 + 7 = \square + \square$ **any numbers with a sum of 12**

2. $8 + 8 = \square + \square$ **any numbers with a sum of 16**

3. $\square + \square = 6 - 4$ **$0 + 2$ or $1 + 1$**

4. $\square + \square = 6 - 6$ **$0 + 0$**

5. $\square - \square = 4$ **any numbers with a difference of 4**

6. $\square - \square = 8 - 4$ **any numbers with a difference of 4**

7. $\square - \square < 8 - 4$ **any numbers with a difference less than 4**

8. $\square - \square > 8 - 4$
any numbers with a difference greater than 4

Use sticky notes labeled 0–9. Place a note in the box to make the number sentence true. Use each note once. When you've finished, remove the sticky notes and record your answers.

9. $5 - \boxed{?} = 4$ **1**
10. $\boxed{?} + \boxed{?} = 5$ **2, 3**

11. $13 - \boxed{?} = 7$ **6**
12. $\boxed{?} + 4 = 4$ **0**

13. $\boxed{?} + \boxed{?} = 9$ **4, 5**
14. $\boxed{?} = 19 - 10$ **9**

15. $15 = \boxed{?} + \boxed{?}$ **7, 8**

Use sticky notes labeled 0–9. Place a note in the box to make the number sentence true. Use each note once. When you've finished, remove the sticky notes and record your answers.

16. $\boxed{?} + \boxed{?} < 2$ **0, 1**
17. $\boxed{?} + \boxed{?} < 6$ **2, 3**

18. $11 > \boxed{?} + 6$ **4**
19. $12 = \boxed{?} + \boxed{?}$ **5, 7**

20. $14 < \boxed{?} + 6$ **9**
21. $\boxed{?} < \boxed{?}$ **6, 8**

Complete the number sentence to make it true.
Some problems have several correct answers.

22. $17 = 9 + \underline{?}$ **8**

23. $17 < 9 + \underline{?}$ **any number greater than 8**

24. $17 > 9 + \underline{?}$ **any number less than 8**

25. $8 + 9 < \underline{?}$ **any number greater than 17**

26. $8 + 9 > \underline{?}$ **any number less than 17**

27. $17 - 9 < \underline{?}$ **any number greater than 8**

TRY IT What's Missing?

Students will practice writing a missing number to make a number sentence true. Have students turn to the What's Missing? activity page in their Activity Book and read the directions with them.

Students should copy the problems from the Activity Book into their Math Notebook as necessary and solve them there.

Objectives

- Determine a missing number in an equation or an inequality.

Tips

Remind students that some exercises have more than one correct answer.

Missing Values (A)
What's Missing?

Complete the number sentence to make it true.
Some problems have several correct answers.

1. $8 + \square = 13$ **5**

2. $15 - \square = 12$ **3**

3. $\square - 5 = 17$ **22**

4. $\square = 17 - 9$ **8**

5. $18 - \square = 9$ **9**

6. $\square = 19 - 4$ **15**

7. $13 > \square + 9$ **any number less than 4**

8. $11 + 2 > \square$ **any number less than 13**

9. $6 + 5 = \square + \square$ **any number with a sum of 11**

TRY IT

Missing Values (B)

Lesson Overview		
Skills Update	5 minutes	ONLINE
LEARN Use Inverse Relationships	15 minutes	ONLINE
LEARN Multiplication and Division	30 minutes	OFFLINE
TRY IT Missing Values in Number Sentences	10 minutes	OFFLINE

▶ Lesson Objectives

Determine a missing number in an equation or an inequality.

▶ Prerequisite Skills

- Write and solve addition or subtraction number sentences to represent problem-solving situations with sums and minuends up through 1,000.
- Use an equation to represent a relationship between quantities.
- Use an inequality to represent a relationship between quantities.

▶ Content Background

Students will continue to use their understanding of operation symbols $(+, -, \times, \div)$, relation symbols $(<, >, =)$, and inverse operations to find a missing value that will make a number sentence true. Students will see problems such as the following:

- $30 = 25 + \square$
- $10 + 20 = 3 \times \square$
- $17 > 9 + \square$

Students will learn that number sentences with an equals symbol and one missing value, such as the first two examples, have only one correct answer. They will learn that a number sentence with a greater-than or less-than symbol (an inequality), such as the last example, can be true with a range of different values in the blank space. As students complete these types of problems, they will become more fluent with expressions, number sentences, and the type of thinking that will be more useful for algebra in the future.

▶ Advance Preparation

Print the Centimeter Grid Paper. Cut two rectangles 3 rows by 5 columns from the paper. Keep the unused paper for use in the activity.

Materials to Gather

SUPPLIED

Multiplication and Division activity page

Missing Values in Number Sentences activity page

blocks – B (15 of any color)

Centimeter Grid Paper (printout)

ALSO NEEDED

scissors, adult

LEARN Use Inverse Relationships

Students will use part-part-total charts and the inverse relationship of addition and subtraction to help them find missing numbers in number sentences. Provide paper and pencil for student calculations.

LEARN Multiplication and Division

Students will use arrays and the inverse relationship of multiplication and division to help them find missing numbers in number sentences. Remind students that an array is an arrangement of objects in rows and columns. Also remind them that rows are horizontal—they go across from left to right—and columns are vertical, or up-and-down.

Gather the blocks and the rectangles you prepared from the grid paper print-out. Set the rectangles aside until later in the activity. Have students turn to the Multiplication and Division activity page in their Activity Book. Students should copy the problems from the Activity Book into their Math Notebook as necessary and solve them there.

1. Tell students that expressions can include any operation. They have already worked with addition and subtraction expressions; now they will work with multiplication and division expressions.

2. Discuss the Worked Examples with students. Go over the multiplication problems on the left. Explain that multiplication involves equal groups and that an array is one way to arrange objects so that each row shows an equal group.

3. Have students look at Problem 1 on the activity page. Ask students to use their B blocks to show 3 groups of 5 circles as illustrated on the activity page. Tell students that when there are 3 groups of 5, they say "3 times 5" and write 3×5. Point to 3×5 on the activity page.

4. Tell students that they can use what they know about multiplication to solve number sentences. Work through each number sentence in Problem 1, relating back to the array as necessary. Then ask students how each expression is alike. The value of each expression is 15.

5. Guide students through the number sentences in Problem 2. Have students see how each previous number sentence helps them complete the next number sentence. Have them compare the values of each expression and see that again, they all have a value of 15. Have students note the different ways 15 is shown.

6. Have students complete the number sentences in Problems 3 and 4. As students complete the number sentences in each problem, have them identify the value of each expression. The value of each expression in Problem 3 is 40 and the value of each expression in Problem 4 is 16

7. Point out the grid in Problem 5. Remind students that they have seen multiplication as combining equal groups, such as 3 groups of 5 equals 15. Display one of the prepared rectangle grids to show 3 rows of 5 as on the activity page.

Objectives

- Determine a missing number in an equation or an inequality.

Objectives

- Determine a missing number in an equation or an inequality.

Tips

Allow students to use B blocks or grid paper to make arrays or grids.

8. Explain that the grid can also show that 5 groups of 3 equals 15. Turn the rectangle so that it shows 5 rows of 3.

9. Explain that division is the opposite of multiplication. It undoes multiplication; it is the inverse operation of multiplication. Tell students that division is separating a total amount into equal groups. Write 15 divided by 3 equals 5. Show students one of the rectangles you prepared. Cut the rows of the rectangle into 3 separate strips of 5 squares to show division. Point out that the total, 15, is separated into 3 equal groups and there are 5 squares in each group.

10. Display the other prepared rectangle grid. Explain that the grid can also show 15 divided by 5 equals 3. Cut the rows of this rectangle into 5 separate strips of 3 squares. Point out that the total, 15, is separated into 5 equal groups and there are 3 squares in each group. Use the cut-up rectangles as a guide to help students complete the number sentences in Problem 5.

11. Point to Problem 6, and have students complete the first sentence below the grid. Emphasize that when students need to solve a division problem, they can think of the related multiplication problem. Point to $20 \div 5 = \square$. Guide students to think: How many groups of 5 make 20? 4 groups of 5 equals 20, or $4 \times 5 = 20$, and therefore $20 \div 5 = 4$

12. Guide students to complete the other number sentences in Problem 6, using the grid and the related multiplication facts. Look back at the Worked Example. Direct students' attention to the division problems and see if they can explain how the grid in the Worked Example can help solve the division number sentences.

13. Have students complete the remaining problems. Guide them to find the value of the complete expression to determine the value of the missing number. Remind them to use multiplication to find the missing number in the division expressions.

Missing Values (B)
Multiplication and Division

Worked Examples

You can use arrays or grids to help you find missing numbers in multiplication and division number sentences.

PROBLEM 1 Use the array or grid to help find the missing number to make each number sentence true.

MULTIPLICATION
$35 = 5 \times \square$
$35 = 7 \times \square$

SOLUTION

The array shows 5 rows of 7 or $5 \times 7 = 35$.
Turn the array sideways to show 7 rows of 5 or $7 \times 5 = 35$.

ANSWER
$35 = 5 \times 7$
$35 = 7 \times 5$

PROBLEM 2 Use the array or grid to help find the missing number to make each number sentence true.

DIVISION
$35 \div 5 = \square$
$35 \div 7 = \square$

SOLUTION

The grid shows 35 squares. Cut it into 5 rows of 7 squares to show that $35 \div 5 = 7$. Turn the grid sideways and cut it into 7 rows of 5 squares to show that $35 \div 7 = 5$.

ANSWER
$35 \div 5 = 7$
$35 \div 7 = 5$

This array shows 3 rows of 5 circles. Use your blocks to make this array. Then use the array to help answer the questions.
Write the missing number to make the number sentence true.

1. $3 \times 5 = \square$ **15**
   $15 = \square \times 5$ **3**
   $5 + 5 + 5 = \square \times 5$ **3**

2. $5 \times 3 = \square$ **15**
   $9 + \square = 3 \times 5$ **6**
   $5 + 10 = \square$ **15**

Write the missing number to make the number sentence true.

3. $4 \times 10 = \square$ **40**
   $40 = \square \times 10$ **4**
   $10 + 10 + 10 + 10 = 10 \times \square$ **4**
   $60 - \square = 40$ **20**
   $4 \times 10 = \square + 20$ **20**

4. $2 \times 8 = \square$ **16**
   $8 + 8 = 8 \times \square$ **2**
   $8 \times \square = 16$ **2**
   $20 - \square = 2 \times 8$ **4**
   $8 + 8 = 10 + \square$ **6**

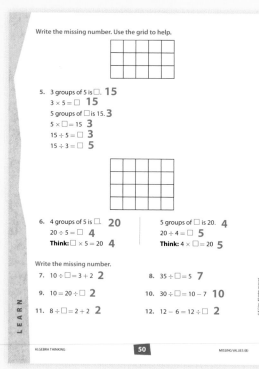

Write the missing number. Use the grid to help.

5. 3 groups of 5 is ☐. **15**
   3 × 5 = ☐ **15**
   5 groups of ☐ is 15. **3**
   5 × ☐ = 15 **3**
   15 ÷ 5 = ☐ **3**
   15 ÷ 3 = ☐ **5**

6. 4 groups of 5 is ☐. **20**   5 groups of ☐ is 20. **4**
   20 ÷ 5 = ☐ **4**   20 ÷ 4 = ☐ **5**
   Think: ☐ × 5 = 20 **4**   **Think:** 4 × ☐ = 20 **5**

Write the missing number.

7. 10 ÷ ☐ = 3 + 2 **2**   8. 35 ÷ ☐ = 5 **7**

9. 10 = 20 ÷ ☐ **2**   10. 30 ÷ ☐ = 10 − 7 **10**

11. 8 ÷ ☐ = 2 + 2 **2**   12. 12 − 6 = 12 ÷ ☐ **2**

LEARN

OFFLINE

10 min

TRY IT Missing Values in Number Sentences

Objectives

- Determine a missing number in an equation or an inequality.

Students will practice using everything they know about operations and expressions to determine the missing value in a number sentence. In problems such as $? \times 3 = 10 - 4$, remind students to find the value of the expression, $10 - 4$, first. When students cannot do a problem in their head, they should be encouraged to use everything they know about the operations. This includes making a part-part-total chart for addition and subtraction, making arrays or using a grid for multiplication or division, and using inverse relationships (or opposite operations) to help solve problems with any of the four operations.

Have students turn to the Missing Values in Number Sentences activity page in their Activity Book and read the directions with them. Students should copy the problems from the Activity Book into their Math Notebook as necessary and solve them there.

Tips

Remind students that addition and subtraction are inverse, or opposite, operations, as are multiplication and division. They can use inverse operations to find missing values in expressions.

Missing Values (B)
Missing Values in Number Sentences

Write the missing number.

1. 65 + ☐ = 92 **27**

2. 87 − ☐ = 45 **42**

3. ☐ + 34 = 71 **37**

4. ☐ − 23 = 35 **58**

5. 8 × ☐ = 30 + 10 **5**

6. ☐ × 3 = 10 − 4 **2**

7. 30 ÷ ☐ = 3 × 2 **5**

8. 5 + 0 = 50 ÷ ☐ **10**

TRY IT

Missing Values (C)

Lesson Overview

Skills Update	5 minutes	ONLINE
LEARN Add or Subtract and Compare	15 minutes	ONLINE
LEARN Compare to Find Missing Values	20 minutes	OFFLINE
TRY IT Simplify and Solve	10 minutes	OFFLINE
CHECKPOINT	10 minutes	ONLINE

▶ Lesson Objectives

Determine a missing number in an equation or an inequality.

▶ Prerequisite Skills

- Write and solve addition or subtraction number sentences to represent problem-solving situations with sums and minuends up through 1,000.
- Use an equation to represent a relationship between quantities.
- Use an inequality to represent a relationship between quantities.

Materials to Gather

SUPPLIED
Compare to Find Missing Values activity page
Simplify and Solve activity page

▶ Content Background

Students will continue to use their understanding of operation symbols $(+, -, \times, \div)$, relation symbols $(<, >, =)$, and inverse operations to find a missing value that will make a number sentence true. Students will see problems such as the following:

- $30 = 25 + \square$
- $10 + 20 = 3 \times \square$
- $17 > 9 + \square$

Students will learn that number sentences with an equals symbol and one missing value, such as the first two examples, have only one correct answer. They will learn that a number sentence with a greater-than or less-than symbol (an inequality), such as the last example, can be true with a range of different values in the blank space. As students complete these types of problems, they will become more fluent with expressions, number sentences, and the type of thinking that will be more useful for algebra in the future.

When students are asked to *simplify*, they are being asked to find a value that is equal to another value but more simple to understand. For example, to simplify 2×5, they would write 10.

LEARN Add or Subtract and Compare

Objectives

- Determine a missing number in an equation or an inequality.

Students will decide which of three answer choices makes a number sentence true. In some of the problems, they will simplify by adding or subtracting to find the value of an expression. Then they will compare the expressions on each side of the comparison symbol. Guide students to see that it is easiest to find the answer that makes the expressions equal and then decide how to make one expression greater than or less than the other. Provide paper and pencil for students calculations.

LEARN Compare to Find Missing Values

Objectives

- Determine a missing number in an equation or an inequality.

Students will determine the missing number in number sentences in which they have to compare the two sides of the number sentence.

Have students turn to the Compare to Find Missing Values activity page in their Activity Book. Students should copy the problems from the Activity Book into their Math Notebook as necessary and solve them there.

1. Tell students that they will learn how to find a missing number in a number sentence when they have to compare the two sides of the number sentence.

2. Have students read aloud the number sentence in the Worked Examples: $2 \times 5 < 5 + ?$

   Ask: What is the expression on the left? 2×5

   Ask: What is the expression on the right? $5 + ?$

   Ask: What comparison symbol separates the two expressions? $<$; less-than symbol

3. Have students read the first two lines of the solution.

   Ask: What is the small, raised 10? It is the value of 5×2.

   Ask: Which expression is the unknown expression, or the one that you don't know the value of? $5 + ?$; the expression on the right

4. Have students read the rest of the solution.

   Ask: Why does the 6 make this number sentence true? The 6 added to the 5 equals 11. We already simplified 2×5 to get 10. The number sentence now says 10 is less than 11, which is true.

5. Have students read the answer.

   Ask: Why can the answer be any number that is greater than 6? As long as 10 is less than the value of the expression on the right side, the number sentence is correct. When number sentences have a less-than or a greater-than symbol, there can be more than one correct answer.

6. Guide students through each problem, helping them simplify expressions. They should write answers for the Think statements when provided. Encourage students to find the number that would make the expressions equal, and then decide if the missing number should be greater or less.

Tips

Have students place a clear plastic sheet over the activity page and use a dry-erase marker to write the missing numbers.

Tips

Remind students that some exercises have more than one correct answer.

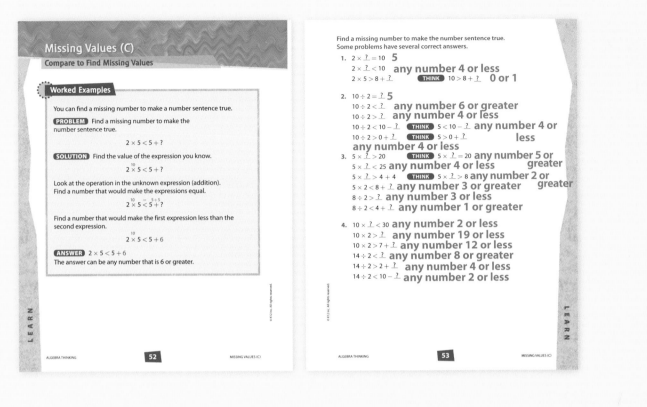

Missing Values (C)
Compare to Find Missing Values

Worked Examples

You can find a missing number to make a number sentence true.

PROBLEM Find a missing number to make the number sentence true.

$$2 \times 5 < 5 + ?$$

SOLUTION Find the value of the expression you know.

$$2 \times 5 < 5 + ?$$
(10 above 2×5)

Look at the operation in the unknown expression (addition). Find a number that would make the expressions equal.

$$2 \times 5 < 5 + ?$$
(10 = 5 + 5 above)

Find a number that would make the first expression less than the second expression.

$$2 \times 5 < 5 + 6$$
(10 above 2×5)

ANSWER $2 \times 5 < 5 + 6$
The answer can be any number that is 6 or greater.

ALGEBRA THINKING | 52 | MISSING VALUES (C)

Find a missing number to make the number sentence true. Some problems have several correct answers.

1. $2 \times ? = 10$ **5**
   $2 \times ? < 10$ **any number 4 or less**
   $2 \times 5 > 8 + ?$ **THINK** $10 > 8 + ?$ **0 or 1**

2. $10 \div 2 = ?$ **5**
   $10 \div 2 < ?$ **any number 6 or greater**
   $10 \div 2 > ?$ **any number 4 or less**
   $10 \div 2 < 10 - ?$ **THINK** $5 < 10 - ?$ **any number 4 or less**
   $10 \div 2 > 0 + ?$ **THINK** $5 > 0 + ?$ **any number 4 or less**

3. $5 \times ? > 20$ **THINK** $5 \times ? = 20$ **any number 5 or greater**
   $5 \times ? < 25$ **any number 4 or less**
   $5 \times ? > 4 + 4$ **THINK** $5 \times ? > 8$ **any number 2 or greater**
   $5 \times 2 < 8 + ?$ **any number 3 or greater**
   $8 \div 2 > ?$ **any number 3 or less**
   $8 \div 2 < 4 + ?$ **any number 1 or greater**

4. $10 \times ? < 30$ **any number 2 or less**
   $10 \times 2 > ?$ **any number 19 or less**
   $10 \times 2 > 7 + ?$ **any number 12 or less**
   $14 \div 2 < ?$ **any number 8 or greater**
   $14 \div 2 > 2 + ?$ **any number 4 or less**
   $14 \div 2 < 10 - ?$ **any number 2 or less**

ALGEBRA THINKING | 53 | MISSING VALUES (C)

TRY IT Simplify and Solve

OFFLINE 10 min

Students will practice finding missing values in number sentences. When number sentences with missing values have a greater-than or less-than symbol, there can be more than one correct answer. Remind students that they have to find only one number that makes the number sentence true. Have students turn to the Simplify and Solve activity page in their Activity Book and read the directions with them.

Students should copy the problems from the Activity Book into their Math Notebook as necessary and solve them there.

Objectives

- Determine a missing number in an equation or an inequality.

Tips

Remind students to look for the number that makes the expressions equal and then find a number that makes the unknown expression either greater or less, whichever is correct for solving the problem.

Tips

Remind students that some exercises have more than one correct answer.

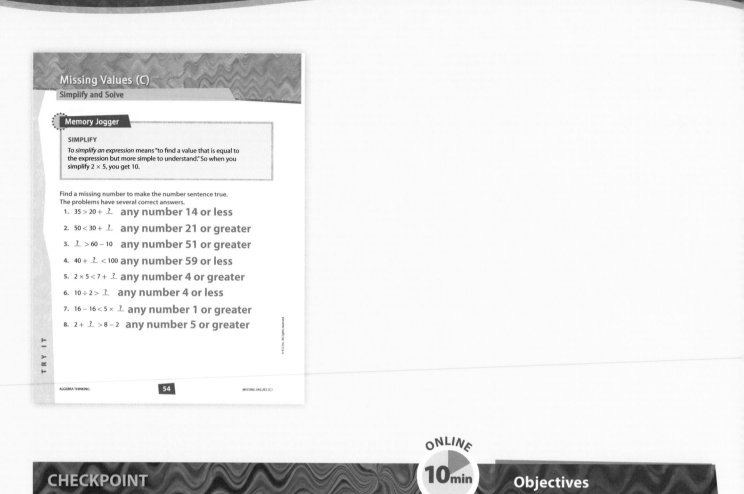

Missing Values (C)
Simplify and Solve

Find a missing number to make the number sentence true.
The problems have several correct answers.

1. $35 > 20 + \underline{?}$ **any number 14 or less**
2. $50 < 30 + \underline{?}$ **any number 21 or greater**
3. $\underline{?} > 60 - 10$ **any number 51 or greater**
4. $40 + \underline{?} < 100$ **any number 59 or less**
5. $2 \times 5 < 7 + \underline{?}$ **any number 4 or greater**
6. $10 \div 2 > \underline{?}$ **any number 4 or less**
7. $16 - 16 < 5 \times \underline{?}$ **any number 1 or greater**
8. $2 + \underline{?} > 8 - 2$ **any number 5 or greater**

TRY IT

CHECKPOINT

ONLINE 10 min

Students will complete an online Checkpoint. If necessary, read the directions, problems, and answer choices to students and help them with keyboard or mouse operations.

Objectives

- Determine a missing number in an equation or an inequality.

Number Patterns

▶ Lesson Objectives

- Extend a linear pattern, such as stating what number comes next in a series.
- Recognize and describe a linear pattern, such as counting by 5s or multiplying 5 times a number to reach 100, by its rule.

▶ Prerequisite Skills

- Describe linear patterns, such as 3, 6, 9, using wheels on 1 tricycle, 2 tricycles, 3 tricycles as an example.
- Determine a next term and extend a linear pattern, such as 3, 6, 9, … as the wheels on 1 tricycle, 2 tricycles, 3 tricycles, and extending it to 12 wheels on 4 tricycles as an example.

▶ Content Background

Students will describe and extend linear patterns.

A *linear pattern* is a number pattern in which each successive number increases or decreases by the same value. A rule describes a linear pattern. You can use a rule to extend a pattern. For example, if the rule is "add 5," the numbers increase by 5. To find the next number, add 5 to the last number shown.

- Linear pattern: 5, 10, 15, 20
- Rule: add 5
- Next number: 25 (20 + 5)

Skip counting creates a linear pattern. For example, skip counting by 2s creates the linear pattern 2, 4, 6, 8, … . The rule for this pattern is "add 2."

Materials to Gather

SUPPLIED

Find the Rule activity page

Describe and Extend activity page

OFFLINE 5min

Students will identify a pattern and find the next number in a sequence. They will see an example of how patterns can represent things in everyday situations. Have students record patterns and rules in their Math Notebook.

- Determine a next term and extend a linear pattern, such as 3, 6, 9, ... as the wheels on 1 tricycle, 2 tricycles, 3 tricycles, and extending it to 12 wheels on 4 tricycles as an example.

1. Tell students you are going to look at number patterns. Start counting by 2s, saying 2, 4, 6, and ask student to continue the pattern until 20. 8, 10, 12, 14, 16, 18, 20

2. **Ask:** Can you say a rule that tells how to get the next number in the pattern? The rule is "add 2."

3. Count by 2s, saying 74, 76, 78. Have students continue the pattern for a few more numbers. Ask for the rule for getting the next number. 80, 82, 84; The rule is "add 2."

4. Count by 2s, saying 83, 85, 87. Have students continue the pattern and say the rule. 89, 91, 93; The rule is "add 2."

   Say: Patterns describe things that we see every day. Note that one hand has 5 fingers (write 5), two hands have 10 fingers (write 10), and so on.

   Have students write 5, 10, _?_, _?_, _?_ in their Math Notebook. Have students continue the pattern and say the rule. Notice that each time we add a hand we add 5 more fingers. The rule is "add 5."

5. Have students write answers for the following questions:

   Ask: Here's a pattern that can show the number of wheels on tricycles. If I have zero tricycles, how many wheels do I have? I have zero wheels. Students write 0.

   Ask: If I have one tricycle, how many wheels do I have? Students write 3.

   Ask: If I have one more tricycle, how many wheels do I have? Students write 6.

   Have students continue the pattern and say the rule. The rule is "add 3."

OFFLINE 15min

Students will fill in missing numbers in patterns and state the rule for the pattern. They will then use what they know about patterns to fill in missing numbers in charts. Emphasize that charts can be used to organize information.

- Extend a linear pattern, such as stating what number comes next in a series.

1. Explain to students that they can use rules to find the next number in many patterns. Write the following pattern, showing the missing numbers as blanks. Have students write the missing numbers and say the rule. If students have difficulty, have them look at the 39 and see how much is added to get to 43.

   - 31, _?_, 39, 43, _?_, 51. **Rule:** plus 4. **Answer:** 31, _35_, 39, 43, _47_, 51

2. Write these patterns and have students fill in the missing numbers and say the rule. If students have difficulty, remind them that rules can involve subtraction as well as addition.

   - 100, 90, _?_, _?_, 60, _?_ **Rule:** subtract 10. **Answer:** 100, 90, _80_, _70_, 60, _50_

   - _?_, 94, 90, _?_, 82, _?_, _?_ **Rule:** subtract 4. **Answer:** _98_, 94, 90, _86_, 82, _78_, _74_

3. For further practice, give students a starting number and a rule and have them create number patterns. For example, give the starting number 30 and the rule "subtract 5." Students should write the number pattern 30, 25, 20, 15, 10, 5, 0. Vary the starting number and the rule. Challenge students with a rule that combines two operations such as "add 10, subtract 3." A number pattern with that type of rule might look like this: 0, 7, 14, 21, 28, ….

4. Explain to students that patterns can be helpful in counting things in everyday situations. Have students make the following charts and use what they know about patterns to fill in the missing numbers:

Ticket Prices	
Number of tickets	Price
1	$5
2	$10
3	$15
4	$20
5	$25
6	$30
7	$35
8	$40
9	$45

Seats	
Number of rows	Seats in each row
1	14
2	28
3	42
4	56
5	70

5. Ask students what rule they used to fill out the Ticket Prices chart. Some students will say they added 5 to the previous amount. Some students may notice that you can multiply the number of tickets in the left column by 5 to get the amount in the right column. Explain to students that there's an advantage to using the number in the left column to get the number in the right right. If they want to know how much 100 tickets would cost, they would simply multiply by 5 rather than adding 5 to the previous amount 100 times.

OFFLINE
15 min

LEARN Find the Rule

Students will describe and extend number patterns. Have students turn to the Find the Rule activity page in their Activity Book and read the directions with them. Students should copy the problems from the Activity Book into their Math Notebook as necessary and solve them there.

1. Discuss the Worked Examples with students. Ask them to read the first sentence and the problem.

Ask: What is the pattern? 4, 8, 12, 16

Ask: Why did Sarah see that pattern when she counted the legs of horses?
Horses have 4 legs.

2. Have students read the solution and the answer.

Ask: Why is "add 4" the answer? Each number is 4 more than the number just before it in the pattern.

3. Have students complete Problems 1–4.

4. Read the information in the Problem 5 chart. Have students copy the chart into their Math Notebook. Have them describe the pattern in their own words.
1 nest, 2 eggs; 2 nests, 4 eggs; 3 nests, 6 eggs...

Ask: What is the rule? double the number of nests, or multiply the number of nests by 2

Say: That rule will help us know how many eggs would be in any number of nests without having to count eggs. Write the rule under the chart. multiply by 2

Ask: How many eggs would there be in 20 nests? 40 eggs

5. Go through a similar explanation for Problem 6.

6. Have students solve Problem 7. They may draw a chart to help them.

Number Patterns
Find the Rule

Worked Examples

You can find a rule for a number pattern.

PROBLEM While counting the legs of horses in a field, Sarah saw this pattern: 4, 8, 12, 16.

| 4 | 8 | 12 | 16 |

What is the rule for this pattern?

SOLUTION Think about how the numbers change. Each number is 4 more than the previous number so the rule is: add 4.

ANSWER add 4

Identify the rule for the number pattern.

1. | 50 | 45 | 40 | 35 | 30 | 25 | subtract 5

2. | 20 | 30 | 40 | 50 | 60 | add 10

3. | 20 | 18 | 16 | 14 | 12 | subtract 2

Fill in the missing numbers in the pattern and give the rule.

4. | 44 | ? | 54 | 59 | ? | ? |
49, 64, 69; add 5

L E A R N

L E A R N

Read the story problem and follow the directions.

5. Look at the nests and eggs chart. If you know how many nests there are, what is the rule to know how many eggs there are?

multiply by 2

Eggs in a Nest	
Number of nests	Number of eggs
1	2
2	4
3	6
4	8
5	10

6. This chart shows how many birdhouses were sold and how much money was collected. If you know how many birdhouses were sold, what is the rule to know how much money was collected?

multiply by 10

Birdhouses Sold	
Number of birdhouses	Dollars collected
1	$10
2	$20
3	$30
4	$40
5	$50

7. One ostrich egg weighs about 3 pounds. What rule can you use to find the weight of 10 ostrich eggs?

multiply by 3

TRY IT Describe and Extend

Objectives

- Recognize and describe a linear pattern, such as counting by 5s or multiplying 5 times a number to reach 100, by its rule.

Students will practice extending patterns. Have students turn to the Describe and Extend activity page in their Activity Book and read the directions with them.

Students should copy the problems from the Activity Book into their Math Notebook as necessary and solve them there.

Number Patterns
Describe and Extend

Read the problem and follow the directions.

1. What number comes next in this pattern?
   23, 26, 29, 32, 35, 38, ?   **41**

2. What number comes next in this pattern?
   13, 25, 37, 49, ?   **61**

3. May counted down the number of days left in her vacation. She counted "21, 14, 7." Which rule describes the pattern?   **subtract 7**

Choose the answer.

4. Trish was watching people cross a bridge. She counted the number of feet she saw and said "2, 4, 6, 8, 10." Which rule describes this pattern?
   (A.) add 2   B. add 4
   C. add 10   D. add 12

5. Which pattern follows the rule "subtract 3"?
   A. 12, 9, 6, 1   B. 99, 66, 33, 11
   (C.) 55, 52, 49, 46   D. 3, 6, 9, 12

6. Which **two** rules describe this pattern?
   10, 15, 20, 25, 30
   (A.) add 5   B. add 10
   (C.) count by 5s   D. count by 10s

7. Which **two** rules describe this pattern?
   6, 12, 18, 24, 30
   (A.) add 6   B. add 10
   (C.) count by 6s   D. count by 10s

8. Bala was practicing for a cross-country running competition. At the end of 1 week he had run 5 miles, at the end of 2 weeks he had run 10 miles, and at the end of 3 weeks he had run 15 miles. He made this chart to keep track. Which rule describes the pattern?

Running Distances	
Weeks	Total miles
1	5
2	10
3	15
4	20

   A. add 10
   B. add 7
   (C.) multiply by 5
   D. multiply by 10

TRY IT

ALGEBRA THINKING   57   NUMBER PATTERNS

ALGEBRA THINKING   58   NUMBER PATTERNS

CHECKPOINT

Objectives

- Extend a linear pattern, such a stating what number comes next in a series.

- Recognize and describe a linear pattern, such as counting by 5s or multiplying 5 times a number to reach 100, by its rule.

Students will complete an online Checkpoint. If necessary, read the directions, problems, and answer choices to students and help them with keyboard or mouse operations.

Story Problems and Patterns (A)

Lesson Overview

Skills Update	5 minutes	ONLINE
GET READY Number Patterns	10 minutes	ONLINE
LEARN Find the Pattern	15 minutes	ONLINE
LEARN Story Problems	20 minutes	OFFLINE
TRY IT Tables and Patterns	10 minutes	OFFLINE

▶ Lesson Objectives

Solve a simple story problem that involves a function.

▶ Prerequisite Skills

- Solve problems involving simple number patterns.
- Extend a linear pattern, such as stating what number comes next in a series.
- Recognize and describe a linear pattern, such as counting by 5s or multiplying 5 times a number to reach 100, by its rule.

▶ Content Background

Students will use linear pattern rules to solve simple story problems.

A *linear pattern* is a number pattern in which each successive number increases or decreases by the same value. A rule describes a linear pattern.

Skip counting creates a linear pattern. For example, skip counting by 2s creates the linear pattern 2, 4, 6, 8, …. The rule for this pattern is "add 2."

▶ Advance Preparation

Print the Input-Output Tables.

Materials to Gather

SUPPLIED

Story Problems activity page

Input-Output Tables (printout)

Tables and Patterns activity page

GET READY Number Patterns

ONLINE
10min

Students will review different rules for creating and continuing numerical patterns. They will then use patterns to solve everyday problems.

Objectives

- Solve problems involving simple number patterns.
- Extend a linear pattern, such as stating what number comes next in a series.
- Recognize and describe a linear pattern, such as counting by 5s or multiplying 5 times a number to reach 100, by its rule.

LEARN Find the Pattern

ONLINE 15 min

Objectives

- Solve a simple story problem that involves a function.

Tips

If students have difficulty with patterns, use input numbers that are sequential so students can see the pattern.

Students will solve simple story problems that involve patterns. They will use a function machine. In this machine, a number goes in and is changed using a rule such as "add 5" or "multiply by 2." Then the machine sends the changed number out. Students can keep track of the numbers that go in and come out using a T chart, also called an input-output table. The input-output table has two columns: input and output. Students will use the patterns they see in the table to figure out the rule that is changing the numbers.

As time permits, play a function-machine game in which you think of a rule (don't tell students the rule you chose), students give you an input number, and you say the output number. For example, if your rule is "multiply by 3" and a student calls out "10," you should answer "30." Have students record the spoken numbers in an input-output table. Repeat this process with the same rule. Continue until students guess your rule. Then change places and have students choose the rule while you call out a number. Students will solve the problem, and you will guess the rule.

LEARN Story Problems

OFFLINE 20 min

Objectives

- Solve a simple story problem that involves a function.

Tips

Provide counting objects or paper and pencil for students to complete calculations.

Students will fill in missing numbers for a given rule in an input-output table. They will also solve simple story problems by using an input-output table. They will identify and extend a pattern to solve the problems. Model for students how to organize the information from a story problem into an input-output table.

Gather the Input-Output Tables printout. Set the printout aside until later in the activity. Have students turn to the Story Problems activity page in their Activity Book. Students should copy the problems from the Activity Book into their Math Notebook as necessary and solve them there.

1. Explain to students that certain types of story problems work just like a function machine, in which a number goes in and the machine adds to it, multiplies it, or does other operations on it, and another number comes out. For these problems, it's helpful to use an input-output table.

2. Have students look at the Worked Examples. The table shows the number of crayons needed for different numbers of students. Explain to students that this is like a function machine. Since 1 student needs 5 crayons, they could imagine that 1 goes in and 5 comes out of the machine. They see that 2 students need 10 crayons, so 2 goes into the machine and 10 comes out. Since 3 students need 15 crayons, they can say that if 3 goes into the machine, 15 comes out.

   Ask: Can you find the rule that says what the machine does to the number that goes in so that it becomes the number that comes out? The rule is "multiply by 5."

   Using this rule, students can figure out how many crayons they'll need for 10 students or 100 students without building the whole chart.

3. Emphasize that students can build the chart one step at a time by adding 5 crayons for each new student, or they can look at the chart as a function machine and multiply the number of students by 5 to find out how many crayons are needed for any number of students.

4. Have students complete Problems 1–4 on their own. Give students the Input-Output Tables printout. They can use the printout to create the input-output table to solve Problem 4.

Number of students	Number of crayons
1	5
2	10
3	15
4	**20**
5	**25**
10	**50**
100	**500**

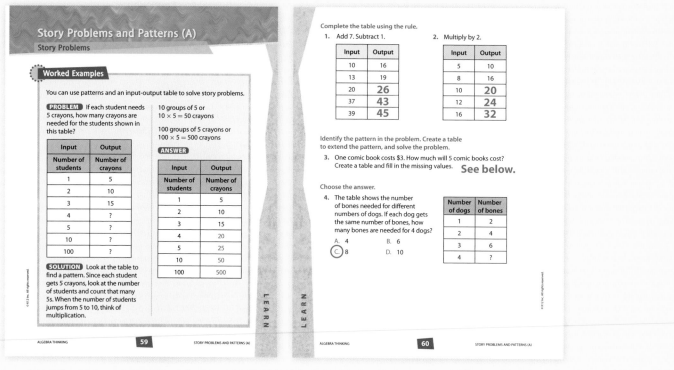

Additional Answers

3. $15

Number of comic books	Total price
1	$3
2	$6
3	$9
4	$12
5	$15

OFFLINE
10 min

TRY IT Tables and Patterns

Students will practice solving story problems by identifying and extending patterns using an input-output table. Have students turn to the Tables and Patterns activity page in their Activity Book and read the directions with them.

Students should copy the problems from the Activity Book into their Math Notebook as necessary and solve them there.

Objectives

- Solve a simple story problem that involves a function.

Tips

Have students create their tables on the Input-Output Tables printout. Also, have counting objects or paper and pencil available for students to complete their calculations.

Story Problems and Patterns (A)

Tables and Patterns

Read the problem and solve.

1. Complete the input-output table by using the rule "add 5, subtract 2."

Input	Output
32	35
34	37
36	**39**
38	**41**
40	**43**

2. Complete the input-output table by using the rule "subtract 5, add 3."

Input	Output
5	3
10	8
15	**13**
20	**18**
25	**23**

3. LaBella is making a sign showing the cost to ski at Big Ski Hill. She wants to charge $12 per hour.

Big Ski Hill Prices	
Hours	Total cost
1	$12
2	$24
3	**$36**
4	**$48**

4. Frank is making a sign for his ice rink showing the cost to skate. He wants to charge $8 an hour.

Ice Skating Prices	
Hours	Total cost
1	$8
2	$16
3	**$24**
4	**$32**

TRY IT

Identify the pattern. Create a table to extend the pattern and solve.

5. It takes Anne 10 minutes to walk once around her block. She knows it will take 20 minutes to walk around the block 2 times and 30 minutes to walk around the block 3 times. How many minutes will it take Anne to walk around the block 5 times? **50**

Block	Minutes
1	10
2	20
3	30
4	40
5	50

TRY IT

Story Problems and Patterns (B)

Lesson Overview

GET READY Boat Games	10 minutes	ONLINE
LEARN Beach Math	20 minutes	OFFLINE
TRY IT Make a Chart	20 minutes	OFFLINE
CHECKPOINT	10 minutes	ONLINE

▶ Lesson Objectives

Solve a simple story problem that involves a function.

▶ Prerequisite Skills

- Solve problems involving simple number patterns.
- Extend a linear pattern, such as stating what number comes next in a series.
- Recognize and describe a linear pattern, such as counting by 5s or multiplying 5 times a number to reach 100, by its rule.

▶ Content Background

Students will continue to use linear pattern rules to solve simple story problems.

A *linear pattern* is a number pattern in which each successive number increases or decreases by the same value. A rule describes a linear pattern.

Skip counting creates a linear pattern. For example, skip counting by 2s creates the linear pattern 2, 4, 6, 8, …. The rule for this pattern is "add 2."

▶ Advance Preparation

Print the Input-Output Tables.

GET READY Boat Games

ONLINE
10 min

Students will review extending number patterns by counting on or repeatedly adding or subtracting a number. They will enter the number that will fill in the blank in the pattern. Students may repeat the game to try to improve their score.

Objectives

- Solve problems involving simple number patterns.
- Extend a linear pattern, such as stating what number comes next in a series.
- Recognize and describe a linear pattern, such as counting by 5s or multiplying 5 times a number to reach 100, by its rule.

LEARN Beach Math

Objectives

- Solve a simple story problem that involves a function.

Students will use patterns counting on by a number, repeatedly adding a number, or multiplying by a number to solve problems. Gather the Input-Output Tables printout. Have students turn to the Beach Math activity page in their Activity Book. Students should copy the problems from the Activity Book into their Math Notebook as necessary and solve them there.

Tips

Be sure students understand how to create and label the input-output tables on the Input-Output Tables printout.

1. Discuss the Worked Examples with students. Explain to students that 1 skateboard has 4 wheels.

2. Explain that to find the number of wheels on 2 skateboards, students can add 4 plus 4 to get 8.

3. Work together to go over the table. Show students that one way to create the table is by repeatedly adding 4 to find how many wheels are needed for 10 skateboards.

4. Ask students if they can identify another pattern in the number of wheels. Students may notice that the number of wheels increases by 4 each time and therefore they can also count by 4s to extend the pattern and find the answer. Point out that the number of skateboards times 4 equals the number of wheels.

5. Have students complete Problems 1–6 on their own. Ask them to describe the patterns they see in the input-output tables. Encourage them to describe the patterns in terms of counting by a number, repeatedly adding a number, or multiplying by a number.

6. Give students the Input-Output Tables printout. Students can use the printout to create the input-output tables to solve the rest of the story problems on the activity page.

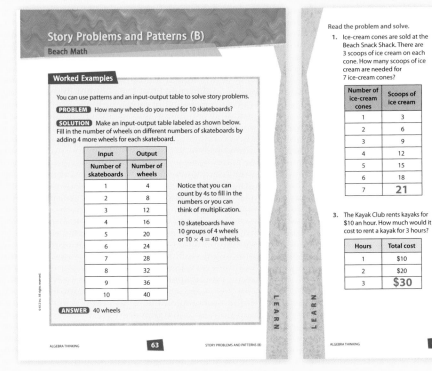

5. Marc wants to buy beach balls for his friends.
He knows that 1 beach ball costs $2, 2 beach balls
cost $4, and 3 beach balls cost $6. How much will
4 beach balls cost?

   A. $7   (B.) $8
   C. $9   D. $10

6. A ride on the Ferris wheel costs $5 per person.
How much would it cost for 6 people to ride
the Ferris wheel?

   A. $5   B. $10
   C. $25   (D.) $30

L E A R N

OFFLINE
20min

TRY IT   Make a Chart

Objectives

- Solve a simple story problem
  that involves a function.

Students will solve story problems by completing input-output tables. Gather the
Make a Chart activity page and the Input-Output Tables printout. Students can
use the printout to create the tables to solve each story problem.

Tips

Be sure students understand how to
set up and label the columns in the
input-output tables.

Story Problems and Patterns (B)

Make a Chart

Complete the table using the rule.

1. Add 5.

Input	Output
25	30
27	32
29	**34**
31	**36**
33	**38**

2. Multiply by 2. Add 3.

Input	Output
2	7
4	11
6	**15**
8	**19**
10	**23**

Make a table to solve the problem.

3. Each player gets 4 rings to toss at the ring toss game.
How many rings are needed for 4 games?   **See right.**

4. Sam uses 6 lemons to make 1 glass of lemonade.
How many lemons does Sam need to make 6 glasses
of lemonade?   **See right.**

Additional Answers

3. 16 rings

Games	Number of rings
1	4
2	8
3	12
4	16

4. 36 lemons

Glasses of lemonade	Number of lemons
1	6
2	12
3	18
4	24
5	30
6	36

T R Y   I T

Objectives

- Solve a simple story problem that involves a function.

Students will complete an online Checkpoint. If necessary, read the directions, problems, and answer choices to students and help them with keyboard or mouse operations.

Unit Review

Lesson Overview

UNIT REVIEW Look Back	10 minutes	ONLINE
UNIT REVIEW Checkpoint Practice	50 minutes	ONLINE
⏩ **UNIT REVIEW** Prepare for the Checkpoint		

▶ Lesson Objectives

This lesson reviews the following objectives:

- Use a mathematical expression to represent a relationship between quantities.
- Use an equation to represent a relationship between quantities.
- Use an inequality to represent a relationship between quantities.
- Select the appropriate symbol to show an operation or a relationship that makes a number sentence true.
- Determine a missing number in an equation or an inequality.
- Extend a linear pattern, such as stating what number comes next in a series.
- Recognize and describe a linear pattern, such as counting by 5s or multiplying 5 times a number to reach 100, by its rule.
- Solve a simple story problem that involves a function.

Materials to Gather

There are no materials to gather for this lesson.

▶ Advance Preparation

In this lesson, students will have an opportunity to review previous activities in the Algebra Thinking unit. Look at the suggested activities in Unit Review: Prepare for the Checkpoint online and gather any needed materials.

UNIT REVIEW Look Back ONLINE 10 min

Objectives

- Review unit objectives.

Students will review key concepts from the unit to prepare for the Unit Checkpoint.

UNIT REVIEW Checkpoint Practice ONLINE 50 min

Objectives

- Review unit objectives.

Students will complete an online Checkpoint Practice to prepare for the Unit Checkpoint. If necessary, read the directions, problems, and answer choices to students. Have students answer the problems on their own. Carefully review the answers with students.

⏩ UNIT REVIEW Prepare for the Checkpoint

What you do next depends on how students performed in the previous activity, Unit Review: Checkpoint Practice. If students had difficulty with any of the problems, complete the appropriate review activity listed in the table online.

Unit Checkpoint

UNIT CHECKPOINT Online   60 minutes   **ONLINE**

▶ Unit Objectives

This lesson assesses the following objectives:

- Use a mathematical expression to represent a relationship between quantities.
- Use an equation to represent a relationship between quantities.
- Use an inequality to represent a relationship between quantities.
- Select the appropriate symbol to show an operation or a relationship that makes a number sentence true.
- Determine a missing number in an equation or an inequality.
- Extend a linear pattern, such as stating what number comes next in a series.
- Recognize and describe a linear pattern, such as counting by 5s or multiplying 5 times a number to reach 100, by its rule.
- Solve a simple story problem that involves a function.

Materials to Gather

There are no materials to gather for this lesson.

UNIT CHECKPOINT Online

Students will complete the Unit Checkpoint online. If necessary, read the directions, problems, and answer choices to students and help them with keyboard or mouse operations.

Objectives

- Assess unit objectives.

Whole Number Multiplication Sense

▶ Unit Objectives

- Use objects or sketches to solve a multiplication problem.
- Use a model to explain multiplication as repeated addition of the same quantity.
- Use an area model to explain multiplication.
- Demonstrate an understanding of how multiplication affects whole numbers.
- Explain and apply the commutative property of multiplication.
- Explain and apply the zero property of multiplication.
- Explain and apply the multiplication property of 1.
- Demonstrate automatic recall of multiplication facts.
- Explain and apply the associative property of multiplication.

▶ Big Ideas

- Multiplication and division can be represented by models and by using math symbols.
- Multiplication can be understood as repeated addition or can be represented through area models.
- Inverses undo each other. Addition and subtraction are inverses, and multiplication and division are inverses.
- The commutative and associative properties can be used to simplify expressions.
- Multiplying any number by 1, the multiplicative identity, results in a product that is the given number.

▶ Unit Introduction

In this unit, students will focus on multiplication. They will become familiar with factors (the numbers that are multiplied) and products (answers). Students know their 2s, 5s, and 10s multiplication facts and have shown multiplication as arrays and repeated addition. They will work in this unit with the area model to explain multiplication. They will explain the effects of multiplication on numbers and notice that multiplying generally results in numbers greater than they started with. They will revisit the commutative property, which says that the order in which two numbers are multiplied doesn't affect the result, and they'll investigate what happens when numbers are multiplied by zero and 1. They will work on their multiplication facts through 10×10. They will track the facts they've covered on a multiplication facts chart, and will post the facts they've fully memorized on a multiplication facts poster on the wall.

▶ Keywords

area model	factor	multiplication symbol
array	grid	multiply
associative property of multiplication	identity property of multiplication	operation
commutative property of multiplication	linear pattern	product
	multiple	repeated addition
expression	multiplication	skip count
	multiplication facts	zero property of multiplication

Model and Explain Multiplication

Lesson Overview

GET READY Model with Arrays	5 minutes	ONLINE
LEARN Model with Equal Groups	15 minutes	ONLINE
LEARN Model with Base-10 Blocks	15 minutes	OFFLINE
TRY IT Model Multiplication	15 minutes	OFFLINE
CHECKPOINT	10 minutes	ONLINE

▶ ## Lesson Objectives

- Use objects or sketches to solve a multiplication problem.
- Use a model to explain multiplication as repeated addition of the same quantity.

▶ ## Prerequisite Skills

- Use concrete objects or sketches of arrays to model multiplication problems.
- Use concrete objects or sketches to model and explain multiplication as repeated addition.

▶ ## Content Background

Students have used arrays and repeated addition to solve multiplication problems. They may already know their multiplication facts for 2s, 5s, and 10s. In this lesson, students will use objects and sketches to model and explain multiplication problems for other factors.

Multiplication is an operation used when there are equal groups. The multiplication symbol is used to say "groups of" or "rows of." For example, 3 groups of 5 objects would be shown with the expression 3×5. The expression is read "3 times 5." On the other hand, 5 groups of 3 objects would be shown with the expression 5×3 and read "5 times 3."

A multiplication number sentence is composed of two numbers, called factors, that are multiplied to produce the solution, or product. An array is a rectangular arrangement of objects in rows and columns. The number of rows is the first factor in a multiplication number sentence, and the number of columns is the second factor. The total number of objects in the entire array is the product.

Materials to Gather

SUPPLIED

base-10 blocks

blocks – B (40 of any color)

Model Multiplication activity page

GET READY Model with Arrays

Objectives

Students will represent multiplication as arrays for the 2s, 5s, and 10s facts. They will review the concepts that multiplication is about equal groups and that a multiplication fact can be shown as an array or as groups of objects. For example, 5 ×2 can be shown with 5 rows of 2 objects or 5 groups of 2 objects.

- Use concrete objects or sketches of arrays to model multiplication problems.
- Use concrete objects or sketches to model and explain multiplication as repeated addition.

LEARN Model with Equal Groups

Objectives

Students will use online objects and sketches to solve multiplication problems. They will model multiplication problems as equal groups and explain multiplication as repeated addition of the same quantity on a number line.

- Use objects or sketches to solve a multiplication problem.
- Use a model to explain multiplication as repeated addition of the same quantity.

LEARN Model with Base-10 Blocks

Objectives

Students will use objects to solve multiplication problems that have one factor greater than 10. They will use base-10 blocks to model the equal groups and then combine all the tens and all the ones to find the total.

Gather the base-10 blocks.

- Use objects or sketches to solve a multiplication problem.
- Use a model to explain multiplication as repeated addition of the same quantity.

1. Write 3 × 100 in the Math Notebook. Explain that it would take a long time to draw a sketch to show this multiplication problem. Tell students that they can use base-10 blocks to model the problem.

2. Ask students how many groups of 100 should be shown and how they can show the problem with the fewest blocks. Three groups of 100 should be shown; using 3 hundreds flats is the way to show this with the fewest blocks.

3. **Ask:** How can we find the total? Answers might include counting by 100s or adding 3 hundreds.

4. Repeat Steps 1–3 using the problem 6 × 10. Guide students to determine that they should use tens rods to model the problem.

5. Write 4 × 22.

   Ask: How many groups should we show? 4

   Ask: How many should be shown in each group? 22

   Guide students to show 2 tens rods and 2 ones cubes in each of 4 groups.

6. Discuss with students that it would be difficult to count by 22s to find the total.

   Ask: How can we group the blocks to find the total? Discussion should include grouping the tens and the ones to find the total.

7. Have students combine all the tens rods and all the ones cubes. Then have students count the tens and the ones to find the total.

   Ask: What is 4 × 22? 88

   Have students explain how they found their answer.

Tips

Have students write the addition sentence vertically so they can add all the ones and then add the tens.

8. Have students write a repeated addition problem to check their answer.
$22 + 22 + 22 + 22 = 88$

9. Repeat Steps 5–8 with the following problems.
- 3×23 Three groups of 23 should be shown; 23 should be shown in each group; $3 \times 23 = 69$; $23 + 23 + 23 = 69$.
- 3×25 Three groups of 25 should be shown; 25 should be shown in each group; $3 \times 25 = 75$; $25 + 25 + 25 = 75$.

10. **Say:** Peter has 4 bags of pennies. Each bag has 15 pennies. How can you use base-10 blocks to show this problem? Answers should include showing 4 groups, each consisting of 1 tens rod and 5 ones cubes.

11. Have students model the problem. Then have them tell the multiplication problem that describes what they have shown. 4×15

Finally have students tell the addition sentence they can use to solve the problem. $15 + 15 + 15 + 15 = 60$

OFFLINE

15min

TRY IT Model Multiplication

Students will practice using objects or sketches to solve multiplication problems and will explain multiplication as repeated addition. Gather the B blocks for students to use as counting objects. Have students turn to the Model Multiplication activity page in their Activity Book and read the directions with them.

Students should copy the problems from the Activity Book into their Math Notebook as necessary and solve them there.

Objectives

- Use objects or sketches to solve a multiplication problem.
- Use a model to explain multiplication as repeated addition of the same quantity.

Tips

Allow students to use models to help them answer the problems.

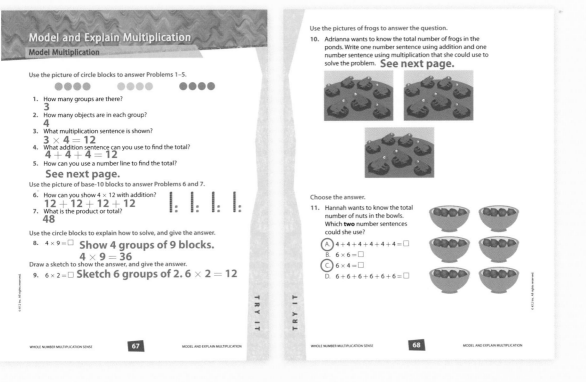

Model and Explain Multiplication
Model Multiplication

Use the picture of circle blocks to answer Problems 1–5.

1. How many groups are there?
3
2. How many objects are in each group?
4
3. What multiplication sentence is shown?
$3 \times 4 = 12$
4. What addition sentence can you use to find the total?
$4 + 4 + 4 = 12$
5. How can you use a number line to find the total?
See next page.

Use the picture of base-10 blocks to answer Problems 6 and 7.

6. How can you show 4×12 with addition?
$12 + 12 + 12 + 12$
7. What is the product or total?
48

Use the circle blocks to explain how to solve, and give the answer.

8. $4 \times 9 = \square$ **Show 4 groups of 9 blocks.**
$4 \times 9 = 36$

Draw a sketch to show the answer, and give the answer.

9. $6 \times 2 = \square$ **Sketch 6 groups of 2. $6 \times 2 = 12$**

Use the pictures of frogs to answer the question.

10. Adrianna wants to know the total number of frogs in the ponds. Write one number sentence using addition and one number sentence using multiplication that she could use to solve the problem. **See next page.**

Choose the answer.

11. Hannah wants to know the total number of nuts in the bowls. Which **two** number sentences could she use?

A. $4 + 4 + 4 + 4 + 4 + 4 = \square$
B. $6 \times 6 = \square$
C. $6 \times 4 = \square$
D. $6 + 6 + 6 + 6 + 6 = \square$

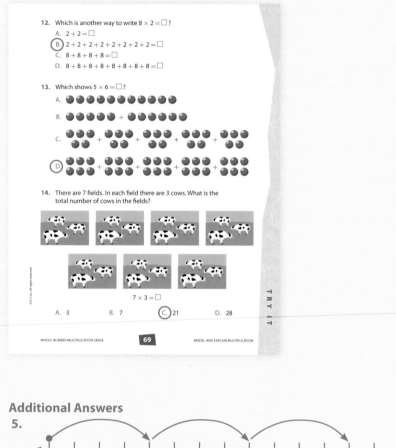

12. Which is another way to write $8 \times 2 = \square$?
    A. $2 + 2 = \square$
    B. $2 + 2 + 2 + 2 + 2 + 2 + 2 + 2 = \square$
    C. $8 + 8 + 8 + 8 = \square$
    D. $8 + 8 + 8 + 8 + 8 + 8 + 8 = \square$

13. Which shows $5 \times 6 = \square$?

14. There are 7 fields. In each field there are 3 cows. What is the total number of cows in the fields?

    $7 \times 3 = \square$

    A. 3   B. 7   C. 21   D. 28

T R Y   I T

Additional Answers

5.

10. $7 + 7 + 7 = \square$
    $3 \times 7 = \square$
    Both answers are 21.

ONLINE
10 min

CHECKPOINT

Students will complete an online Checkpoint. If necessary, read the directions, problems, and answer choices to students and help them with keyboard or mouse operations.

Objectives

- Use objects or sketches to solve a multiplication problem.
- Use a model to explain multiplication as repeated addition of the same quantity.

Area Models for Multiplication (A)

▶ Lesson Objectives

Use an area model to explain multiplication.

▶ Prerequisite Skills

Use concrete objects or sketches of arrays to model multiplication problems.

▶ Content Background

Students have used objects arranged in arrays to model and explain multiplication as repeated addition. In this lesson, students will learn what area models are and will use them to explain multiplication.

Multiplication is an operation used when there are equal groups. The multiplication symbol is used to say "groups of" or "rows of." For example, 3 groups of 5 objects would be shown with the expression 3×5. The expression is read "3 times 5." On the other hand, 5 groups of 3 objects would be shown with the expression 5×3 and read "5 times 3."

A multiplication number sentence is composed of two numbers, called factors, that are multiplied to produce the solution, or product. An array is a rectangular arrangement of objects in rows and columns. The number of rows is the first factor in a multiplication number sentence, and the number of columns is the second factor. The total number of objects in the entire array is the product.

The area model for multiplication is shown as the area of a rectangle in a grid showing the square units. An area model can also be a rectangle made of base-10 blocks that are in rows of tens rods and ones cubes lying end to end.

▶ Common Errors and Misconceptions

- Students might add the second factor too many or too few times. For example, for 4×5, students might add $4 + 4 + 4 + 4$.
- Students might undercount or overcount when using the count-by-n strategy.

▶ Advance Preparation

Print the Centimeter Grid Paper.

Materials to Gather

SUPPLIED

blocks – E (40 of any color)

Centimeter Grid Paper (printout)

Area Models activity page

GET READY Arrays and Multiplication

Students will review representing multiplication as arrays for the 2s and 5s facts. They will review using skip counting and repeated addition to find the product, or answer.

- Use concrete objects or sketches of arrays to model multiplication problems.

LEARN Show Multiplication with Area Models

Objectives

Students will learn what an area model is. They will use area models to represent and explain multiplication. They'll learn that an array of squares can be pushed together to translate into an area model of equal rows on a grid. And they'll see that the equal rows form a rectangle.

- Use an area model to explain multiplication.

Gather the Centimeter Grid Paper.

DIRECTIONS FOR USING THE GRID LEARNING TOOL

1. Tell students that they can make an area model by shading squares on the tool.

2. Have students choose a color. Then have them shade squares to show 2×4. Tell them that they will shade 2 rows of 4 squares.

3. Guide students to shade the squares in one corner of their grid paper to make a picture that resembles their online model.

   Ask: What is the product of 2 times 4? 8

4. Have students count the shaded squares. Then have them say the addition sentence they can use to find the value of 2×4. $4 + 4 = 8$

5. Have students clear the grid.

6. Have students shade squares to show 4×6. Check that they have shaded adjacent squares to form a rectangle made up of 4 rows of 6 squares.

7. Have students tell you the multiplication sentence shown by the area model. $4 \times 6 = 24$

8. Repeat Steps 2–5 with the following problems:

   - 7×4 28; $4 + 4 + 4 + 4 + 4 + 4 + 4 = 28$
   - 3×7 21; $7 + 7 + 7 = 21$

9. Have students use their grid paper to copy a 3×7 grid like the one they made on the screen. Have them label the grid with the multiplication sentence and the addition problem they can use to find the value.
   Students should shade 3 rows of 7 squares on the grid paper and write $3 \times 7 = 21$ and $7 + 7 + 7 = 21$.

10. Have students shade the grid to show 3×4. Then have them say the multiplication fact. Students should shade 3 rows of 4 squares and say $3 \times 4 = 12$.

11. Near the 3 rows of 4, have students shade the grid to show 4×3 and say the multiplication fact. Students should shade 4 rows of 3 squares and say $4 \times 3 = 12$.

12. Have students compare the two models they just shaded. Discuss how the models are alike, including the fact that the product is the same.

Ask: Is multiplication still repeated addition when it is represented as an area model? Yes, because you see 3 rows of 4 or 3 groups of 4 and you can add $4 + 4 + 4$ to find the total of 12.

13. Have students shade 3×4 and 4×3 on their grid paper. Have them write the multiplication fact and the repeated addition fact next to each area model.

TRY IT Area Models

OFFLINE
20min

Objectives

- Use an area model to explain multiplication.

Students will practice using area models to explain and solve multiplication problems. Gather the E blocks and the Centimeter Grid Paper; students will use these to solve some problems. Have students turn to the Area Models activity page in their Activity Book and read the directions with them.

Students should copy the problems from the Activity Book into their Math Notebook as necessary and solve them there.

Area Models for Multiplication (A)
Area Models

Use color tiles to show the multiplication expression.
Then find the product.

1. 6×3
6 rows of 3 tiles; 18

2. 5×4
5 rows of 4 tiles; 20

Multiply.

3. $2 \times 9 = \square$
18

4. $3 \times 9 = \square$
27

5. $4 \times 8 = \square$
32

6. $6 \times 7 = \square$
42

Use grid paper to show how to solve the problem.

7. $6 \times 8 = \square$
Shade a rectangle with 6 rows of 8 squares.
$6 \times 8 = 48$

8. $7 \times 5 = \square$
Shade a rectangle with 7 rows of 5 squares.
$7 \times 5 = 35$

9. $8 \times 3 = \square$
Shade a rectangle with 8 rows of 3 squares.
$8 \times 3 = 24$

Choose the answer.

10. Which shows $4 \times 5 = \square$?

A.

B.

C.

D.

11. $5 \times 7 = \square$

A. 7   B. 12   C. 30   D. 35

12. $9 \times 9 = \square$

A. 9   B. 18   C. 81   D. 99

Area Models for Multiplication (B)

Lesson Overview

LEARN Blocks and Grids	20 minutes	ONLINE
LEARN Model and Add	20 minutes	OFFLINE
TRY IT Solve with Area Models	10 minutes	OFFLINE
CHECKPOINT	10 minutes	ONLINE

▶ Lesson Objectives

Use an area model to explain multiplication.

▶ Prerequisite Skills

Use concrete objects or sketches of arrays to model multiplication problems.

Materials to Gather

SUPPLIED

Base-10 Grid Paper (printout)

Solve with Area Models activity page

▶ Content Background

Students will learn more about factors and multiplication. This lesson uses Base-10 Grid Paper. The Base-10 Grid Paper has smaller and more numerous squares than Centimeter Grid Paper. The Base-10 Grid Paper is marked with a darker line every 10 squares, thus the name referring to base 10. The purpose of the Base-10 Grid Paper is to allow students to multiply greater numbers and to count by 10 for quicker calculation.

▶ Common Errors and Misconceptions

- Students might add the second factor too many or too few times. For example, for 4×5, students might add $4 + 4 + 4 + 4$.
- Students might undercount or overcount when using the count-by-n strategy.

▶ Advance Preparation

Print the Base-10 Grid Paper.

LEARN Blocks and Grids

ONLINE 20min

Objectives

- Use an area model to explain multiplication.

Students will use area models to show multiplication problems with factors of 10 or greater. They will use online base-10 blocks to represent the problem and then use the online Grid Learning Tool to shade the area represented by a multiplication expression. The purpose of this activity is to guide students toward a faster and easier way to multiply. For instance, the expression 5×23, when shaded on a grid, clearly shows the product. Students can look at the shaded area and can easily count the tens and ones. This builds students' conceptual understanding of multiplication and prepares them for learning to do multiplication without the aid of models in the future.

DIRECTIONS FOR USING THE GRID LEARNING TOOL

1. Tell students that they can represent multiplication expressions on the grid. Have them choose a color. Then have them show 5 × 7 by shading 5 rows of 7 squares.

   Ask: How many squares are shaded? 35

   Ask: What is the product of 5 × 7? 35

   Have students record the problem in their Math Notebook. 5 × 7 = 35

2. Have students click the down arrow at the bottom of the screen to show two grids. Ask students to show the expression 5 × 13 by shading 5 rows of 13. To shade a row of 13, students should shade a row of 10 in the grid on the left and shade 3 squares in the same row in the grid on the right.

   Ask: How many squares are shaded? 65

   Ask: What is the product of 5 × 13? 65

   Have students record the problem in their Math Notebook. 5 × 13 = 65

   Observe how students figure out how many squares there are. Most will count rows of 10 and then count the rest of the squares. If they do not use this method, suggest it to them.

3. Have students click the down arrow at the bottom of the screen to show three grids. Ask students to show the expression 5 × 23 by shading 5 rows of 23. Have students use the grid to determine the product. Have them record the problem in their Math Notebook. 5 × 23 = 115

4. Have students do the following problems in the same way:
   - 8 × 12 96
   - 10 × 25 250

   As time permits, have students make up problems, show them on the grid, and record the problems and answers in their Math Notebook.

LEARN Model and Add

OFFLINE
20min

Objectives

- Use an area model to explain multiplication.

Students will use area models to represent and solve multiplication problems. They will use Base-10 Grid Paper to make area models. The models represent multiplication expressions where one factor is greater than 10. Then students will find products in a variety of ways, including using repeated addition expressed vertically.
Gather the Base-10 Grid Paper.

Tips

Encourage students to try a variety of methods to find each product.

1. Write the problem 5 × 23. Then have students shade squares on grid paper to show the problem. Encourage students to explain how they can use the markings on the grid paper to help them quickly count 10s. They can count the rows of tens first and then count the ones.

2. Have students write 5 × 23 next to the area model and write the product. 115

3. Ask students how they can use repeated addition to check their product. They can add 23 five times.

   Have students write 23 + 23 + 23 + 23 + 23 vertically on the grid paper.

   Ask: How many times will you write 23? 5
   Ask: How do you know? There are 5 groups, or rows, of 23.

4. Encourage students to use the squares of the grid to align the tens and ones digits of their addition. Observe them as they find the sum of the ones and then the sum of the tens. Watch to see if students use skip counting to find the sums. If they do not skip count, suggest that they try it.

5. Write the problem 6 × 11. Have students shade squares on the grid paper to show the problem.

6. **Ask:** How can you use the sketch to find the product of 6 times 11? I can count the number of shaded squares.

7. Have students find the product by counting the squares on the grid paper. Have them write the multiplication problem. 6 × 11 = 66

8. **Ask:** How can you use repeated addition to find the product? I can add 11 six times.

   Have students write the vertical addition problem and the sum on the grid paper next to the multiplication problem.

9. Discuss with students which method they prefer to use to find the product.

10. Have students sketch area models on grid paper for the following multiplication expressions. Have them find each product two different ways, recording their solutions on the grid paper.

    - 3 × 27 81
    - 6 × 27 162

11. **Ask:** How could you use what you know about 3 × 27 to find the product of 6 × 27? Six is the double of three, so I could just double the product of 3 × 27 to find the product of 6 × 27.

	¹	¹2	3	
		2	3	
		2	3	
		2	3	
	+	2	3	
	1	1	5	

Objectives

- Use an area model to explain multiplication.

Students will work with area models to show multiplication. Gather the Base-10 Grid Paper. Have students turn to the Solve with Area Models activity page in their Activity Book and read the directions with them.

   Students should copy the problems from the Activity Book into their Math Notebook as necessary and solve them there.

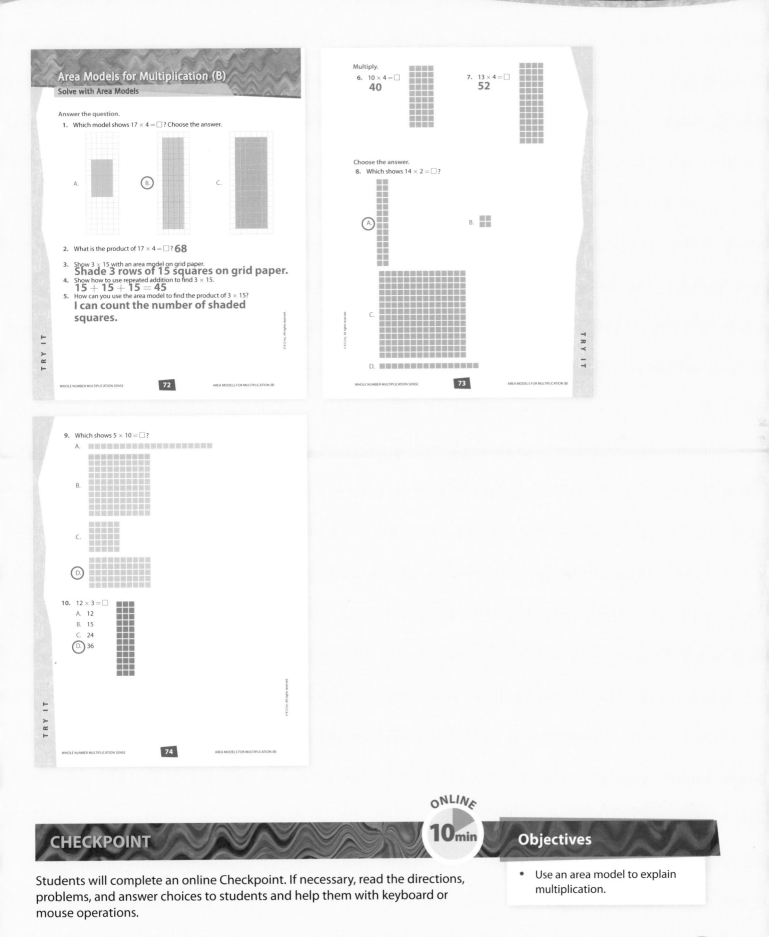

Area Models for Multiplication (B)
Solve with Area Models

Answer the question.

1. Which model shows $17 \times 4 = \square$? Choose the answer.

   A.   B. (circled)   C.

2. What is the product of $17 \times 4 = \square$? **68**

3. Show 3×15 with an area model on grid paper.
   Shade 3 rows of 15 squares on grid paper.

4. Show how to use repeated addition to find 3×15.
   15 + 15 + 15 = 45

5. How can you use the area model to find the product of 3×15?
   I can count the number of shaded squares.

TRY IT

Multiply.

6. $10 \times 4 = \square$
   40

7. $13 \times 4 = \square$
   52

Choose the answer.

8. Which shows $14 \times 2 = \square$?

   A. (circled)   B.

   C.

   D.

TRY IT

9. Which shows $5 \times 10 = \square$?
   A.
   B.
   C.
   D. (circled)

10. $12 \times 3 = \square$
    A. 12
    B. 15
    C. 24
    D. 36 (circled)

TRY IT

ONLINE
10 min

CHECKPOINT

Students will complete an online Checkpoint. If necessary, read the directions, problems, and answer choices to students and help them with keyboard or mouse operations.

Objectives

- Use an area model to explain multiplication.

Understand Multiplication

Lesson Overview

GET READY Model Multiplication	10 minutes	OFFLINE
LEARN Effect of Multiplication	15 minutes	OFFLINE
LEARN Multiplication Patterns	15 minutes	OFFLINE
TRY IT Multiplication Results	10 minutes	OFFLINE
CHECKPOINT	10 minutes	ONLINE

▶ Lesson Objectives

Demonstrate an understanding of how multiplication affects whole numbers.

▶ Prerequisite Skills

Use objects or sketches to solve a multiplication problem.

▶ Content Background

Students may already have a basic knowledge of multiplication and understand how to model and solve multiplication problems. In this lesson, they will learn how multiplication affects whole numbers, gaining an understanding that with multiplication, the product is usually greater than the factors. They will explore multiplying by 1 and zero and the effects of those numbers on the product. They will identify patterns of multiples. (For example, multiples of 2 are even numbers; multiples of 5 end in the digit 5 or zero; and multiples of 10 end in the digit zero.) Seeing these general patterns will help students develop a broader understanding of mathematics. Students will be introduced to the term *multiples* and will learn that when they skip count by 10s, starting at zero, they are saying the multiples of 10.

▶ Common Errors and Misconceptions

Students might not understand that the two factors in a multiplication expression have different meanings. For example, 3 sets of 6 dots is written as 3×6, not 6×3. However, the product of each expression is 18.

▶ Advance Preparation

Print the Hundred Chart, and use the Number Line Creator Tool to print a page with four number lines from 0 to 20.

DIRECTIONS FOR USING THE NUMBER LINE CREATOR TOOL

To create number lines from 0 to 20:

1. Set Range:	2. Select Options:	3. Print Number Line:
• Start Number Line at: 0 • End Number Line at: 20	• Tick Marks: ones • Labels: ones	• Page Orientation: landscape • Number Lines per Sheet: 4

Materials to Gather

SUPPLIED

number lines from the Number Line Creator Tool

base-10 blocks

Hundred Chart (printout)

Multiplication Results activity page

GET READY Model Multiplication

OFFLINE 10 min

Objectives

- Use objects or sketches to solve a multiplication problem.

Students will make a sketch to model a multiplication expression. They will then write a related addition expression and skip count to solve.

1. Have students write the expression 4 × 5. Ask them to sketch 4 × 5 in any way they like. Options include:
   - An array with 4 rows of 5 circles (or dots, stars, or other objects)
   - A drawing of 4 groups of 5 circles
   - A grid showing 4 rows of 5 squares shaded
   - A number line starting at zero and showing 4 jumps of 5

2. Near their drawing, have students write the expression as repeated addition. 5 + 5 + 5 + 5 = 20

3. Have students skip count by 5s to find the total. Have them record the answer. 5, 10, 15, 20

4. Remind students of the different ways they could have represented the expression so that they are familiar with various ways to show multiplication.

Tips

Reinforce that the first factor is the number of groups and the second factor is the number in each group.

LEARN Effect of Multiplication

OFFLINE 15 min

Objectives

- Demonstrate an understanding of how multiplication affects whole numbers.

Students will explore how multiplication affects whole numbers. They will learn the following patterns.

When both factors are greater than 1,
- The product is greater than either factor.
- The product will be to the right of both factors on the number line.

When a factor is zero,
- The product is zero.

When a factor is 1 (and there are only two factors),
- The product is the other factor.

Gather the number lines you printed from the Number Line Creator Tool.

1. **Say:** In an addition problem where two numbers greater than zero are added, the sum is greater than either of the addends.

   To illustrate this, show the problem 8 + 7 on a number line.

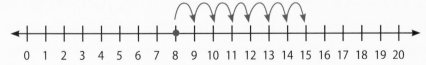

   Have students notice that the sum is to the right of each number being added, so it's greater than either number being added.

2. Remind students that multiplication is repeated addition.

   Ask: If you multiply two numbers greater than 1, do you think the product will always be greater than or less than the factors? The product will always be greater than the factors.

Have students work the problem 3 × 5 on a number line as an example.

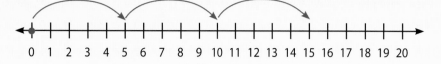

Point out that the product (15) is greater than either of the factors (3 and 5).

Ask: When you multiply two numbers greater than 1, will the answer always be greater than either of the numbers? Yes

Have students make up some problems, such as 2 × 10 and 3 × 100, to verify that this seems to be true.

3. **Say:** When both numbers in a problem are greater than 1, you can think of the problem on a number line and see that there's more than one jump. So the product is definitely greater than the number you started with. For example, if the problem is 3 × 5, there's more than one jump of 5. The product will definitely be greater than 5. The same is true if the factors in the problem are reversed. In our example, if you change the problem to 5 × 3, there's more than one jump of 3.

4. Tell students that as long as both factors are greater than 1, the product is always greater than either factor. On the number line, the product will always be to the right of either factor. The answer to 3 × 5 is 15; this product is to the right of both 3 and 5.

5. **Ask:** When is the product not greater than both factors? when a factor is zero or 1

   Ask: What happens when you multiply by zero? When you multiply by 1? When I multiply by zero, I get zero. When I multiply by 1, I get the other factor.

6. Summarize for students.

   Say: When multiplying two numbers, the product is usually greater than the factors. The only times this is not true are when multiplying by zero or 1. When zero is a factor, the product is always zero, and when 1 is a factor, the product is the other factor.

LEARN Multiplication Patterns

OFFLINE 15 min

Objectives

- Demonstrate an understanding of how multiplication affects whole numbers.

Students will learn the term *multiple* and will identify patterns that result when multiplying two factors.
   Gather the base-10 blocks and the Hundred Chart.

1. Have students model the expression 1 × 10 using base-10 blocks. Students should show 1 tens rod.

   Ask students to say and write the number sentence and the product.
   1 × 10 = 10

   Repeat for the expressions 2 × 10, 3 × 10, and 4 × 10.

   Ask students why no ones cubes are needed. Since we're showing 1 ten, 2 tens, 3 tens, and so on, we can show them with just tens rods.

   Have students notice that each product has a zero in the ones place, showing that there are no ones.

2. Have students circle each product. Explain that these are all multiples of 10.

   Have students skip count by 10 (10, 20, 30, and so on). Explain that when they skip count by 10, they are saying the multiples of 10. Have students notice that all multiples of 10 end with the digit zero in the ones place.

3. Have students skip count by 5s on the Hundred Chart. Have them shade each multiple of 5 and then look for a pattern.

   Ask: What do you notice about multiples of 5? Multiples of 5 always end in the digit 5 or zero.

4. Write the following expressions in two columns as shown:

1×5	2×5
3×5	4×5
5×5	6×5
7×5	8×5
9×5	10×5

   Have students use base-10 blocks to show the products of 1×5, 2×5, 3×5, and 4×5. Have them record the products. Ask them to explain why there are always either 5 ones cubes or zero ones cubes when making multiples of 5. Guide students to see that when multiplying by an odd number, the product will have 5 ones and when multiplying by an even number, the product will have only tens rods and zero ones because two 5s equal one 10.

5. Have students solve the following problems and look for a pattern:

$4 \times 10 = 40$	$6 \times 10 = 60$	$8 \times 10 = 80$	$5 \times 10 = 50$
$4 \times 5 = 20$	$6 \times 5 = 30$	$8 \times 5 = 40$	$5 \times 5 = 25$

   Discuss the pattern. Help students recognize that multiplying 5 times a number is the same as half of 10 times the same number—in other words, the product of 10 and a number is twice the product of 5 and that same number.

6. Explore multiples of 2 by having students count by 2s and write the following expressions for multiples of 2:

1×2	2×2	3×2	4×2	5×2
6×2	7×2	8×2	9×2	10×2

   Ask students to identify each product as an even or odd number. All products are even numbers.

   Explain that all multiples of 2 are even numbers because when you multiply by 2, you make groups of 2, and every multiple of 2 is an even number.

TRY IT Multiplication Results

OFFLINE
10 min

Objectives

Students will practice determining the result of multiplication on whole numbers. Have students turn to the Multiplication Results activity page in their Activity Book and read the directions with them.

Students should copy the problems from the Activity Book into their Math Notebook as necessary and solve them there.

- Demonstrate an understanding of how multiplication affects whole numbers.

Understand Multiplication
Multiplication Results

Tell whether the product is zero, equal to one factor, or greater than both factors.

1. 5×6 **greater than**
2. 1×4 **equal to**
3. 3×0 **zero**
4. 9×3 **greater than**
5. 0×5 **zero**
6. 8×1 **equal to**

Answer the question.

7. Jared multiplies a number by 2. Will the product be even or odd? How do you know?

    Even; all multiples of 2 are even.

8. Look at this set of numbers: 10, 25, 35, 40, 50.
Are these numbers multiples of 5? How do you know?

    Yes; they end in 5 or zero.

Choose the statement that is true.

9. Gina is going to multiply 5×6.
    - A. It's impossible to know if the answer will be greater than 6.
    - (B.) The answer is greater than 6.
    - C. It's impossible to know if the answer will be less than 6.
    - D. The answer is less than 6.

10. Ralph is going to multiply two numbers greater than 1.
    - A. The answer will sometimes be less than either number.
    - B. The answer will always be less than either number.
    - C. The answer will sometimes be greater than either number.
    - (D.) The answer will always be greater than either number.

11. Rachel is going to use a number line to multiply 2×7.
    - (A.) The answer will always be to the right of 7.
    - B. The answer will sometimes be to the left of 7.
    - C. The answer will always be to the left of 7.
    - D. The answer will sometimes be to the right of 7.

12. Janice is going to multiply a whole number greater than zero by 10.
    - (A.) The last digit in the product will be zero.
    - B. The last digit in the product will always be 2.
    - C. The last digit in the product will either be zero or 5.
    - D. The product will always be an even number ending in 0, 2, 4, 6, or 8.

TRY IT

TRY IT

CHECKPOINT

ONLINE 10 min

Students will complete an online Checkpoint. If necessary, read the directions, problems, and answer choices to students and help them with keyboard or mouse operations.

Objectives

- Demonstrate an understanding of how multiplication affects whole numbers.

Commutative Property of Multiplication

Lesson Overview

GET READY Area Models	5 minutes	ONLINE
LEARN Change the Order	10 minutes	ONLINE
LEARN Factor Switch	15 minutes	ONLINE
LEARN Three Factors	15 minutes	ONLINE
TRY IT Apply the Commutative Property	10 minutes	OFFLINE

▶ Lesson Objectives

Explain and apply the commutative property of multiplication.

▶ Prerequisite Skills

Demonstrate understanding that the order in which numbers are multiplied does not affect the product.

Materials to Gather

SUPPLIED

Apply the Commutative Property
   activity page

▶ Content Background

Students now have a basic knowledge of multiplication, and they understand how to model and solve multiplication problems by skip counting or using repeated addition. In this lesson, they will be reminded that a multiplication expression can be represented by rows and squares. For instance, the expression 7×10 is represented by 7 rows of 10 squares. This can be solved easily by skip counting by 10s. In contrast, the expression 10×7 is represented with 10 rows of 7 squares. Since it's more difficult to skip count by 7s, students will use the commutative property of multiplication to change the order of the factors and will multiply 7×10 to get the product. They will learn about the commutative property of multiplication.

The commutative property of multiplication states that two numbers can be multiplied in any order and the product does not change. For example, $5 \times 3 = 15$ and $3 \times 5 = 15$, so $5 \times 3 = 3 \times 5$.

▶ Common Errors and Misconceptions

Students might not realize that the two factors in a multiplication expression have different meanings. For example, 3 sets of 6 dots is written as 3×6, not 6×3. However, the product of each expression is 18.

ONLINE
5 min

GET READY Area Models

Students will see multiplication represented using an area model. They will see 5×8 represented as 5 rows of 8 squares. Then they'll see that when the model is turned sideways, it shows 8×5 or 8 rows of 5 squares. In each case, while the problem is different, the product or total number of squares is the same.

Objectives

- Demonstrate understanding that the order in which numbers are multiplied does not affect the product.

LEARN Change the Order

ONLINE 10 min

Objectives

- Explain and apply the commutative property of multiplication.

Students will explore the commutative property of multiplication. They will see multiplication problems shown using an area model with squares on a grid. They'll see that the order of the factors does not affect the product.

Remind students that the first factor is the number of rows and the second factor is the number of squares in each row, or the number of columns. If necessary, help students solve the the problem by writing it as repeated addition. For example, $10 \times 7 = 7 + 7 + 7 + 7 + 7 + 7 + 7 + 7 + 7 + 7$, and $7 \times 10 = 10 + 10 + 10 + 10 + 10 + 10 + 10$. This will help students see how the order of the factors affects how the problem is solved but doesn't affect the product.

LEARN Factor Switch

ONLINE 15 min

Objectives

- Explain and apply the commutative property of multiplication.

Students will practice using the commutative property of multiplication to solve problems. They will see that $7 \times 5 = 35$ and use that to solve 5×7.

LEARN Three Factors

ONLINE 15 min

Objectives

- Explain and apply the commutative property of multiplication.

Students have been using the commutative property of multiplication to solve problems that have only two factors. The commutative property always deals with only two factors at a time, but it can be used in problems with more than two factors to make the problems easier to solve.

In multiplication, any of the factors can be switched with another factor and the product will be the same. In this activity, students will first review how they commonly use the commutative property of addition in problems with three or more numbers, making those problems easier to solve. They will then use the commutative property of multiplication to make multiplication problems easier when there are three factors. For instance, $5 \times 7 \times 2$ is easily solved when reordered as $5 \times 2 \times 7$.

TRY IT Apply the Commutative Property

OFFLINE 10 min

Objectives

- Explain and apply the commutative property of multiplication

Students will practice applying the commutative property of multiplication. Have students turn to the Apply the Commutative Property activity page in their Activity Book and read the directions with them.

Students should copy the problems from the Activity Book into their Math Notebook as necessary and solve them there.

Commutative Property of Multiplication

Apply the Commutative Property

Use the commutative property of multiplication to find the product.

1. $9 \times 5 = 45$
   $5 \times 9 = \underline{?}$ **45**

2. $7 \times 4 = 28$
   $4 \times 7 = \underline{?}$ **28**

3. $6 \times 8 = 48$
   $8 \times 6 = \underline{?}$ **48**

4. $3 \times 5 = 15$
   $5 \times 3 = \underline{?}$ **15**

Find the missing number.

5. $7 \times 3 = 3 \times \square$ **7**

6. $6 \times 4 = 4 \times \square$ **6**

7. $\square \times 2 = 2 \times 9$ **9**

8. $5 \times \square = 10 \times 5$ **10**

Change the order to make the numbers easier to multiply. Then solve.

9. $2 \times 8 \times 5 = \square \times \square \times \square = \square$
   2, 5, 8; 80

10. $7 \times 6 \times 0 = \square \times \square \times \square = \square$
    7, 0, 6; 0

Answer the question.

11. Theresa knows that $8 \times 3 = 24$.
    Explain how she can quickly give the answer to 3×8 by using the commutative property. **See below.**

Choose the answer.

12. If $6 \times 3 = 18$, which sentence is true?

    A. The answer to 3×6 will be greater than 18.

    B. The answer to 3×6 will be equal to 18.

    C. The answer to 3×6 will be less than 18.

WHOLE NUMBER MULTIPLICATION SENSE **77** COMMUTATIVE PROPERTY OF MULTIPLICATION

T R Y I T

Additional Answers

11. **Example:** She knows that changing the order of the numbers that are multiplied doesn't change the product, so 3×8 will also equal 24. Other correct answers are acceptable.

Multiplication Facts for 0, 1, 3

Lesson Overview

Skills Update	5 minutes	ONLINE
GET READY Groups of Objects	5 minutes	ONLINE
LEARN Factors of Zero and 1	10 minutes	OFFLINE
LEARN Multiplication Facts Chart	20 minutes	OFFLINE
LEARN Multiply 3s	10 minutes	OFFLINE
TRY IT Multiplication Practice	10 minutes	ONLINE

▶ Lesson Objectives

- Explain and apply the zero property of multiplication.
- Explain and apply the multiplication property of 1.
- Demonstrate automatic recall of multiplication facts.

▶ Prerequisite Skills

- Demonstrate understanding of the rule for multiplying by zero.
- Demonstrate understanding that any number multiplied by 1 results in the same number ($n \times 1 = n$).

▶ Content Background

Students have a basic understanding of multiplication. They will expand on this knowledge by learning about the zero property of multiplication and the multiplication property of 1. They will focus on fact memorization with the goal of automatically recalling the 3s multiplication facts. Students have already learned the multiplication facts for 2s, 5s, and 10s, and they should continue to practice those.

As students study math, they will learn that both zero and 1 are special numbers. In multiplication, for example, the result of multiplying any number by 1 is that same number, but multiplying any number by zero always results in the answer of zero. These two facts are very important for students to remember.

Skip counting provides a firm foundation for multiplication. However, students must memorize and automatically recall their multiplication facts to truly succeed in math.

The commutative property of multiplication states that two numbers can be multiplied in any order and the product does not change. Even if the property is still not completely understood by students, they should recognize that once they know the product of 8×2 is 16, they also know the product of 2×8.

▶ Advance Preparation

Print the Multiplication Facts Chart, the Multiplication Facts Poster, and the Centimeter Grid Paper. Tape together the pieces of the Multiplication Facts Poster.

Materials to Gather

SUPPLIED

blocks – B (7 of any color)
Multiplication Facts Chart (printout)
Multiplication Facts Poster (printout)
Centimeter Grid Paper (printout)

ALSO NEEDED

coloring pencils or crayons

GET READY Groups of Objects

Students will practice representing multiplication expressions with the factors zero and 1. Remind students that the numbers that are multiplied are called *factors* and the answer is called the *product*.

Students will see that a number multiplied by 1 equals the number itself. They will see that a number multiplied by zero equals zero. They will see that 4×0 can be shown as 4 groups of zero objects. Remind students that 0×4 would be shown by zero groups of 4 objects.

- Demonstrate understanding of the rule for multiplying by zero.
- Demonstrate understanding that any number multiplied by 1 results in the same number ($n \times 1 = n$).

LEARN Factors of Zero and 1

Objectives

Students will model multiplication by zero and 1. Then they will practice solving problems with factors of zero and 1.

Gather the B blocks.

1. Make one pile of 7 B blocks.

   Say: Here is one group of 7 circles. What multiplication problem does it represent? 1×7

   Ask: What is the product? 7

   Have the students use the same 7 blocks to show the problem 7×1. Students should spread the 7 blocks out to show 7 groups of 1.

   Ask: What is the product? 7

   Ask students what the rule is for multiplying by 1. Students should explain that 1 times any number is just that number, and any number times 1 is just the number you started with.

2. Ask students to show you zero groups of 7, and then 7 groups of zero. Ask what the product is in each case. zero

   Ask students to show you zero groups of 10,000 and tell you the product. zero

   Have students explain the rule for multiplying by zero. Students should explain that any number times zero is zero, or zero times any number is zero.

3. Tell students that since they know the rules for multiplying by zero and 1, they can do any problem with a factor of zero or 1 quickly. Say each of these problems. Ask students to tell you the product.

   - 7×0 0
   - 10×1 10
   - 0×9 0
   - 35×1 35
   - 1×17 17
   - 245×0 0
   - $0 \times 2,000$ 0
   - 450×1 450
   - 1×42 42

4. Present the following simple story problems, which apply the zero property of multiplication. Ask students to give each answer.

   - There are zero paintbrushes in each box of art supplies. There are 24 boxes of art supplies. How many paintbrushes are there? $24 \times 0 = 0$; zero paintbrushes
   - There are 562 boxes in the warehouse. Each box has zero items. How many items are in all the boxes together? $562 \times 0 = 0$; zero items

Objectives

- Explain and apply the zero property of multiplication.
- Explain and apply the multiplication property of 1.

Tips

Write the multiplication problems in the Math Notebook, if you wish, and have students write each product.

5. If students answer either of the above story problems incorrectly, show them the expression for that problem and explain how the story problem is an example of the zero property of multiplication. Remind students that multiplying any number by zero results in an answer of zero.

LEARN Multiplication Facts Chart

Objectives

- Demonstrate automatic recall of multiplication facts.

Tips

Make a set of multiplication flash cards for problems with factors of 0, 1, 2, 5, and 10. Show students the cards and ask them to say the product. If they have the fact memorized, they can record the product on the chart.

Students will use a Multiplication Facts Chart to record the multiplication facts they have learned. They will also use the Multiplication Facts Poster that was assembled to hang on the wall. On the poster, students will record only the products of facts they have memorized. Those are the products they can say without pausing to do a mental calculation. In multiplication, the order in which factors are multiplied doesn't affect the product (multiplication is commutative). Thus, when students learn 3×4, they will also know 4×3 and can record both products on the Multiplication Facts Chart.

Gather the Multiplication Facts Poster and Multiplication Facts Chart.

1. Show students the Multiplication Facts Chart and the Multiplication Facts Poster. Explain that the small chart will be used to record which multiplication facts they've learned, and the poster will record those that are truly memorized. Explain that the goal is to memorize all the multiplication facts. Remind them that they already know many of the facts.

2. Guide students in how to use the chart to record products. Explain that the numbers on the bottom and on the left of the chart are factors, and each number on the bottom will pair with a number on the left to create a multiplication fact. Students will write each fact's product in the square where the column and row meet. (Be sure students go along the bottom to get the first factor and up for the second factor. Doing this will help them later when they do graphing, using the same routine to find points on a graph.)

3. Begin at the bottom and work from left to right: 0×0, 1×0, 2×0, 3×0, to 10×0. Have students match each factor along the bottom to zero on the left and record the product in the 0s and 1s chart.

4. Explain that since they know the products when the second factor is zero, they also know the products when the first factor is zero. Guide students to fill in the column that corresponds to multiplying by zero.

5. Repeat Steps 3 and 4 for the 1s multiplication facts. The highlighted area of the 0s and 1s chart shows the products of the 0s and 1s facts that students should write.

6. Check students' recall of the 2s, 5s, and 10s facts before recording those products in the chart. Remind students that they can skip count by 2s, 5s, or 10s to solve these facts.

7. At the end of the activity, have students record the product for any 0s, 1s, 2s, 5s, or 10s facts they have memorized on the Multiplication Facts Poster. The highlighted areas on the charts show the products that students should write.

8. Have students write the facts on the Multiplication Facts Chart and write the products in pencil on the Multiplication Facts Poster. (In several days, if students have truly memorized the facts and can recall them quickly, they can write them on the poster with a colored marker.)

Multiplication Facts Chart
Completed for 0s and 1s

	0	1	2	3	4	5	6	7	8	9	10
10	0	10									
9	0	9									
8	0	8									
7	0	7									
6	0	6									
5	0	5									
4	0	4									
3	0	3									
2	0	2									
1	0	1	2	3	4	5	6	7	8	9	10
0	0	0	0	0	0	0	0	0	0	0	0
×	0	1	2	3	4	5	6	7	8	9	10

Multiplication Facts Chart
Completed for 2s, 5s, and 10s

	0	1	2	3	4	5	6	7	8	9	10
10	0	10	20	30	40	50	60	70	80	90	100
9	0	9	18			45					90
8	0	8	16			40					80
7	0	7	14			35					70
6	0	6	12			30					60
5	0	5	10	15	20	25	30	35	40	45	50
4	0	4	8			20					40
3	0	3	6			15					30
2	0	2	4	6	8	10	12	14	16	18	20
1	0	1	2	3	4	5	6	7	8	9	10
0	0	0	0	0	0	0	0	0	0	0	0
×	0	1	2	3	4	5	6	7	8	9	10

LEARN Multiply 3s

Objectives

- Demonstrate automatic recall of multiplication facts.

Students will model and solve the 3s multiplication facts. Because students know 0×3, 1×3, and 2×3, they will start at 3×3. There are only six facts to memorize. With the commutative facts, students will fill in 11 new facts in the Multiplication Facts Chart.

Gather the Multiplication Facts Chart, Centimeter Grid Paper, and coloring pencils or crayons.

1. Have students draw and color an area model to show 7×3 (7 rows of 3) on the grid paper.

2. Ask students to skip count by 3s to find the product. 3, 6, 9, 12, 15, 18, 21

3. Have students record the multiplication sentence below the area model. $7 \times 3 = 21$

4. Repeat Steps 1–3 for these facts: 3×3, 4×3, 5×3, 6×3, 8×3, and 9×3. Examples of area models on grid paper are shown.

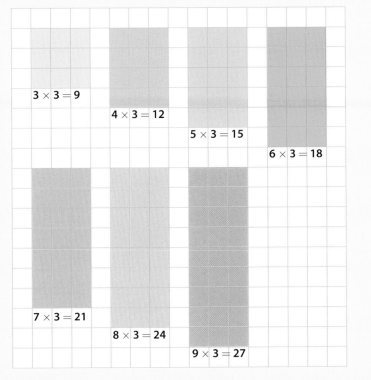

$3 \times 3 = 9$
$4 \times 3 = 12$
$5 \times 3 = 15$
$6 \times 3 = 18$
$7 \times 3 = 21$
$8 \times 3 = 24$
$9 \times 3 = 27$

5. Remind students that changing the order of the factors in a multiplication problem does not change the product. Point out they also know the following facts because of the commutative property: 3×4, 3×5, 3×6, 3×7, 3×8, and 3×9.

6. Have students write the new 3s facts on the Multiplication Facts Chart and write the products in pencil on the Multiplication Facts Poster. (In several days, if students have truly memorized the facts and can recall them quickly, they can write them on the poster with a colored marker.)

Note: The highlighted area on the Multiplication Facts Chart shows the 3s multiplication facts that students should have filled in during this activity. The other, nonhighlighted products in the chart are the ones that they previously learned.

Multiplication Facts Chart
Completed for 3s

10	0	10	20	30	40	50	60	70	80	90	100
9	0	9	18	27		45					90
8	0	8	16	24		40					80
7	0	7	14	21		35					70
6	0	6	12	18		30					60
5	0	5	10	15	20	25	30	35	40	45	50
4	0	4	8	12		20					40
3	0	3	6	9	12	15	18	21	24	27	30
2	0	2	4	6	8	10	12	14	16	18	20
1	0	1	2	3	4	5	6	7	8	9	10
0	0	0	0	0	0	0	0	0	0	0	0
×	0	1	2	3	4	5	6	7	8	9	10

TRY IT Multiplication Practice

ONLINE 10 min

Objectives

Students will use online flash cards to practice their 3s multiplication facts. They should say each answer aloud. They can flip the card to check their answer or they can go on to the next card if they know their answer is correct. If students have difficulty memorizing the 3s, have them count by 3s to 30 to get familiar with the numbers that are multiples of 3.

- Explain and apply the zero property of multiplication.
- Explain and apply the multiplication property of 1.
- Demonstrate automatic recall of multiplication facts.

Multiplication Facts (A)

Lesson Overview

GET READY Multiplication Review	10 minutes	**ONLINE**
LEARN Use 2s Facts to Solve Multiplication	20 minutes	**OFFLINE**
LEARN Recall 4s Facts	20 minutes	**ONLINE**
TRY IT Practice Multiplication	10 minutes	**OFFLINE**

▶ Lesson Objectives

Demonstrate automatic recall of multiplication facts.

▶ Prerequisite Skills

- Demonstrate automatic recall of multiplication facts for 2 through 10 × 2.
- Demonstrate automatic recall of multiplication facts for 5 through 10 × 5.
- Demonstrate understanding that the order in which numbers are multiplied does not affect the product.

▶ Content Background

Students will practice previously learned multiplication facts and will also learn the 4s facts. They will learn a strategy that will help them memorize their 4s facts.

Skip counting provides a foundation for multiplication. However, students must memorize and automatically recall their multiplication facts to truly succeed in math. They should begin to realize that changing the order in which numbers are multiplied does not affect the product. (For example, if they know $8 \times 2 = 16$, they will also know the product of 2×8.)

▶ Advance Preparation

Print the Centimeter Grid Paper. Have the Multiplication Facts Chart and Multiplication Facts Poster ready or print new ones if needed.

Materials to Gather

SUPPLIED

Centimeter Grid Paper (printout)

Multiplication Facts Chart (printout)

Multiplication Facts Poster (printout)

Practice Multiplication activity page

GET READY Multiplication Review

Students will continue to practice multiplication facts. They will use online flash cards to practice these facts. Have students say or write the answer.

Objectives

- Demonstrate automatic recall of multiplication facts for 2 through 10 × 2.
- Demonstrate automatic recall of multiplication facts for 5 through 10 × 5.
- Demonstrate understanding that the order in which numbers are multiplied does not affect the product.

LEARN Use 2s Facts to Solve Multiplication

Students will use their knowledge of the 2s multiplication facts to learn multiplication facts for 4s.

Gather the Centimeter Grid Paper, Multiplication Facts Chart, and Multiplication Facts Poster.

1. Ask students to create an area model on the grid paper to show 3 × 4. Remind students that the first factor, 3, names the number of rows and the second factor, 4, names the number in each row.
2. Have students count by 4s to find the product. 4, 8, 12
3. Write the multiplication fact 3 × 4 = 12.
4. Explain to students that skip counting by 4s is not necessarily as easy as skip counting by 2s and that they can use their 2s facts to solve facts for 4.
5. **Say:** Since 2 × 2 = 4, or double 2 is 4, you can double the 2s facts to find the facts for 4.
6. Ask students to find the product of 6 × 2. 12

   Explain that they can double that product to find the product of 6 × 4.

   Ask: What is the double of 12? 24

   Explain that to find the product of 6 × 4, they can use 6 × 2 = 12, double the 12, and identify 24 as the product of 6 × 4.
7. Have students find the products for the following problems using whatever strategy is easiest for them: 1 × 4, 2 × 4, 3 × 4, 4 × 4, 5 × 4, 6 × 4, 7 × 4, 8 × 4, and 9 × 4.

   For some problems, students may choose to find the 2s fact and double the product. For example, to solve 8 × 4, students would think of 8 × 2 = 16. The answer to 8 × 4 would be the double of 16. Thus, 8 × 4 = 32.

   For other problems, students may choose to reverse the order of the factors to turn the problem into one they know. For example, 5 × 4 could be turned into 4 × 5, which students will know equals 20. Or students may wish to substitute a similar problem and then add to or subtract from the product as needed. For 9 × 4, a student might think of 10 × 4 = 40 and then take away 4 to find that 9 × 4 = 36. Any strategy that students use is okay. But remind them that ultimately they need to memorize the facts so that there is no mental calculation.

Objectives

- Demonstrate automatic recall of multiplication facts.

Tips

If students have difficulty seeing that 4 times a number is the double of 2 times a number, have them use the grid paper to shade 6 × 4 (6 rows of 4). Then draw a line under the second row to show students how the grid can be seen as two sets of 6 rows of 2.

Multiplication Facts Chart
Completed for 4s

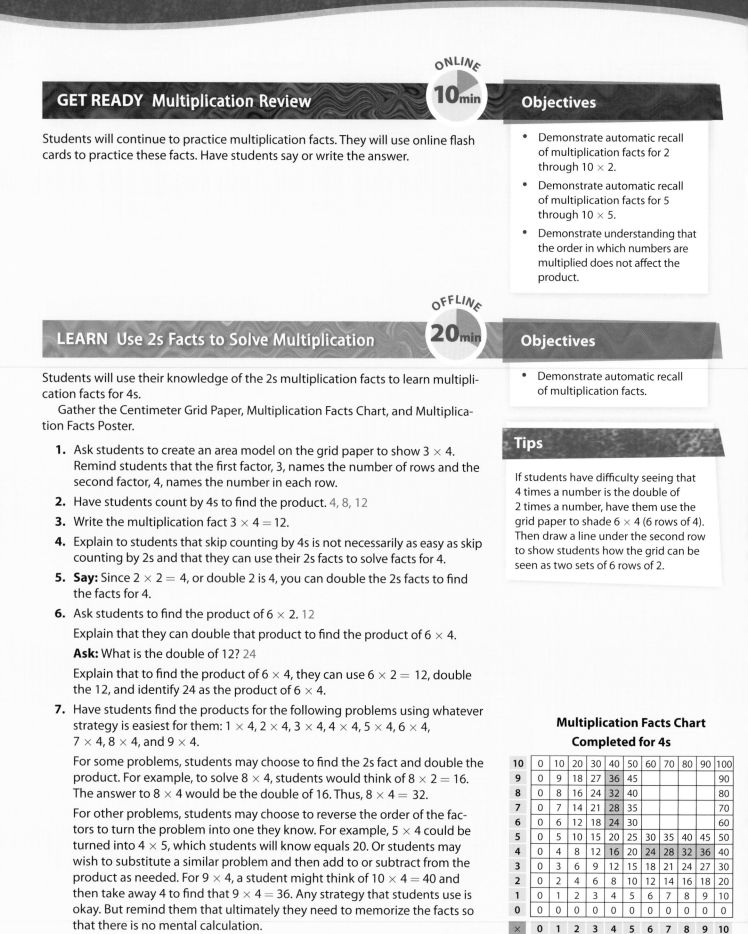

10	0	10	20	30	40	50	60	70	80	90	100
9	0	9	18	27	36	45					90
8	0	8	16	24	32	40					80
7	0	7	14	21	28	35					70
6	0	6	12	18	24	30					60
5	0	5	10	15	20	25	30	35	40	45	50
4	0	4	8	12	16	20	24	28	32	36	40
3	0	3	6	9	12	15	18	21	24	27	30
2	0	2	4	6	8	10	12	14	16	18	20
1	0	1	2	3	4	5	6	7	8	9	10
0	0	0	0	0	0	0	0	0	0	0	0
×	0	1	2	3	4	5	6	7	8	9	10

8. Have students write the 4s facts in pencil on the Multiplication Facts Chart and write the products on the Multiplication Facts Poster. (In several days, if students have truly memorized the facts and can recall them quickly, they can write them on the poster with a colored marker.)

LEARN Recall 4s Facts

ONLINE 20 min

Students will practice recalling the multiplication facts for 4. They will type the answer to a problem and check their answer. Then they'll use online flash cards to further reinforce their knowledge of 4s facts.

Objectives

- Demonstrate automatic recall of multiplication facts.

TRY IT Practice Multiplication

OFFLINE 10 min

Students will practice solving multiplication problems. Have students turn to the Practice Multiplication activity page in their Activity Book and read the directions with them.

Students should copy the problems from the Activity Book into their Math Notebook as necessary and solve them there.

Objectives

- Demonstrate automatic recall of multiplication facts.

Multiplication Facts (A)
Practice Multiplication

Multiply.

1. $2 \times 3 = \underline{?}$ **6**　　　2. $8 \times 4 = \underline{?}$ **32**

3. $\begin{array}{r} 4 \\ \times 4 \\ \hline 16 \end{array}$　4. $\begin{array}{r} 3 \\ \times 5 \\ \hline 15 \end{array}$　5. $\begin{array}{r} 3 \\ \times 0 \\ \hline 0 \end{array}$　6. $\begin{array}{r} 4 \\ \times 2 \\ \hline 8 \end{array}$

7. $8 \times 3 = \underline{?}$ **24**　　8. $4 \times 6 = \underline{?}$ **24**

9. $3 \times 4 = \underline{?}$ **12**　　10. $4 \times 10 = \underline{?}$ **40**

11. $3 \times 1 = \underline{?}$ **3**　　12. $3 \times 10 = \underline{?}$ **30**

13. $\begin{array}{r} 4 \\ \times 3 \\ \hline 12 \end{array}$　14. $\begin{array}{r} 7 \\ \times 3 \\ \hline 21 \end{array}$　15. $\begin{array}{r} 4 \\ \times 5 \\ \hline 20 \end{array}$　16. $\begin{array}{r} 4 \\ \times 9 \\ \hline 36 \end{array}$

17. $7 \times 4 = \underline{?}$ **28**　　18. $6 \times 3 = \underline{?}$ **18**

19. $4 \times 1 = \underline{?}$ **4**　　20. $3 \times 3 = \underline{?}$ **9**

21. $1 \times 4 = \underline{?}$ **4**　　22. $6 \times 4 = \underline{?}$ **24**

23. $4 \times 8 = \underline{?}$ **32**　　24. $9 \times 4 = \underline{?}$ **36**

25. $\begin{array}{r} 10 \\ \times 4 \\ \hline 40 \end{array}$　　26. $\begin{array}{r} 0 \\ \times 10 \\ \hline 0 \end{array}$

TRY IT

WHOLE NUMBER MULTIPLICATION SENSE　**78**

Multiplication Facts (B)

Lesson Overview

GET READY Multiplication Review	10 minutes	ONLINE
LEARN Multiplication Facts for 6	10 minutes	ONLINE
LEARN Multiplication Facts for 7	15 minutes	ONLINE
LEARN Multiplication Fact Match	15 minutes	OFFLINE
TRY IT Facts for 6 and 7	10 minutes	OFFLINE

▶ Lesson Objectives

Demonstrate automatic recall of multiplication facts.

▶ Prerequisite Skills

- Demonstrate automatic recall of multiplication facts for 2 through 10 × 2.
- Demonstrate automatic recall of multiplication facts for 5 through 10 × 5.
- Demonstrate understanding that the order in which numbers are multiplied does not affect the product.

▶ Content Background

Students will practice previously learned multiplication facts and will also learn the facts for 6 and 7. They will learn a strategy that will help them memorize their facts for 6 and 7.

Skip counting provides a foundation for multiplication. However, students must memorize and automatically recall their multiplication facts to truly succeed in math. They should begin to realize that changing the order in which numbers are multiplied does not affect the product. (For example, if they know $8 \times 2 = 16$, they will also know the product of 2×8.)

▶ Advance Preparation

Have the Multiplication Facts Chart and Multiplication Facts Poster ready or print new ones if needed.

Prepare a set of index cards for the new multiplication facts. Each card should have the fact on one side and the answer on the other.

- 6×6 36
- 7×6 42
- 8×6 48
- 9×6 54
- 6×7 42
- 7×7 49
- 8×7 56
- 9×7 63

Materials to Gather

SUPPLIED

Multiplication Facts Chart (printout)

Multiplication Facts Poster (printout)

index cards – labeled with multiplication facts

Facts for 6 and 7 activity page

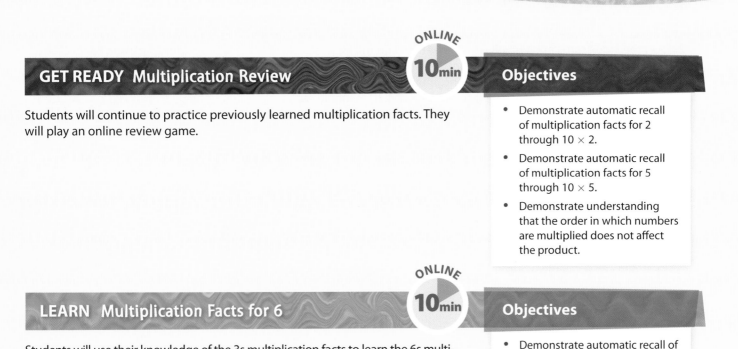

GET READY Multiplication Review

ONLINE 10 min

Students will continue to practice previously learned multiplication facts. They will play an online review game.

Objectives

- Demonstrate automatic recall of multiplication facts for 2 through 10 × 2.
- Demonstrate automatic recall of multiplication facts for 5 through 10 × 5.
- Demonstrate understanding that the order in which numbers are multiplied does not affect the product.

LEARN Multiplication Facts for 6

ONLINE 10 min

Students will use their knowledge of the 3s multiplication facts to learn the 6s multiplication facts. Students will also use the commutative property, which states that the order in which two numbers are multiplied does not affect the product.

In general, students should use whatever strategy works for them to learn and memorize the multiplication facts. The strategies explained can help students get an answer until they have the facts memorized, but there is no substitute for memorizing the facts eventually. Memorization is essential for doing multiplication of greater numbers.

Objectives

- Demonstrate automatic recall of multiplication facts.

LEARN Multiplication Facts for 7

ONLINE 15 min

Students will learn and practice their multiplication facts for 7. Encourage students to use whatever strategy seems easiest to find the products for these multiplication facts. Emphasize that the goal is to memorize the facts so that students don't have to spend time making mental calculations.

Objectives

- Demonstrate automatic recall of multiplication facts.

LEARN Multiplication Fact Match

OFFLINE 15 min

Students will review the multiplication facts for 6 and 7 by adding the facts to the Multiplication Facts Chart. They will continue to practice these facts by playing a memory game in which they provide either the answer for a multiplication expression or the expression that goes with the answer. This game will help students get familiar with the multiples of 6 and 7 so they can start to memorize these eight facts.

Gather the Multiplication Facts Chart, Multiplication Facts Poster, and labeled index cards.

1. Have students write the products of the new multiplication facts for 6 and 7 on the Multiplication Facts Chart. They should write the products for $6 \times 6, 7 \times 6, 8 \times 6, 9 \times 6, 6 \times 7, 7 \times 7, 8 \times 7,$ and 9×7.

Objectives

- Demonstrate automatic recall of multiplication facts.

2. Sort the index cards into two piles: the facts for 6 and the facts for 7. Take one pile at a time and turn the cards answer-side up. Have students flip through the four cards for the 6s, looking at the answer and saying the matching problem. (For example, if students see 54, they should say 9 × 6.) Do this for several rounds, shuffling the cards after each round. Then turn the cards problem-side up and have students say the matching answers. Repeat for several rounds, shuffling the cards after each round.

3. Repeat Step 2 with the four cards for the 7s facts.

4. Shuffle the two stacks together and continue to practice. Note that there will be two cards with 42 as an answer, 7 × 6 and 6 × 7. Either problem is acceptable when this answer card comes up.

5. Have students write the products for the 6s and 7s in pencil on the Multiplication Facts Poster. (In several days, if students have truly memorized the facts and can recall them quickly, they can write them on the poster with a colored marker.)

Multiplication Facts Chart Completed for 6s and 7s

10	0	10	20	30	40	50	60	70	80	90	100
9	0	9	18	27	36	45	54	63			90
8	0	8	16	24	32	40	48	56			80
7	0	7	14	21	28	35	42	49	56	63	70
6	0	6	12	18	24	30	36	42	48	54	60
5	0	5	10	15	20	25	30	35	40	45	50
4	0	4	8	12	16	20	24	28	32	36	40
3	0	3	6	9	12	15	18	21	24	27	30
2	0	2	4	6	8	10	12	14	16	18	20
1	0	1	2	3	4	5	6	7	8	9	10
0	0	0	0	0	0	0	0	0	0	0	0
×	0	1	2	3	4	5	6	7	8	9	10

OFFLINE
10 min

TRY IT Facts for 6 and 7

Objectives

- Demonstrate automatic recall of multiplication facts.

Students will practice multiplication facts by solving problems. Have students turn to the Facts for 6 and 7 activity page in their Activity Book and read the directions with them.

Students should copy the problems from the Activity Book into their Math Notebook as necessary and solve them there.

Before students do the problems on the activity page, have them practice any facts they have not yet memorized. Next they should complete all the problems on the activity page that they can do quickly, then go back and complete the rest.

Multiplication Facts (B)

Facts for 6 and 7

Multiply.

1. 6 × 3 = 18
2. 7 × 9 = 63
3. 7 × 7 = 49
4. 6 × 8 = 48
5. 6 × 5 = 30
6. 6 × 1 = 6
7. 7 × 4 = 28
8. 7 × 3 = 21
9. 9 × 7 = 63
10. 2 × 6 = 12
11. 6 × 7 = 42
12. 4 × 5 = 20

13. 7 × 6 = ? **42**
14. 4 × 5 = ? **20**
15. 8 × 6 = ? **48**
16. 3 × 7 = ? **21**
17. 6 × 10 = ? **60**
18. 0 × 3 = ? **0**
19. 7 × 1 = ? **7**
20. 9 × 7 = ? **63**
21. 7 × 2 = ? **14**
22. 7 × 6 = ? **42**
23. 2 × 7 = ? **14**
24. 3 × 6 = ? **18**
25. 5 × 7 = ? **35**
26. 7 × 6 = ? **42**
27. 9 × 6 = ? **54**
28. 10 × 7 = ? **70**

T R Y   I T

WHOLE NUMBER MULTIPLICATION SENSE   **79**   MULTIPLICATION FACTS (B)

Multiplication Facts (C)

GET READY Multiplication Fact Recall	5 minutes	ONLINE
LEARN Multiply by 8	15 minutes	OFFLINE
LEARN Multiply by 9	15 minutes	OFFLINE
LEARN Fact Practice for 8s and 9s	15 minutes	ONLINE
TRY IT Multiplication Minutes	10 minutes	OFFLINE

▶ Lesson Objectives

Demonstrate automatic recall of multiplication facts.

▶ Prerequisite Skills

- Demonstrate automatic recall of multiplication facts for 2 through 10×2.
- Demonstrate automatic recall of multiplication facts for 5 through 10×5.
- Demonstrate understanding that the order in which numbers are multiplied does not affect the product.

▶ Content Background

Students will practice previously learned multiplication facts and will also learn the 8s and 9s facts. They will learn strategies that will help them memorize their 8s and 9s facts.

Multiplication facts provide the foundation for learning to multiply greater numbers and for eventually doing long division. While the many strategies students have learned help them find answers, students need to memorize and automatically recall their multiplication facts to truly succeed in math. They should realize that changing the order in which numbers are multiplied does not affect the product. (For example, if they know $8 \times 6 = 48$, they will also know the product of 6×8.)

▶ Advance Preparation

Have the Multiplication Facts Chart ready or print a new one if needed. Have Multiplication Facts Poster available.

Materials to Gather

SUPPLIED

Multiplication Facts Chart (printout)
Multiplication Facts Poster (printout)
Multiplication Minutes activity page

GET READY   Multiplication Fact Recall

Objectives

Students will play a game in which they practice previously learned multiplication facts.

Remind students that they can switch the order of the factors to solve a multiplication problem.

- Demonstrate automatic recall of multiplication facts for 2 through 10 × 2.
- Demonstrate automatic recall of multiplication facts for 5 through 10 × 5.
- Demonstrate understanding that the order in which numbers are multiplied does not affect the product.

LEARN   Multiply by 8

Objectives

Students will use their knowledge of doubling multiplication facts to learn the 8s multiplication facts. They will also use the commutative property, which states that the order in which two numbers are multiplied does not affect the product.

Gather the Multiplication Facts Chart.

- Demonstrate automatic recall of multiplication facts.

Tips

Have students try to count by 8s to help them get familiar with the multiples of 8.

1. Explain to students that they are now ready to learn their 8s facts and that since they already know 0 × 8 through 7 × 8, they only have to learn two new facts—8 × 8 and 9 × 8. Emphasize that the goal is to memorize the facts so they don't have to pause and calculate to get a product.

2. Tell students that they can use their knowledge of other facts to solve the 8s multiplication facts.

   Say: Since 8 is the double of 4, you can double the 4s facts to find the facts for 8. For instance, to find 3 × 8, you could think of 3 × 4 = 12 and double it to get 3 × 8 = 24.

   For 6 × 8, you could think of 6 × 4 = 24 and double it to get 6 × 8 = 48.

   For 8 × 8, you could think of 8 × 4 = 32 and double it to get 8 × 8 = 64.

   For 9 × 8, it's easier to just think of 10 × 8 = 80 and take away one 8 to get 9 × 8 = 72.

3. Explain to students that, if needed, they could think of the commutative fact. For example, instead of 7 × 8, they could think of 8 × 7. Then they could think "2 × 7 is 14, double that to get 4 × 7 is 28, and double that to get 8 × 7 is 56." Remind students that these mental gyrations are only ways to get the answer until they have the facts memorized.

4. Have students write the two new facts for 8 (8 × 8 and 8 × 9) on the Multiplication Facts Chart. When these facts have been filled in, the only space left will be for the fact 9 × 9.

Multiplication Facts Chart
Completed for 8s

×	0	1	2	3	4	5	6	7	8	9	10
10	0	10	20	30	40	50	60	70	80	90	100
9	0	9	18	27	36	45	54	63	72		90
8	0	8	16	24	32	40	48	56	64	72	80
7	0	7	14	21	28	35	42	49	56	63	70
6	0	6	12	18	24	30	36	42	48	54	60
5	0	5	10	15	20	25	30	35	40	45	50
4	0	4	8	12	16	20	24	28	32	36	40
3	0	3	6	9	12	15	18	21	24	27	30
2	0	2	4	6	8	10	12	14	16	18	20
1	0	1	2	3	4	5	6	7	8	9	10
0	0	0	0	0	0	0	0	0	0	0	0

LEARN Multiply by 9

Students will learn strategies to memorize the 9s multiplication facts. They will record the new 9s fact on the Multiplication Facts Chart.

Gather the Multiplication Facts Chart and Multiplication Facts Poster.

1. Show students the following hands-on method for learning 9s facts:
   - Hold out both hands in front of you with your thumbs close together and touching, fingers spread apart.
   - Number the fingers from left to right 1–10.

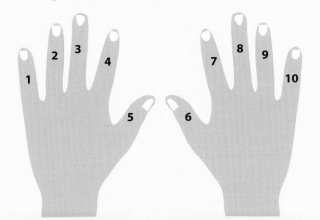

   - Have students bend one finger at a time and count to say the number that this finger represents. For practice, call out numbers and have students bend the correct finger. For example, if you call out "4," students should bend the index finger on their left hand.
   - Tell students that their fingers are a special calculator they can use for the 9s multiplication facts.
   - Explain that to find any product from 1 × 9 through 10 × 9, they should bend the finger representing the first factor and count the number of fingers to the left of the bent finger. That number tells how many tens are in the product. The number of fingers to the right of the bent finger tells the number of ones in the product. For example, to find 4 × 9, students should bend the index finger on the left hand (the finger marked 4). There are 3 fingers to the left of the bent finger, so there are 3 tens, or 30, and 6 fingers to the right of the bent finger, so there are 6 ones. So 4 × 9 = 36. For 7 × 9, bend the seventh finger (index finger on the right hand). There are 6 fingers, or 6 tens, to the left of the bent finger and 3 fingers, or 3 ones, to the right of the bent finger, so 7 × 9 = 63. Remind students that they must count all the fingers to the left and right of the bent finger, including the thumbs. After doing this process just a few times, students will become adept at quickly seeing the answer.
   - Point out to students that when they drop a finger, the number of fingers to the left will always be one less than the finger they dropped. If they drop finger number 8 to do 8 × 9, there will be 7 fingers to the left, so 8 × 9 will start with 7 in the tens place. But since there are 9 fingers up altogether, if there are 7 fingers to the left there must be 2 fingers to the right. So 8 × 9 = 72. For 7 × 9 we drop finger number 7, so there are 6 fingers to the left and there must be 3 to the right; thus, 7 × 9 = 63.

Tips

Provide B blocks for students to use to complete the multiplication and determine the products, if you wish.

2. Tell students that they can see this pattern if they look at the 9s facts. The sum of the digits in the product always equals 9.

   $1 \times 9 = 9;$ 9
   $2 \times 9 = 18;$ $1 + 8 = 9$
   $3 \times 9 = 27;$ $2 + 7 = 9$
   $4 \times 9 = 36;$ $3 + 6 = 9$
   $5 \times 9 = 45;$ $4 + 5 = 9$
   $6 \times 9 = 54;$ $5 + 4 = 9$
   $7 \times 9 = 63;$ $6 + 3 = 9$
   $8 \times 9 = 72;$ $7 + 2 = 9$
   $9 \times 9 = 81;$ $8 + 1 = 9$
   $10 \times 9 = 90;$ $9 + 0 = 9$

3. Have students use a strategy to complete the facts for 9: 1×9, 2×9, 3×9, 4×9, 5×9, 6×9, 7×9, 8×9, 9×9, and 10×9. Students should write the facts in their Math Notebook.

4. Have students write the product for 9×9 on the Multiplication Facts Chart.

5. Explain that since students know their multiplication facts, they also are beginning to learn division facts. Point to the Multiplication Facts Poster. Select a product and have students identify the corresponding multiplication facts. For example, point to 28. Students should identify the facts 4×7 and 7×4. Tell students that 28 divided by 7 is 4, and 28 divided by 4 is 7. Complete several examples but do not push this concept too hard. Encourage students to see the relationship between multiplication and division.

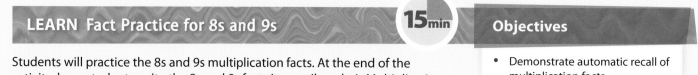

LEARN Fact Practice for 8s and 9s

ONLINE
15 min

Objectives

Students will practice the 8s and 9s multiplication facts. At the end of the activity, have students write the 8s and 9s facts in pencil on their Multiplication Facts Poster. (In several days, if students have truly memorized the facts and can recall them quickly, they can write them on the poster with a colored marker.)

- Demonstrate automatic recall of multiplication facts.

TRY IT Multiplication Minutes

OFFLINE 10 min

Objectives

- Demonstrate automatic recall of multiplication facts.

Students will practice the multiplication facts for 8 and 9. Have students turn to the Multiplication Minutes activity page in their Activity Book and read the directions with them.

Students should copy the problems from the Activity Book into their Math Notebook as necessary and solve them there.

Before students do the problems on the activity page, have them practice any facts they have not yet memorized. Next they should complete all the problems on the activity page that they can do quickly, then go back and complete the rest.

Multiplication Facts (C)
Multiplication Minutes

Multiply.

1.	8	2.	9	3.	9	4.	6	5.	9
	× 8		× 8		× 9		× 5		× 1
	64		**72**		**81**		**30**		**9**

6.	9	7.	2	8.	9	9.	7	10.	8
	× 4		× 7		× 3		× 9		× 2
	36		**14**		**27**		**63**		**16**

11. 8 × 10 = ? **80**　　　12. 5 × 8 = ? **40**

13. 1 × 8 = ? **8**　　　14. 3 × 4 = ? **12**

15. 9 × 10 = ? **90**　　　16. 8 × 3 = ? **24**

17. 9 × 5 = ? **45**　　　18. 8 × 9 = ? **72**

19. 9 × 2 = ? **18**　　　20. 9 × 6 = ? **54**

21. 1 × 9 = ? **9**　　　22. 3 × 8 = ? **24**

23. 4 × 9 = ? **36**　　　24. 5 × 8 = ? **40**

25. 6 × 9 = ? **54**　　　26. 8 × 8 = ? **64**

TRY IT

WHOLE NUMBER MULTIPLICATION SENSE　　**80**　　MULTIPLICATION FACTS (C)

Multiplication Facts (D)

Lesson Overview

LEARN Strategy Review	20 minutes	ONLINE
LEARN Multiplication Facts 0–10	15 minutes	ONLINE
TRY IT Fast Facts	15 minutes	ONLINE
CHECKPOINT	10 minutes	ONLINE

▶ **Lesson Objectives**

Demonstrate automatic recall of multiplication facts.

▶ **Prerequisite Skills**

- Demonstrate automatic recall of multiplication facts for 2 through 10 × 2.
- Demonstrate automatic recall of multiplication facts for 5 through 10 × 5.
- Demonstrate understanding that the order in which numbers are multiplied does not affect the product.

▶ **Content Background**

Students will practice previously learned multiplication facts and will focus on memorizing the facts.

Multiplication facts provide the foundation for learning to multiply greater numbers and for eventually doing long division. While the many strategies students have learned help them find answers, students need to memorize and automatically recall their multiplication facts to truly succeed in math. They should realize that changing the order in which numbers are multiplied does not affect the product. (For example, if they know $8 \times 6 = 48$, they will also know the product of 6×8.)

▶ **Advance Preparation**

Have the Multiplication Facts Poster available.

Materials to Gather

SUPPLIED

Multiplication Facts Poster (printout)

LEARN Strategy Review

ONLINE **20**min

Students will use online flash cards to practice multiplication facts and strategies. They will start with the 9s facts so they can focus on the most challenging facts first.

Emphasize that the strategies for getting the product of a multiplication fact are only for use until the fact is memorized. Ultimately, students should know the products without doing any calculating.

Students will be using all the multiplication strategies they have learned. Keep this list handy for reference; you may also want to write it in the Math Notebook.

Objectives

- Demonstrate automatic recall of multiplication facts.

- Any number times zero equals zero.

- Any number times 1 equals that number.

- To multiply a number by 2, just add the number to itself, or double it. For example, $6 \times 2 = 6 + 6$.

- When solving facts for 3, skip count by 3s or switch the factors and use repeated addition. For 7×3, think 3×7 and add $7 + 7 + 7 = 21$.

- When solving facts for 4, double the 2s fact to find the product. 4×7 is the same as 2×7 doubled.

- When solving facts for 5, skip count by 5s. Or multiply by 10 and figure out what half of that answer is—that number will be the 5s fact.

- When solving for 6, double the 3s fact to find the product. 6×7 is the same as 3×7 doubled.

- When solving facts for 7, memorize 7×7. For all the other 7s facts, reverse the order of the factors and use a rule for the other factor. For 7×3, think of 3×7, which you can solve by adding $7 + 7 + 7$.

- When solving facts for 8, double the 4s facts to find the product. 8×7 is the same as 4×7 doubled.

- When solving facts for 9, use finger multiplication, or multiply the number by 10 and subtract the number. For 9×8, think 10×8 and then take away 8 to get $9 \times 8 = 72$.

ONLINE

15 min

LEARN Multiplication Facts 0–10

Students will complete an online game to review multiplication facts. At the end of the activity, have students add any additional facts they have mastered to the Multiplication Facts Poster. Students should write the facts in pencil. (In several days, if students have truly memorized the facts and can recall them quickly, they can write them on the poster with a colored marker.)

Objectives

- Demonstrate automatic recall of multiplication facts.

TRY IT Fast Facts

Objectives

- Demonstrate automatic recall of multiplication facts.

Students will practice multiplication facts with factors 0 through 10 with the Fast Facts Learning Tool.

DIRECTIONS FOR USING THE FAST FACTS LEARNING TOOL

1. Have students enter their name and car number as well as choose the color of the car.
2. Choose the following options:
   - Choose the facts you want to practice: Multiplication
   - Choose multiples: Click a gray number in column 1 to choose all the multiples of that number. (For example, clicking the 8 in column 1 will select all the 8s facts.) You can also choose any individual facts with which students need additional practice.
   - Mode: Race Mode
3. Have students type the answer to each problem as it appears on the screen. After students finish, review the results. Note problems students answered incorrectly. Also note their time.
4. Repeat the activity. Have students try to beat their time and improve their accuracy.
5. If time remains, customize the "Choose multiples" screen and have students review the facts with which they had difficulty.

CHECKPOINT

Objectives

- Demonstrate automatic recall of multiplication facts.

Students will complete an online Checkpoint. If necessary, read the directions, problems, and answer choices to students and help them with keyboard or mouse operations.

Associative Property

GET READY Group to Add and Multiply	10 minutes	OFFLINE
LEARN Different Ways to Group Factors	30 minutes	OFFLINE
TRY IT Group and Multiply	10 minutes	OFFLINE
CHECKPOINT	10 minutes	ONLINE

▶ Lesson Objectives

Explain and apply the associative property of multiplication.

▶ Prerequisite Skills

Demonstrate understanding of the associative properties of addition and multiplication.

▶ Content Background

Students may already have a basic understanding that in addition, the addends can be grouped in any order to make the addition easier. This is called the associative property of addition. In this lesson, students will focus on a similar idea in multiplication that says when multiplying three or more numbers, they can be grouped in any way. This is called the associative property of multiplication.

The associative property of multiplication, sometimes known as the grouping property of multiplication, states that changing the way factors are grouped does not change the product. You can use parentheses to group factors to show which numbers are to be multiplied first. Students will learn about parentheses and will use them to group factors.

The order of operations principle states that factors in a horizontal row must be multiplied from left to right. However, if there are parentheses around a subgroup of these factors, always multiply the grouped factors first. For example, if students want to multiply $7 \times 5 \times 2$, they could multiply 7×5 to get 35 and then multiply 35×2 to get 70. However, if students use the associative property of multiplication to group 5 and 2 first, the problem becomes easier: $7 \times (5 \times 2)$. By multiplying within the parentheses to get 10, they then multiply 7 and 10 to get 70.

▶ Advance Preparation

Gather or label index cards to make number and symbol cards. You will need 2 sets of numerals 0 through 9; two multiplication symbols, ×; and the parentheses symbols—one card with an opening parenthesis symbol, (, and another card with a closing parenthesis symbol,).

Materials to Gather

SUPPLIED

Group and Multiply activity page

ALSO NEEDED

index cards – labeled

GET READY Group to Add and Multiply

OFFLINE 10 min

Students will review the associative properties of addition and multiplication. The associative properties of addition and multiplication state that changing the grouping of addends or factors does not affect the sum or product, respectively.

There are no materials to gather for this activity. Use the Math Notebook for writing the examples and problems.

1. Write $(8 + 5) + 5$. Point to the parentheses and explain that the parentheses tell which two numbers to add first.

2. **Say:** The associative property of addition says that changing the grouping of addends does not change the sum. Therefore, we can move the parentheses when adding three addends.

    Write $8 + (5 + 5)$.

3. Have students find each sum.

4. **Ask:** Which addition problem is easier to solve? Students may say $8 + (5 + 5)$ is easier to solve because 5 plus 5 is 10, and adding to 10 is easier than adding to 13.

5. Write $(3 + 7) + 2$. Discuss the benefits of solving the problem as written or grouping the addends differently. Help students see that 3 plus 7 is 10, and making 10 is a good strategy to use when adding three or more numbers.

6. Repeat Step 5 with $(5 + 6) + 4$. Guide students to see that $6 + 4$ makes 10, so they might want to move the parentheses on this problem.

7. Write $(6 \times 7) \times 0$. Point out that this expression is multiplication and not addition.

8. **Say:** The associative property of multiplication is like the associative property of addition. You can change the grouping of factors without changing the product.

9. Write $6 \times (7 \times 0)$.

    Say: Sometimes moving the parentheses makes it easier to multiply. Discuss with students how they would solve each expression and which expression was easier to simplify.

10. Write the following expressions. Have students determine whether they would like to solve the problem as written or group the factors differently.
    - $5 \times (2 \times 3)$
    - $(2 \times 5) \times 5$

11. Help students see that the product of 2 and 5 is 10, and it is easy to multiply by 10.

Objectives

- Demonstrate understanding of the associative properties of addition and multiplication.

Tips

Have students find sums or products in different groupings to help determine which grouping is easier to solve.

LEARN Different Ways to Group Factors

OFFLINE 30 min

Students will explain and apply the associative property of multiplication. They will use parentheses to group factors in a multiplication problem. Students will find the product of three factors.

Gather the number and symbol cards. Use the Math Notebook for writing the examples and problems.

1. Arrange the number and symbol cards to show $(2 \times 3) \times 4$. Remind students that the parentheses tell which two numbers to multiply first.

Objectives

- Explain and apply the associative property of multiplication.

2. **Ask:** How will you solve this problem? First, I will multiply 2 and 3. Then I will multiply the product by 4.

   Have students solve the problem.

3. Move the parentheses cards to show 2 × (3 × 4). Have students solve the problem.

4. **Ask:** What do you notice about the product of both problems? They are the same—24.

5. Repeat Steps 1–4 using 2 × 4 × 5, positioning the parentheses cards to group 2 × 4 first and 4 × 5 next.

6. **Say:** The associative property of multiplication says that changing the grouping of factors does not change the product. Therefore, when multiplying three factors, you can change the grouping to find the product.

7. Arrange the number and symbol cards to show (7 × 5) × 2. Have students solve the problem.

   Move the parentheses cards to show 7 × (5 × 2). Have students solve the problem.

   Review that 5 × 2 = 10, making the problem 7 × 10. Discuss that multiplying 5 and 2 first makes it easier to solve 7 × 5 × 2 because students are confident about multiplying any number by 10. Then review that 7 × 5 = 35, making the problem 35 × 2. Conclude that 7 × 10 is easier to solve than 35 × 2.

8. Arrange the number and symbol cards to show (3 × 4) × 5. Have students solve the problem any way they can. The problem 12 × 5 can be seen as ten 5s, which is 50, and two more 5s to get 60.

   Move the parentheses cards to show 3 × (4 × 5). Have students solve the problem.

   Ask: Which grouping was easier to solve? Students may say that multiplying 4 and 5 first makes it easier to solve 3 × 4 × 5 because multiplying 3 times 20 is easier than 12 times 5.

9. Repeat Step 8 using 2 × 5 × 6.

10. Arrange the number cards face down on the table. Have students choose three cards and place them in a row.

11. Have students place the multiplication symbol cards between the number cards to form a multiplication expression. Then have students use the parentheses cards to group the factors in a way that makes the problem easiest to solve.

12. Have students explain why they chose to position the parentheses cards as they did.

13. Repeat Steps 10–12 several times. Have students find the products of the simpler expressions—ones that use lesser numbers.

14. Write the following statement:

    If (5 × 7) × 3 = 105, then what is 5 × (7 × 3)?

    Help students see that the same three factors are used in both expressions, but the grouping is different. Guide students to determine that the product is the same. Remind students that the associative property of multiplication says that changing the grouping of factors does not change the product.

15. Write the following statement:

    If 8 × (4 × 5) = 160, then what is (8 × 4) × 5?

    Students should determine the product is 160.

Tips

Make the number cards one color, the multiplication symbol cards a second color, and the parentheses symbol cards a third color for visual distinction.

TRY IT Group and Multiply

- Explain and apply the associative property of multiplication.

Students will practice applying the associative property of multiplication. Have students turn to the Group and Multiply activity page in their Activity Book and read the directions with them.

Students should copy the problems from the Activity Book into their Math Notebook as necessary and solve them there. Note that for Problems 1 and 2 students do not find the value of the expressions, but they just show another way to regroup the factors. For Problems 1–5, the answers shown are sample answers. Answers will vary.

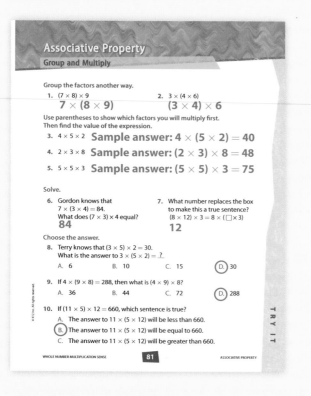

Associative Property
Group and Multiply

Group the factors another way.

1. $(7 \times 8) \times 9$
   $\mathbf{7 \times (8 \times 9)}$

2. $3 \times (4 \times 6)$
   $\mathbf{(3 \times 4) \times 6}$

Use parentheses to show which factors you will multiply first. Then find the value of the expression.

3. $4 \times 5 \times 2$ **Sample answer: $4 \times (5 \times 2) = 40$**

4. $2 \times 3 \times 8$ **Sample answer: $(2 \times 3) \times 8 = 48$**

5. $5 \times 5 \times 3$ **Sample answer: $(5 \times 5) \times 3 = 75$**

Solve.

6. Gordon knows that
   $7 \times (3 \times 4) = 84$.
   What does $(7 \times 3) \times 4$ equal?
   84

7. What number replaces the box to make this a true sentence?
   $(8 \times 12) \times 3 = 8 \times (\square \times 3)$
   12

Choose the answer.

8. Terry knows that $(3 \times 5) \times 2 = 30$.
   What is the answer to $3 \times (5 \times 2) = \underline{?}$
   A. 6 B. 10 C. 15 (D.) 30

9. If $4 \times (9 \times 8) = 288$, then what is $(4 \times 9) \times 8$?
   A. 36 B. 44 C. 72 (D.) 288

10. If $(11 \times 5) \times 12 = 660$, which sentence is true?
    A. The answer to $11 \times (5 \times 12)$ will be less than 660.
    (B.) The answer to $11 \times (5 \times 12)$ will be equal to 660.
    C. The answer to $11 \times (5 \times 12)$ will be greater than 660.

WHOLE NUMBER MULTIPLICATION SENSE · **81** · ASSOCIATIVE PROPERTY

TRY IT

CHECKPOINT

- Explain and apply the associative property of multiplication.

Students will complete an online Checkpoint. If necessary, read the directions, problems, and answer choices to students and help them with keyboard or mouse operations.

Unit Review

Lesson Overview

UNIT REVIEW Look Back	10 minutes	**ONLINE**
UNIT REVIEW Checkpoint Practice	50 minutes	**ONLINE**
▶ **UNIT REVIEW** Prepare for the Checkpoint		

▶ Unit Objectives

This lesson assesses the following objectives:

- Use objects or sketches to solve a multiplication problem.
- Use a model to explain multiplication as repeated addition of the same quantity.
- Use an area model to explain multiplication.
- Demonstrate an understanding of how multiplication affects whole numbers.
- Explain and apply the commutative property of multiplication.
- Explain and apply the zero property of multiplication.
- Explain and apply the multiplication property of 1.
- Demonstrate automatic recall of multiplication facts.
- Explain and apply the associative property of multiplication.

▶ Advance Preparation

In this lesson, students will have an opportunity to review previous activities in the Whole Number Multiplication Sense unit. Look at the suggested activities in Unit Review: Prepare for the Checkpoint online and gather any needed materials.

Materials to Gather

There are no materials to gather for this lesson.

ONLINE 10min

UNIT REVIEW Look Back

Students will review key concepts from the unit to prepare for the Unit Checkpoint.

Objectives

- Review unit objectives.

ONLINE 50min

UNIT REVIEW Checkpoint Practice

Students will complete an online Checkpoint Practice to prepare for the Unit Checkpoint. If necessary, read the directions, problems, and answer choices to students. Have students answer the problems on their own. Review any missed problems with students.

Objectives

- Review unit objectives.

▶ UNIT REVIEW Prepare for the Checkpoint

What you do next depends on how students performed in the previous activity, Unit Review: Checkpoint Practice. If students had difficulty with any of the problems, complete the appropriate review activity listed in the table online.

Unit Checkpoint

UNIT CHECKPOINT Online | 60 minutes | **ONLINE**

▶ Unit Objectives

This lesson assesses the following objectives:

- Use objects or sketches to solve a multiplication problem.
- Use a model to explain multiplication as repeated addition of the same quantity.
- Use an area model to explain multiplication.
- Demonstrate an understanding of how multiplication affects whole numbers.
- Explain and apply the commutative property of multiplication.
- Explain and apply the zero property of multiplication.
- Explain and apply the multiplication property of 1.
- Demonstrate automatic recall of multiplication facts.
- Explain and apply the associative property of multiplication.

Materials to Gather

There are no materials to gather for this lesson.

UNIT CHECKPOINT Online

ONLINE 60min

Objectives

- Assess unit objectives.

Students will complete the Unit Checkpoint online. If necessary, read the directions, problems, and answer choices to students and help them with keyboard or mouse operations.

Whole Number Multiplication

▶ Unit Objectives

- Use objects or sketches to solve a multiplication story problem.
- Solve a multiplication problem involving a multidigit factor and a one-digit factor.
- Use multiplication to solve a story problem that involves equal groups.
- Use multiplication to solve a story problem that involves equal measures.
- Create a story problem that can be represented by a multiplication number sentence.

▶ Big Ideas

- Multiplication and division can be represented by models and by using math symbols.
- The use of letters, numbers, and mathematical symbols makes possible the translation of complex situations or long word statements into concise mathematical sentences or expressions.

▶ Unit Introduction

In this unit, students will learn the step-by-step process, the algorithm, to solve multiplication computation problems in which a one-digit factor is multiplied by a multidigit factor. They will model story problems and then use their multiplication computation skills to solve multiplication story problems involving equal groups or equal measures. Finally they will create their own story problems and show how their problems can be represented by number sentences. Overall students will move from solving both computation and story problems with concrete objects to being able to solve them with numbers and symbols by using number sentences and the multiplication algorithm.

▶ Keywords

division
equal groups

equal measures
factor
grid

partial product
product

Multiplication Story Problems

▶ Lesson Objectives

Use objects or sketches to solve a multiplication story problem.

▶ Prerequisite Skills

Use models and math symbols to represent multiplication.

▶ Content Background

Students will learn to solve story problems involving multiplication. They will review the concept that multiplication involves combining equal groups. The multiplication symbol ($\times$) represents the phrase "groups of." For example, the expression 5×8 represents 5 groups of 8 objects. As students move toward more difficult problems, it is important for them to model problems with objects and sketches to see the connection between the meaning of multiplication and the way to calculate problems.

A multiplication number sentence has at least two numbers, called factors, that are multiplied to produce the solution, or product.

An array is a rectangular arrangement of objects in rows and columns. The number of rows in the array is the first factor in a multiplication number sentence, and the number of columns in the array is the second factor. The expression 5×8 would be shown as 5 rows of 8. The total number of objects in the entire array is the product.

▶ Common Errors and Misconceptions

- Students might need exposure to a variety of models (such as rectangular array or area) when learning multiplication as a conceptual operation. Using only repeated addition models and the term *times* can lead to a basic misunderstanding of multiplication. This misunderstanding will complicate future use of multiplication when working with decimals and fractions.

- Students might view multiplication and division algorithms as rules to be followed. This leads to a misunderstanding that the numbers involved are separate digits rather than grouped amounts representing place values. The result is often an incorrect answer because of students' misunderstanding of estimation, place value, and reasonableness of results.

Materials to Gather

SUPPLIED

blocks – B (all)

base-10 blocks

Model Multiplication Story Problems activity page

Model and Solve Problems activity page

GET READY Represent Multiplication with Symbols

Students will practice representing multiplication. They will write the factors shown in a multiplication model and then write the product.

- Use models and math symbols to represent multiplication.

LEARN Model Multiplication Story Problems

Students will use objects and sketches to model and solve multiplication story problems. They will learn to match the words and phrases in a story problem to the numbers in a multiplication sentence.

- Use objects or sketches to solve a multiplication story problem.

Gather the B blocks and base-10 blocks. Have students turn to the Model Multiplication Story Problems activity page.

Students should copy the problems from the Activity Book to their Math Notebook as necessary and solve them there.

1. Read Worked Example 1 with students. Explain how the model represents the rows of seeds.

2. Look at the multiplication number sentence. Show students how each number in the multiplication sentence matches a statement in the story problem.

3. Remind students that the first factor in a multiplication number sentence tells the number of groups, or rows, and the second factor tells the number in each group, or row.

4. Have students use skip counting or repeated addition to check the product.

5. Read Worked Example 2 with students.

6. Discuss the sketch with students. Explain that each rectangle represents a vase and the tulips represent the flowers Ted put in each vase. Explain how the objects in the sketch match the information in the story problem.

7. Have students use skip counting or repeated addition to check the product. Discuss with students how they can use the sketch to check the product.

8. Read Worked Example 3 with students.

9. Explain how the groups of base-10 blocks represent the posters and stickers in the story problem.

10. Point out that grouping all the tens rods together and all the ones cubes together makes it easier to count them. Have students use skip counting or repeated addition to check the product.

11. Have students complete Problems 1–5 on their own. Then have students share their models and sketches. Ask them to identify the phrases in the problems that match the numbers in each multiplication number sentence.

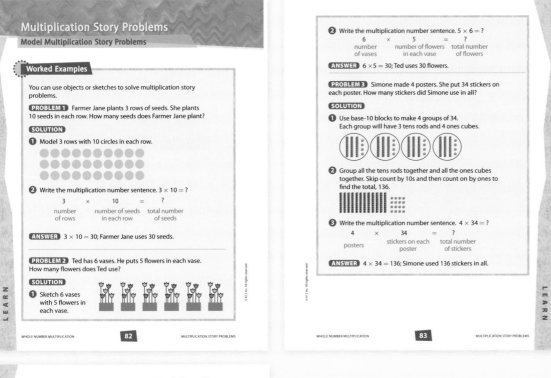

Multiplication Story Problems
Model Multiplication Story Problems

Worked Examples

You can use objects or sketches to solve multiplication story problems.

PROBLEM 1 Farmer Jane plants 3 rows of seeds. She plants 10 seeds in each row. How many seeds does Farmer Jane plant?

SOLUTION

❶ Model 3 rows with 10 circles in each row.

❷ Write the multiplication number sentence. $3 \times 10 = ?$

$$3 \times 10 = ?$$

number of rows   number of seeds in each row   total number of seeds

ANSWER $3 \times 10 = 30$; Farmer Jane uses 30 seeds.

PROBLEM 2 Ted has 6 vases. He puts 5 flowers in each vase. How many flowers does Ted use?

SOLUTION

❶ Sketch 6 vases with 5 flowers in each vase.

❷ Write the multiplication number sentence. $5 \times 6 = ?$

$$6 \times 5 = ?$$

number of vases   number of flowers in each vase   total number of flowers

ANSWER $6 \times 5 = 30$; Ted uses 30 flowers.

PROBLEM 3 Simone made 4 posters. She put 34 stickers on each poster. How many stickers did Simone use in all?

SOLUTION

❶ Use base-10 blocks to make 4 groups of 34. Each group will have 3 tens rods and 4 ones cubes.

❷ Group all the tens rods together and all the ones cubes together. Skip count by 10s and then count on by ones to find the total, 136.

❸ Write the multiplication number sentence. $4 \times 34 = ?$

$$4 \times 34 = ?$$

posters   stickers on each poster   total number of stickers

ANSWER $4 \times 34 = 136$; Simone used 136 stickers in all.

Use circle blocks to model the problem. **Models will vary.**
Write the multiplication number sentence and solve.

1. Farmer Ted has 8 containers. He puts 2 tomato plants in each container. How many tomato plants does he use? **See below.**

2. There are 7 baskets of peppers. There are 5 peppers in each basket. How many peppers are there altogether? **See below.**

Make a sketch to model the problem. **Sketches will vary.**
Write the multiplication number sentence and solve.

3. Jane buys 2 bags of onions. There are 10 small onions in each bag. How many onions are there in all? **See below.**

4. There are 9 shelves. There are 3 pumpkins on each shelf. How many pumpkins are on the shelves altogether? **See below.**

Use base-10 blocks to model the problem. **Models will vary.**
Write the multiplication number sentence and solve.

5. Andre has 4 packs of seeds. Each pack has 32 seeds. How many seeds does Andre have?

Sample answer: Students make 4 groups of blocks; each group has 3 tens rods and 2 ones cubes. $4 \times 32 = ?$; $4 \times 32 = 128$

Additional Answers

1. **Sample answer:** Students make 8 groups of 2 circles. $8 \times 2 = ?$; $8 \times 2 = 16$

2. **Sample model:** Students make 7 groups of 5 circles. $7 \times 5 = ?$; $7 \times 5 = 35$

3. **Sample sketch:** Students make a sketch of 2 groups of 10 circles. $2 \times 10 = ?$; $2 \times 10 = 20$

4. **Sample answer:** Students make a sketch of 9 groups of 3 circles. $9 \times 3 = ?$; $9 \times 3 = 27$

TRY IT Model and Solve Problems

Students will practice modeling and solving multiplication problems. Gather the B blocks. Have students turn to the Model and Solve Problems activity page in their Activity Book and read the directions with them.

Students should copy the problems from the Activity Book into their Math Notebook as necessary and solve them there.

Objectives

- Use objects or sketches to solve a multiplication story problem.

Tips

Encourage students to find each product in different ways to check their answers.

Multiplication Story Problems
Model and Solve Problems

Use the model to solve.

1. Ryan has 4 boxes of model cars. There are 7 cars in each box. How many model cars does Ryan have in all?

$4 \times 7 = \underline{?}$
28

2. Jessie placed her seashells in 3 piles. She put 24 shells in each pile. How many seashells does Jessie have altogether?

$3 \times 24 = \underline{?}$
72

3. Dawn has 8 bags of bagels. Each bag has 4 bagels in it. How many bagels does Dawn have? Choose the answer.

A. 8
B. 16
C. 12
D. 32

4. A carton of eggs has 2 rows. There are 6 eggs in each row. How many eggs are in the carton? Choose the answer.

A. 8
B. 12
C. 16
D. 24

WHOLE NUMBER MULTIPLICATION   85   MULTIPLICATION STORY PROBLEMS

TRY IT

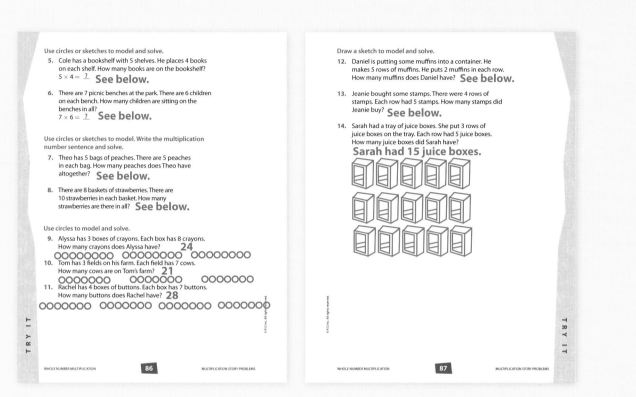

Use circles or sketches to model and solve.

5. Cole has a bookshelf with 5 shelves. He places 4 books on each shelf. How many books are on the bookshelf?
$5 \times 4 = \underline{?}$ **See below.**

6. There are 7 picnic benches at the park. There are 6 children on each bench. How many children are sitting on the benches in all?
$7 \times 6 = \underline{?}$ **See below.**

Use circles or sketches to model. Write the multiplication number sentence and solve.

7. Theo has 5 bags of peaches. There are 5 peaches in each bag. How many peaches does Theo have altogether? **See below.**

8. There are 8 baskets of strawberries. There are 10 strawberries in each basket. How many strawberries are there in all? **See below.**

Use circles to model and solve.

9. Alyssa has 3 boxes of crayons. Each box has 8 crayons. How many crayons does Alyssa have? **24**

10. Tom has 3 fields on his farm. Each field has 7 cows. How many cows are on Tom's farm? **21**

11. Rachel has 4 boxes of buttons. Each box has 7 buttons. How many buttons does Rachel have? **28**

Draw a sketch to model and solve.

12. Daniel is putting some muffins into a container. He makes 5 rows of muffins. He puts 2 muffins in each row. How many muffins does Daniel have? **See below.**

13. Jeanie bought some stamps. There were 4 rows of stamps. Each row had 5 stamps. How many stamps did Jeanie buy? **See below.**

14. Sarah had a tray of juice boxes. She put 3 rows of juice boxes on the tray. Each row had 5 juice boxes. How many juice boxes did Sarah have?

Sarah had 15 juice boxes.

Additional Answers

5. 20; Models will vary. Sample model: Students make an array of 5 rows of 4 circles.

6. 42; Models will vary. Sample answer: Students make a sketch of 7 groups of 6 circles.

7. $5 \times 5 = ?$
$5 \times 5 = 25$
Models will vary. Sample model: Students make an array of 5 rows of 5 circles.

8. $8 \times 10 = ?$
$8 \times 10 = 80$
Models will vary. Sample model: Students make a sketch of 8 groups of 10 circles

12. Daniel has 10 muffins.

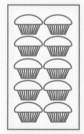

13. Jeanie bought 20 stamps.

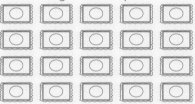

CHECKPOINT

ONLINE **10min**

Objectives

Students will complete an online Checkpoint. If necessary, read the directions, problems, and answer choices to students and help them with keyboard or mouse operations.

- Use objects or sketches to solve a multiplication story problem.

Multiply Multidigit by 1-Digit Numbers

▶ Lesson Objectives

Solve a multiplication problem involving a multidigit factor and a one-digit factor.

▶ Prerequisite Skills

Demonstrate automatic recall of multiplication facts.

Materials to Gather

SUPPLIED

Multiply Two Ways activity page

▶ Content Background

Students know how to multiply a one-digit number by another one-digit number. In this lesson, students will learn to solve problems by multiplying a one-digit number by a multidigit number, a number that has more than one digit.

In many problems, students will have equal groups and will be asked for the total. Until they learn to multiply using a standard step-by-step process, they will have a greater risk of error when they add large groups. Suppose they were asked to find the total of 9 groups of 4,352 objects. They would be forced to find the sum of 9 addends of 4,352. The potential for error is great. Multiplication simplifies the entire process, and students should understand this benefit of knowing how to multiply.

Students need to understand why the standard process adults use to multiply actually works. Therefore, rather than moving into a step-by-step process (called an algorithm) that has no meaning, students will begin to learn multiplication by using what they know about place value and simple multiplication facts, recording that information as they work through the problems.

Learning to multiply in this way accomplishes two things:

- Students will understand the meaning behind the multiplication process. They will eventually use it as a shortcut.
- Students will also learn strategies for mentally multiplying some problems they would otherwise think they had to write down.

▶ Common Errors and Misconceptions

- Students might add the second factor too many or too few times when using repeated addition. For example, for 5×4, students might add $4 + 4 + 4 + 4$.
- Students might undercount or overcount when using the count-by-n strategy.

- Students might view multiplication and division algorithms as rules to be followed. This leads to a misunderstanding that the numbers involved are separate digits rather than grouped amounts representing place values. The result is often an incorrect answer because of students' misunderstanding of estimation, place value, and reasonableness of results.

GET READY Multiplication Fast Facts

ONLINE 5 min

Students will continue to practice automatic recall of multiplication facts by playing a timed game. Note which facts are difficult for students and practice them with flash cards, such as the 6s or 7s facts.

Objectives

- Demonstrate automatic recall of multiplication facts.

LEARN Multiply with Partial Products

ONLINE 15 min

Students will learn how to use partial products to multiply a multidigit factor by a one-digit factor. It is important to participate with students during this activity to understand the partial-product method of multiplication.

Students will use place value to break the greater number up and show it in expanded form. They will multiply each number in the expanded form by the one-digit factor to get part of the product. These parts are called partial products. Then students will add the partial products to find the product of the original problem.

Objectives

- Solve a multiplication problem involving a multidigit factor and a one-digit factor.

Tips

Review place value and expanded form with students. This review will help them use partial products to multiply.

LEARN Standard Multiplication Algorithm

ONLINE 10 min

Students will learn how to multiply a multidigit factor and a one-digit factor, using a step-by-step procedure, or algorithm. Emphasize that students can always solve a problem with partial products to check their solutions.

Objectives

- Solve a multiplication problem involving a multidigit factor and a one-digit factor.

TRY IT Multiply Two Ways

OFFLINE 20 min

Students will practice finding the product of a multidigit factor and a one-digit factor by using partial products or the standard algorithm. They should use the method they're most comfortable with for a given problem. When they use the standard algorithm, watch that they keep each digit of the answer in the proper place value position. Have students turn to the Multiply Two Ways activity page in their Activity Book and read the directions with them.

Students should copy the problems from the Activity Book into their Math Notebook as necessary and solve them there.

Objectives

- Solve a multiplication problem involving a multidigit factor and a one-digit factor.

Tips

To help students align the digits in the standard algorithm, use a pencil to draw light, vertical lines separating the digits in the ones, tens, and hundreds places.

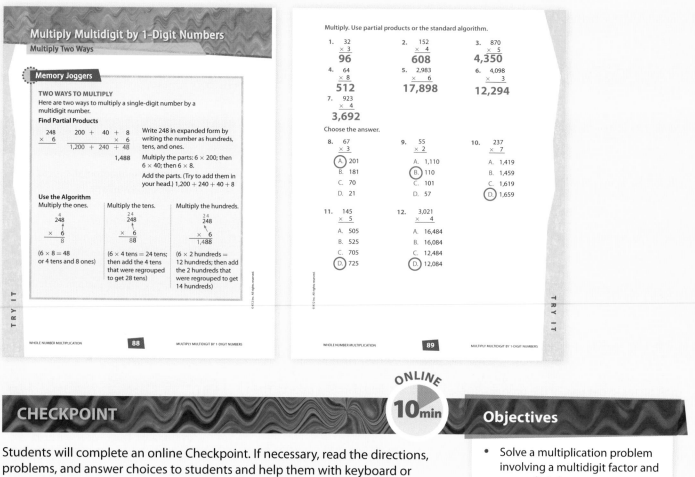

Multiply Multidigit by 1-Digit Numbers
Multiply Two Ways

Memory Joggers

TWO WAYS TO MULTIPLY
Here are two ways to multiply a single-digit number by a multidigit number.

Find Partial Products

$$\begin{array}{r} 248 \\ \times\ 6 \end{array} \qquad \begin{array}{r} 200\ +\ 40\ +\ 8 \\ \times\ 6 \\ \hline 1{,}200\ +\ 240\ +\ 48 \end{array}$$

1,488

Write 248 in expanded form by writing the number as hundreds, tens, and ones.

Multiply the parts: 6 × 200; then 6 × 40; then 6 × 8.

Add the parts. (Try to add them in your head.) 1,200 + 240 + 40 + 8

Use the Algorithm

Multiply the ones.	Multiply the tens.	Multiply the hundreds.
$\begin{array}{r}4\\248\\ \times\ 6\\ \hline 8\end{array}$	$\begin{array}{r}2\ 4\\248\\ \times\ 6\\ \hline 88\end{array}$	$\begin{array}{r}2\ 4\\248\\ \times\ 6\\ \hline 1{,}488\end{array}$
(6 × 8 = 48 or 4 tens and 8 ones)	(6 × 4 tens = 24 tens; then add the 4 tens that were regrouped to get 28 tens)	(6 × 2 hundreds = 12 hundreds; then add the 2 hundreds that were regrouped to get 14 hundreds)

Multiply. Use partial products or the standard algorithm.

1. $\begin{array}{r}32\\ \times\ 3\\ \hline 96\end{array}$ 2. $\begin{array}{r}152\\ \times\ 4\\ \hline 608\end{array}$ 3. $\begin{array}{r}870\\ \times\ 5\\ \hline 4{,}350\end{array}$

4. $\begin{array}{r}64\\ \times\ 8\\ \hline 512\end{array}$ 5. $\begin{array}{r}2{,}983\\ \times\ 6\\ \hline 17{,}898\end{array}$ 6. $\begin{array}{r}4{,}098\\ \times\ 3\\ \hline 12{,}294\end{array}$

7. $\begin{array}{r}923\\ \times\ 4\\ \hline 3{,}692\end{array}$

Choose the answer.

8. $\begin{array}{r}67\\ \times\ 3\end{array}$
   - Ⓐ 201
   - B. 181
   - C. 70
   - D. 21

9. $\begin{array}{r}55\\ \times\ 2\end{array}$
   - A. 1,110
   - Ⓑ 110
   - C. 101
   - D. 57

10. $\begin{array}{r}237\\ \times\ 7\end{array}$
   - A. 1,419
   - B. 1,459
   - C. 1,619
   - Ⓓ 1,659

11. $\begin{array}{r}145\\ \times\ 5\end{array}$
   - A. 505
   - B. 525
   - C. 705
   - Ⓓ 725

12. $\begin{array}{r}3{,}021\\ \times\ 4\end{array}$
   - A. 16,484
   - B. 16,084
   - C. 12,484
   - Ⓓ 12,084

ONLINE 10min

CHECKPOINT

Students will complete an online Checkpoint. If necessary, read the directions, problems, and answer choices to students and help them with keyboard or mouse operations.

Objectives

- Solve a multiplication problem involving a multidigit factor and a one-digit factor.

Multiply Equal Groups (A)

Lesson Overview		
Skills Update	5 minutes	ONLINE
GET READY Model and Solve	5 minutes	ONLINE
LEARN Multiply with Equal Groups	15 minutes	ONLINE
LEARN Multiplication Story Problems	20 minutes	OFFLINE
TRY IT Multiply Groups and Objects	15 minutes	OFFLINE

▶ Lesson Objectives

Use multiplication to solve a story problem that involves equal groups.

▶ Prerequisite Skills

- Use grouping to solve simple multiplication problems.
- Use objects or sketches to solve a multiplication story problem.

▶ Content Background

Students will solve multiplication story problems involving equal groups of objects. They will multiply multidigit numbers by one-digit numbers.

Multiplication is an operation used when there are equal groups. The multiplication symbol ($\times$) represents the phrase "groups of." For example, the expression 5×8 represents 5 groups of 8 objects. As students move toward more difficult problems, they will move away from models and sketches. They will solve problems using the partial-product method or the standard algorithm (the traditional steps for muliplication). The partial-product method involves writing a multidigit number in expanded form (for example, $324 = 300 + 20 + 4$) and then multiplying each part by a single-digit factor. Using this method helps students make a connection between the meaning of multiplication and the steps to calculate problems.

▶ Common Errors and Misconceptions

- Students might add the second factor too many or too few times when using repeated addition. For example, for 5×4, students might add $4 + 4 + 4 + 4$.
- Students might undercount or overcount when using the count-by-n strategy.
- Students might view multiplication and division algorithms as rules to be followed. This leads to a misunderstanding that the numbers involved are separate digits rather than grouped amounts representing place values. The result is often an incorrect answer because of students' misunderstanding of estimation, place value, and reasonableness of results.

Materials to Gather

SUPPLIED

Multiplication Story Problems
activity page

Multiply Groups and Objects
activity page

GET READY Model and Solve

Students will use models to solve a multiplication story problem that involves equal groups. They will see that the answer is the same whether they solve the problem with repeated addition or with multiplication.

Objectives

- Use grouping to solve simple multiplication problems.
- Use objects or sketches to solve a multiplication story problem.

LEARN Multiply with Equal Groups

Students will learn to solve story problems involving equal groups. Encourage students to use whatever method they are most comfortable with to solve the problems.

Objectives

- Use multiplication to solve a story problem that involves equal groups.

LEARN Multiplication Story Problems

Students will use multiplication to solve story problems that involve equal groups. Have students turn to the Multiplication Story Problems activity page in their Activity Book and read the directions with them.

Students should copy the problems from the Activity Book into their Math Notebook as necessary and solve them there.

1. Tell students that they will multiply to solve the story problems on the activity page.

2. Read the Worked Example together. Emphasize that each phrase in the problem represents a part of the multiplication sentence. Guide students to see that the 1,500 ants represent the number of groups, and the 6 legs per ant represent the number in each group. Point out that it would be difficult to draw 1,500 groups of 6, so they can just use numbers to solve the problem.

3. Point out the multiplication number sentence used to solve the problem. Tell students there are two ways to find the answer to this sentence, partial products and the standard algorithm.

4. Go over the two ways to solve the problem. Point out that both ways lead to the same answer, 9,000 legs.

5. Have students complete Problems 1–4. Encourage them to use the multiplication method that works best for each problem. Encourage them to use the standard steps for multiplying (the algorithm) when the numbers are too difficult to work with in their head. When students use the algorithm, help them line up the numbers and multiply the one-digit number by the ones, tens, and hundreds, regrouping where necessary. Remind them to show how they solved each problem.

Objectives

- Use multiplication to solve a story problem that involves equal groups.

Tips

Provide base-10 blocks for students to model and solve the multiplication problems.

Multiply Equal Groups (A)
Multiplication Story Problems

Worked Examples

You can multiply to solve story problems that involve equal groups.

PROBLEM An ant has 6 legs. How many legs would there be in a colony of 1,500 ants?

SOLUTION Multiply to solve the problem. Use the method that is easiest for you.

❶ Turn the problem into a sentence. $6 \times 1,500 = ?$

❷ Solve using partial products.

$$
\begin{array}{r}
1,500 \longrightarrow 1,000 + 500 \\
\times \quad 6 \qquad \times \quad 6 \qquad 6 \\
\hline
6,000 + 3,000 \\
9,000
\end{array}
$$

or

Solve using the algorithm.

Multiply the ones.
$$
\begin{array}{r}
1,500 \\
\times \quad 6 \\
\hline
0
\end{array}
$$

Multiply the tens.
$$
\begin{array}{r}
1,500 \\
\times \quad 6 \\
\hline
00
\end{array}
$$

Multiply the hundreds.
$$
\begin{array}{r}
3 \\
1,500 \\
\times \quad 6 \\
\hline
000
\end{array}
$$

Multiply the thousands.
$$
\begin{array}{r}
3 \\
1,500 \\
\times \quad 6 \\
\hline
9,000
\end{array}
$$

ANSWER $6 \times 1,500 = 9,000$
There would be 9,000 legs.

L E A R N

Multiply to solve each problem.

1. A sheep has 4 feet.
   There are 200 sheep in the herd.
   How many feet are there altogether?

   _?_ feet **800**

2. A chicken has 2 legs.
   There are 67 chickens in the coop.
   How many legs are there altogether?

   _?_ legs **134**

3. An octopus has 8 arms.
   If there are 642 octopuses in the ocean, how many arms are there altogether?

   _?_ arms **5,136**

4. A starfish has 5 arms.
   There are 830 starfish at the aquarium.
   How many arms are there altogether?

   _?_ arms **4,150**

L E A R N

OFFLINE
15 min

TRY IT Multiply Groups and Objects

Students will practice using multiplication to solve story problems. Have students turn to the Multiply Groups and Objects activity page in their Activity Book and read the directions with them.

Students should copy the problems from the Activity Book into their Math Notebook as necessary and solve them there.

Objectives

- Use multiplication to solve a story problem that involves equal groups.

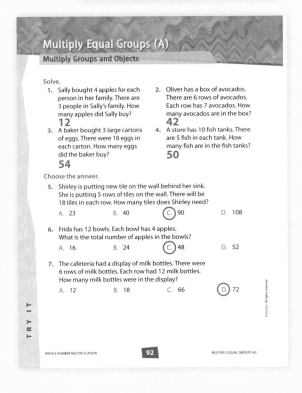

Multiply Equal Groups (A)
Multiply Groups and Objects

Solve.
1. Sally bought 4 apples for each person in her family. There are 3 people in Sally's family. How many apples did Sally buy?
   12

2. Oliver has a box of avocados. There are 6 rows of avocados. Each row has 7 avocados. How many avocados are in the box?
   42

3. A baker bought 3 large cartons of eggs. There were 18 eggs in each carton. How many eggs did the baker buy?
   54

4. A store has 10 fish tanks. There are 5 fish in each tank. How many fish are in the fish tanks?
   50

Choose the answer.

5. Shirley is putting new tile on the wall behind her sink. She is putting 5 rows of tiles on the wall. There will be 18 tiles in each row. How many tiles does Shirley need?
   A. 23   B. 40   C. 90   D. 108

6. Frida has 12 bowls. Each bowl has 4 apples. What is the total number of apples in the bowls?
   A. 16   B. 24   C. 48   D. 52

7. The cafeteria had a display of milk bottles. There were 6 rows of milk bottles. Each row had 12 milk bottles. How many milk bottles were in the display?
   A. 12   B. 18   C. 66   D. 72

TRY IT

Multiply Equal Groups (B)

Lesson Overview

Skills Update	5 minutes	ONLINE
LEARN Train Station Multiplication	20 minutes	ONLINE
LEARN Multiplication Computation	20 minutes	OFFLINE
TRY IT Multiply to Solve	15 minutes	OFFLINE

▶ Lesson Objectives

Use multiplication to solve a story problem that involves equal groups.

▶ Prerequisite Skills

- Use grouping to solve simple multiplication problems.
- Use objects or sketches to solve a multiplication story problem.

▶ Content Background

Students will continue to solve multiplication story problems involving equal groups of objects. They will multiply multidigit numbers by one-digit numbers.

Multiplication is an operation used when there are equal groups. The multiplication symbol ($\times$) represents the phrase "groups of." For example, the expression 5×8 represents 5 groups of 8 objects. As students move toward more difficult problems, they will move away from models and sketches. They will solve problems using the partial-product method, or the standard algorithm (the traditional steps for muliplication). The partial-product method involves writing a multidigit number in expanded form (for example, $324 = 300 + 20 + 4$) and then multiplying each part by a single-digit factor. Using this method helps students make a connection between the meaning of multiplication and the steps to calculate problems.

▶ Common Errors and Misconceptions

- Students might add the second factor too many or too few times when using repeated addition. For example, for 5×4, students might add $4 + 4 + 4 + 4$.
- Students might undercount or overcount when using the count-by-n strategy.
- Students might view multiplication and division algorithms as rules to be followed. This leads to a misunderstanding that the numbers involved are separate digits rather than grouped amounts representing place values. The result is often an incorrect answer because of students' misunderstanding of estimation, place value, and reasonableness of results.

LEARN Train Station Multiplication

ONLINE 20 min

Students will use multiplication to solve story problems. They may use different methods to solve the problems. When solving 4 × 45, some students will use the partial-product method, where they multiply 4 × 40 and 4 × 5 and add the products together. Others will use the standard algorithm (the traditional steps for multiplying) to solve the problem.

Objectives

- Use multiplication to solve a story problem that involves equal groups.

Tips

Encourage students to use the multiplication method with which they are most comfortable to solve each problem. Have paper and pencil available.

LEARN Multiplication Computation

OFFLINE 20 min

Students will use computation to solve story problems involving equal groups. Have students turn to the Multiplication Computation activity page in their Activity Book.

Students should copy the problems from the Activity Book to their Math Notebook as necessary and solve them there.

1. Tell students they will multiply to solve the story problems on the activity page.
2. Read the Worked Example together. Emphasize that each phrase in the problem represents a part of the multiplication number sentence. Guide students to see that the 347 mini boxes represent the number of equal groups and the 8 crayons represent the number in each group. They should use the sentence 347 × 8 to solve the problem.
3. Encourage students to use the multiplication method with which they are most comfortable to solve the problem.
4. Have students complete Problems 1 and 2 on their own. They may use either the partial-product method or the standard algorithm.
5. Remind students to show how they solved each problem.

Objectives

- Use multiplication to solve a story problem that involves equal groups.

Tips

Review the partial-product method and the standard algorithm with students.

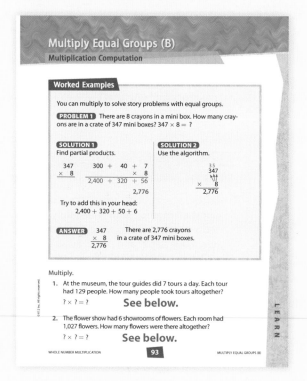

Additional Answers

1. $7 \times 129 = 903$

Partial Products

$$
\begin{array}{r}
100 \ + \ 20 \ + \ 9 \\
\times \ 7 \\
\hline
700 \ + \ 140 \ + \ 63 \\
\textbf{903}
\end{array}
$$

Algorithm

$$
\begin{array}{r}
{}^{2\,6} \\
129 \\
\times \quad 7 \\
\hline
903
\end{array}
$$

2. $6 \times 1{,}027 = 6{,}162$

Partial Products

$$
\begin{array}{r}
1{,}000 \ + \ 20 \ + \ 7 \\
\times \ 6 \\
\hline
6{,}000 \ + \ 120 \ + \ 42 \\
\textbf{6{,}162}
\end{array}
$$

Algorithm

$$
\begin{array}{r}
{}^{1\,4} \\
1{,}027 \\
\times \quad 6 \\
\hline
6{,}162
\end{array}
$$

TRY IT Multiply to Solve

Students will practice solving story problems using multiplication. Have students turn to the Multiply to Solve activity page in their Activity Book and read the directions with them.

   Students should copy the problems from the Activity Book into their Math Notebook as necessary and solve them there.

- Use multiplication to solve a story problem that involves equal groups.

Multiply Equal Groups (B)
Multiply to Solve

Solve.

1. Janelle bought 6 large boxes of mangos. There were 14 mangos in each box. How many mangos did Janelle buy?
   84

2. The camp counselor gave 3 plums to each camper. There were 125 campers. How many plums did the counselor give out?
   375

3. Kelly knit 9 rows in her sweater. Each row had 203 stitches. How many stitches did Kelly knit?
   1,827

4. A nut factory had 1,987 almonds in each crate. If there were 4 crates, how many almonds did the factory have?
   7,948

Choose the answer.

5. Simone was paving a pathway in her yard. She had 9 rows of small paving stones. Each row had 102 stones. How many paving stones did she use?
   A. 102
   B. 111
   C. 908
   D. 918

6. The caterer has 106 plates. He wants to put 4 potatoes on each plate. How many potatoes does the caterer need?
   A. 424
   B. 404
   C. 110
   D. 64

7. Cindy drew some squares on her paper. She drew 15 rows of squares. Each row had 6 squares. How many squares did Cindy draw?
   A. 105
   B. 90
   C. 75
   D. 21

8. A grocery store had 5 crates of toothpaste. Each crate had 1,921 tubes of toothpaste. How many tubes of toothpaste did the grocery store have?
   A. 5,505
   B. 5,605
   C. 9,505
   D. 9,605

TRY IT

Multiplication with Equal Measures

▶ Lesson Objectives

Use multiplication to solve a story problem that involves equal measures.

▶ Prerequisite Skills

- Use objects or sketches to solve a multiplication story problem.
- Solve a multiplication problem involving a multidigit factor and a one-digit factor.

▶ Content Background

Students have learned how to solve multiplication story problems. In this lesson, they will solve story problems involving equal measures.

Multiplication is usually associated with combining equal groups of objects. The equal groups can also be groups of equal measures like distances, amounts of time, or amounts of money. For example, if students line up 6 toothpicks, end to end, and each toothpick is 2 inches long, they have 6 equal groups of 2. They can use multiplication to find the total length of the line of toothpicks.

▶ Common Errors and Misconceptions

- Students might add the second factor too many or too few times when using repeated addition. For example, for 5×4, students might add $4 + 4 + 4 + 4$.
- Students might undercount or overcount when using the count-by-n strategy.
- Students might view multiplication and division algorithms as rules to be followed. This leads to a misunderstanding that the numbers involved are separate digits rather than grouped amounts representing place values. The result is often an incorrect answer because of students' misunderstanding of estimation, place value, and reasonableness of results.

Materials to Gather

SUPPLIED

Equal-Measures Story Problems activity page

Solve Equal-Measures Story Problems activity page

GET READY Multidigit Multiplication

Objectives

- Solve a multiplication problem involving a multidigit factor and a one-digit factor.

Students will solve multiplication problems involving a multidigit factor and a one-digit factor. They will see how using known multiplication facts can help them solve related facts.

1. Have students solve $8 \times 1,000$ (write the problem vertically) using the traditional steps in which they multiply 8 times each digit.

2. Explain to students that solving a problem like this is very easy when they understand place value. They can just multiply 8 times the 1 in the thousands place to get 8 in the thousands place and all the other places will just have zeros. So it's like multiplying 8×1 and putting 3 zeros at the end of that number to get 8,000. Encourage students to make a connection between this concept and the problem $8 \times 1,000$.

3. Have students solve 8×100.

4. Discuss how multiplying a number by 100 is like putting 2 zeros at the end of that number. Encourage students to make a connection between this idea and the problem 8×100.

5. Give students the problem 8×99. Before students solve the problem, discuss how the numbers are close to the problem 8×100. See if students can use the problem 8×100 to solve 8×99.

6. Have students solve the problem and discuss their solutions. Guide students to say that the product of 8×99 can be seen as 99×8, or 99 groups of 8. Since they know that 100 groups of 8 would be 800, they could surmise that 99 groups of 8 would be $800 - 8$, or 792.

7. Help students see these tricks and twists to multiplication to increase their agility with mental mathematics.

LEARN Multiply Equal Measures

Objectives

- Use multiplication to solve a story problem that involves equal measures.

Students will learn to solve multiplication story problems involving equal measures such as time, money, length, and capacity. Have them work the problems on paper and enter the answers on the screen to check their work. Students should solve problems using whatever method they are most comfortable with.

LEARN Equal-Measures Story Problems

Objectives

- Use multiplication to solve a story problem that involves equal measures.

Students will practice solving multiplication story problems involving equal measures such as time, capacity, length, and height. Have students turn to the Equal-Measures Story Problems activity page in their Activity Book and read the directions with them.

Students should copy the problems from the Activity Book into their Math Notebook as necessary and solve them there.

1. Ask students to explain when they can use multiplication to solve a story problem. Students should explain that they multiply when the story problem is about combining equal groups.

2. Discuss several examples of different measurements that can be thought of as equal groups, such as distance, height, length, time, weight, or capacity. Explain that students can multiply these equal measures just as they would multiply equal groups.

3. Read the Worked Example with students. Point out that 48 inches is the amount that gets added over and over. Tell them that this amount gets added 6 times. Explain that since multiplication is repeated addition, they can multiply 6 times 48 to solve the problem. Make sure students understand how the multiplication number sentence was determined.

4. Read each problem with students. Ask them which amount gets added over and over, and how many times it gets added. Have students tell you the multiplication number sentence that can be used to solve each problem, and then solve it.

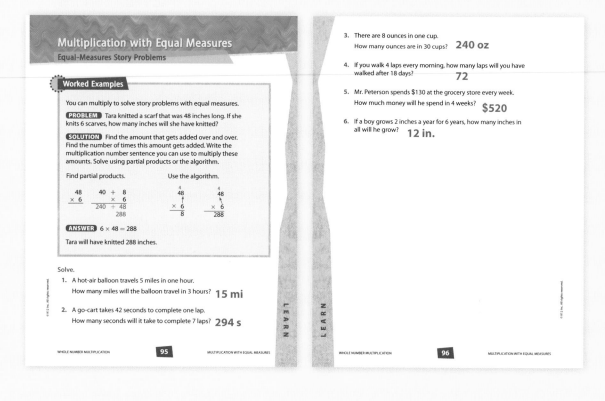

Multiplication with Equal Measures
Equal-Measures Story Problems

Worked Examples

You can multiply to solve story problems with equal measures.

PROBLEM Tara knitted a scarf that was 48 inches long. If she knits 6 scarves, how many inches will she have knitted?

SOLUTION Find the amount that gets added over and over. Find the number of times this amount gets added. Write the multiplication number sentence you can use to multiply these amounts. Solve using partial products or the algorithm.

Find partial products.   Use the algorithm.

$$\begin{array}{r} 48 \\ \times\ 6 \end{array} \quad \begin{array}{r} 40\ +\ 8 \\ \times\ 6 \\ \hline 240\ +\ 48 \\ 288 \end{array} \qquad \begin{array}{r} {}^{4}\\ 48 \\ \times\ 6 \\ \hline 8 \end{array} \quad \begin{array}{r} {}^{4}\\ 48 \\ \times\ 6 \\ \hline 288 \end{array}$$

ANSWER $6 \times 48 = 288$

Tara will have knitted 288 inches.

Solve.

1. A hot-air balloon travels 5 miles in one hour.
   How many miles will the balloon travel in 3 hours? **15 mi**

2. A go-cart takes 42 seconds to complete one lap.
   How many seconds will it take to complete 7 laps? **294 s**

3. There are 8 ounces in one cup.
   How many ounces are in 30 cups? **240 oz**

4. If you walk 4 laps every morning, how many laps will you have walked after 18 days? **72**

5. Mr. Peterson spends $130 at the grocery store every week.
   How much money will he spend in 4 weeks? **$520**

6. If a boy grows 2 inches a year for 6 years, how many inches in all will he grow? **12 in.**

L E A R N

L E A R N

TRY IT Solve Equal-Measures Story Problems

- Use multiplication to solve a story problem that involves equal measures.

Students will practice solving multiplication story problems involving equal measures. Have students turn to the Solve Equal-Measures Story Problems activity page in their Activity Book and read the directions with them.

Students should copy the problems from the Activity Book into their Math Notebook as necessary and solve them there.

Multiplication with Equal Measures
Solve Equal-Measures Story Problems

Solve.

1. Eli bought 3 bunches of roses. If each bunch cost $9, how much did Eli spend on roses? **$27**

2. Freddie charged $88 for a car tune-up. He did a tune-up on 6 vehicles last month. How much did he earn doing tune-ups last month? **$528**

3. Megan buys 110 pounds of dog food a year for each dog. How much will Megan need to buy for 2 dogs? **220 lb**

4. There are 1,760 yards in 1 mile. How many yards are in 5 miles? **8,800 yd**

Choose the answer.

5. Monica ran 2 miles each day for 5 days. What is the total distance Monica ran?
   A. 7 miles   (B.) 10 miles
   C. 15 miles   D. 20 miles

6. Mia earns $250 every month. How much will Mia earn in 7 months?
   A. $1,400   B. $1,450
   (C.) $1,750   D. $1,850

7. The blue whale is as long as 6 elephants put together. If each elephant is 15 feet long, how long is a blue whale?
   A. 60 feet   (B.) 90 feet
   C. 95 feet   D. 100 feet

8. Melanie is renting a house. The rent costs $1,850 each month. How much will she have to pay for 4 months?
   A. $4,200   B. $4,400
   C. $7,200   (D.) $7,400

WHOLE NUMBER MULTIPLICATION   **97**   MULTIPLICATION WITH EQUAL MEASURES

TRY IT

CHECKPOINT

- Use multiplication to solve a story problem that involves equal measures.

Students will complete an online Checkpoint. If necessary, read the directions, problems, and answer choices to students and help them with keyboard or mouse operations.

Write Multiplication Stories (A)

Lesson Overview

Skills Update	5 minutes	ONLINE
GET READY Solve Multiplication Story Problems	10 minutes	ONLINE
LEARN Types of Multiplication Story Problems	20 minutes	OFFLINE
LEARN Write Your Own Story Problems	20 minutes	OFFLINE
TRY IT Match a Number Sentence to a Problem	5 minutes	ONLINE

▶ Lesson Objectives

Create a story problem that can be represented by a multiplication number sentence.

▶ Prerequisite Skills

- Use multiplication to solve a story problem that involves equal groups.
- Use multiplication to solve a story problem that involves equal measures.
- Solve a multiplication problem involving a multidigit factor and a one-digit factor.

▶ Content Background

Students have a basic understanding of multiplication and how to solve multiplication story problems. In this lesson, they will create their own multiplication story problems.

Usually students solve problems written by others. However, one of the best ways to learn and practice a new skill is to teach it to someone else. By writing problems of their own, students become the teacher. They must think about all the parts needed to write a good multiplication story problem.

As students study and work through the variety of multiplication story problems, and also create some of their own, they may notice many different types of problems. Some of the different types of problems are those with arrays and area models and those involving equal groups and equal measures. Students are not expected to memorize or explain these types of problems. However, encouraging them to use variety in the types of problems they write will help them better understand multiplication story problems.

Materials to Gather

SUPPLIED

Types of Multiplication Story Problems activity page

GET READY Solve Multiplication Story Problems

Objectives

Students will solve a multiplication story problem.

- Use multiplication to solve a story problem that involves equal groups.
- Solve a multiplication problem involving a multidigit factor and a one-digit factor.

LEARN Types of Multiplication Story Problems

Objectives

Students will review what they know about story problems, multiplication, and ways of showing multiplication. They will learn the steps to write story problems. They will use this information to write their own multiplication story problems.

First follow the directions in Steps 1–5 with students. Then have students turn to the Types of Multiplication Story Problems activity page in their Activity Book.

- Create a story problem that can be represented by a multiplication number sentence.

Tips

Allow students to sketch each problem to determine if it is an array, area-model, equal-groups, or equal-measures problem.

1. Review different types of multiplication story problems. Present each situation below and ask students to give an example, either verbally or with a drawing.
   - Array **Example:** 5 rows of 10 seats; $5 \times 10 = 50$
   - Area model **Example:** squares on a grid that is 3 squares by 4 squares; $3 \times 4 = 12$
   - Equal groups **Example:** 6 packs of 100; $6 \times 100 = 600$
   - Equal measures **Example:** running 50 meters 5 times; $5 \times 50 = 250$

2. Discuss how to get ideas for story problems, and present examples. Guide students in picking a general theme, getting specific, and then thinking of what to include in the problem.

   Say: If you want to write a story problem, first you need a good story! Start by picking a theme.

   Present an example about hamsters.

   Say: Let's pick animals, more specifically hamsters. Now we have to think about what hamsters do that can be included in a problem.

   Ask: What are some things hamsters do? Hamsters eat, sleep, run on the hamster wheel, put food in their pouch, and build nests.

   Say: Now let's start thinking of problems. If we want problems with greater numbers, we might need many hamsters. So let's say we have a hamster farm with a lot of hamsters.

   Ask: How many hamsters should we have on the farm? Accept any number greater than 100.

3. Explain that the next step is thinking of problems that involve multiplying. Point out that for each problem, students need to write a multiplication number sentence.

4. Together, write a problem about the hamsters on the farm. Identify the multiplication number sentence for that problem. **Example:** There are 475 hamsters on the farm. Each hamster eats 2 pounds of food each month. How many pounds of food do the hamsters eat in one month altogether? The number sentence is $475 \times 2 = ?$

5. Brainstorm with students other themes they could use to write multiplication stories. Have students move from general theme to specific topic to items to include in the problem. Use the following questions:

   - What is your theme? **Example:** circus, zoo, party, library, weather

   - What specifically would your problem be about? **Example:** clowns, lions, balloons, books, snowfall

   - Give an example of something you would multiply. **Example:** price of a ticket to the show, amount of food the lions eat each day, number of balloons each guest gets, number of books in piles, amount of snow in 4 weeks

6. Have students turn to the Types of Multiplication Story Problems activity page in their Activity Book and read the directions with them. Students should copy the problems from the Activity Book into their Math Notebook as necessary and solve them there. (Note: Students only need to identify the types of story problems; they do not need to solve the multiplication problems presented.)

7. Read the Worked Example with students. To make sure they understand why an area model is the best model for the problem, ask how they would make the area model that shows the details in the problem. Students should say that they would make a grid with 9 rows, each with 12 squares.

8. Read Problem 1 with students. Ask them which type of story problem best matches this particular problem. Guide them to see that this is an equal-groups problem. There are the same number of objects in each group. 3 hamster pellets; 365 hamsters

9. Read Problem 2 with students. Ask them which type of story problem best matches this particular problem. Guide them to see that this is an equal-measures problem. Ask them what amount gets added over and over. the number of times Hamie Hamster runs around the wheel

10. Read Problem 3 with students. Ask them which type of story problem best matches this particular problem. Guide them to see that this is an area-model problem because the pictures form a grid of squares. Ask them how many rows there are and how many pictures in each row. 24 rows; 3 pictures in each row

    Remind students that in an area model, the objects are touching, and point out that this problem says that the photos will be side by side, with edges touching.

11. Read Problem 4 with students. Ask them which type of story problem best matches this particular problem. Guide them to see that this is an array problem. Ask them how many rows there are, and how many cages are in each row. 5 rows; 28 cages in each row

12. Have students solve Problems 5 and 6 on their own. Read the problems to them if needed. Allow time to discuss their answers.

Additional Answers

1. equal-groups problem; There are groups with the same number of objects in each group.

2. equal-measures problem; The same amount gets added over and over.

3. area-model problem; There are squares in a rectangular grid.

4. array problem; There are rows of objects with the same number in each row.

OFFLINE

20min

LEARN Write Your Own Story Problems

Objectives

- Create a story problem that can be represented by a multiplication number sentence.

Students will write story problems for a given multiplication sentence. Have students turn to the Types of Multiplication Story Problems activity page in their Activity Book. Students will refer to this page in this activity.

1. Explain to students that they will write their own multiplication story problem.

2. Write the multiplication number sentence 6×204 on a sheet of paper. Have students make up an equal-groups story problem about hamsters by using this number sentence. Encourage students to use their imagination. Share this example with students:
   - The 6 oldest hamsters collected seeds. They each collected 204 seeds in their pouches. How many seeds did they collect altogether?

3. Ask students to share their story problem. Check that their story matches the multiplication number sentence.

4. Have students look at the Types of Multiplication Story Problems activity page. Review the different ways that multiplication can be shown—by an array, by an area model, by equal groups, and by equal measures.

5. Have students write another story problem that uses the same number sentence as the earlier problem (6 × 204). This problem should use an array.
Example: The hamsters made 6 rows of 204 pellets to play a game.

6. Repeat Step 5 to write another story problem that uses an area model.
Example: The hamsters set out their square seating pads to watch the game. They made 6 rows with 204 seats in each row. They placed their seating pads right next to each other forming a giant grid.

7. Repeat Step 5 to write another story problem involving equal measures.
Example: A hamster lined up 204 pellets. Each pellet is 3 millimeters long. How long is the line of pellets?

8. Discuss with students how the different story problems are alike and how they are different.

TRY IT Match a Number Sentence to a Problem

ONLINE
5min

Objectives

Students will complete an online Try It. If necessary, read the directions, problems, and answer choices to students and help them with keyboard or mouse operations.

- Create a story problem that can be represented by a multiplication number sentence.

Write Multiplication Stories (B)

Lesson Overview

LEARN Multiplication Story Problem Book	40 minutes	OFFLINE
TRY IT Story Writing	10 minutes	ONLINE
CHECKPOINT	10 minutes	ONLINE

▶ Lesson Objectives

Create a story problem that can be represented by a multiplication number sentence.

▶ Prerequisite Skills

- Use multiplication to solve a story problem that involves equal groups.
- Use multiplication to solve a story problem that involves equal measures.
- Solve a multiplication problem involving a multidigit factor and a one-digit factor.

▶ Content Background

Students have a basic understanding of multiplication and how to solve multiplication story problems. In this lesson, they will continue to create their own multiplication story problems.

Usually students solve problems written by others. However, one of the best ways to learn and practice a new skill is to teach it to someone else. By writing problems of their own, students become the teacher. They must think about all the parts needed to write a good multiplication story problem.

As students study and work through the variety of multiplication story problems, and also create some of their own, they may notice many different types of problems. Some of the different types of problems are those with arrays and area models and those involving equal groups and equal measures. Students are not expected to memorize or explain these types of problems. However, encouraging them to use variety in the types of problems they write will help them better understand multiplication story problems.

▶ Advance Preparation

Cut each sheet of wide-line handwriting paper into halves as shown.

▶ Safety

Make sure students handle the scissors carefully and be sure to store them in a safe place. Supervise students as they work with the stapler.

Materials to Gather

SUPPLIED

Types of Multiplication Story Problems activity page

ALSO NEEDED

scissors, pointed-end safety

household objects – stapler

glue stick

crayons or markers

paper, construction – 2 sheets

paper, wide-line handwriting – 2 sheets

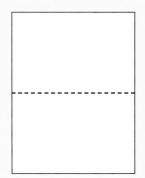

Objectives

- Create a story problem that can be represented by a multiplication number sentence.

Tips

Instead of stapling along the fold, use a hole punch and string to secure the pages. Students may add more pages to their book.

Students will use what they know about story problems, multiplication, and ways of showing multiplication to create a book of multiplication story problems. Their book will have four problems. The directions say that students should use a different model for multiplication for each problem—array, area model, equal groups, and equal measures. But if students wish, they may use the same model for all the problems. Or they may use any combination of models.

The examples in this activity all use the same numbers (8 and 173). This is so students can see the same numbers used with the four types of models. But students may use different numbers in each problem if they wish.

Encourage students to create problems that are challenging enough to show off their multiplication skills. They may choose to show the worked solutions on the individual pages in their book, or they may prefer to show the answers to all problems on the book's last page.

Gather the construction paper, stapler, glue stick, crayons or markers, and the four half-sheets of lined paper. Have students turn to the Types of Multiplication Story Problems activity page in their Activity Book. They will refer to this page in Step 6.

1. Review with students how to write their own multiplication story problem. Suggest that they begin with an amusement park theme.

2. Write the number sentence $8 \times 173 = ?$ on a sheet of paper. Tell students that they will be using this multiplication number sentence to write story problems.

3. Share this example with students:
   - Each log of the Raging Rapids Water Slide seats 8 people. If 173 logs went down the slide in one day, how many people rode the water slide?

   Point out how the number sentence was used in the example.

4. Have students create their own amusement park problem using the number sentence $8 \times 173 = ?$ Encourage them to use their imagination.

5. Ask students to read their story problem aloud. Check that their story matches the number sentence.

6. Have students look at the Types of Multiplication Story Problems activity page. Review the different ways that multiplication can be shown—by an array, by an area model, by equal groups, and by equal measures.

7. Have students write another problem using the same number sentence. This problem should use an array. **Example:** In the parking lot, there are 8 rows of cars. There are 173 cars in each row. How many cars are there in all?

8. Repeat Step 7 for a problem that uses an area model. **Example:** People are having lunch in the picnic area of the amusement park. There are 8 rows of square blankets. There are 173 blankets in each row. How many picnic blankets are there in all?

9. Repeat Step 7 for a problem involving equal measures. **Example:** Each roller coaster car is 8 feet long. If 173 roller coaster cars are placed end to end, how long would the coaster be?

10. Discuss with students how their story problems are alike and how their problems are different.

11. Distribute the four half-sheets of lined paper.

12. Explain to students that they will make their own multiplication story problem book. Encourage them to choose a theme for their problems. If they are having difficulty coming up with ideas, have them look through magazines or newspapers to help them think of a theme.

13. Have students write four multiplication story problems. Tell them to write one problem of each type (equal groups, array, area model, and equal measures) and to write each problem on a separate piece of lined paper.

14. Have students assemble a multiplication story problem book. Give students the sheets of construction paper.

    Fold the sheets of construction paper in half and staple on the fold as shown.

15. Use the front page as the cover. Have students glue each story problem onto a page in their book.

16. Suggest that students title their book and create an illustration for each problem. They can use pictures from magazines, clip art, or their own drawings.

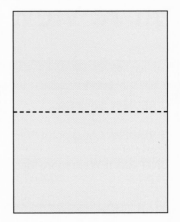

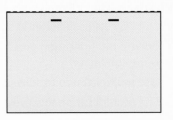

TRY IT Story Writing

ONLINE **10**min

Objectives

Students will complete an online Try It. If necessary, read the directions, problems, and answer choices to students and help them with keyboard or mouse operations.

- Create a story problem that can be represented by a multiplication number sentence.

CHECKPOINT

ONLINE **10**min

Objectives

Students will complete an online Checkpoint. If necessary, read the directions, problems, and answer choices to students and help them with keyboard or mouse operations.

- Create a story problem that can be represented by a multiplication number sentence.

Unit Review

Lesson Overview

UNIT REVIEW Look Back	10 minutes	**ONLINE**
UNIT REVIEW Checkpoint Practice	50 minutes	**ONLINE**
➥ **UNIT REVIEW** Prepare for the Checkpoint		

▶ Unit Objectives

This lesson reviews the following objectives:

- Use objects or sketches to solve a multiplication story problem.
- Solve a multiplication problem involving a multidigit factor and a one-digit factor.
- Use multiplication to solve a story problem that involves equal groups.
- Use multiplication to solve a story problem that involves equal measures.
- Create a story problem that can be represented by a multiplication number sentence.

Materials to Gather

There are no materials to gather for this lesson.

▶ Advance Preparation

In this lesson, students will have an opportunity to review previous activities in the Whole Number Multiplication unit. Look at the suggested activities in Unit Review: Prepare for the Checkpoint online and gather any needed materials.

UNIT REVIEW Look Back

Students will review key concepts from the unit to prepare for the Unit Checkpoint.

Objectives

- Review unit objectives.

UNIT REVIEW Checkpoint Practice

Students will complete an online Checkpoint Practice to prepare for the Unit Checkpoint. If necessary, read the directions, problems, and answer choices to students. Have students answer the problems on their own. Review any missed problems with students.

Objectives

- Review unit objectives.

➥ **UNIT REVIEW** Prepare for the Checkpoint

What you do next depends on how students performed in the previous activity, Unit Review: Checkpoint Practice. If students had difficulty with any of the problems, complete the appropriate review activity listed in the table online.

Unit Checkpoint

UNIT CHECKPOINT Online   60 minutes   ONLINE

▶ Unit Objectives

This lesson assesses the following objectives:

- Use objects or sketches to solve a multiplication story problem.
- Solve a multiplication problem involving a multidigit factor and a one-digit factor.
- Use multiplication to solve a story problem that involves equal groups.
- Use multiplication to solve a story problem that involves equal measures.
- Create a story problem that can be represented by a multiplication number sentence.

Materials to Gather

There are no materials to gather for this lesson.

UNIT CHECKPOINT Online

ONLINE
60min

Objectives

- Assess unit objectives.

Students will complete the Unit Checkpoint online. If necessary, read the directions, problems, and answer choices to students and help them with keyboard or mouse operations.

Whole Number Division Sense

▶ Unit Objectives

- Use objects or sketches to solve a division problem.
- Explain division as repeated subtraction.
- Explain the meaning of the ÷ symbol.
- Explain and apply the division property of 1.
- Demonstrate understanding that division by zero is undefined.
- Recognize the meaning of the three symbols for division.
- Explain division as the sharing of a quantity into equal groups.
- Demonstrate an understanding of the inverse relationship between multiplication and division.
- Use the inverse relationship of multiplication and division to compute and check results.
- Demonstrate an understanding of the effects of division on whole numbers.

▶ Big Ideas

- Multiplication and division can be represented by models and by using math symbols.
- Division can be understood as repeated subtraction or as division of a quantity into equal groups.
- Addition, subtraction, multiplication, and division can be represented by models and by using math symbols.
- Inverses undo each other. Addition and subtraction are inverse operations, and multiplication and division are inverse operations.

▶ Unit Introduction

In this unit, students will develop a further understanding of division. They will practice using the terms *dividend*, *divisor*, and *quotient*. Students will model division problems with concrete objects and sketches. They will explain division as repeated subtraction and explain the meaning of the division symbol. They will explain that division by 1 leaves a number unchanged, and they will demonstrate an understanding that division by zero has no answer. They will learn the three symbols for division: the standard division symbol, the fraction bar, and the long-division symbol. It is important for students to understand that these symbols have the same meaning even though they're used in different situations. Students will explain division as sharing a quantity into equal groups. They will see the inverse relationship between multiplication and division. Finally students will take a step back and generalize to see that when numbers are divided, the answer, or quotient, is less than the number being divided, the dividend. The exception is when dividing by 1 or zero.

▶ Keywords

dividend	equal groups	inverse relationship
division	equal sharing	multiplication fact family
division by 1	fraction bar	quotient
division symbol (÷)	inverse operations	repeated subtraction
divisor		

Model and Explain Division

GET READY Explore Division	10 minutes	OFFLINE
LEARN Model Equal Groups	10 minutes	OFFLINE
LEARN Use Repeated Subtraction	15 minutes	OFFLINE
TRY IT Represent Division Problems	15 minutes	OFFLINE
CHECKPOINT	10 minutes	ONLINE

▶ Lesson Objectives

- Use objects or sketches to solve a division problem.
- Explain division as repeated subtraction.
- Explain the meaning of the ÷ symbol.

▶ Prerequisite Skills

- Use models and math symbols to represent division.
- Use forming equal groups with remainders to solve simple division problems.
- Use repeated subtraction to do division problems.
- Recognize that the ÷ sign refers to division.
- Correctly use the ÷ symbol.

▶ Content Background

Students will learn to explain division as sharing. They will be introduced to division modeled as equal groups, repeated subtraction, and equal measures. Finally they will explain the meaning of the division symbol (÷) and recognize the three different symbolic representations of division.

Division is an operation involving distributing an amount equally. Students can use division to find the number of equal groups or equal measures when they know both the total number and the number that shows how the total will be shared. They can also find the number being shared when they know both the total number and the number of groups or units of measure.

Since students understand fair sharing from an early age, use that idea to begin discussing division. Students need to say "divided by" when stating division problems and writing division symbols. Do not use the phrase "divided into." Likewise, do not ask how many times a number "goes into" another number.

When writing a division number sentence, the first number tells the total number and is called the *dividend*. The next number tells the number students are dividing by and is called the *divisor*. The answer tells how many groups or objects or units have been shared and is called the *quotient*.

This format will be used with students throughout this lesson.

24	÷	4	=	6
dividend	divided by	divisor	equals	quotient

Materials to Gather

SUPPLIED

blocks – B (all colors)

number lines from the Number Line Creator Tool

Represent Division Problems activity page

ALSO NEEDED

index cards – 5

▶ Common Errors and Misconceptions

Students might view multiplication and division algorithms as rules to be followed. This leads to a misunderstanding that the numbers involved are separate digits rather than grouped amounts representing place values. The result is often an incorrect answer because of students' misunderstanding of estimation, place value, and reasonableness of results.

▶ Advance Preparation

DIRECTIONS FOR USING THE NUMBER LINE CREATOR TOOL

To create number lines from 0 to 35:

1. Set Range:	2. Select Options:	3. Print Number Line:
• Start Number Line at: 0 • End Number Line at: 35	• Tick Marks: ones	• Page Orientation: landscape • Number Lines per Sheet: 2

GET READY Explore Division

OFFLINE **10**min

Students will explore multiplication and division with models and objects. They will use multiplication to find the total number of objects in equal groups. Then they will divide objects into equal groups, use repeated subtraction, and identify remainders.
Gather the blocks and the index cards.

Objectives

- Use models and math symbols to represent division.
- Use repeated subtraction to do division problems.
- Recognize that the ÷ sign refers to division.
- Correctly use the ÷ symbol.

1. Display 5 groups of circles with 4 circles in each group.

2. **Ask:** How many groups are there? 5

3. **Ask:** How many circles are in each group? 4

4. Explain that multiplication is used to find the total amount by combining equal groups.

5. **Ask:** How many circles are there in all? 20

6. Write 5 × 4 = 20. Explain that the multiplication sentence is read as "5 groups of 4 equals 20 in all."

7. **Say:** You have 20 pretzels and you want to share them equally among 5 people.

   Explain that 20 divided by 5, or 20 objects placed into 5 equal groups, describes this situation. Write 20 ÷ 5 = ? Point out the division symbol and identify it as such.

8. Repeat the sharing situation. Tell students that they will use the circles to represent pretzels and the index cards to represent the groups. Have students count out 20 circles and lay the 5 index cards on a flat surface.

9. Have students place one circle in each of the 5 groups until all the circles have been distributed. This is an example of what the students' completed answer should look like.

10. **Ask:** How many circles are in each group? 4

    Refer back to the division sentence and write the answer. $20 \div 5 = 4$

11. **Ask:** How many pretzels does each person get? 4

12. **Say:** This time, you have 23 pretzels that you want to divide by 5 by making groups of 5.

    Have students write the division expression to represent 23 divided by 5. Be sure students use the division symbol correctly. $23 \div 5$

13. Explain that students will use repeated subtraction to solve this problem.

14. Have students show 23 circles. Then have them take away a group of 5 circles.

    Say: This is one group of 5.

    Then have students take away another group of 5.

    Say: This is another group of 5.

    Explain that by repeatedly taking away groups of 5, students are modeling repeated subtraction.

15. Continue having students take away groups of 5 until there are no more groups of 5.

16. **Ask:** How many groups of 5 did you subtract? 4

17. **Ask:** How many are left over? 3

LEARN Model Equal Groups

Objectives

Students will use objects and sketches to solve division problems. They will model equal sharing by divvying up totals and dividing amounts to make equal groups.
Gather the blocks.

- Use objects or sketches to solve a division problem.
- Explain the meaning of the ÷ symbol.

1. **Say:** Winnie has 18 flowers. She wants to put an equal number of flowers into 3 vases. How many flowers will be in each vase?

2. Draw 3 large ovals on paper and explain to students that the ovals represent the vases. Make the ovals large enough so that 6 circles will fit inside each one.

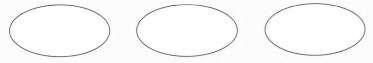

3. Display 18 circles.

    Say: These are 18 little round flowers. To solve the problem, put the same number of flowers in each of the 3 vases.

4. Have students solve the problem by placing the circles into the vases. They will find that there are 6 flowers in each vase. Here is an example of how the circles could be arranged in groups.

Tips

Connect each number in the division sentence to the words in the story problem.

5. Write 18 ÷ 3 = 6.

   Say: This problem is read as "18 divided by 3 equals 6."

   Point to the division symbol. Tell students that in this problem, there are a total of 18 objects (flowers), placed into 3 equal groups, with 6 in each group.

6. **Say:** Alexander has 24 seeds. He plants 4 seeds in each pot. How many pots does he use?

7. Have students count out 24 circles and separate them into groups of 4 circles.

   Ask: How many groups did you make? 6

   Here is an example of how the circles could be arranged.

8. Write 24 ÷ 4 = 6. Be sure to leave space between this number sentence and the previous one. Have students read the problem as "24 divided by 4 equals 6."

   Ask: What does the division symbol show? It shows that 24 objects (seeds) placed into equal groups of 4 makes 6 groups.

9. **Say:** Sometimes when we divide, we have a certain quantity, such as 18 flowers, that we need to divide to make a certain number of groups. This is what we do when we put flowers in 3 vases, or when we share equally with friends. We can represent these problems by showing the total divided by the number of groups using a division symbol.

10. Point to 18 ÷ 3 = 6. Write "number in all" below the 18, "number of groups" below the 3, and "number in each group" below the 6.

18	÷	3	=	6
number in all		number of groups		number in each group

11. **Say:** Other times when we divide, we have a certain quantity, such as 24 seeds, that we divide into groups with a certain number in each group, and we have to find how many groups there are. We can represent these problems by showing the total divided by the number in each group using a division symbol.

12. Point to 24 ÷ 4 = 6. Write "number in all" below the 24, "number in each group" below the 4, and "number of groups" below the 6.

24	÷	4	=	6
number in all		number in each group		number of groups

13. Have students use sketches to solve the following problems. After they solve each problem, write the accompanying division sentence. Have students state each division sentence, saying "divided by" as they read the division symbol.

    • Serena has 16 mystery books. She puts 8 books on each shelf. How many shelves does she use? 2
      Here is a sample sketch.

      16 ÷ 8 = 2

- Ron has 20 stickers and wants to put an equal number on 5 rockets. How many stickers will be on each rocket? 4
Here is a sample sketch.

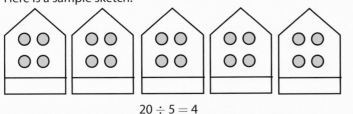

$$20 \div 5 = 4$$

LEARN Use Repeated Subtraction

OFFLINE
15min

Students will use repeated subtraction to solve division problems. They will take away groups of circles, make backward jumps on a number line, and write subtraction sentences to show repeated subtraction.

Gather the blocks and the number lines you printed from the Number Line Creator Tool.

1. **Say:** We can use division to separate a total amount into a given number of equal groups. We can also use division to make equal groups of a given amount. We can use repeated subtraction to determine the number of equal groups.

2. **Ask:** Winnie has 35 painted eggs and wants to put 5 eggs in each basket. How many baskets does she need?

3. Have students count out a total of 35 circles. Guide students to repeatedly take away groups of 5 to see how many groups of 5 are in 35. Students should make 7 groups of 5.

4. **Ask:** What division number sentence means "35 objects placed into equal groups of 5"? 35 divided by 5 equals 7.

5. Write $35 \div 5 = 7$. Ask students what each number represents. They should explain that 35 is the total amount, 5 is the number in each group, and 7 is the number of groups.

35	÷	5	=	7
number in all		number in each group		number of groups

6. Point to the 7, and tell students that the answer to a division problem is called a quotient.

7. Remind students that when they solved $35 \div 5$, they repeatedly took away 5. Explain to students that this can also be done with a number line.

8. Display the labeled number line. Have students start at 35 and make backward jumps of 5 to zero. Have student show their jumps with a curved arrow and label them with -5.

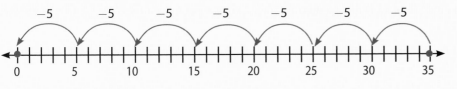

9. **Ask:** How many jumps did you make? 7

   Say: You have shown 35 divided by 5 equals 7

   Point to the number sentence.

Objectives

- Use objects or sketches to solve a division problem.
- Explain division as repeated subtraction.
- Explain the meaning of the ÷ symbol.

Tips

Have students use circles or a number line to solve $63 \div 9$ and $40 \div 8$. Compare solutions to the repeated subtraction solutions.

$$35 - 5 = 30$$
$$30 - 5 = 25$$
$$25 - 5 = 20$$
$$20 - 5 = 15$$
$$15 - 5 = 10$$
$$10 - 5 = 5$$
$$5 - 5 = 0$$

10. Review the subtraction shown on the number line.

11. Summarize the activity with students. They can model division with objects and sketches. They can explain the meaning of the division symbol and can solve division problems by using repeated subtraction with numbers and on a number line. They know that a division problem can ask how many groups with a certain number of objects they can make from a given number of objects. Or it can ask how many would be in each group if they divided a given number of objects into a given number of groups. Students have seen that the problem $35 \div 5 = ?$ can ask how many groups of 5 they can make with 35 objects, or how many would be in each group if they divided 35 into 5 equal groups.

OFFLINE
15 min

TRY IT Multiply or Divide and Check

Students will practice using objects, sketches, and repeated subtraction to solve division problems. Have students turn to the Represent Division Problems activity page in their Activity Book and read the directions with them.

Students should copy the problems from the Activity Book into their Math Notebook as necessary and solve them there.

Objectives

- Use objects or sketches to solve a division problem.
- Explain division as repeated subtraction.
- Explain the meaning of the ÷ symbol.

Model and Explain Division
Represent Division Problems

Use repeated subtraction to solve the problem.

1. $18 \div 6 = ?$
    See next page.

2. $36 \div 9 = ?$
    See next page.

Use circle blocks to solve the problem.

3. $35 \div 7 = ?$
    See next page.

4. $? = 28 \div 7$
    See next page.

Draw a sketch to show how to solve the problem.

5. $? = 18 \div 3$
    See next page.

6. $20 \div 4 = ?$
    See next page.

Use circle blocks to show how to use repeated subtraction to solve the problem.

7. Kristina has 18 grapes.
    She wants to give 2 grapes to each person.
    How many people can she give grapes to?
    See next page.

8. Mark has 40 tiles.
    He wants to put 4 tiles onto each tray.
    How many trays will Mark need? **See next page.**

Use a sketch to solve the problem.

9. Johnny has a bag of 12 cat treats.
    He gives 3 treats to each cat.
    How many cats are there?
    4; Sketches will vary.
    Example: 4 groups with
    3 circles in each group.

WHOLE NUMBER DIVISION SENSE **100** MODEL AND EXPLAIN DIVISION

Choose the answer.

10. Geoff wanted to solve this problem.

    $25 \div 5 = ?$

    Which operation should he use?

    A. addition
    B. multiplication
    C. subtraction
    D. division ⃝

11. Kent wanted to solve this problem.

    $? = 36 \div 6$

    Which operation should he use?

    A. subtraction
    B. addition
    C. division ⃝
    D. multiplication

12. Which sketch shows $15 \div 3 = ?$

WHOLE NUMBER DIVISION SENSE **101** MODEL AND EXPLAIN DIVISION

Additional Answers

1. $18 - 6 = 12$
   $12 - 6 = 6$
   $6 - 6 = 0$
   6 was subtracted 3 times, so $18 \div 6 = 3$.

2. $36 - 9 = 27$
   $27 - 9 = 18$
   $18 - 9 = 9$
   $9 - 9 = 0$
   9 was subtracted 4 times, so $36 \div 9 = 4$.

3. 5; Students should divide the 35 circle blocks into 7 equal groups with 5 circle blocks in each group or subtract 7 from 35 five times.

4. 4; Students should divide the 28 circle blocks into 7 equal groups with 4 circle blocks in each group or subtract 7 from 28 four times.

5. 6; Students should draw 3 groups of 6 or 6 groups of 3.
   $18 \div 3 = 6$

6. 5; Students should draw 4 groups of 5 or 5 groups of 4.
   $20 \div 4 = 5$

7. 9; **Example:** Start with 18 circle blocks. Move 2 circle blocks to another pile. Move another 2 circle blocks to a new pile. Keep moving 2 circle blocks to new piles until the 18 circle blocks are divided into piles of 2. Count the number of piles.

8. 10; **Example:** Start with 40 circle blocks. Move 4 circle blocks to another pile. Move another 4 circle blocks to a new pile. Keep moving 4 circle blocks to new piles until the 40 circle blocks are divided into piles of 4. Count the number of piles.

ONLINE
10 min

CHECKPOINT

Students will complete an online Checkpoint. If necessary, read the directions, problems, and answer choices to students and help them with keyboard or mouse operations.

Objectives

- Explain division as repeated subtraction.

Applying Division Symbols and Rules

Lesson Overview

LEARN Division Three Ways	15 minutes	**ONLINE**
LEARN Dividing with 1 and Zero	15 minutes	**OFFLINE**
LEARN Practice with Flash Cards	10 minutes	**ONLINE**
TRY IT Division Symbols and Properties	10 minutes	**OFFLINE**
CHECKPOINT	10 minutes	**ONLINE**

▶ Lesson Objectives

- Explain and apply the division property of 1.
- Demonstrate understanding that division by zero is undefined.
- Recognize the meaning of the three symbols for division.

▶ Prerequisite Skills

- Use models and math symbols to represent division.
- Demonstrate understanding that any number multiplied by 1 results in the same number ($n \times 1 = n$).
- Use repeated subtraction to do division problems.
- Use equal sharing to do division problems.
- Recognize that the $\div$ sign refers to division.
- Correctly use the $\div$ symbol.

▶ Content Background

Students have a basic understanding of division. They will apply their understanding to explore division properties and different representations of division. Students will learn three different ways to represent a division problem. They will also learn the result of dividing a number by 1 or zero and dividing zero by a number. When dividing a number by 1, the quotient is always the original number. When dividing a number by zero, the answer is undefined. It is acceptable for students to say there is no answer.

There are three different symbols to show division. These are the standard division symbol, as in $6 \div 2$; the fraction bar, as in $\frac{6}{2}$; and the long-division symbol, as in $2\overline{)6}$. In each of these examples, the division problem should be read as "6 divided by 2." Becoming familiar with the different representations of division will help students with division and assist them in the future study of fractions. Use the following chart to guide students to say and write fractions properly.

Division Sentence	Say	Write
$12 \div 4 = 3$	12 divided by 4 equals 3	12 and say "divided by" as you write the standard division symbol
$\frac{12}{4} = 3$	12 divided by 4 equals 3	12 and say "divided by" as you write the fraction bar
$4\overline{)12}$ with 3 above	12 divided by 4 equals 3	12 and say "divided by" as you draw the long-division symbol, $\overline{)}$

Avoid using the phrase "4 goes into 12" with students. Say "12 divided by 4," or "4 divides 12." Although students may be splitting 12 "into" 4 groups, it makes no sense to say that 4 goes into 12. Students should consistently relate what they are doing to division. The expression "goes into" becomes a rote phrase that can lead to misconceptions for students.

▶ Common Errors and Misconceptions

- Students might view multiplication and division algorithms as rules to be followed. This leads to a misunderstanding that the numbers involved are separate digits rather than grouped amounts representing place values. The result is often an incorrect answer because of students' misunderstanding of estimation, place value, and reasonableness of results.

- Students might not relate their knowledge of division (its symbols, procedures, and facts) to what they already know in order to make meaningful, everyday connections.

ONLINE 15 min

LEARN Division Three Ways

Students will learn the three symbols to show division. They will complete division problems using these symbols. They will see division written in the following three ways: $6 \div 2$; $\frac{6}{2}$, and $2\overline{)6}$. Help students say each division problem properly. In all cases, they should read the problem as "[dividend] divided by [divisor]." For example, all three examples here would be read as "6 divided by 2."

Objectives

- Recognize the meaning of the three symbols for division.

OFFLINE 15 min

LEARN Dividing with 1 and Zero

Students will investigate division by 1 and zero. They will also explore dividing zero by any number. They will see why dividing by zero has no possible answer.
   There are no materials to gather for this activity.

Objectives

- Explain and apply the division property of 1.

- Demonstrate understanding that division by zero is undefined.

- Recognize the meaning of the three symbols for division.

DIVIDING BY 1

1. Tell students that when you divide a number by 1, the answer is the same as the number you are dividing. To help students understand this concept, begin by reviewing multiplication by 1. Explain to students that any number multiplied by 1 is the original number because there is only one group. Give an example: If you have 1 group of 5 grapes, you have 5 grapes altogether.

2. Tell students that if you divide the 5 grapes into 1 group there would be 5 grapes in the group because $5 \div 1 = 5$. Point to each number in the division sentence and explain its meaning.

5	$\div$	1	$=$	5
number in all	$\div$	number of groups	$=$	number in each group

3. Tell students that, similar to multiplication, any number divided by 1 is the original number.

4. Have students practice this concept by finding the quotient in each of the following problems:
   - $27 \div 1 = ?$ 27
   - $87 \div 1 = ?$ 87

   - $1\overline{)35}$? 35
   - $\dfrac{259}{1} = ?$ 259

   - $\dfrac{6,367}{1} = ?$ 6,367
   - $2,345,657,765 \div 1 = ?$ 2,345,657,765

   Point out that the last problem may seem challenging but students can still find the quotient following the rule for dividing by 1.

DIVIDING BY ZERO

5. Explain to students that unlike division by 1, division by zero has no possible answer. Use the idea of repeated subtraction to explain this concept to students.

   Say: It doesn't make sense to ask how many times you can subtract zero from a quantity of objects to get to zero. You could subtract zero forever and you would never get to zero.

6. Explain that when dividing by zero, there is no answer. Write $63 \div 9 = ?$ Explain that students could find the answer by solving this problem: $? \times 9 = 63$. They would get an answer of 7. Write 7 as the quotient.

7. Write $6 \div 0 = ?$ Again, explain that students could find the answer by solving $? \times 0 = 6$, but no number would work because $? \times 0$ would always be 0, not 6 or any other number. (**Note:** $0 \div 0 = ?$ is a different case, which is reserved for later courses.)

8. Show students the following problems. Ask students to solve them and to explain their answers.
   - $35 \div 0 = ?$
   - $87 \div 0 = ?$

   - $0\overline{)87}$?
   - $\dfrac{259}{0} = ?$

   - $\dfrac{6,367}{0} = ?$
   - $2,345,657,765 \div 0 = ?$

   These problems have no possible answer.

> ### Tips
>
> If students have difficulty grasping the concept of division by zero and 1, have them model problems with circle blocks.

DIVIDING ZERO BY A NUMBER

9. Explain to students that while there is no answer when a number is divided by zero, they can divide zero by a number. Discuss with students the example $0 \div 3 = 0$. If 0 objects are placed into 3 groups, there are 0 objects in each group.

10. Have students answer the following problems and explain their answers:

- $0 \div 5 = ?\ 0$
- $0 \div 37 = ?\ 0$
- $7\overline{)0} \quad \overset{?\ \ 0}{}$
- $9\overline{)0} \quad \overset{?\ \ 0}{}$
- $\dfrac{0}{8} = ?\ 0$
- $0 \div 3{,}300{,}486 = ?\ 0$

Students should explain that the answer is always zero because 0 objects placed into any number of groups always results in 0 objects in each group. Also, any number times zero is zero.

11. Review with students the following division rules:

- Any number divided by 1 is the original number.
- There is no possible answer when a number is divided by zero.
- Zero divided by any number is always zero.

12. Give students the following problems and have them answer aloud:

- $64 \div 1 = ?\ 64$
- $81 \div 0 = ?\ $ no possible answer
- $0 \div 55 = ?\ 0$

ONLINE 10 min

LEARN Practice with Flash Cards

Students will use online flash cards to practice dividing with 1 and zero. They will practice doing division problems that use the three representations for division. Students should call out the problems as well as the answers and then click to see if they are correct. They should become accustomed to the fact that any number divided by 1 is the same number, and that zero divided by a number is zero, but a number divided by zero has no answer.

Objectives

- Explain and apply the division property of 1.
- Demonstrate understanding that division by zero is undefined.
- Recognize the meaning of the three symbols for division.

OFFLINE 10 min

TRY IT Division Symbols and Properties

Students will practice writing the different ways to show a division problem. Have students say the problem as they write it. Students will also practice dividing with 1 and zero. Have students turn to the Division Symbols and Properties activity page in their Activity Book and read the directions with them.

Students should copy the problems from the Activity Book into their Math Notebook as necessary and solve them there.

Objectives

- Explain and apply the division property of 1.
- Demonstrate understanding that division by zero is undefined.
- Recognize the meaning of the three symbols for division.

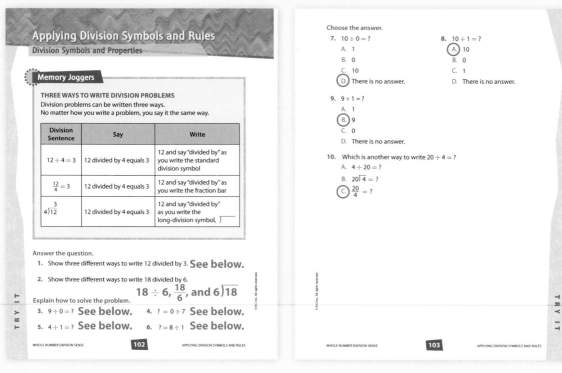

Applying Division Symbols and Rules
Division Symbols and Properties

Memory Joggers

THREE WAYS TO WRITE DIVISION PROBLEMS
Division problems can be written three ways.
No matter how you write a problem, you say it the same way.

Division Sentence	Say	Write
$12 \div 4 = 3$	12 divided by 4 equals 3	12 and say "divided by" as you write the standard division symbol
$\frac{12}{4} = 3$	12 divided by 4 equals 3	12 and say "divided by" as you write the fraction bar
$4\overline{)12}^{\,3}$	12 divided by 4 equals 3	12 and say "divided by" as you write the long-division symbol, $\overline{)}$

Answer the question.
1. Show three different ways to write 12 divided by 3. **See below.**
2. Show three different ways to write 18 divided by 6.
$$18 \div 6,\ \frac{18}{6},\ \text{and}\ 6\overline{)18}$$
Explain how to solve the problem.
3. $9 \div 0 = ?$ **See below.** 4. $? = 0 \div 7$ **See below.**
5. $4 \div 1 = ?$ **See below.** 6. $? = 8 \div 1$ **See below.**

Choose the answer.
7. $10 \div 0 = ?$
   A. 1
   B. 0
   C. 10
   (D.) There is no answer.

8. $10 \div 1 = ?$
   (A.) 10
   B. 0
   C. 1
   D. There is no answer.

9. $9 \div 1 = ?$
   A. 1
   (B.) 9
   C. 0
   D. There is no answer.

10. Which is another way to write $20 \div 4 = ?$
   A. $4 \div 20 = ?$
   B. $20\overline{)4} = ?$
   (C.) $\frac{20}{4} = ?$

Additional Answers

1. $12 \div 3$, $\frac{12}{3}$, and $3\overline{)12}$
3. There is no answer when you try to divide by zero.
4. Zero divided into 7 groups would be zero in each group, or zero divided into groups of 7 would be zero groups. Zero divided by any number is zero.
5. Four objects divided into 1 group will give 4 objects in the group. If you divide any number by 1, the answer is always the same as the given number.
6. Eight objects divided into 1 group will give 8 objects in the group. If you divide any number by 1, the answer is always the same as the given number.

CHECKPOINT

ONLINE 10 min

Students will complete an online Checkpoint. If necessary, read the directions, problems, and answer choices to students and help them with keyboard or mouse operations.

Objectives

- Explain and apply the division property of 1.
- Demonstrate understanding that division by zero is undefined.
- Recognize the meaning of the three symbols for division.

Division as Sharing

Lesson Overview

Skills Update	5 minutes	ONLINE
LEARN Division Fact Practice	10 minutes	ONLINE
LEARN Division and Equal Sharing	20 minutes	OFFLINE
TRY IT Explain Division	15 minutes	OFFLINE
CHECKPOINT	10 minutes	ONLINE

▶ Lesson Objectives

Explain division as the sharing of a quantity into equal groups.

▶ Prerequisite Skills

- Use equal sharing to do division problems.
- Use objects or sketches to solve a division problem.

▶ Content Background

Students will use models and sketches to explain division as a way to share a quantity equally.

One way to divide is to separate objects into "fair shares" or equal groups. For example, $16 \div 8 = 2$ means students place 16 objects into groups of 8 to make 2 equal groups, or they separate 16 objects into 8 equal groups with 2 objects in each group. In either case, 16 is the dividend, 8 is the divisor, and the answer, or quotient, is 2. When dividing to form equal groups, students are given the total and the number of groups, and they have to find the number in each group. For example, if they have 21 divided by 3 and they want to find out how many would be in each group, they would "deal out" the objects, one by one, into the groups until they had no objects left. Then they would count the number in each group. There are 7 in each group, so $21 \div 3 = 7$.

▶ Common Errors and Misconceptions

Students might not relate their knowledge of division (its symbols, procedures, and facts) to what they already know in order to make meaningful, everyday connections.

Materials to Gather

SUPPLIED

blocks – B (all colors)

Explain Division activity page

ONLINE

10min

LEARN Division Fact Practice

Students will play a game to practice division facts. Have students say each problem aloud. For the first few problems, ask them to explain what the problem means. For example, for the problem $21 \div 7$, students should say either "How many groups of 7 can you make with 21 objects?" or "If you shared 21 objects among 7 people, how many objects would each person get?" In either case, the correct answer is 3.

Objectives

- Explain division as the sharing of a quantity into equal groups.

- Explain division as the sharing of a quantity into equal groups.

Students know how to model division problems to explain division as repeated subtraction. Now they will learn how to model division problems to explain division as equal sharing.

With repeated subtraction, students show the number of groups they can make with a given number. With equal sharing, they imagine the total amount shared among a given number of people. For example, say students want to model the problem $21 \div 3 = ?$ With repeated subtraction, they would show this as the number of groups of 3 they can make with 21. But with equal sharing, they would show it as the total, 21, shared among 3 people. They would distribute the 21 objects into 3 equal groups. With either method, the answer is the same, 7.

Gather the blocks.

1. **Say:** Suppose we have 21 fish to separate evenly into 3 bowls.

2. Have students use 21 circles to represent the fish and draw 3 large ovals to represent the fishbowls to model the story.

3. **Ask:** How could we write the story as a division problem?

   Guide students to write the division problem three different ways. In each case, students should write and say the "21," then say "divided by" as they write the division symbol, and then write and say "3." Be sure they write "= ?" for the first two ways and that they put a question mark above the long-division symbol.

   $$21 \div 3 = ?, \frac{21}{3} = ?, \text{ and } 3\overline{)21}^{?}$$

4. Have students say the problem: "21 divided by 3 equals ?"

5. Point to the division symbol, and ask students what it means in this problem. Students should say it means separating 21 fish into 3 equal groups.

6. Have students act out the problem. Tell them to place one fish (one circle) in each fishbowl (oval) and repeat this until all the circles have been used and there is an equal number in each fishbowl.

   Ask: How many fish are in each bowl? 7

7. Have students write the quotient in each division problem they wrote. Have them read each problem aloud as "21 divided by 3 equals 7."

   $$21 \div 3 = 7; \frac{21}{3} = 7; \text{ and } 3\overline{)21}^{7}$$

8. Present the following problem: There are 45 raffle tickets to sell for the club fundraiser. There are 9 people in the club. How many tickets does each person have to sell so that everyone sells an equal amount?

9. Ask students to solve the problem. Allow them to solve this problem in the way that is easiest for them. Have them explain division as equal sharing as they do the problem. Some students may wish to use a sketch or circles, while other will just want to use a number sentence and work it out on paper.

10. Have students write the division sentence three ways and explain the meaning. Students should explain that 45 shared equally in 9 groups is 5 in each group, so each member has to sell 5 tickets.

11. Have students make up a division problem that involves equal sharing, and have them write it in their Math Notebook. Suggest a theme of interest to the students. Have them model the problem and show how to write the division three ways.

TRY IT Explain Division

Objectives

- Explain division as the sharing of a quantity into equal groups.

Students will practice explaining division as equal sharing. Gather the blocks. Have students turn to the Explain Division activity page in their Activity Book and read the directions with them.

Students should copy the problems from the Activity Book into their Math Notebook as necessary and solve them there.

Division as Sharing
Explain Division

Draw a sketch to show how to solve the problem. Give your answer.

1. Aisha wanted to put 15 muffins in a box. She could put 3 muffins in each row. How many rows would she need? **See below.**

2. Destiny wanted to put 18 baseballs in 3 bags. If she put the same number of baseballs in each bag, how many baseballs would she put in each bag? **See below.**

Use circle blocks to show how to solve the problem. Give your answer.

3. Julianne has 42 marbles to share with 6 people. She wants to give each person the same number of marbles. How many marbles will each person get? **See below.**

4. Frankie has 36 carrot sticks to share with 4 people. He wants to give each person the same number of carrot sticks. How many carrot sticks will each person get? **See below.**

WHOLE NUMBER DIVISION SENSE   104   DIVISION AS SHARING

Choose the answer.

5. Beverly wanted to solve this problem. Thirty avocado trees were planted in 5 rows. There were the same number of trees in each row. How many trees were planted in each row?

   Which shows a correct way to solve this problem?

   A. 6 trees in each row
   B. 5 trees in each row
   C. 5 trees in each row
   D. 10 trees in each row

6. Maria wanted to solve this problem. The band director wants his band marching in 3 equal columns. If there are 24 members in the band, how many will be in each column?

   Which shows a correct way to solve this problem?

   A. 3 band members in each column
   B. 4 band members in each column
   C. 8 band members in each column
   D. 6 band members in each column

WHOLE NUMBER DIVISION SENSE   105   DIVISION AS SHARING

Additional Answers

1. Students should draw 5 rows with 3 muffins in each row. Aisha would need 5 rows for the muffins.

2. Students should draw 3 bags with 6 baseballs in each bag. Destiny would put 6 baseballs in each bag.

3. Students should divide 42 circles into 6 equal groups. Each person will get 7 marbles.

4. Students should divide 36 circles into 4 equal groups. Each person will get 9 carrot sticks.

CHECKPOINT

Objectives

- Explain division as the sharing of a quantity into equal groups.

Students will complete an online Checkpoint. If necessary, read the directions, problems, and answer choices to students and help them with keyboard or mouse operations.

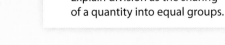

Relating Multiplication and Division

Lesson Overview

GET READY Number Relationships	5 minutes	OFFLINE
LEARN Repeated Addition and Subtraction	15 minutes	ONLINE
LEARN Related Division Facts	15 minutes	ONLINE
LEARN Related Multiplication Facts	10 minutes	ONLINE
TRY IT Inverse Operations	10 minutes	OFFLINE
CHECKPOINT	5 minutes	ONLINE

▶ Lesson Objectives

Demonstrate an understanding of the inverse relationship between multiplication and division.

▶ Prerequisite Skills

- Use models or drawings to show how addition and subtraction are inversely related.
- Use objects or sketches to solve a multiplication problem.
- Use objects or sketches to solve a division problem.

▶ Content Background

Students have an understanding of the relationship between addition and subtraction and the concept that one operation can undo the other. Students also understand that multiplication is the same as using repeated addition, and division is the same as using repeated subtraction. In this lesson, they will learn about the inverse relationship between multiplication and division. They will be able to identify related multiplication and division facts and complete fact families.

Inverse operations undo each other. For example, in the problem $3 \times 4 = 12$, the operation that would undo multiplying by 4 is dividing by 4. So the inverse of $3 \times 4 = 12$ is $12 \div 4 = 3$. When studying inverses, or opposite operations, students also use the related facts in a fact family. The facts related to $3 \times 4 = 12$ and $12 \div 4 = 3$ are $4 \times 3 = 12$ and its inverse, $12 \div 3 = 4$.

In multiplication and division, an array can be a helpful visual tool. An array is a drawing of objects in rows and columns. An array for $3 \times 4 = 12$ would have 3 rows with 4 objects in each row.

▶ Common Errors and Misconceptions

Students might view multiplication and division algorithms as rules to be followed. This leads to a misunderstanding that the numbers involved are separate digits rather than grouped amounts representing place values. The result is often an incorrect answer because of students' misunderstanding of estimation, place value, and reasonableness of results.

array for $3 \times 4 = 12$

GET READY Number Relationships

Students will demonstrate the relationship between addition and subtraction. They will use models and sketches to solve related multiplication and division problems. Gather the blocks.

- Use models or drawings to show how addition and subtraction are inversely related.
- Use objects or sketches to solve a multiplication problem.
- Use objects or sketches to solve a division problem.

1. Write $3 + 2 = 5$. Have students use circle blocks to model the problem by showing a group of 3 circles and a group of 2 circles, then putting them together to show the total, 5.

2. Ask students how they can use subtraction to check the sum of $3 + 2$.
   Students should explain that they can use either $5 - 2 = 3$ (the inverse of $3 + 2$) or the related fact, $5 - 3 = 2$, to check the sum.
   Have students use circles to model the subtraction.

3. Discuss with students how addition and subtraction are related. Be sure students understand that addition and subtraction are opposite, or inverse, operations and that addition and subtraction undo each other.

4. Tell students that they can look at multiplication and division as opposites as well. Have them draw an array to model the problem $3 \times 6 = 18$. Students should show 3 rows of 6. Explain that the array represents the problem
   $3 \times 6 = 18$.

5. Have students label their array $3 \times 6 = 18$.

6. Have students use their array to show that 18 divided by 6 is 3. They can circle the rows to show the division. Have students write $18 \div 6 = 3$ under the multiplication sentence.

7. Summarize by explaining to students that just as addition and subtraction are opposites, multiplication and division are opposites. The opposite of $3 + 2 = 5$ is $5 - 2 = 3$, and the opposite of $3 \times 6 = 18$ is $18 \div 6 = 3$.

LEARN Repeated Addition and Subtraction

Students will learn about the inverse relationship between multiplication and division. They will use their understanding of repeated addition for multiplication and repeated subtraction for division to see that multiplication and division are opposite, or inverse, operations.

- Demonstrate an understanding of the inverse relationship between multiplication and division.

LEARN Related Division Facts

Students will identify the inverse division fact for a given multiplication fact. They'll also identify the inverse multiplication fact for a given division fact. And they'll learn about fact families.

- Demonstrate an understanding of the inverse relationship between multiplication and division.

LEARN Related Multiplication Facts

Students will use online flash cards to practice identifying inverse multiplication and division facts. Have students say each fact aloud and then say the inverse fact and check their answer.

Objectives

- Demonstrate an understanding of the inverse relationship between multiplication and division.

TRY IT Inverse Operations

Students will practice identifying related multiplication and division problems. Have students turn to the Inverse Operations activity page in their Activity Book and read the directions with them.

Students should copy the problems from the Activity Book into their Math Notebook as necessary and solve them there.

Objectives

- Demonstrate an understanding of the inverse relationship between multiplication and division.

Tips Draw an array to model the given division or multiplication fact to help students identify the inverse fact.

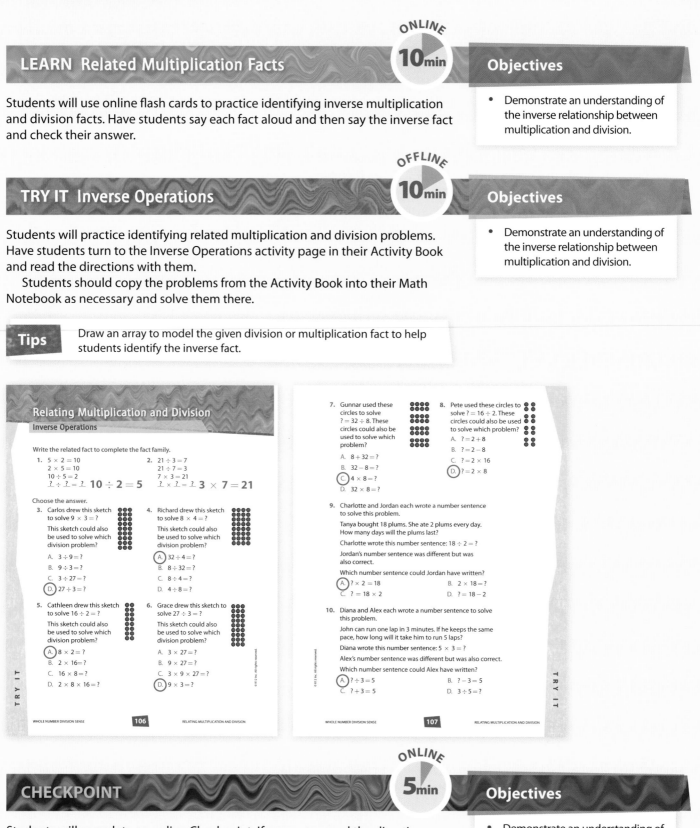

CHECKPOINT

Students will complete an online Checkpoint. If necessary, read the directions, problems, and answer choices to students and help them with keyboard or mouse operations.

Objectives

- Demonstrate an understanding of the inverse relationship between multiplication and division.

Use Inverse Relationships

Lesson Overview

GET READY Complete the Fact Family	5 minutes	OFFLINE
LEARN Check with Multiplication	20 minutes	OFFLINE
LEARN Use Multiplication to Divide	15 minutes	ONLINE
TRY IT Multiply or Divide and Check	10 minutes	OFFLINE
CHECKPOINT	10 minutes	ONLINE

▶ Lesson Objectives

Use the inverse relationship of multiplication and division to compute and check results.

▶ Prerequisite Skills

Demonstrate an understanding of the inverse relationship between multiplication and division.

▶ Content Background

Students have an understanding of the inverse relationship between multiplication and division. In this lesson, they will learn to use the inverse relationship to solve division problems and check results.

Inverse operations undo each other. For example, in the problem $3 \times 4 = 12$, the operation that would undo multiplying by 4 is dividing by 4. So the inverse of $3 \times 4 = 12$ is $12 \div 4 = 3$. When studying inverses, or opposite operations, students also use the related facts in a fact family. The facts related to $3 \times 4 = 12$ and $12 \div 4 = 3$ are $4 \times 3 = 12$ and the inverse, $12 \div 3 = 4$.

Understanding the relationship between multiplication and division allows students to use multiplication to solve division problems and helps them check their work.

Materials to Gather

SUPPLIED

Check with Multiplication activity page

Multiply or Divide and Check activity page

GET READY Complete the Fact Family

Objectives

- Demonstrate an understanding of the inverse relationship between multiplication and division.

Students will review the multiplication and division facts that make up a multiplication fact family. They will see that a multiplication fact and its related fact make up two parts of a fact family. (For example, $5 \times 8 = 40$ and $8 \times 5 = 40$ are two parts of the same fact family.) Two multiplication facts and their inverses make up the four facts in a multiplication fact family.

There are no materials to gather for this activity.

1. Write the following facts with missing parts as indicated.

   - $5 \times 8 = 40$
   - $8 \times \underline{?} = 40$ 5
   - $40 \div 8 = 5$
   - $40 \div \underline{?} = 8$ 5

2. Have students fill in the missing parts, and ask what patterns they see. **Sample answers:** The multiplication problems have the same factors in reverse order. Both multiplication problems have the answer 40. The division problems both have a dividend of 40. All problems use the same three numbers.

   Remind students that these four facts make up a multiplication fact family.

3. Point to the two multiplication facts and explain that these are related facts because they are both multiplication facts and they both use the same numbers.

4. Point to the two division facts and explain that these are related facts because they are both division facts and they both use the same numbers.

5. Point from each multiplication fact to its corresponding division fact and tell students that each division fact is the inverse of its corresponding multiplication fact. Point from the division facts back to the multiplication facts and tell students that each multiplication fact is the inverse of its corresponding division fact. Have students notice that when we say the inverse to a fact, the numbers are in reverse order.

Tips

Remind students that the value on each side of the equals symbol should be the same.

LEARN Check with Multiplication

Objectives

- Use the inverse relationship of multiplication and division to compute and check results.

Students will review multiplication fact families. They will solve division story problems and use multiplication to check division problems.

Have students turn to the Check with Multiplication activity page in their Activity Book. Students should copy the problems from the Activity Book to their Math Notebook as necessary and solve them there.

1. Read the first Worked Example with students. Remind students that the four facts in a multiplication fact family use the same three numbers. After going over the Worked Example, have students say the four facts aloud to hear the pattern of the numbers.

2. Have students complete Problems 1–3 on their own. Point out that in Problem 3, the fact given is a division fact and that students' first step should be to find the inverse multiplication fact. Then they should find the related division fact that uses the same numbers as the first one, and write that fact. Finally they should write the inverse multiplication fact for the division fact they just wrote. Check students' answers.

Tips

Write each story problem on a sheet of paper. Have students identify the numbers and key words that indicate how to solve the problem.

3. Read the second Worked Example with students.

4. Have students complete Problems 4–6 on their own. Check students' answers. If students have difficulty with these problems, help them see that division can be used to solve all three problems.

ONLINE 15 min

LEARN Use Multiplication to Divide

Students will practice their division facts using an online game.

Objectives

- Use the inverse relationship of multiplication and division to compute and check results.

Tips

Encourage students to use the inverse multiplication facts to solve the division problems.

TRY IT Multiply or Divide and Check

OFFLINE
10 min

Objectives

- Use the inverse relationship of multiplication and division to compute and check results.

Students will practice using the inverse relationship of multiplication and division to compute and check results. Have students turn to the Multiply or Divide and Check activity page in their Activity Book and read the directions with them.

Students should copy the problems from the Activity Book into their Math Notebook as necessary and solve them there.

Tips Help students identify phrases in the story problems that indicate whether a total is being divided into equal parts, or equal parts are being combined.

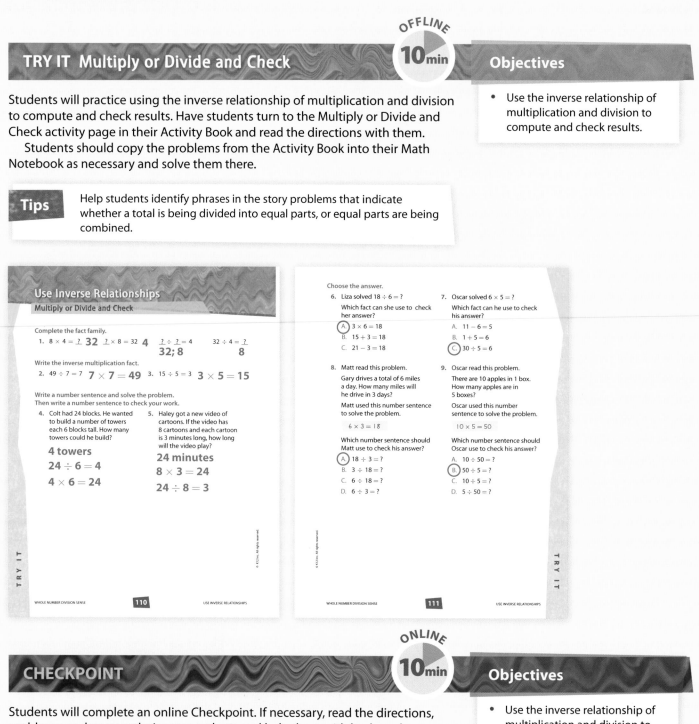

Use Inverse Relationships
Multiply or Divide and Check

Complete the fact family.

1. $8 \times 4 = ?$ **32** $? \times 8 = 32$ **4** $? \div ? = 4$ $32 \div 4 = ?$
   32; 8   **8**

Write the inverse multiplication fact.

2. $49 \div 7 = 7$ **$7 \times 7 = 49$** 3. $15 \div 5 = 3$ **$3 \times 5 = 15$**

Write a number sentence and solve the problem.
Then write a number sentence to check your work.

4. Colt had 24 blocks. He wanted to build a number of towers each 6 blocks tall. How many towers could he build?

   4 towers

   $24 \div 6 = 4$

   $4 \times 6 = 24$

5. Haley got a new video of cartoons. If the video has 8 cartoons and each cartoon is 3 minutes long, how long will the video play?

   24 minutes

   $8 \times 3 = 24$

   $24 \div 8 = 3$

Choose the answer.

6. Liza solved $18 \div 6 = ?$
   Which fact can she use to check her answer?
   - (A.) $3 \times 6 = 18$
   - B. $15 + 3 = 18$
   - C. $21 - 3 = 18$

7. Oscar solved $6 \times 5 = ?$
   Which fact can he use to check his answer?
   - A. $11 - 6 = 5$
   - B. $1 + 5 = 6$
   - (C.) $30 \div 5 = 6$

8. Matt read this problem.
   Gary drives a total of 6 miles a day. How many miles will he drive in 3 days?
   Matt used this number sentence to solve the problem.
   $$6 \times 3 = 18$$
   Which number sentence should Matt use to check his answer?
   - (A.) $18 \div 3 = ?$
   - B. $3 \div 18 = ?$
   - C. $6 \div 18 = ?$
   - D. $6 \div 3 = ?$

9. Oscar read this problem.
   There are 10 apples in 1 box. How many apples are in 5 boxes?
   Oscar used this number sentence to solve the problem.
   $$10 \times 5 = 50$$
   Which number sentence should Oscar use to check his answer?
   - A. $10 \div 50 = ?$
   - (B.) $50 \div 5 = ?$
   - C. $10 \div 5 = ?$
   - D. $5 \div 50 = ?$

TRY IT

ONLINE
10 min

CHECKPOINT

Objectives

- Use the inverse relationship of multiplication and division to compute and check results.

Students will complete an online Checkpoint. If necessary, read the directions, problems, and answer choices to students and help them with keyboard or mouse operations.

Effects of Division

▶ Lesson Objectives

Demonstrate an understanding of the effects of division on whole numbers.

▶ Prerequisite Skills

Use objects or sketches to solve a division problem.

▶ Content Background

Students will examine the effects of division on whole numbers. They will learn that when they divide a whole number by another whole number less than the dividend and greater than 1, the quotient is a lesser number than the original dividend. Also, when they divide by 1, they get the same number as the dividend.

Every division sentence has a dividend, a divisor, and a quotient. The dividend is the number being divided, the divisor is the number students are dividing by, and the quotient is the answer.

$$\underset{\text{dividend}}{30} \div \underset{\text{divisor}}{6} = \underset{\text{quotient}}{5}$$

An important note to emphasize now and remember for students' future work with division: They only get an answer that is less than the dividend when they divide by a whole number that is greater than 1 and also less than the dividend. When a whole number is divided by a number less than 1, the answer will actually be greater than the dividend. Students will realize this fact when they study division by fractions and decimals less than 1.

▶ Common Errors and Misconceptions

Students might view multiplication and division algorithms as rules to be followed. This leads to a misunderstanding that the numbers involved are separate digits rather than grouped amounts representing place values. The result is often an incorrect answer because of students' misunderstanding of estimation, place value, and reasonableness of results.

Materials to Gather

SUPPLIED

There are no supplied materials to gather for this lesson.

ALSO NEEDED

index cards – 3 (optional)

LEARN Compare the Quotient and Dividend

Objectives

- Demonstrate an understanding of the effects of division on whole numbers.

Students will use logic, patterns, and what they know about multiplication and division to understand the effects of division on whole numbers.

Gather the index cards, if using.

1. Write $3 \times 4 = 12$.

   Say: When you multiply two whole numbers greater than 1, the product is greater than either number.

   Have students give another example to show this.

2. **Ask:** What happens when you multiply a number by 1? The number stays the same.

   Have students give an example of multiplying a number by 1.

3. **Ask:** What happens when you multiply a number by 0? The product is zero.

   Have students give an example of multiplying a number by 0.

4. Tell students they will explore division and how the answer, or quotient, compares to the starting amount, or dividend.

5. Write the following division problem and corresponding term for each number.

$$\underset{\text{dividend}}{12} \quad \div \quad \underset{\text{divisor}}{3} \quad = \quad \underset{\text{quotient}}{4}$$

6. Give the definition of each term. Have students write the definitions in their Math Notebook or on index cards.

   dividend: the total number being divided

   divisor: the number you are dividing by

   quotient: the answer

7. Present the following problem:

   - The dividend is 30 and the divisor is 6. What is the quotient?

8. Have students write the fact all three ways, identify the dividend and the divisor, and show the quotient.

$$30 \div 6 = 5 \qquad \frac{30}{6} = 5 \qquad 6\overline{)30}^{\,5}$$

   30 is the dividend, 6 is the divisor, and 5 is the quotient.

9. Repeat Step 8 for each of the following problems:

   - The dividend is 21 and the divisor is 3. What is the quotient? 7 is the quotient.
   - The dividend is 15 and the divisor is 5. What is the quotient? 3 is the quotient.
   - The dividend is 20 and the divisor is 4. What is the quotient? 5 is the quotient.

10. Ask students to underline the dividend and circle the quotient in each problem. Ask them what they notice about the value of the quotient compared to the dividend. The quotient is less than the dividend in each case.

11. Ask students if they think this will always happen. Ask them if they can think of a case where it isn't true.

    Have students explore this by dividing 12 by 6, 4, 3, 2, and 1. Guide students to see that when the divisor is 1, the dividend and the quotient are equal, so this is an exception to the rule.

Tips

Have students make a poster showing a division problem with the dividend, divisor, and quotient labeled and defined.

LEARN Parts of a Division Sentence

ONLINE **10**min

Objectives

- Demonstrate an understanding of the effects of division on whole numbers.

Students will practice division vocabulary terms. They will identify the highlighted number in a division number sentence as the dividend, divisor, or quotient.

LEARN Dividend, Divisor, and Quotient

ONLINE **15**min

Objectives

- Demonstrate an understanding of the effects of division on whole numbers.

Students will observe what happens when certain parts of a division problem remain the same while other parts change. They will see the dividend stay the same and the divisor increase. And they will see the dividend increase while the divisor stays the same. Remind students that the dividend is the total amount that is being divided up and the divisor can be seen as the number of people sharing the total. So if the total stays the same and the number of people sharing increases, each person's share decreases. The mathematical way to say this is

- If the dividend stays the same and the divisor increases, the quotient decreases.

On the other hand, if the total amount increases and the number of people sharing stays the same, each person's share increases. The mathematical way to say this is

- If the dividend increases and the divisor stays the same, the quotient increases.

TRY IT Division Results

ONLINE **10**min

Objectives

- Demonstrate an understanding of the effects of division on whole numbers.

Students will complete an online Try It. If necessary, read the directions, problems, and answer choices to students and help them with keyboard or mouse operations.

CHECKPOINT

ONLINE **5**min

Objectives

- Demonstrate an understanding of the effects of division on whole numbers.

Students will complete an online Checkpoint. If necessary, read the directions, problems, and answer choices to students and help them with keyboard or mouse operations.

Unit Review

Lesson Overview

UNIT REVIEW Look Back	10 minutes	**ONLINE**
UNIT REVIEW Checkpoint Practice	50 minutes	**ONLINE**
➜ **UNIT REVIEW** Prepare for the Checkpoint		

▶ Unit Objectives

This lesson reviews the following objectives:

- Use objects or sketches to solve a division problem.
- Explain division as repeated subtraction.
- Explain the meaning of the ÷ symbol.
- Explain and apply the division property of 1.
- Demonstrate understanding that division by zero is undefined.
- Recognize the meaning of the three symbols for division.
- Explain division as the sharing of a quantity into equal groups.
- Demonstrate an understanding of the inverse relationship between multiplication and division.
- Use the inverse relationship of multiplication and division to compute and check results.
- Demonstrate an understanding of the effects of division on whole numbers.

Materials to Gather

There are no materials to gather for this lesson.

▶ Advance Preparation

In this lesson, students will have an opportunity to review previous activities in the Whole Number Division Sense unit. Look at the suggested activities in Unit Review: Prepare for the Checkpoint online and gather any needed materials.

UNIT REVIEW Look Back

ONLINE 10min

Objectives

- Review unit objectives.

Students will review key concepts from the unit to prepare for the Unit Checkpoint.

UNIT REVIEW Checkpoint Practice

ONLINE 50min

Objectives

- Review unit objectives.

Students will complete an online Checkpoint Practice to prepare for the Unit Checkpoint. If necessary, read the directions, problems, and answer choices to students. Have students answer the problems on their own. Review any missed problems with students.

➜ **UNIT REVIEW** Prepare for the Checkpoint

What you do next depends on how students performed in the previous activity, Unit Review: Checkpoint Practice. If students had difficulty with any of the problems, complete the appropriate review activity listed in the table online.

Unit Checkpoint

UNIT CHECKPOINT Online   60 minutes   ONLINE

▶ Unit Objectives

This lesson assesses the following objectives:

- Use objects or sketches to solve a division problem.
- Explain division as repeated subtraction.
- Explain the meaning of the ÷ symbol.
- Explain and apply the division property of 1.
- Demonstrate understanding that division by zero is undefined.
- Recognize the meaning of the three symbols for division.
- Explain division as the sharing of a quantity into equal groups.
- Demonstrate an understanding of the inverse relationship between multiplication and division.
- Use the inverse relationship of multiplication and division to compute and check results.
- Demonstrate an understanding of the effects of division on whole numbers.

Materials to Gather

There are no materials to gather for this lesson.

ONLINE
60min

UNIT CHECKPOINT Online

Students will complete the Unit Checkpoint online. If necessary, read the directions, problems, and answer choices to students and help them with keyboard or mouse operations.

Objectives

- Assess unit objectives.

Whole
Number Division

▶ Unit Objectives

- Use objects or sketches to solve a division story problem.
- Solve a division problem that has a multidigit dividend, a one-digit divisor, and no remainder.
- Use division to solve a story problem that involves equal groups.
- Use division to solve a story problem that involves equal measures.
- Determine unit cost.
- Create a story problem that can be represented by a division number sentence.

▶ Big Ideas

The use of letters, numbers, and mathematical symbols makes possible the translation of complex situations or long word statements into concise mathematical sentences or expressions.

▶ Unit Introduction

In this unit, students will use objects and sketches to solve division story problems. They will learn to divide a multidigit number by a one-digit number using the steps for solving division problems, known as the division algorithm. They will use their skills to solve story problems that involve equal groups and equal measures. They will also learn to solve problems that determine unit cost of items. Finally they will put their skill and imagination to work writing their own division story problems.

▶ Keywords

dividend
divisor

equal groups
equal measures

quotient
remainder

Dividing with Remainders

▶ Lesson Objectives

Use objects or sketches to solve a division story problem.

▶ Prerequisite Skills

Use objects or sketches to solve a division problem.

▶ Content Background

Students have a basic understanding of division. They will learn to use objects and sketches to solve division story problems. They will also see what happens when objects do not divide evenly and there are some objects left over.

Division is an operation involving equal sharing. The idea of separating an amount comes from the concept of division. Students can use division to find the number of equal groups when they know the number of objects and the number in each group. They can also find the number being shared when they know the total and the number of groups. Since students understand "fair sharing" from an early age, this idea is a great place to begin discussing division.

Students need to be trained to say "divided by" when stating division problems and writing division symbols. Division can be shown in the following three ways:

Division Sentence	Say	Write
$12 \div 4 = 3$	12 divided by 4 equals 3	12 and say "divided by" as you write the standard division symbol
$\frac{12}{4} = 3$	12 divided by 4 equals 3	12 and say "divided by" as you write the fraction bar
$4\overline{)12}\,{}^{3}$	12 divided by 4 equals 3	12 and say "divided by" as you draw the long-division symbol, $)$

Use this chart to help students practice reading division problems aloud. Avoid using the phrase "4 goes into 12" with students. Say "12 divided by 4," or "4 divides 12." Although students may be splitting 12 "into" 4 groups it makes no sense to say that 4 goes into 12. Students should consistently relate what they are doing to division. The expression "goes into" becomes a rote phrase that can lead to misconceptions for students.

Materials to Gather

SUPPLIED

blocks – B (all colors)

Divide with Leftover Objects activity page

Division Story Problems activity page

Students will see that dividing in everyday situations does not always work out evenly. Students will learn to interpret the leftover amount, typically called the remainder.

Determining what the remainder means in a certain situation may result in the following:

- Ignoring the remainder
- Using the remainder itself as the answer, depending on the question
- Increasing the answer by 1
- Writing the remainder as a fraction of the divisor

When writing the solution to a problem such as $23 \div 4$, students will write "5 r 3 or $5\frac{3}{4}$," indicating the 3 left over as a remainder.

Students should be encouraged to use proper division language. The total amount is the *dividend*. The number that the dividend is divided by is the *divisor*. The answer, or solution, is the *quotient*.

▶ Common Errors and Misconceptions

Students might view multiplication and division algorithms as rules to be followed. This leads to a misunderstanding that the numbers involved are separate digits rather than grouped amounts representing place values. The result is often an incorrect answer because of students' misunderstanding of estimation, place value, and reasonableness of results.

GET READY Divide Peanuts into Equal Groups

OFFLINE 5 min

Students will practice solving division problems by using objects and sketches. Gather the blocks.

1. **Say:** Suppose you had 18 peanuts and wanted to give each elephant 3 peanuts. How many elephants would get peanuts?

2. Have students use circles to show repeated subtraction to model 18 divided by 3. Have them place 18 circles in a pile and take away 3 circles at a time. Students should determine they can subtract 3 from 18 six times. So they could give peanuts to 6 elephants.

3. Explain to students that by taking 18 (the number in all) and dividing it by 3 (the number in each group) they get 6 (the number of groups).

4. Write the division number sentence $18 \div 3 = 6$.

Objectives

- Use objects or sketches to solve a division problem.

Tips

Remind students they can express division with three different symbols:
$18 \div 3 = 6$, $\frac{18}{3} = 6$, and $3\overline{)18}$.

LEARN Divide with Leftover Objects

OFFLINE 30 min

Students will solve division story problems involving remainders. They will learn how to interpret the remainder of a division problem. They will also use models and sketches to solve division story problems.

Gather the blocks. Have students turn to the Divide with Leftover Objects activity page in their Activity Book and read the directions with them. Students should copy the problems from the Activity Book into their Math Notebook as necessary and solve them there.

Objectives

- Use objects or sketches to solve a division story problem.

1. **Say:** In some division story problems, the objects can be divided into equal groups with none left over. In these situations, we say that the objects divide evenly. But in other problems, there is an amount left over. We call this amount the remainder. In this activity, you'll learn how to solve division story problems with remainders.

2. Write the word *remainder*. Tell students that the remainder is the amount left over after a whole amount is divided into equal groups.

3. Read the Worked Examples with students. Point out that in all four problems, the situation starts out the same—a baker has 23 muffins and wants to place 4 in each box. Have students use circles to show the story problem situation. Students will find that there will be 5 boxes filled with 4 muffins each and there will be 3 muffins left over. Point out that the remainder is shown with a lowercase "r" followed by the number left over.

4. Compare the questions asked in the four problems.
   - How many boxes of 4 can the baker completely fill?
   - How many muffins will be left over after he fills as many boxes of 4 as he can with the muffins?
   - How many boxes does he need if he is selling all 23 muffins?
   - How many boxes (including parts of boxes) can the baker fill?

5. Tell students that the same story problem situation can yield different answers depending on the question that's asked. In these examples, there is a remainder, and that remainder is dealt with differently depending on what the problem asks.

   Say: Compare the answers to Problems 1 and 3. In Problem 1, we ignored the 3 leftover muffins because they wouldn't have completely filled a box. But in Problem 3, those 3 muffins are important because we know that the baker plans to sell all the muffins. Since a box is needed for those muffins, we rounded to the next greatest number, 6.

6. Guide students in solving Problems 1–12. Help them make models and sketches to solve the problems. Assist them in answering the questions. Remind students that remainders can be handled different ways, depending on the question that's asked in the problem.
   - They can be dropped.
   - They can be expressed as a fraction.
   - They can be used to increase the quotient by 1.
   - They can be used as the answer.

   Remind students that the question asked in the problem determines what to do with the remainder.

7. Read Problems 13–16 with students. Then have students solve the problems on their own. When they have finished, have them explain how they solved the problems and how they interpreted and expressed the remainders.

Dividing with Remainders
Divide with Leftover Objects

> **Worked Examples**
>
> You can use objects or sketches to solve division story problems in which the objects do not divide evenly. What you do with the amount left over depends on what the story problem asks.
>
> **PROBLEM 1** A baker has 23 muffins and wants to place 4 in each box. How many boxes of 4 can the baker completely fill?
>
> **SOLUTION** $23 \div 4 = ?$
>
> Use circles to show 23 objects divided into groups of 4. You will have 5 complete groups and 3 objects left over.
>
> $23 \div 4 = 5 \text{ r } 3$
>
> Since the question asked how many boxes of 4 the baker can completely fill, the answer is 5. Ignore the 3 muffins left over.
>
> **ANSWER** The baker can completely fill 5 boxes.
>
> **PROBLEM 2** A baker has 23 muffins and wants to place 4 in each box. How many muffins will be left over after he fills as many boxes of 4 as he can with the muffins?
>
> **SOLUTION** $23 \div 4 = ?$
>
> Use circles to show 23 objects divided into groups of 4. You will have 5 complete groups and 3 objects left over. Since the question asked how many muffins will be left over, the answer is 3.
>
> $23 \div 4 = 5 \text{ r } 3$
>
> **ANSWER** 3 muffins will be left over.

LEARN

WHOLE NUMBER DIVISION   112   DIVIDING WITH REMAINDERS

PROBLEM 3 A baker has 23 muffins and wants to place 4 in each box. How many boxes does he need if he is selling all 23 muffins?

SOLUTION 23 ÷ 4 = ?

Use circles to show 23 objects divided into groups of 4. You will have 5 complete groups and 3 objects left over. Since the baker wants to sell all the muffins, he needs 5 boxes for the complete groups and a sixth box for the leftover muffins.

23 ÷ 4 = 5 r 3

ANSWER The baker needs 6 boxes.

PROBLEM 4 A baker has 23 muffins and wants to place 4 in each box. How many boxes (including parts of boxes) can the baker fill?

SOLUTION 23 ÷ 4 = ?

Use circles to show 23 objects divided into groups of 4. You will have 5 complete groups and 3 objects left over. Since the question asks how many boxes (including parts of boxes) the baker can fill, the answer is $5\frac{3}{4}$. The $\frac{3}{4}$ stands for the 3 muffins left over out of a group of 4.

23 ÷ 4 = 5 r 3

ANSWER The baker can fill $5\frac{3}{4}$ boxes.

Use circles and this story problem to solve Problems 1–3.
The circus clown wants to share 10 balloons among 3 children. How many balloons would each child get?

1. How do you write the problem? **See below.**

2. What should you do with the remainder? **See below.**

3. What is the answer? **See below.**

Use a sketch and this story problem to solve Problems 4–6.
The bakery donated 13 pies to the children's band to serve at the parties after their shows. If there are 2 shows, how many pies will be served after each show?

4. How do you write the problem? **See below.**

5. What should you do with the remainder? **See below.**

6. What is the answer? **See below.**

Use a sketch or circles and this story problem to solve Problems 7–9.
The scout leader is renting buses to take 35 campers to the campsite. Each bus holds 10 campers. How many buses should the scout leader rent to take everyone on the camping trip?

7. How do you write the problem? **See below.**

8. What should you do with the remainder? **See below.**

9. What is the answer? **See below.**

L E A R N

L E A R N

WHOLE NUMBER DIVISION **113** DIVIDING WITH REMAINDERS

WHOLE NUMBER DIVISION **114** DIVIDING WITH REMAINDERS

Additional Answers

1–3. Sample model: 3 groups of 3 circles each, with 1 additional circle alone

1. 10 ÷ 3 = 3 with 1 balloon left over

2. Drop it, because you can't divide 1 balloon among 3 children.

3. Each child would get 3 balloons.

4–6. Sample sketch: 2 groups of 6 circles, with 1 additional circle alone

4. 13 ÷ 2 = 6 with 1 pie left over

5. Show it as a fraction, $\frac{1}{2}$.

6. A pie can be split into two equal pieces, and each piece can be served at one of the parties; $6\frac{1}{2}$ pies will be served after each show.

7–9. Sample sketch and model: 4 rectangles, each large enough to hold 10 circles; 3 rectangles should have 10 circles each and the fourth should have 5 circles.

7. 35 ÷ 10 = 3 with 5 people left over

8. Increase the quotient by 1.

9. The scout leader should rent 4 buses.

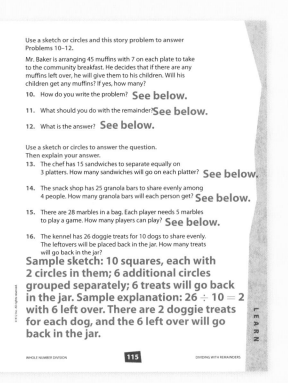

Use a sketch or circles and this story problem to answer Problems 10–12.

Mr. Baker is arranging 45 muffins with 7 on each plate to take to the community breakfast. He decides that if there are any muffins left over, he will give them to his children. Will his children get any muffins? If yes, how many?

10. How do you write the problem? **See below.**

11. What should you do with the remainder? **See below.**

12. What is the answer? **See below.**

Use a sketch or circles to answer the question. Then explain your answer.

13. The chef has 15 sandwiches to separate equally on 3 platters. How many sandwiches will go on each platter? **See below.**

14. The snack shop has 25 granola bars to share evenly among 4 people. How many granola bars will each person get? **See below.**

15. There are 28 marbles in a bag. Each player needs 5 marbles to play a game. How many players can play? **See below.**

16. The kennel has 26 doggie treats for 10 dogs to share evenly. The leftovers will be placed back in the jar. How many treats will go back in the jar?

Sample sketch: 10 squares, each with 2 circles in them; 6 additional circles grouped separately; 6 treats will go back in the jar. Sample explanation: 26 ÷ 10 = 2 with 6 left over. There are 2 doggie treats for each dog, and the 6 left over will go back in the jar.

LEARN

WHOLE NUMBER DIVISION · 115 · DIVIDING WITH REMAINDERS

Additional Answers

10–12. Sample sketch and model: 6 ovals, each with 7 circles inside it; 3 additional circles that are not in an oval

10. $45 \div 7 = 6$ plates with 3 muffins left over

11. Use the remainder to answer the question.

12. Mr. Baker's children will get 3 muffins.

13. **Sample model:** 3 groups of 5 circles each; 5 sandwiches will go on each platter. **Sample explanation:** $15 \div 3 = 5$; There is no remainder.

14. **Sample sketch:** 4 groups of 6 rectangles; Each group would also have a small rectangle that is ¼ the size of the others. Each person gets $6\frac{1}{4}$ granola bars.
    Sample explanation: $25 \div 4 = 6$ with 1 left over; The leftover bar can be cut into 4 pieces; each person gets one of the 4 pieces, or $\frac{1}{4}$ piece. So $25 \div 4 = 6\frac{1}{4}$.

15. **Sample model:** 5 groups of 5 circles each, and 3 additional circles grouped separately; 5 players can play.
    Sample explanation: $28 \div 5 = 5$ with 3 left over; Drop the remainder and say that 5 players can play.

TRY IT Division Story Problems

OFFLINE
10 min

Objectives

- Use objects or sketches to solve a division story problem.

Students will practice using objects or sketches to solve division story problems. Gather the blocks. Have students turn to the Division Story Problems activity page in their Activity Book and read the directions with them.

Students should copy the problems from the Activity Book into their Math Notebook as necessary and solve them there.

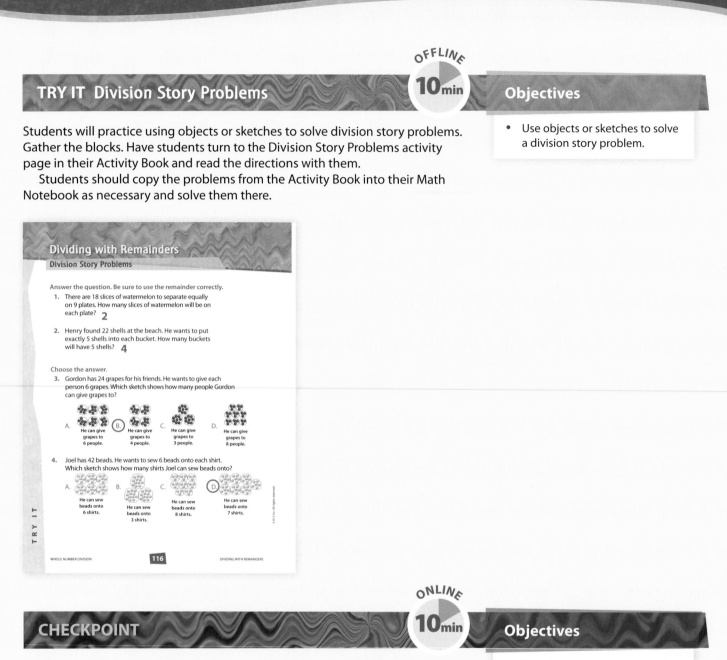

Dividing with Remainders
Division Story Problems

Answer the question. Be sure to use the remainder correctly.

1. There are 18 slices of watermelon to separate equally on 9 plates. How many slices of watermelon will be on each plate? **2**

2. Henry found 22 shells at the beach. He wants to put exactly 5 shells into each bucket. How many buckets will have 5 shells? **4**

Choose the answer.

3. Gordon has 24 grapes for his friends. He wants to give each person 6 grapes. Which sketch shows how many people Gordon can give grapes to?

A. He can give grapes to 6 people.
B. He can give grapes to 4 people.
C. He can give grapes to 3 people.
D. He can give grapes to 8 people.

4. Joel has 42 beads. He wants to sew 6 beads onto each shirt. Which sketch shows how many shirts Joel can sew beads onto?

A. He can sew beads onto 6 shirts.
B. He can sew beads onto 3 shirts.
C. He can sew beads onto 8 shirts.
D. He can sew beads onto 7 shirts.

WHOLE NUMBER DIVISION   **116**   DIVIDING WITH REMAINDERS

TRY IT

CHECKPOINT

ONLINE
10 min

Objectives

- Use objects or sketches to solve a division story problem.

Students will complete an online Checkpoint. If necessary, read the directions, problems, and answer choices to students and help them with keyboard or mouse operations.

Divide Greater Numbers

Lesson Overview

GET READY Model Division	5 minutes	OFFLINE
LEARN Model and Record Multidigit Division	25 minutes	OFFLINE
LEARN The Division Algorithm	15 minutes	ONLINE
TRY IT Record Division Practice	15 minutes	OFFLINE

▶ Lesson Objectives

Solve a division problem that has a multidigit dividend, a one-digit divisor, and no remainder.

▶ Prerequisite Skills

Use objects or sketches to solve a division problem.

▶ Content Background

Students will learn the algorithm, or step-by-step process, for dividing a multi-digit number by a single-digit number. They will start by using base-10 blocks so they can see the connection between place value and the steps in the division algorithm.

Avoid using the phrases "goes into" and "bring down." While students may be splitting 40 "into" 5 groups, it makes no sense to say that 5 goes into 40. They should consistently relate what they are doing to division. The expression "goes into" becomes a rote phrase that has no meaning for students. Say "divided by" or "divides." Also, when students do the division algorithm, keep them focused on the meaning. They shouldn't have rote phrases in their head such as "subtract and bring down." Learning for understanding will have great benefit as students progress to higher mathematics.

Students need to understand why the traditional process adults use to divide actually works. So rather than moving into an algorithm that has no meaning, they will learn long division using what they know about place value and simple division facts and recording that information as they work through the problems. Students will learn to record their steps in a way that's similar to what they would do in the traditional algorithm. They will also see that understanding the place value can lead them to a shortcut in recording the steps. Students will record division problems in two ways, as shown here.

Learning to divide in this way accomplishes two things:

1. Students will understand the meaning behind the division process that they will eventually use as a shortcut.
2. Students will develop strategies for mentally dividing some problems they would otherwise think they had to write down.

Materials to Gather

SUPPLIED

base-10 blocks
Long Division – Hundreds (printout)
Long Division – Thousands (printout)
Model and Record Multidigit Division activity page
Record Division Practice activity page

$$
\begin{array}{r}
113 \\
4\overline{)452} \\
-400 \\
\hline
52 \\
-\ 40 \\
\hline
12 \\
-\ 12 \\
\hline
0
\end{array}
\qquad
\begin{array}{r}
1\ 4\ 7 \\
5\overline{)7\ ^2 3\ ^3 5}
\end{array}
$$

▶ Common Errors and Misconceptions

- Students might view multiplication and division algorithms as rules to be followed. This leads to a misunderstanding that the numbers involved are separate digits rather than grouped amounts representing place values. The result is often an incorrect answer because of students' misunderstanding of estimation, place value, and reasonableness of results.

- Students might not relate their knowledge of division (its symbols, procedures, and facts) to what they already know in order to make meaningful, everyday connections.

▶ Advance Preparation

Print two copies of Long Division – Hundreds and one copy of Long Division – Thousands.

GET READY Model Division

OFFLINE 5 min

Objectives

- Use objects or sketches to solve a division problem.

Students will use base-10 blocks to model division of a three-digit number by a one-digit number.

Gather the base-10 blocks.

1. Review with students the different ways they have modeled division with circles and sketches. As you talk about division, use the words *dividend*, the number that is being divided; *divisor*, the number you are dividing by; and *quotient*, the answer. Explain that students can also use base-10 blocks to model division, especially division with greater numbers.

2. Write 484 ÷ 4.

   Say: Let's find the quotient. Since this problem would be too hard to draw, we can use base-10 blocks to model it.

3. Have students model the dividend by counting out 4 hundreds flats, 8 tens rods, and 4 ones blocks.

4. Guide students to divide the blocks into 4 equal groups to model dividing by 4. Suggest they divide the hundreds flats first, then the tens rods, and finally the ones cubes. Students will see that they can put 1 hundreds flat, 2 tens rods, and 1 ones cube in each of the 4 groups.

5. Have students record the problem and quotient. 484 ÷ 4 = 121

6. Summarize by telling students that they can divide greater numbers by modeling the dividend with base-10 blocks and dividing the blocks into equal groups.

LEARN Model and Record Multidigit Division

OFFLINE 25 min

Objectives

- Solve a division problem that has a multidigit dividend, a one-digit divisor, and no remainder.

Students will learn an algorithm (or steps) for long division. First they will use base-10 blocks to reinforce the concept of division, and will record results of division problems in a simple way. They will then do long division by working with blocks. Finally they will do the long-division algorithm, which is the step-by-step procedure, without blocks.

Gather the base-10 blocks and the Long Division – Hundreds printout. Have students turn to the Model and Record Multidigt Division activity page in their Activity Book and read the directions with them. Students should copy the problems from the Activity Book into their Math Notebook as necessary and solve them there.

LONG DIVISION WITH BASE-10 BLOCKS

1. Tell students they will learn to divide greater numbers. First they'll use base-10 blocks. Then they'll learn a long-division algorithm, or step-by-step process.

2. Give students 9 hundreds flats, 3 tens rods, and 6 ones cubes, and write the number the blocks make (936). Have them divide the blocks into 3 equal groups.

   Ask: What is the value of the blocks in each group? 312

3. Have students write the division number sentence and record the answer. 936 ÷ 3 = 312

4. Remind students that they've seen different ways to write division problems and that depending on the problem, some ways are more helpful than others.

5. Write the division problem using the long-division symbol. 3)936

   Say: When we do division problems with greater numbers, we write them like this because we can use this to figure out the answer. Let's redo the problem and record each step as we go.

6. Have students put the blocks back to create the original number, 936.

7. Tell students that they will now record the dividing of the 936 blocks. They won't record all the subtraction yet.

8. Instruct students to write the problem in their Math Notebook as described here. Students should write and say the number 936, then write the long-division symbol and say "divided by," and then write a 3 outside and to the left of the division symbol and say "three."

9. Ask students to underline the 9. Point out that division starts with the greatest place value. Have students separate the 9 hundreds flats into 3 groups.

   Ask: How many hundreds flats are in each group? 3

   If students say 300, tell them that is the value of the three blocks.

10. Students should record this by putting the 3 above the 9. Have them notice how the 3 is over the hundreds place. Explain that the 3 is in the hundreds place and has a value of 300.

11. Explain that with this method students can see how many blocks they've divided so far by multiplying. Point to the 3 in the hundreds place of the answer and say the number sentence: 300 × 3 = 900. This shows that all 9 hundreds flats have been divided evenly.

12. Have students underline the 3 in 936. Then have them divide the tens rods into 3 groups.

    Ask: How many tens rods are in each group? 1

    Say: We can say that 3 tens divided by 3 is 1 ten, so write a 1 above the 3 in the tens place. Now check by multiplying 10 × 3 = 30 to show that all 3 tens rods have been divided evenly.

13. Have students underline the 6 in 936. Then have them divide the ones cubes into 3 groups.

    Ask: How many ones cubes are in each group? 2

    Say: We can say that 6 ones divided by 3 is 2 ones, so write a 2 above the 6 in the ones place. Now check by multiplying 2 × 3 = 6 to show that all ones cubes have been divided evenly.

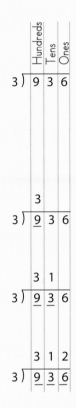

14. Work with students to complete the following problems, underlining each digit as they work through the steps, and modeling with blocks. When students feel confident, have them try a problem without the blocks. With the blocks, students will see that in some cases there are no tens or ones, but they will know the answer from looking at the groups of blocks. However, when students do problems without blocks, you may have to point out the need to record a zero when no tens or ones are divided.

$$482 \div 2\ 241 \qquad 906 \div 3\ 302 \qquad 800 \div 4\ 200$$

LONG DIVISION: THE ALGORITHM

15. Tell students that when the digits in the place value divide evenly, division is very simple. Explain that now they will explore what happens when there are leftover hundreds or tens.

16. Have students use base-10 blocks to solve 926 divided by 2. Remind them that when they divide by 2, they are making two equal groups. If they're not sure what to do with the extra hundreds flat, suggest that they break it into tens and add those tens to the tens rods piles. Check that students get the quotient 463.

17. **Say:** Let's redo the problem and record each step as we go.

Say: Write 926 divided by 2 by using the long-division symbol on the Long Division – Hundreds printout. Underline the 9 in the hundreds place. Start with the hundreds. Divide the 9 hundreds flats into two groups. There are 4 hundreds flats in each group. Write a 4 in the hundreds place of the quotient over the 9 to show that we put 4 hundreds in each group.

Hundreds	Tens	Ones	
4	6	3	
2)9	2	6	
− 8	0	0	$400 \times 2 = 800$
1	2	6	

18. **Say:** To show how many of our 926 we've divided up, we say "4 hundreds" (point to the 4 and then the hundreds label) "times 2" (point to the divisor 2) "is 8 hundreds," so 800 of the 926 blocks have been divided up. We subtract 800 from 926 and have 126 blocks left to divide.

Have students fill in this step on their printout.

19. Point out that there is 1 hundred left over. Tell students that since they can't put it in two groups, they need to break it into tens.

Ask: How many tens does the hundreds flat make? 10

Ask: How many tens do we have altogether now? 12

20. Have students underline the 12 tens.

Say: Now we have 12 tens to divide.

Ask: How many tens can we put in each group? 6

Have students write a 6 in the tens place of the quotient.

Hundreds	Tens	Ones	
4	6	3	
2)9	2	6	
− 8	0	0	$400 \times 2 = 800$
1	2	6	
− 1	2	0	$60 \times 2 = 120$
		6	

Say: Now to see how many more blocks were divided up, we say "6 tens" (point to the 6 and to the tens label) and ask how many that is. Six tens is equal to 60. Six tens or 60 times 2 is 120. We subtract the 120 and see that we have only 6 ones left to divide.

21. Have students underline the 6.

Ask: If we take the 6 ones and divide them into two groups, how many are in each group? 3

Have students record the 3 in the ones column of the quotient.

Say: To see how many more blocks we've divided up, we say "3 ones times 2 is 6 ones," and we record it in the ones column under the 6 at the bottom.

Once again we subtract to get zero, which tells us we've divided up all the blocks.

Now we can say that 926 ÷ 2 is 463.

Hundreds	Tens	Ones	
4	6	3	
2)9	2	6	
− 8	0	0	$400 \times 2 = 800$
1	2	6	
− 1	2	0	$60 \times 2 = 120$
		6	
−		6	$3 \times 2 = 6$
		0	

Point out that it divided evenly. There were no blocks left over. The 800, the 120, and the 6 add up to 926.

22. Read the first Worked Example on the Activity Book page with students. Tell them that this is a recap of the steps for the problem they've just solved.

23. Have students look at Problem 1, copy it onto their Long Division – Hundreds printout, and solve it.

24. Have students complete Problems 2 and 3 on their own, still using the printout and the blocks. At this point, students may feel that there has been a lot to write.

25. After students have done Problem 3, look at the second Worked Example, which shows a shortcut method for doing division. It works especially well with one-digit divisors. Most students will find it quite useful for problems in which the regrouping is easy. With this shortcut method, the regrouping is recorded as shown. If students imagine the blocks or imagine dividing up $100, $10, and $1 bills, this method becomes quite easy.

Divide Greater Numbers
Model and Record Multidigit Division

Worked Examples

You can use base-10 blocks to understand the standard algorithm for division.

PROBLEM $2\overline{)926}$

SOLUTION

1. Write the problem on the Long Division – Hundreds printout.

2. Start with the hundreds. Underline the 9. Divide the 9 hundreds flats evenly into 2 groups. There are 4 hundreds flats in each group. Write a 4 in the hundreds place of the quotient over the 9 to show that you put 4 hundreds in each group.

3. Think "4 hundreds times 2 is 8 hundreds, so 800 of the 926 blocks have been divided up." Subtract 800 from 926; there are 126 blocks left to divide.

$$2\overline{)926} \\ -800 \quad 400 \times 2 = 800 \\ 126$$

4. Write 800 under 926 on the printout. Also write a minus symbol. Subtract.

5. Think "There are 126 blocks left to divide. Of that, there is 1 hundred. I can't put 1 hundred into 2 groups, so I have to break it into tens." Regroup the hundreds flat into 10 tens rods. Add those to the 2 tens you already have; that makes 12 tens.

WHOLE NUMBER DIVISION   **117**   DIVIDE GREATER NUMBERS

---

6. Underline the 12 tens. Divide 12 tens by 2. The answer is 6 tens. Write a 6 in the tens place of the quotient on the printout.

$$463 \\ 2\overline{)926} \\ -800 \quad 400 \times 2 = 800 \\ 126 \\ -120 \quad 60 \times 2 = 120 \\ 6$$

7. 6 tens times 2 is 12 tens or 60 times 2 equals 120, so you've divided up 120 more of out 926. Write 120 under the 126 on your printout. Subtract.

8. There are 6 ones left to divide. Divide the ones cubes into 2 groups; there are 3 in each group. Record the 3 in the ones column of the quotient. Think "3 ones times 2 is 6 ones." Write 6 in the ones column under the 6 at the bottom. Subtract to get zero. This shows you've divided up all the blocks. You can say this problem as "926 divided by 2 equals 463."

$$463 \\ 2\overline{)926} \\ -800 \quad 400 \times 2 = 800 \\ 126 \\ -120 \quad 60 \times 2 = 120 \\ 6 \\ -6 \quad 3 \times 2 = 6 \\ 0$$

ANSWER 463
$2\overline{)926}$

WHOLE NUMBER DIVISION   **118**   DIVIDE GREATER NUMBERS

Copy these problems to the Long Division – Hundreds printout and solve.

1.
$$\begin{array}{r} 135 \\ 5\overline{)675} \\ -500 \\ \hline 175 \\ -150 \\ \hline 25 \\ -25 \\ \hline 0 \end{array}$$

$100 \times 5 = 500$
$30 \times 5 = 150$
$5 \times 5 = 25$

2. $4\overline{)908}$

$$\begin{array}{r} 227 \\ 4\overline{)908} \\ -800 \\ \hline 108 \\ -80 \\ \hline 28 \\ -28 \\ \hline 0 \end{array}$$

3. $2\overline{)726}$

$$\begin{array}{r} 363 \\ 2\overline{)726} \\ -600 \\ \hline 126 \\ -120 \\ \hline 6 \\ -6 \\ \hline 0 \end{array}$$

LEARN

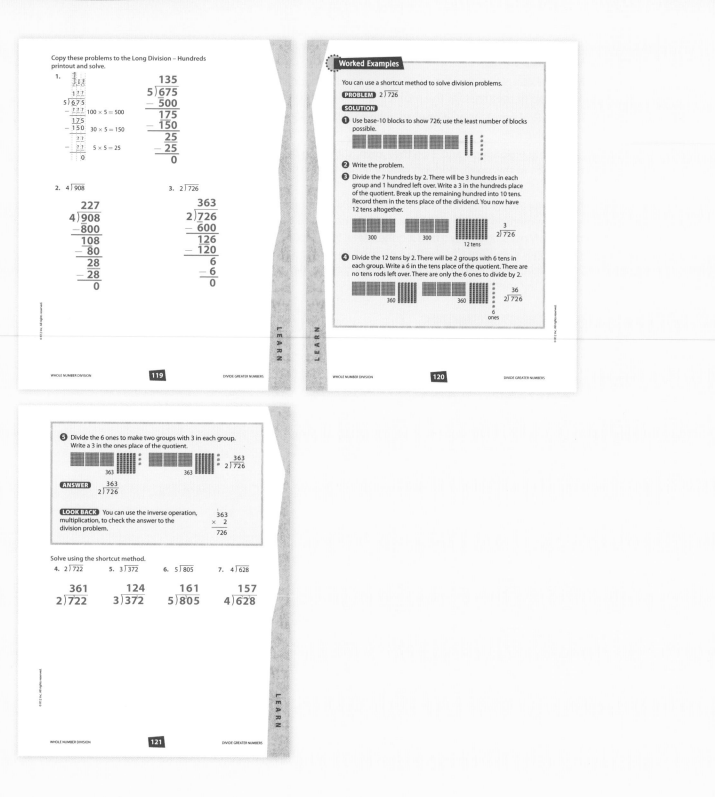

Worked Examples

You can use a shortcut method to solve division problems.

PROBLEM $2\overline{)726}$

SOLUTION

1 Use base-10 blocks to show 726; use the least number of blocks possible.

2 Write the problem.

3 Divide the 7 hundreds by 2. There will be 3 hundreds in each group and 1 hundred left over. Write a 3 in the hundreds place of the quotient. Break up the remaining hundred into 10 tens. Record them in the tens place of the dividend. You now have 12 tens altogether.

300   300   12 tens $\dfrac{3}{2\overline{)726}}$

4 Divide the 12 tens by 2. There will be 2 groups with 6 tens in each group. Write a 6 in the tens place of the quotient. There are no tens rods left over. There are only the 6 ones to divide by 2.

360   360   6 ones $\dfrac{36}{2\overline{)726}}$

LEARN

5 Divide the 6 ones to make two groups with 3 in each group. Write a 3 in the ones place of the quotient.

363   363 $\dfrac{363}{2\overline{)726}}$

ANSWER $\dfrac{363}{2\overline{)726}}$

LOOK BACK You can use the inverse operation, multiplication, to check the answer to the division problem.

$$\begin{array}{r} \overset{1}{363} \\ \times\ 2 \\ \hline 726 \end{array}$$

Solve using the shortcut method.

4. $2\overline{)722}$

$$\begin{array}{r} 361 \\ 2\overline{)722} \end{array}$$

5. $3\overline{)372}$

$$\begin{array}{r} 124 \\ 3\overline{)372} \end{array}$$

6. $5\overline{)805}$

$$\begin{array}{r} 161 \\ 5\overline{)805} \end{array}$$

7. $4\overline{)628}$

$$\begin{array}{r} 157 \\ 4\overline{)628} \end{array}$$

LEARN

LEARN The Division Algorithm

ONLINE 15 min

Students will learn the algorithm to solve division problems involving one-digit divisors and dividends up to four digits. They will see base-10 blocks modeling the division to reinforce the division algorithm. They will also see a shortcut method for long division that will enable them to do problems without writing each step.

TRY IT Record Division Practice

OFFLINE 15 min

Students will practice using the division algorithm to divide a multidigit number by a one-digit number.

When students do a multiple-choice problem, they should look at the problem and the answers choices and see if they can choose the correct answer without doing long division. For example, when students get to Problem 4, have them look at the problem and answer choices and see if they can find the answer with only mental calculations. (Since the problem is close to 500 ÷ 5, the answer will be around 100.)

Gather the Long Division – Hundreds and Long Division – Thousands printouts. Have students turn to the Record Division Practice activity page in their Activity Book and read the directions with them.

Students should copy the problems from the Activity Book into their Math Notebook as necessary and solve them there. They may use the Long Division – Hundreds and Long Division – Thousands printouts if desired.

Objectives

- Solve a division problem that has a multidigit dividend, a one-digit divisor, and no remainder.

Objectives

- Solve a division problem that has a multidigit dividend, a one-digit divisor, and no remainder.

Tips

Encourage students to use the shortcut method when the numbers are easy.

Divide Greater Numbers

Record Division Practice

Solve.
1. 7)‾854 **122**
2. 4)‾972 **243**

Choose the answer.
3. 238 ÷ 7 = ?
   A. 54   B. 48   C. 43   (D.) 34
4. 495 ÷ 5 = ?
   A. 109   (B.) 99   C. 90   D. 89

Solve.
5. 8)‾1,640 **205**
6. 3)‾1,350 **450**
7. 8)‾2,752 **344**

WHOLE NUMBER DIVISION   122   DIVIDE GREATER NUMBERS

DIVIDE GREATER NUMBERS **233**

Story Problems with Equal Groups (A)

Lesson Overview

Skills Update	5 minutes	ONLINE
LEARN Divide a Collection of Marbles	20 minutes	ONLINE
LEARN Use Long Division	25 minutes	OFFLINE
TRY IT Solve Problems with Equal Groups	10 minutes	OFFLINE

▶ Lesson Objectives

Use division to solve a story problem that involves equal groups.

▶ Prerequisite Skills

Use objects or sketches to solve a division story problem.

▶ Content Background

The *division algorithm* is a set of steps for solving division problems. Students will learn to use this algorithm to divide a multidigit number by a one-digit number. They will use their skills to solve division story problems.

Division is an operation involving equal sharing. The idea of separating an amount comes from the concept of division. Students can use division to find the number of equal groups when they know the number of objects and the number in each group. They can also find the number in each group when they know the total and the number of groups. Since students understand "fair sharing" from an early age, this idea is a great place to begin discussing division.

Students need to be trained to say "divided by" when stating division problems and writing division symbols. Division can be shown in the following three ways:

Division Sentence	Say	Write
$12 \div 4 = 3$	12 divided by 4 equals 3	12 and say "divided by" as you write the standard division symbol
$\frac{12}{4} = 3$	12 divided by 4 equals 3	12 and say "divided by" as you write the fraction bar
$4\overline{)12}^{\,3}$	12 divided by 4 equals 3	12 and say "divided by" as you draw the long-division symbol, $\overline{)}$

Avoid using the phrase "4 goes into 12" with students. Say "12 divided by 4," or "4 divides 12." Although students may be splitting 12 "into" 4 groups, it makes no sense to say that 4 goes into 12. Students should consistently relate what they are doing to division. The expression "goes into" becomes a rote phrase that can lead to misconceptions for students.

Materials to Gather

SUPPLIED

Use Long Division activity page

Solve Problems with Equal Groups activity page

Students will see that dividing in everyday situations does not always work out evenly. They will learn to interpret the leftover amount, typically called the remainder.

Determining what the remainder means in a certain situation may result in the following:

- Ignoring the remainder
- Using the remainder itself as the answer, depending on the question
- Increasing the answer by 1
- Writing the remainder as a fraction of the divisor

When writing the solution to a problem such as $23 \div 4$, students will write "5 r 3 or $5\frac{3}{4}$," indicating the 3 is left over as a remainder.

Students should be encouraged to use proper division language. The total amount is the *dividend*. The number that the dividend is divided by is the *divisor*. The answer, or solution, is the *quotient*.

▶ Common Errors and Misconceptions

Students might not relate their knowledge of division (its symbols, procedures, and facts) to what they already know in order to make meaningful, everyday connections.

LEARN Divide a Collection of Marbles

ONLINE **20**min

Objectives

- Use division to solve a story problem that involves equal groups.

Students will watch an online demonstration of how to use long division to solve a story problem. They will also see the shortcut method for long division and see how to check division with multiplication.

Tips After students watch the demonstration, have them solve the problem on their own to reinforce the procedure.

LEARN Use Long Division

OFFLINE **25**min

Objectives

- Use division to solve a story problem that involves equal groups.

Students will use long division to solve story problems that involve equal groups. They will use place value to align the digits when writing the problem. They will also see the shortcut method of doing long division.

Have students turn to the Use Long Division activity page in their Activity Book.

1. Direct students' attention to the Worked Example. Read the problem with students.

   Ask: What number sentence can be used to solve this problem? $416 \div 8 = ?$

2. Read Step 1 with students. Have them read aloud the problem shown. 416 divided by 8

3. Read Step 2 with students. Point to 416, which is the dividend.

   Say: Since we have less than 8 hundreds, we must regroup the hundreds into tens. Four hundreds equals 40 tens. We combine this with the tens that the number originally had. Forty tens plus 1 ten equals 41 tens. We underline the 4 and the 1 to help us remember that there are 41 tens.

Tips

Allow students to use grid paper to line up the digits according to place value. They can check their work with base-10 blocks if necessary.

4. Read Step 3 with students.

   Say: We divide the 41 tens by 8 and get 5 tens. We write the 5 tens in the tens place of the quotient, or the answer, above the long-division symbol.

5. Read Step 4 with students.

   Say: We multiply the 5 tens, or 50, times 8 to get 400. So far we know we can fill at least 50 boxes with 8 candles each. That will use up 400 of the candles. We write the 400 below 416 and subtract to find out how many candles are left to put into boxes; 416 minus 400 equals 16. We underline the 1 and the 6.

6. Read Step 5 with students.

   Say: There are 16 candles that still need to be put into boxes. If 8 candles fit in a box and we have 16 candles left, how many boxes do we need? 16 divided by 8 equals 2. We need 2 boxes. We write the 2 in the ones place in the quotient. Then we multiply the 2 by 8 to see how many candles filled the 2 boxes. We write the 16 below and subtract.

7. **Say:** There are no candles left over. So the quotient, 52, is our answer.

8. If students are comfortable with the long-division solution, go over the shortcut method. The shortcut method is very useful when the regrouped numbers are small and the students know the multiplication facts needed for the problem. Help students see that the process followed in the short-cut method is the same as that in long division, but in the shortcut method, some steps are done in their head and there is much less writing. (If students are unclear about the long-division solution, continue practicing long division, focusing on place value. When they're more confident, go over the shortcut method shown in Solution 2.)

9. Guide students in solving Problems 1 and 2. Refer to the steps in the Worked Example if needed.

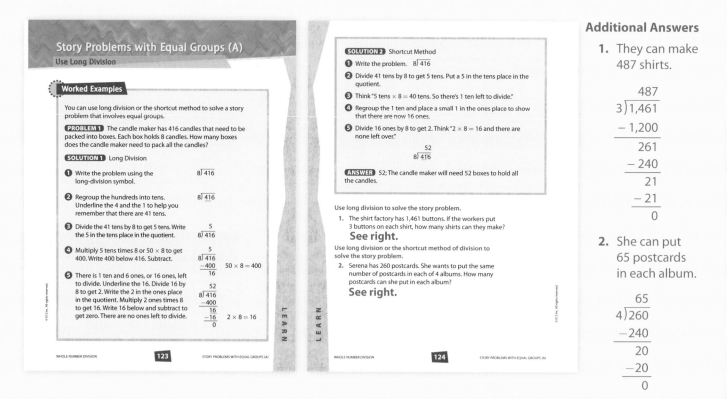

TRY IT Solve Problems with Equal Groups

Objectives

- Use division to solve a story problem that involves equal groups.

Students will practice using division to solve story problems that involve equal groups. Have students turn to the Solve Problems with Equal Groups activity page in their Activity Book and read the directions with them.

Students should copy the problems from the Activity Book into their Math Notebook as necessary and solve them there.

Story Problems with Equal Groups (A)
Solve Problems with Equal Groups

Solve.

Rosa can make 82 playlists.

1. Rosa has 738 songs in her library. She wants to make playlists with 9 songs in each. How many playlists can Rosa make?

$$\begin{array}{r} 82 \\ 9\overline{)738} \\ -720 \\ \hline 18 \\ -18 \\ \hline 0 \end{array}$$

2. The theater company made $3,647 selling tickets. If each ticket sold for $7, how many tickets were sold? **See below.**

3. The farmer put 5 pumpkins into each box. He boxed 256 pumpkins in one month. How many complete boxes did he fill? **See below.**

4. The 27 players on the baseball team are traveling to their game in cars. Each car can take 5 players. How many cars will be needed? **See below.**

5. Colleen has 33 bagels. She wants to give 5 bagels to each person, and she wants to give bagels to as many people as possible. How many bagels will she have left over? **See below.**

Challenge Question

Solve.

6. The florist has 2,005 roses. She makes bouquets with 5 roses in each. How many bouquets can she make? **See below.**

TRY IT

WHOLE NUMBER DIVISION   125   STORY PROBLEMS WITH EQUAL GROUPS (A)

Additional Answers

2. The company sold 521 tickets.

$$\begin{array}{r} 521 \\ \$7\overline{)\$3,647} \\ -3,500 \\ \hline 147 \\ -140 \\ \hline 7 \\ -7 \\ \hline 0 \end{array}$$

3. The farmer filled 51 complete boxes.

$$\begin{array}{r} 51 \text{ r } 1 \\ 5\overline{)256} \\ -250 \\ \hline 6 \\ -5 \\ \hline 1 \end{array}$$

4. 6 cars will be needed.

$$\begin{array}{r} 5 \text{ r } 2 \\ 5\overline{)27} \\ -25 \\ \hline 2 \end{array}$$

5. Colleen will have 3 bagels left over.

$$\begin{array}{r} 6 \text{ r } 3 \\ 5\overline{)33} \\ -30 \\ \hline 3 \end{array}$$

6. The florist can make 401 bouquets.

$$\begin{array}{r} 401 \\ 5\overline{)2,005} \\ -2,000 \\ \hline 5 \\ -5 \\ \hline 0 \end{array}$$

Story Problems with Equal Groups (B)

Lesson Overview

GET READY Divide Bread	10 minutes	OFFLINE
LEARN Interpret Remainders	20 minutes	ONLINE
LEARN Long Division with Remainders	20 minutes	OFFLINE
TRY IT Divide with Remainders	10 minutes	OFFLINE

▶ Lesson Objectives

Use division to solve a story problem that involves equal groups.

▶ Prerequisite Skills

Use objects or sketches to solve a division story problem.

▶ Content Background

The *division algorithm* is a set of steps for solving division problems. Students will continue to learn to use this algorithm to divide a multidigit number by a one-digit number. They will use their skills to solve division story problems.

Division is an operation involving equal sharing. The idea of separating an amount comes from the concept of division. Students can use division to find the number of equal groups when they know the number of objects and the number in each group. They can also find the number in each group when they know the total and the number of groups. Since students understand "fair sharing" from an early age, this idea is a great place to begin discussing division.

Students need to be trained to say "divided by" when stating division problems and writing division symbols. Division can be shown in the following three ways:

Division Sentence	Say	Write
$12 \div 4 = 3$	12 divided by 4 equals 3	12 and say "divided by" as you write the standard division symbol
$\frac{12}{4} = 3$	12 divided by 4 equals 3	12 and say "divided by" as you write the fraction bar
$4\overline{)12}^{\,3}$	12 divided by 4 equals 3	12 and say "divided by" as you draw the long-division symbol, $\overline{)}$

Avoid using the phrase "4 goes into 12" with students. Say "12 divided by 4," or "4 divides 12." Although students may be splitting 12 "into" 4 groups, it makes no sense to say that 4 goes into 12. Students should consistently relate what they are doing to division. The expression "goes into" becomes a rote phrase that can lead to misconceptions for students.

Students will see that dividing in everyday situations does not always work out evenly. Students will learn to interpret the leftover amount, typically called the remainder.

Materials to Gather

SUPPLIED

Long Division with Remainders activity page

Divide with Remainders activity page

Determining what the remainder means in a certain situation may result in the following:

- Ignoring the remainder
- Using the remainder itself as the answer, depending on the question
- Increasing the answer by 1
- Writing the remainder as a fraction of the divisor

When writing the solution to a problem such as 23 ÷ 4, students will write "5 r 3 or $5\frac{3}{4}$," indicating the 3 left over as a remainder.

Students should be encouraged to use proper division language. The total amount is the *dividend*. The number that the dividend is divided by is the *divisor*. The answer, or solution, is the *quotient*.

▶ Common Errors and Misconceptions

Students might not relate their knowledge of division (its symbols, procedures, and facts) to what they already know in order to make meaningful, everyday connections.

▶ Advance Preparation

Write this problem on a sheet of paper.

> Rosa wants to share all 25 loaves of bread she baked among 4 tables.
> How many loaves of bread should be placed on each table?
>
> A. 6 loaves   B. 7 loaves   C. 1 loaf   D. $6\frac{1}{4}$ loaves

GET READY Divide Bread

Students will use sketches to solve a division story problem that does not divide evenly—in other words, a problem that has a remainder. They will identify which representation of the remainder in the answer is best.

Gather the problem you wrote about Rosa.

1. Read students the problem about Rosa.

> Rosa wants to share all 25 loaves of bread she baked among 4 tables.
> How many loaves of bread should be placed on each table?
>
> A. 6 loaves   B. 7 loaves   C. 1 loaf   D. $6\frac{1}{4}$ loaves

2. Have students draw squares to represent the tables and circles within the squares to represent the loaves of bread. After students have shown 6 loaves for each table, discuss that the numbers do not divide evenly, and that there is 1 loaf left over.

3. Have students draw the leftover loaf near the tables, but not as part of any table. Discuss what they might do with that leftover loaf of bread. Guide students to see that the leftover loaf could be cut into equal parts.

4. Ask students what they would do with a leftover loaf of bread that they wanted to share among 4 friends. **Example:** I would cut it into 4 equal pieces so that each person had a piece.

Objectives

- Use objects or sketches to solve a division story problem.

Tips

Allow students to model the problem with circles if they have difficulty or when they check their answers.

5. Have students draw lines on the leftover loaf of bread to indicate how it can be shared among the 4 tables.

   Ask: What fraction of the loaf will each table get? one-fourth

6. Have students draw one-fourth of a loaf on each table.

7. Direct students' attention to the answer choices. Point out that choice A ignores the remainder and choice B increases the answer by 1. Talk about how, for this problem, the remainder does not need to be ignored because it can be used. Likewise, talk about how increasing the remainder is not appropriate because there cannot be 7 loaves of bread for each table.

8. Refer students to answer choices C and D. Point out that choice C lists the remainder as the answer and choice D shows the remainder as a fraction of the divisor.

9. Have students write $4\overline{)25}$ and 6 r 1 as the quotient.

   Say: You can write the remainder as a fraction. Write the remainder, 1, over the divisor, 4.

   Point out the location of the divisor in the division problem.

$$\begin{array}{r} 6 \text{ r } 1 \\ 4\overline{)25} \end{array}$$

10. Discuss with students how answer choice D is the best for this story problem because the leftover loaf can be divided into fractional parts.

$$\begin{array}{r} 6 \text{ r } 1 \text{ or } 6\frac{1}{4} \\ 4\overline{)25} \end{array}$$

11. Have students write and say the division fact used to solve the problem.

    $25 \div 4 = 6\frac{1}{4}$

LEARN Interpret Remainders

ONLINE 20min

Students will watch an online demonstration of how to solve a division story problem with a remainder and how to interpret the remainder to answer the question. They will also see how different questions require different interpretations of the remainder.

Objectives

- Use division to solve a story problem that involves equal groups.

LEARN Long Division with Remainders

OFFLINE 20min

Students will use long division to solve a story problem. They will use the problem to decide what to do with the remainder. Have students turn to the Long Division with Remainders activity page in their Activity Book.

1. Read the problem in the Worked Example with students. Have them write the division in their Math Notebook as you go through each step.

2. When students have done the division and have the answer 41 r 1, ask them what they should do with the 1 remaining roll. Cut the roll into 3 pieces.

3. Go over Step 6 with students. This step shows how to use the remainder and the amount they're dividing by (the divisor) to make a fraction.

4. **Say:** Suppose the baker had 124 spoons and wanted to put them in 3 baskets. How would the answer be different?

   Point out that a spoon can't be equally divided into pieces. Guide students to see that the remainder would be ignored; the baker would put 41 spoons into each basket. The answer would be different because the remainder was ignored, not expressed as a fraction.

Objectives

- Use division to solve a story problem that involves equal groups.

Tips

Allow students to sketch the remainder to help them interpret it. For example, students can sketch a roll to see that it can be divided into 3 equal pieces.

5. Have students solve Problem 1 on their own. They should copy the problem from the Activity Book to their Math Notebook and solve it there.

6. Have students refer to the question in the problem to determine how to interpret the remainder. Discuss whether they should ignore the remainder, add 1 to the quotient, show the remainder as a fraction, or use the remainder as the answer. Students should note that a fraction of a table doesn't make sense, and if they ignore the remainder, 4 people won't have a place to sit.

Help students conclude that to answer this problem, they need to add 1 to the quotient.

7. **Ask:** How many tables are needed? 23 tables

8. If there is time, challenge students to create a problem in which the remainder would be the answer. They may model their problem from a problem in this activity. **Example:** There are 180 people attending a dinner party. Each table seats 8 people. How many people will be at the last table?

Story Problems with Equal Groups (B)
Long Division with Remainders

Worked Examples

You can use division to solve a story problem that involves equal groups. You can use the problem to decide what to do with the remainder.

PROBLEM There are 124 rolls. The baker wants to put an equal number in each of 3 large baskets. How many rolls should she put in each basket?

SOLUTION Divide to solve the problem. Use the method that is easiest for you. One way is shown here.

1. Write the problem using the long-division symbol.

   $3\overline{)124}$

2. Regroup the hundreds into tens. One hundred is equal to 10 tens.
   Add the 10 tens to the 2 tens in the original dividend. You have 12 tens. Underline the 12 in the dividend.

   $3\overline{)124}$

3. Divide the 12 tens by 3 to get 4 tens. Write the 4 in the tens place in the quotient.

   $3\overline{)124}$ (with 4 in quotient)

4. Multiply 4 tens times 3 or 40 × 3 to get 120. Write 120 below 124. Subtract.

   $3\overline{)124}$
   -120 40 × 3 = 120
   4

WHOLE NUMBER DIVISION   126   STORY PROBLEMS WITH EQUAL GROUPS (B)

5. There is 4 left to divide. Divide 4 by 3 to get 1. Write the 1 in the ones place in the quotient. Multiply 1 times 3 to get 3. Write 3 below 4, and subtract. There is 1 left to divide. This is the remainder. Write the remainder in the quotient.

   41 r 1
   $3\overline{)124}$
   -120 40 × 3 = 120
   4
   -3 1 × 3 = 3
   1

6. Decide what to do with the remainder. Since 1 roll can be split into 3 pieces, you can write the remainder as a fraction. The remainder, 1, becomes the top number. The divisor (the number of people you're dividing by), 3, becomes the bottom number.

   $\frac{1}{3}$ remainder / divisor

ANSWER The baker should put $41\frac{1}{3}$ rolls in each basket.

Solve. Use the story problem to decide what to do with the remainder.

1. There are 180 people attending a dinner party. Each table seats 8 people. How many tables are needed?

Long Division

   22 r 4
   $8\overline{)180}$
   -160
   20
   -16
   4

Shortcut Method

   22 r 4
   $8\overline{)180}$

There will be 22 tables with 8 people and there are 4 extra people who need a table. So 23 tables are needed.

WHOLE NUMBER DIVISION   127   STORY PROBLEMS WITH EQUAL GROUPS (B)

STORY PROBLEMS WITH EQUAL GROUPS (B) **241**

TRY IT Divide with Remainders

Objectives

- Use division to solve a story problem that involves equal groups.

Students will practice solving division story problems and interpreting the remainders to answer the questions. Have students turn to the Divide with Remainders activity page in their Activity Book and read the directions with them.

Students should copy the problems from the Activity Book into their Math Notebook as necessary and solve them there.

Story Problems with Equal Groups (B)
Divide with Remainders

Answer the question.

1. Chef Ray is making 245 apple turnovers. He puts 9 turnovers on each pan to bake. How many pans does Chef Ray need? **28**

2. What did you do with the remainder to answer the question in Problem 1? **increased the answer by 1**

3. Karla made 325 cookies. She filled tins with 7 cookies each. She put the leftover cookies on a plate. How many tins did Karla fill? How many cookies did she put on a plate? **46; 3**

4. The cooking class made 27 pies to share among 5 families. How many pies will each family get? $5\frac{2}{5}$

Choose the answer.

5. Nicole has 20 muffins. She gives each person 4 muffins. How many people can she give muffins to?

   A. 4   (B.) 5   C. 8   D. 16

TRY IT

WHOLE NUMBER DIVISION   **128**   STORY PROBLEMS WITH EQUAL GROUPS (B)

Equal-Measure Story Problems

Lesson Overview

Skills Update	5 minutes	ONLINE
GET READY Food Bank Math	5 minutes	ONLINE
LEARN Answers with Remainders	15 minutes	ONLINE
LEARN Division at the Zoo	20 minutes	OFFLINE
TRY IT Story Problems with Division	15 minutes	ONLINE

▶ Lesson Objectives

Use division to solve a story problem that involves equal measures.

▶ Prerequisite Skills

- Solve a division problem that has a multidigit dividend, a one-digit divisor, and no remainder.
- Use division to solve a story problem that involves equal groups.

▶ Content Background

Students should be comfortable dividing with multidigit dividends. In this lesson, they will solve division story problems involving equal measures.

Avoid using phrases that lead students to think this lesson is about measurement, although they should report their answers using the appropriate unit that is given in the problem.

In an equal-measure story problem, several equal-sized measures, or parts, combine to make a total measurement amount. To solve story problems involving equal measures, students can multiply or divide. When they know the number of parts and the measure of each part, they multiply to find the total measurement. For example, each of 3 children drinks 250 milliliters of milk. How many milliliters of milk do they drink altogether? Students multiply 3 times 250 milliliters (the parts) to find the total measurement: $3 \times 250 = 750$. The children drink a total of 750 milliliters of milk.

When students know the total measurement and the measure of one part, they divide to find the number of parts. For example, Amy bought 63 inches of ribbon. She cut it into 7-inch pieces. How many pieces of ribbon did she have? To find the number of 7-inch pieces (the measure of each part), students divide 63 by 7: $63 \div 7 = 9$. Amy has 9 pieces of ribbon.

When students know the total measurement and the number of parts, they can use division to find the measure of each part. For example, John bought 63 inches of wire. He cut it into 9 equal pieces. How long was each piece? To find the length of each piece, divide 63 by 9 (the number of equal pieces): $63 \div 9 = 7$. Each piece is 7 inches long.

▶ Common Errors and Misconceptions

Students might not relate their knowledge of division (its symbols, procedures, and facts) to what they already know in order to make meaningful, everyday connections.

Materials to Gather

Division at the Zoo activity page

GET READY Food Bank Math

ONLINE 5 min

Students will use a story problem about a community food bank to review dividing objects into equal groups without a remainder.

Objectives

- Solve a division problem that has a multidigit dividend, a one-digit divisor, and no remainder.
- Use division to solve a story problem that involves equal groups.

LEARN Answers with Remainders

ONLINE 15 min

Students will practice solving division story problems involving equal measures and will see how to handle a remainder in different story problems on the basis of what the story problem is asking.

Objectives

- Use division to solve a story problem that involves equal measures.

 Tips If you wish, review how to interpret the remainder of a division problem.

LEARN Division at the Zoo

OFFLINE 20 min

Students will solve division story problems involving equal measures. They will interpret the remainder to answer the question. The questions deal with objects, time, and liquid measurement.

Objectives

- Use division to solve a story problem that involves equal measures.

Have students turn to the Division at the Zoo activity page in their Activity Book and read the directions with them. Students should copy the problems from the Activity Book into their Math Notebook as necessary and solve them there.

1. **Say:** Some story problems have an amount that is used over and over to make a total. For example, the amount could be a number of miles or a number of hours. Those amounts are equal measures. You can often solve equal-measures problems with division.

2. Read the problem in the Worked Example. Tell students they know the total amount, $130, and they know the price of one ticket, $9. They want to know how many $9 tickets Mr. Marshall can buy with $130.

3. Read the solution with students. Make sure they understand that the remainder was ignored because the question asked only about whole tickets. The remainder, $4, was not enough to buy a whole ticket.

4. Review with students the four ways to interpret a remainder.

   - Ignore it.
   - Use it as the answer.
   - Increase the answer by 1.
   - Express it as a fraction.

   Remind students that the way to handle a remainder depends on the question being asked.

5. Have students do Problems 1–15 on their own.

Equal-Measure Story Problems

Divison at the Zoo

Worked Examples

Equal-measure problems have an amount that is used over and over to make a total. It could be a total distance; a total amount of money; a total amount of time; or a total amount of water, sand, or other material.

You can use division to solve many story problems involving equal measures.

PROBLEM Mr. Marshall has $130 to spend on tickets to the zoo. Tickets cost $9 each. How many tickets can Mr. Marshall buy?

SOLUTION

1. Figure out what you're being asked to find. The question asks how many $9 tickets Mr. Marshall can buy with $130.
2. Write the number sentence you can use to solve the problem. $130 \div $9 = ?
3. Divide. $9\overline{)130}$ = 14 r 4
4. If there is a remainder, decide what to do with it. The question asks how many $9 tickets Mr. Marshall can buy; the remainder, $4, is not enough to buy a ticket, so ignore it.

ANSWER Mr. Marshall can buy 14 tickets.

Use this story problem to solve Problems 1–5.

A penguin swims 1,240 miles in a month. If the penguin swims 8 miles per hour, how many hours does it swim in a month?

1. What are you being asked to find? **See below.**
2. What division number sentence can you use to solve the problem? **See below.**
3. What is the answer to the division number sentence? **See below.**
4. Is there a remainder? If so, what should you do with it? **See below.**
5. What is the answer to the story problem? **See below.**

Use this story problem to solve Problems 6–10.

The zoo feeds the animals 3,245 pounds of food in 5 days. If the same amount of food is used each day, how many pounds of food are used in a day?

6. What are you being asked to find? **See below.**
7. What division number sentence can you use to solve the problem? **See below.**
8. What is the answer to the division number sentence? **See below.**
9. Is there a remainder? If so, what should you do with it? **See below.**
10. What is the answer to the story problem? **See below.**

Use this story problem to solve Problems 11–15.

The petting zoo had 150 ounces of grain to give to children to feed to the goats. The grain is stored in 8-ounce cups to give out to the children. How many cups are needed to store all the grain?

11. What are you being asked to find? **See right.**
12. What division number sentence can you use to solve the problem? **See right.**
13. What is the answer to the division number sentence? **See right.**
14. Is there a remainder? If so, what should you do with it? **See right.**
15. What is the answer to the story problem? **See right.**

Additional Answers

1. number of hours the penguin swims in a month
2. $1{,}240 \div 8 = ?$
3. 155 hours
4. There is no remainder.
5. A penguin swims 155 hours in a month.
6. number of pounds of food used in a day
7. $3{,}245 \div 5 = ?$
8. There is no remainder.
9. 649 pounds of food are used in a day.
11. number of cups needed to store all the grain
12. $150 \div 8 = ?$
13. 18 r 6
14. There is a remainder of 6. You should use it to increase the answer by 1, because a cup is needed for the leftover 6 ounces of grain.
15. 19 cups are needed to store all the grain.

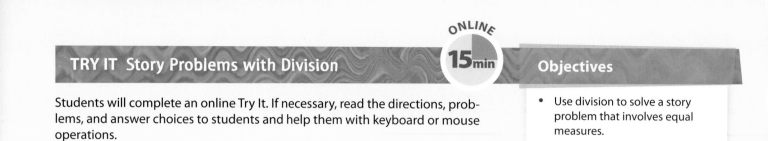

TRY IT Story Problems with Division

Objectives

- Use division to solve a story problem that involves equal measures.

Students will complete an online Try It. If necessary, read the directions, problems, and answer choices to students and help them with keyboard or mouse operations.

Divide Money Amounts

Lesson Overview

GET READY Buy and Divide	5 minutes	ONLINE
LEARN Yard Sale Math	20 minutes	OFFLINE
LEARN Library Division	15 minutes	OFFLINE
TRY IT Find the Cost	10 minutes	ONLINE
CHECKPOINT	10 minutes	ONLINE

▶ Lesson Objectives

Determine unit cost.

▶ Prerequisite Skills

- Solve a division problem that has a multidigit dividend, a one-digit divisor, and no remainder.
- Use division to solve a story problem that involves equal measures.

▶ Content Background

Students will use division to determine how much a single item costs when they are given the price of a number of those items.

Avoid using the phrase *unit cost* with students.

Finding the price of a single item when the price of a number of those items is given is an everyday experience. Be sure students understand that when they work with money and the buying of goods, any remainder of cents always increases the answer to the next highest cent.

Materials to Gather

SUPPLIED

Yard Sale Math activity page
Library Division activity page

GET READY Buy and Divide

ONLINE 5min

Students will practice solving division story problems involving equal measures.

Objectives

- Solve a division problem that has a multidigit dividend, a one-digit divisor, and no remainder.
- Use division to solve a story problem that involves equal measures.

LEARN Yard Sale Math

OFFLINE 20min

Students will learn to find the cost of an item by dividing the total cost by the total number of items.

Have students turn to the Yard Sale Math activity page in their Activity Book.

1. Read the Worked Example with students.

Objectives

- Determine unit cost.

2. Read the directions with students, and have them complete Problems 1–6. Make sure they have completed and answered Problem 1 correctly before they move on to the next problem. They should copy the problems from the Activity Book into their Math Notebook as necessary and solve them there.

3. Assist students as needed with the remaining problems. If students have difficulty, first encourage them to look at the Worked Example and follow the process shown. If they still have difficulty, help them apply the process shown in the Worked Example.

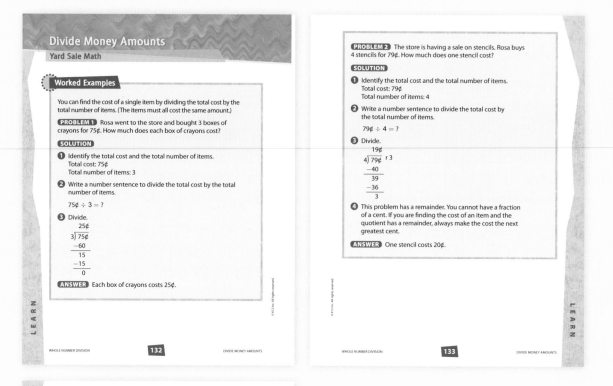

Divide Money Amounts
Yard Sale Math

Worked Examples

You can find the cost of a single item by dividing the total cost by the total number of items. (The items must all cost the same amount.)

PROBLEM 1 Rosa went to the store and bought 3 boxes of crayons for 75¢. How much does each box of crayons cost?

SOLUTION

❶ Identify the total cost and the total number of items.
Total cost: 75¢
Total number of items: 3

❷ Write a number sentence to divide the total cost by the total number of items.

$75¢ ÷ 3 = ?$

❸ Divide.

```
      25¢
  3) 75¢
    −60
     15
    −15
      0
```

ANSWER Each box of crayons costs 25¢.

PROBLEM 2 The store is having a sale on stencils. Rosa buys 4 stencils for 79¢. How much does one stencil cost?

SOLUTION

❶ Identify the total cost and the total number of items.
Total cost: 79¢
Total number of items: 4

❷ Write a number sentence to divide the total cost by the total number of items.

$79¢ ÷ 4 = ?$

❸ Divide.

```
      19¢
  4) 79¢  r 3
    −40
     39
    −36
      3
```

❹ This problem has a remainder. You cannot have a fraction of a cent. If you are finding the cost of an item and the quotient has a remainder, always make the cost the next greatest cent.

ANSWER One stencil costs 20¢.

LEARN

Find the cost of one item.

PRICES
5 DOLLS FOR $25
3 CDS FOR $18
2 DRESSES FOR $16
6 SCARVES FOR $12
3 RINGS FOR 85¢
6 COMIC BOOKS FOR 98¢

YARD SALE

1. one CD **$6**
2. one doll **$5**
3. one scarf **$2**
4. one dress **$8**
5. one comic book **17¢**
6. one ring **29¢**

LEARN Library Division

Students will use a library scenario to determine the cost of a single item, based on the total cost and total number of items.

Have students turn to the Library Division activity page in their Activity Book.

- • Determine unit cost.

1. Read the Worked Example with students.

2. Read the directions with students, and have them complete Problems 1–3. Make sure students have completed and answered Problem 1 correctly before they move on to the next problem. Students should copy the problems from the Activity Book into their Math Notebook as necessary and solve them there.

3. Assist students as needed with the remaining problems. If students have difficulty, first encourage them to look at the Worked Example and follow the process shown. If they still have difficulty, help them apply the process shown in the Worked Example.

Divide Money Amounts
Library Division

Worked Examples

You can find the cost of a single item by dividing the total cost by the total number of items. (The items must all cost the same amount.)

PROBLEM A town is building a new library. The library committee bought 6 computers for $5,400. How much did each computer cost?

SOLUTION

❶ Identify the total cost and the total number of items.
   Total cost: $5,400   Total number of items: 6

❷ Write the problem using the long-division symbol. $?
                                                       6) $ 5,400

❸ Divide. $ 900
           6) $ 5,400

ANSWER Each computer cost $900.

Solve. All items in the problem have the same price.

1. The librarians bought 6 desks for $900. What was the cost of each desk? **$150**

2. The children picked out 8 bean bag chairs for the children's section. The total cost was $520. How much did each bean bag chair cost? **$65**

3. The parents bought the libray 3 digital cameras that the children could borrow. The total cost of the cameras was $2,550. What was the cost of each camera? **$850**

WHOLE NUMBER DIVISION   **135**   DIVIDE MONEY AMOUNTS

L E A R N

TRY IT Find the Cost

Students will complete an online Try It. If necessary, read the directions, problems, and answer choices to students and help them with keyboard or mouse operations.

- • Determine unit cost.

CHECKPOINT

Students will complete an online Checkpoint. If necessary, read the directions, problems, and answer choices to students and help them with keyboard or mouse operations.

- • Use division to solve a story problem that involves equal groups.

- • Use division to solve a story problem that involves equal measures.

- • Determine unit cost.

Write Division Story Problems (A)

▶ Lesson Objectives

Create a story problem that can be represented by a division number sentence.

▶ Prerequisite Skills

- Solve a division problem that has a multidigit dividend, a one-digit divisor, and no remainder.
- Use division to solve a story problem that involves equal measures.

▶ Content Background

Students will learn how to create their own story problems that can be solved by dividing a multidigit number by a one-digit number.

Most often students solve problems others present to them. However, one of the best ways to learn is to teach something yourself. By writing problems of their own, students are placed into the role of teacher and must think about all the parts needed to write a good problem.

When students divide, they separate objects into "fair shares," or equal groups. For example, $16 \div 8 = 2$ means they separate 16 objects into 2 groups with 8 objects in each group. Sixteen is the dividend, 8 is the divisor, and the answer, 2, is the quotient.

A remainder is an amount left over after dividing. With story problems, the remainder can affect the answer. When students solve a story problem, they might ignore the remainder, use it as the answer (depending on what question was asked), use it to increase the quotient by 1, or express it as a fraction of the divisor. How they interpret the remainder depends on the problem itself. For example, students often record the remainder as a fraction when dealing with equal measures. They drop the remainder for situations that ask how many are in each group. They use the remainder for the answer when asked how many are left over. They use the remainder to increase the quotient by 1 for a question like "How many buses are needed?"

Although students will most often see fractions written with a horizontal fraction bar in math, such as $\frac{2}{3}$ or $5\frac{5}{6}$, they will occasionally see a diagonal fraction bar, such as 2/3 or 5 5/6. Students will very likely see the diagonal fraction bar in everyday situations, but be sure they understand that using the horizontal fraction bar in their work will make problems involving fractions easier to interpret and solve.

Materials to Gather

SUPPLIED

Division Story Examples activity page

As students study and work through the variety of division story problems, and also create some of their own, they may notice different types of problems that can be solved by dividing. Some of the different types are sharing an amount, making equal groups from an amount, figuring out equal measures, and finding the cost of one item when they know the cost of many. While students are not expected to learn to identify or explain these types of problems, they should be encouraged to use variety in the types of problems they write.

▶ Common Errors and Misconceptions

Students might not relate their knowledge of division (its symbols, procedures, and facts) to what they already know in order to make meaningful, everyday connections.

GET READY Solve Division Stories

ONLINE 5 min

Students will solve a division story problem that involves equal measures. They will decide how the remainder should be shown.

Objectives

- Use division to solve a story problem that involves equal measures.

LEARN Division Story Examples

OFFLINE 20 min

Students will learn how to write different types of division story problems. They will also review how to interpret remainders in story problems. Then they will write a story problem that has a remainder.

Have students turn to the Division Story Examples activity page in their Activity Book and read the directions with them. Students should copy the problems from the Activity Book into their Math Notebook as necessary and solve them there.

Objectives

- Create a story problem that can be represented by a division number sentence.

1. Read the first Worked Example with students. Then have them describe, in their own words, the process for writing a division story problem.

2. Have students complete Problems 1–3. You may have students respond verbally, by writing, or by sketching.
   - If students have difficulty thinking of ideas for problems, refer them to the steps described in the Worked Example.
   - If students have difficulty coming up with a particular type of problem, such as a problem about sharing, read them the sample answer. Students can then base their problem on the sample.

3. Read the second Worked Example with students. Then have them describe, in their own words, why the answer was increased by 1 because of the remainder.

4. Have students complete Problems 4–6.
   - If students have difficulty with the process for solving the problems, refer them to the steps described in the Worked Example.
   - If students have difficulty deciding between two or more ways to interpret the remainder, talk through each possible scenario. For example, "If we ignore the remainder in Problem 5, there will be 1 pound of grain that isn't put into any of the silos."

5. Have students complete Problems 7 and 8.

- If students have difficulty thinking of ideas for problems, refer them to the steps described in the first Worked Example.

- If students have difficulty coming up with a way to interpret the remainder, read them the sample answer. Students can then base their problem on the sample.

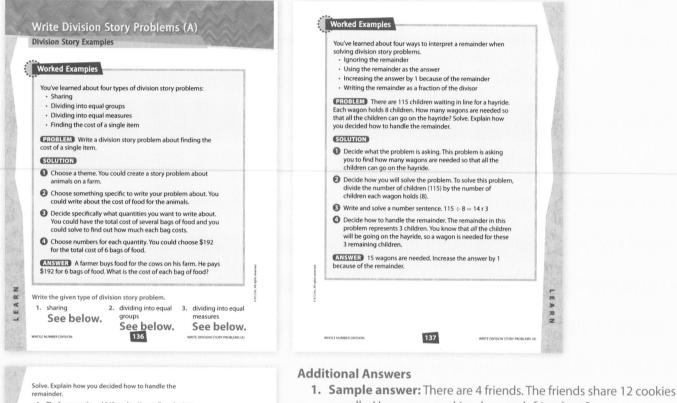

Additional Answers

1. **Sample answer:** There are 4 friends. The friends share 12 cookies equally. How many cookies does each friend get?
$12 \div 4 = 3$; Each friend gets 3 cookies.

2. **Sample answer:** There are 72 cups in 6 packages. Each package has the same number of cups. How many cups are in each package? $72 \div 6 = 12$; There are 12 cups in each package.

3. **Sample answer:** Luke swam 5 laps in the pool. He swam a total distance of 250 meters. How many meters is each lap?
$250 \div 5 = 50$; Each lap is 50 meters long.

4. $348 \div 7 = 49$ r 5; Use the remainder as the answer.
The pigs get 5 apples.

5. $1,000 \div 3 = 333$ r 1 or $333\frac{1}{3}$; Write the remainder as a fraction of the divisor. The farmer will put $333\frac{1}{3}$ pounds of grain in each silo.

6. $267 \div 5 = 53$ r 2; Ignore the remainder. The farmer can bring 53 bottles to each market.

7. **Sample answer:** A group of 4 friends is sharing 13 slices of pizza. How many slices of pizza does each friend get?
$13 \div 4 = 3$ r 1; Write the remainder as a fraction. Each friend gets $3\frac{1}{4}$ slices of pizza.

LEARN Write Your Own Division Story Problems

Objectives

- Create a story problem that can be represented by a division number sentence.

Students will write story problems for a given division sentence.

Have students turn to the Division Story Examples activity page in their Activity Book. They will use the page as a reference in this activity.

1. Have students look at the first Worked Example on the Division Story Examples activity page. Review the different ways division can be shown—sharing, dividing into equal groups, dividing into equal measures, and finding the cost of a single item.

2. Write the number sentence $306 \div 6 = ?$. Tell students that they will use that number sentence to write their own story problem that involves sharing. Encourage students to use their imagination.

   Say: The story problem can be serious. Or it can be silly, like this one:
   - The guinea pigs harvested 306 extra-large pumpkins. They want to share them equally among the 6 guinea pig houses. How many pumpkins will each house get?

3. Ask students to read their story aloud. Check that their story matches the number sentence.

4. Have students write another problem using the same number sentence. This problem should involve finding the cost of a single item. **Sample answer:** The art store sells giant canvases at a price of 6 for $306. How much does each canvas cost?

5. Discuss with students how the two stories they wrote are alike and how they are different. Answers will vary. Students should note that the same number sentence was used in both problems. They should also note that the problems were different types—one was a sharing problem and the other was a problem that required finding the cost of a single item.

6. You may wish to have students write story problems for the other types (dividing into equal groups and equal measures). Have students write at least one problem with a remainder.

TRY IT Identify Matching Story Problems

Objectives

- Create a story problem that can be represented by a division number sentence.

Students will complete an online Try It. If necessary, read the directions, problems, and answer choices to students and help them with keyboard or mouse operations.

Write Division Story Problems (B)

Lesson Overview

GET READY Division Fast Facts	5 minutes	ONLINE
LEARN Division Story Problem Book	35 minutes	OFFLINE
TRY IT Create Division Stories	10 minutes	ONLINE
CHECKPOINT	10 minutes	ONLINE

▶ Lesson Objectives

Create a story problem that can be represented by a division number sentence.

▶ Prerequisite Skills

Solve a division problem that has a multidigit dividend, a one-digit divisor, and no remainder.

▶ Content Background

Students will continue to learn how to create their own story problems that can be solved by dividing a multidigit number by a one-digit number.

Most often students solve problems others present to them. However, one of the best ways to learn is to teach something yourself. By writing problems of their own, students are placed into the role of teacher and must think about all the parts needed to write a good problem.

When students divide, they separate objects into "fair shares," or equal groups. For example, $16 \div 8 = 2$ means they separate 16 objects into 2 groups with 8 objects in each group. Sixteen is the dividend, 8 is the divisor, and the answer, 2, is the quotient.

A remainder is an amount left over after dividing. With story problems, the remainder can affect the answer. When students solve a story problem, they might ignore the remainder, use it as the answer (depending on what question was asked), use it to increase the quotient by 1, or express it as a fraction of the divisor. How they interpret the remainder depends on the problem itself. For example, students often record the remainder as a fraction when dealing with equal measures. They drop the remainder for situations that ask how many are in each group. They use the remainder for the answer when asked how many are left over. They use the remainder to increase the quotient by 1 for a question like "How many buses are needed?"

Although students will most often see fractions written with a horizontal fraction bar in math, such as $\frac{2}{3}$ or $5\frac{5}{6}$, they will occasionally see a diagonal fraction bar, such as 2/3 or 5 5/6. Students will very likely see the diagonal fraction bar in everyday experiences, but be sure they understand that using the horizontal fraction bar in their work will make problems involving fractions easier to interpret and solve.

As students study and work through the variety of division story problems, and also create some of their own, they may notice different types of problems that can be solved by dividing. Some of the different types are sharing an amount, making equal groups from an amount, figuring out equal measures, and finding the cost of one item when they know the cost of many. While students are not expected to learn to identify or explain these types of problems, they should be encouraged to use variety in the types of problems they write.

Materials to Gather

SUPPLIED

Division Story Examples activity page

ALSO NEEDED

paper, construction (2 sheets per student)

paper, wide-line handwriting (2 sheets per student)

pencils, coloring

household objects – magazines or newspapers, stapler

scissors, adult

scissors, pointed-end safety

glue stick

▶ Common Errors and Misconceptions

Students might not relate their knowledge of division (its symbols, procedures, and facts) to what they already know in order to make meaningful, everyday connections.

▶ Advance Preparation

Cut the lined paper into halves as shown.

▶ Safety

Make sure students handle the scissors carefully and be sure to store them in a safe place.

Supervise students as they work with the stapler.

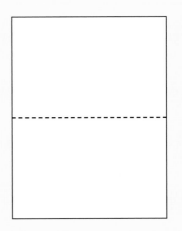

GET READY Division Fast Facts

ONLINE 5 min

Students will use the Fast Facts Learning Tool to solve basic division facts.

DIRECTIONS FOR USING THE FAST FACTS LEARNING TOOL

1. Have students enter their name and car number as well as choose the color of the car.

2. Choose the following options:
   - Choose the facts you want to practice: Division
   - Choose quotients: Click the Problems button, then choose facts to either challenge or build confidence, depending on the student.
   - Mode: Race Mode

3. As each problem appears on the screen, have students type the answer and then press Enter. After students finish, review the results on the Fast Facts Results screen. Note how many problems students answered incorrectly. Also record their time for future reference. You can click under the Lap tables on this screen to see exactly which problems students answered correctly (shown in white) and which ones they missed (shown in red).

4. Repeat the activity. Have students try to beat their time and improve their accuracy.

5. If time remains, customize the Choose quotients screen and specifically choose the facts with which students had difficulty. Then have them run another race.

Objectives

- Demonstrate automatic recall of multiplication facts.
- Use the inverse relationship of multiplication and division to compute and check results.

Tips

If you want to have students get used to the game first, go to Test Drive Mode and enter 5 for the number of problems. Then move to Race Mode.

LEARN Division Story Problem Book

OFFLINE 35 min

Students will use what they know about story problems and division to create a book of division problems. Their book will have four problems.

Gather the construction paper, stapler, glue stick, coloring pencils, magazines or newspapers, scissors, glue stick, and the four half-sheets of lined paper. Have students turn to the Division Story Problems activity page in their Activity Book. They will refer to this page in Step 6.

Objectives

- Create a story problem that can be represented by a division number sentence.

1. Review with students how to write their own division story problem. Suggest that they begin with a baking theme.

2. Write the number sentence $420 \div 4 = ?$ on a sheet of paper. Tell students that they will be using this number sentence to write a story problem.

3. Share this example with students:

   - Jackie had a bag of 420 chocolate chips. She decided to decorate 4 candy houses with the chocolate chips. If she uses the same number of chips on each house, how many chocolate chips will she use for each house?

4. Have students create their own baking problem using the number sentence $420 \div 4 = ?$. Encourage them to use their imagination.

5. Ask students to read their story problem aloud. Check that their story matches the number sentence.

6. Have students look at the Division Story Problems activity page. Review with students the four types of division problems listed on the activity page. Have students give an example of a problem that fits each type.

   - Sharing **Example:** 4 friends share 12 cookies; $12 \div 4 = 3$; Each friend gets 3 cookies.

   - Dividing into equal groups **Example:** 72 cups in 6 packages; $72 \div 6 = 12$; There are 12 cups in each package.

   - Dividing into equal measures **Example:** 5 laps total 250 meters; $250 \div 5 = 50$; Each lap is 50 meters.

   - Finding the cost of a single item **Example:** $20 for 4 books; $20 \div 4 = 5; each book costs $5.

7. Review with students the four ways of interpreting a remainder when solving a division story problem. Students may refer to this list on the Division Story Examples activity page.

   - Ignoring the remainder
   - Using the remainder as the answer
   - Increasing the answer by 1 because of the remainder
   - Writing the remainder as a fraction of the divisor

8. Distribute the four half-sheets of lined paper.

9. Explain that students will make their own division story problem book. Encourage them to choose a theme for their problems. If they are having difficulty coming up with ideas, have them look through magazines or newspapers to help them think of a theme.

10. Have students write four division story problems. Tell them to write one problem of each type (sharing, dividing into equal groups, dividing into equal measures, and finding the cost of a single item) and to write each problem on a separate piece of paper.

11. Have students assemble their division story problem book. Give students the construction paper.

    Fold the construction paper in half and staple on the fold as shown.

12. Use the front page as the cover. Have students glue each story problem onto a page in their book.

13. Suggest that students title their book and create an illustration for each problem. Students can use pictures from magazines, clip art, or their own drawings.

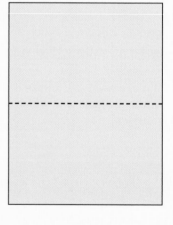

Tips

Encourage students to create problems that are challenging enough to show off their division skills. They may choose to show the worked solutions on the individual pages in their book, or they may prefer to show the answers to all problems on the book's last page.

TRY IT Create Division Stories

Students will complete an online Try It. If necessary, read the directions, problems, and answer choices to students and help them with keyboard or mouse operations.

Objectives

- Create a story problem that can be represented by a division number sentence.

CHECKPOINT

Students will complete an online Checkpoint. If necessary, read the directions, problems, and answer choices to students and help them with keyboard or mouse operations.

Objectives

- Create a story problem that can be represented by a division number sentence.

Unit Review

Lesson Overview

UNIT REVIEW Look Back	10 minutes	ONLINE
UNIT REVIEW Checkpoint Practice	50 minutes	ONLINE
▶ **UNIT REVIEW** Prepare for the Checkpoint		

▶ Unit Objectives

This lesson reviews the following objectives:

- Use objects or sketches to solve a division story problem.
- Solve a division problem that has a multidigit dividend, a one-digit divisor, and no remainder.
- Use division to solve a story problem that involves equal groups.
- Use division to solve a story problem that involves equal measures.
- Determine unit cost.
- Create a story problem that can be represented by a division number sentence.

Materials to Gather

There are no materials to gather for this lesson.

▶ Advance Preparation

In this lesson, students will have an opportunity to review previous activities in the Whole Number Division unit. Look at the suggested activities in Unit Review: Prepare for the Checkpoint online and gather any needed materials.

UNIT REVIEW Look Back

ONLINE 10min

Objectives

- Review unit objectives.

Students will review key concepts from the unit to prepare for the Unit Checkpoint.

UNIT REVIEW Checkpoint Practice

ONLINE 50min

Objectives

- Review unit objectives.

Students will complete an online Checkpoint Practice to prepare for the Unit Checkpoint. If necessary, read the directions, problems, and answer choices to students. Have students answer the problems on their own. Review any missed problems with students.

▶ UNIT REVIEW Prepare for the Checkpoint

What you do next depends on how students performed in the previous activity, Unit Review: Checkpoint Practice. If students had difficulty with any of the problems, complete the appropriate review activity listed in the table online.

Unit Checkpoint

UNIT CHECKPOINT Online	60 minutes	**ONLINE**

▶ Unit Objectives

This lesson assesses the following objectives:

- Use objects or sketches to solve a division story problem.
- Solve a division problem that has a multidigit dividend, a one-digit divisor, and no remainder.
- Use division to solve a story problem that involves equal groups.
- Use division to solve a story problem that involves equal measures.
- Determine unit cost.
- Create a story problem that can be represented by a division number sentence.

Materials to Gather

There are no materials to gather for this lesson.

UNIT CHECKPOINT Online

ONLINE
60min

Students will complete the Unit Checkpoint online. If necessary, read the directions, problems, and answer choices to students and help them with keyboard or mouse operations.

Objectives

- Assess unit objectives.

Semester Review

Lesson Overview

SEMESTER REVIEW Look Back	20 minutes	ONLINE
SEMESTER REVIEW Checkpoint Practice	40 minutes	ONLINE
▶ **SEMESTER REVIEW** Prepare for the Checkpoint		

▶ Semester Objectives

This lesson reviews the following objectives:

- Identify odd and even numbers and describe their characteristics.
- Use expanded form to represent numbers through 10,000.
- Order three or more whole numbers through 10,000.
- Round numbers through 10,000.
- Determine the sum or difference of two whole numbers.
- Recognize and solve a story problem in which two quantities are compared by the use of addition or subtraction.
- Recognize and solve a story problem in which one quantity must be changed to equal another quantity.
- Use an equation to represent a relationship between quantities.
- Use an inequality to represent a relationship between quantities.
- Select the appropriate symbol to show an operation or a relationship that makes a number sentence true.
- Determine a missing number in an equation or an inequality.
- Solve a simple story problem that involves a function.
- Demonstrate automatic recall of multiplication facts.
- Use an area model to explain multiplication.
- Explain and apply the associative property of multiplication.
- Solve a multiplication problem involving a multidigit factor and a one-digit factor.
- Use multiplication to solve a story problem that involves equal groups.
- Use multiplication to solve a story problem that involves equal measures.
- Use objects or sketches to solve a division problem.
- Demonstrate understanding that division by zero is undefined.
- Recognize the meaning of the three symbols for division.
- Demonstrate an understanding of the inverse relationship between multiplication and division.
- Use the inverse relationship of multiplication and division to compute and check results.
- Solve a division problem that has a multidigit dividend, a one-digit divisor, and no remainder.
- Use division to solve a story problem that involves equal groups.
- Use division to solve a story problem that involves equal measures.
- Determine unit cost.

Materials to Gather

There are no materials to gather for this lesson.

▶ Advance Preparation

In this lesson, students will have an opportunity to review previous activities from the semester. Look at the suggested activities in Semester Review: Prepare for the Checkpoint online and be prepared to gather any needed materials.

SEMESTER REVIEW Look Back	ONLINE 20min	Objectives

Objectives

- Review semester objectives.

As students prepare to complete the semester, they should refresh their knowledge of the math they have learned thus far. You may notice that some of the objectives in the Semester Review are not necessarily included in the Semester Checkpoint. Some of these concepts are particularly important to review in order to be successful with the upcoming topics students will encounter, and others contribute to a greater understanding of the concepts that are being assessed. Therefore, a complete review of the objectives in this lesson is recommended.

To review, first students will practice multiplication and division facts using the Fast Facts Learning Tool. Then they will play a Super Genius game, which includes problems that span the topics covered this semester. If students answer a problem incorrectly, the correct answer will display. Be sure to help students understand why the answer is correct before students move on to the next problem. If they miss several problems, have students play the game again.

SEMESTER REVIEW Checkpoint Practice	ONLINE 40min	Objectives

Objectives

- Review semester objectives.

Students will complete an online Checkpoint Practice to prepare for the Semester Checkpoint. If necessary, read the directions, problems, and answer choices to students. Have students answer the problems on their own. Review any missed problems with students.

⮞ SEMESTER REVIEW Prepare for the Checkpoint

What you do next depends on how students performed in the previous activity, Semester Review: Checkpoint Practice. If students had difficulty with any of the problems, complete the appropriate review activity listed in the Unit Review tables online.

Because there are many concepts to review, consider using the Your Choice day to continue preparing for the Semester Checkpoint.

Semester Checkpoint

SEMESTER CHECKPOINT Online	60 minutes	**ONLINE**

▶ Semester Objectives

This lesson assesses the following objectives:

- Order three or more whole numbers through 10,000.
- Round numbers through 10,000.
- Determine the sum or difference of two whole numbers.
- Recognize and solve a story problem in which one quantity must be changed to equal another quantity.
- Use an equation to represent a relationship between quantities.
- Use an inequality to represent a relationship between quantities.
- Select the appropriate symbol to show an operation or a relationship that makes a number sentence true.
- Determine a missing number in an equation or an inequality.
- Explain and apply the associative property of multiplication.
- Solve a multiplication problem involving a multidigit factor and a one-digit factor.
- Use multiplication to solve a story problem that involves equal groups.
- Use multiplication to solve a story problem that involves equal measures.
- Demonstrate understanding that division by zero is undefined.
- Recognize the meaning of the three symbols for division.
- Demonstrate an understanding of the inverse relationship between multiplication and division.
- Use the inverse relationship of multiplication and division to compute and check results.
- Solve a division problem that has a multidigit dividend, a one-digit divisor, and no remainder.
- Use division to solve a story problem that involves equal groups.
- Use division to solve a story problem that involves equal measures.
- Determine unit cost.

Materials to Gather

There are no materials to gather for this lesson.

SEMESTER CHECKPOINT Online

ONLINE **60**min

Objectives

- Assess semester objectives.

Students will complete the Semester Checkpoint online. If necessary, read the directions, problems, and answer choices to students and help them with keyboard or mouse operations.

Whole Numbers and Multiple Operations

Surf Shack

▶ Unit Objectives

- Use the order of operations to evaluate an expression.
- Solve a story problem involving two or more operations.
- Determine whether addition, subtraction, multiplication, or division is the appropriate operation to use to solve a story problem and solve the problem.

▶ Big Ideas

- The use of letters, numbers, and mathematical symbols makes possible the translation of complex situations or long word statements into concise mathematical sentences or expressions.
- The order of operations dictates the order in which operations are to be performed. The order of operations ensures that any numerical expression has exactly one correct value.

▶ Unit Introduction

Students have skills with addition, subtraction, multiplication, and division. They have solved many story problems involving each of these operations. They will now see a wide range of story problems and determine which operation is needed to solve the problem. Students will also begin to work with problems that include more than one operation, such as $2 + 10 \times 3 = ?$ A problem like that would have two possible answers if no agreement existed on which operation should be done first. For that agreement, there are the rules in mathematics called the *order of operations*. In this unit, students will use the proper order of operations to find the value of expressions with more than one operation. They will then solve story problems involving more than one operation.

▶ Keywords

associative property
commutative prwoperty
expression
order of operations

Use the Order of Operations

Lesson Overview

Skills Update	5 minutes	ONLINE
GET READY Use Properties to Add or Multiply	5 minutes	OFFLINE
LEARN Follow the Order of Operations	15 minutes	OFFLINE
LEARN Find the Value of Expressions	10 minutes	ONLINE
TRY IT Practice Finding the Value	15 minutes	OFFLINE
CHECKPOINT	10 minutes	ONLINE

▶ Lesson Objectives

Use the order of operations to evaluate an expression.

▶ Prerequisite Skills

Use the commutative and associative properties to simplify expressions.

Materials to Gather

SUPPLIED

Practice Finding the Value activity page

▶ Content Background

Students will learn about the order of operations and apply the rules to find the value of expressions that involve more than one operation.

The *order of operations* is the set of rules used to evaluate math expressions or solve number sentences. An *expression* is a set of numbers and operations; for example, $3 + 5 \times 4 - 7$. When an expression is written with an equals symbol and a place for the solution, as in $3 + 5 \times 4 - 7 = ?$, use the term *number sentence*.

The international mathematics community developed the order of operations to use when a problem has more than one operation.

When doing division problems, avoid using the phrase *goes into*. For example, in the problem $5\overline{)40}$, avoid saying "5 goes into 40." While students may be split-ting 40 "into" 5 groups, it makes no sense to say that "5 goes into 40." They should to consistently relate what they are doing to division. The phrase *goes into* becomes a rote phrase that has no meaning for students. Students should say "40 divided by 5" or "5 divides 40." Learning the words that will help with under-standing the math will benefit students as they progress to higher mathematics.

RULES FOR THE ORDER OF OPERATIONS WITH NO PARENTHESES

Multiply or divide from left to right in the order that the $\times$ or $\div$ symbols appear. Then add or subtract from left to right in the order that the $+$ or $-$ symbols appear.

The rules for the order of operations prevent confusion when performing computations with more than one operation. Without the rules, students would get different answers depending on which operations they completed first. For example, using the order of operations for $7 + 2 \times 3 = ?$ gives the correct answer 13. The rules say to multiply and divide first so $7 + 2 \times 3$ becomes $7 + 6$. However, when the order of operations is not followed, students are likely to start at the left and say $7 + 2 = 9$ and 9×3 is 27. Order of operations enables everyone in the world to agree that the answer is 13, not 27.

Students will not use parentheses in this lesson. The goal is for them to learn and understand the rules when there are no parentheses. However, at a later time, students will learn that by inserting parentheses in a computation problem, they can change or clarify the order in which operations are performed.

GET READY Use Properties to Add or Multiply

OFFLINE
5 min

Objectives

Students will review the commutative and associative properties of addition and multiplication and apply these properties to simplify expressions.

- Use the commutative and associative properties to simplify expressions.

1. Review the commutative and associative properties of addition through an example.

   - **Say:** The commutative property of addition states that changing the order of the numbers in an addition problem does not change the answer.

   - **Say:** The associative property of addition states that grouping the numbers in an addition problem in different ways does not change the answer.

   - Have students write the expression $40 + 34 + 10$ in their Math Notebook. Remind them that this is an expression because it has numbers and operation symbols. (If it had an equals symbol, it would be a number sentence rather than just an expression.)

   - Ask students how they could change the order of the numbers to make the problem easier to add. You could change the order of 34 and 10 so the expression is $40 + 10 + 34$.

   - Remind students that when they change the order of numbers in an addition problem, they are using the commutative property.

   - **Ask:** Which two numbers would you add first? $40 + 10$

   - Remind students that when they group numbers in an addition problem to make it easier to add, they are using the associative property of addition.

$$40 + 10 + 34$$
$$\vee$$
$$50 + 34 = 84$$

2. Review the commutative and associative properties of multiplication through an example.

   - **Say:** The commutative property of multiplication states that changing the order of the factors does not change the product.

   - **Say:** The associative property of multiplication states that grouping factors in different ways does not change the product.

   - Have students write the expression $5 \times 7 \times 2$ in their Math Notebook.

   - Have students change the order to make the numbers easier to multiply. They may change the order of the 7 and 2, or they may change the order of the 5 and 7. Remind them that changing the order is an example of the commutative property of multiplication.

   - Have students group 5×2 and multiply those first to get 10. Note that the 5×2 might be on the left or right depending on how students changed the order. They should then multiply by 7 to get 70. Tell students they have just used the associative property of multiplication.

two ways to multiply $5 \times 7 \times 2$

$5 \times 2 \times 7$ $7 \times 5 \times 2$
$\vee$ $\vee$
$10 \times 7 = 70$ $7 \times 10 = 70$

3. Have students use the commutative and associative properties of addition and multiplication to find the value of each expression.
   - $61 + 15 + 9$ $61 + 9 + 15 = 85$
   - $7 + 56 + 13$ $7 + 13 + 56 = 76$
   - $4 \times 9 \times 5$ $4 \times 5 \times 9 = 180$
   - $5 \times 9 \times 2$ $5 \times 2 \times 9 = 90$

LEARN Follow the Order of Operations

Students will learn the order of operations and find the value of expressions that have more than one operation.

1. Explain to students that they know the four basic operations (addition, subtraction, multiplication, and division) and that they will use these operations throughout their life to solve problems.

2. Tell students that most problems they have seen so far involved only one operation, but now they will solve problems with more than one operation.

   Say: To find the value of an expression with more than one operation, you need rules to tell you how to find the value correctly.

3. Write the expression $7 + 2 \times 3$. Ask students to find the value of the expression. Most students will calculate from left to right and get the value of 27. Others might multiply first and then add to get the value of 13. Ask students to share their answers and explain how they found the value.

4. Tell students that problems like this one might seem to have two reasonable answers. However, there is only one correct answer. Explain that there are rules so everyone knows what the one correct answer is.

   Say: These rules are called the order of operations. They tell you what order to calculate in so that everyone around the world finds the same value.

5. Go back to the original problem and explain that the value is 13.

6. Present the order of operations to students:
   - Multiply or divide from left to right in the order that the $\times$ or $\div$ symbols appear.
   - Then add or subtract from left to right in the order that the $+$ or $-$ symbols appear.

7. Have students write the rules in their Math Notebook.

8. Ask students to look back at the expression $7 + 2 \times 3$ and explain how using the order of operations results in the correct answer, 13. First you multiply 2×3 and get a product of 6. Then you add $7 + 6$ and get a sum of 13.

9. Write the expression $20 - 5 \times 2$. Ask students to use the order of operations rules to find the correct answer. 10

   If students don't get 10 for the answer, show how the correct answer is found by multiplying first and then subtracting: $5 \times 2 = 10$ and $20 - 10 = 10$.

10. Write the expression $60 - 10 \div 2 \times 3$. Have students record each step as they find the value.

Objectives
- Use the order of operations to evaluate an expression.

Tips

Emphasize working from left to right when applying the rules. Remind students to refer to the order of operations in their Math Notebook, if needed.

Ask: Will you multiply or divide first? How do you know? Divide. The rules say to multiply or divide from left to right in the order the symbols appear, and in this problem division appears first.

Ask: What is 10 divided by 2? 5

Say: Now multiply 5 times 3 and then subtract.

Ask: What is the value of the expression? $60 - 15 = 45$

11. Have students practice using the order of operations to find the value of the following expressions:

   - $72 \div 8 - 5$ $9 - 5 = 4$
   - $9 + 6 \div 3$ $9 + 2 = 11$
   - $8 + 6 \times 5 - 3$ $8 + 30 - 3 = 35$
   - $20 + 12 \div 4 - 2 \times 5$ $20 + 3 - 10 = 13$

LEARN Find the Value of Expressions

ONLINE 10 min

Students will use the order of operations to find the value of expressions. Remind students that when doing problems with multiple operations, they should

   - Multiply or divide from left to right in the order the $\times$ or $\div$ symbols appear.
   - Then add or subtract from left to right in the order the $+$ or $-$ symbols appear.

Objectives

   - Use the order of operations to evaluate an expression.

Tips

Have students say each step in finding the value of each expression.

TRY IT Practice Finding the Value

OFFLINE 15 min

Students will practice using the order of operations to find the value of expressions. Have students turn to the Practice Finding the Value activity page in their Activity Book and read the directions with them.

Students should copy the problems from the Activity Book into their Math Notebook as necessary and solve them there.

Objectives

   - Use the order of operations to evaluate an expression.

Additional Answers

16. Answers will vary. The expression should include all four operations (addition, subtraction, multiplication, and division) and have a value of 24.

    Sample answer: $3 \times 4 + 12 \div 2 + 8 − 2$. Students may also come up with clever answers that use ones or zeros such as $24 \div 24 \times 1 − 1 + 24$ or $1 \div 1 \times 0 − 0 + 24$.

ONLINE

10 min

CHECKPOINT

Students will complete an online Checkpoint. If necessary, read the directions, questions, and answer choices to students and help them with keyboard or mouse operations.

Objectives

- Use the order of operations to evaluate an expression.

Choose the Correct Operation (A)

Lesson Overview

GET READY Create Silly Story Problems	5 minutes	OFFLINE
LEARN Add or Subtract to Solve	15 minutes	OFFLINE
LEARN Multiply or Divide to Solve	15 minutes	OFFLINE
LEARN Identify the Operation and Solve	15 minutes	ONLINE
TRY IT Choose the Operation and Solve	10 minutes	ONLINE

▶ Lesson Objectives

Determine whether addition, subtraction, multiplication, or division is the appropriate operation to use to solve a story problem and solve the problem.

▶ Prerequisite Skills

- Write and solve addition or subtraction number sentences to represent problem-solving situations with sums and minuends up through 1,000.
- Create a story problem that can be represented by a multiplication number sentence.
- Create a story problem that can be represented by a division number sentence.

▶ Content Background

Students will learn to identify which operation—addition, subtraction, multiplication, or division—is appropriate to use to solve a story problem. Then they will solve the problem. They should be able to explain why they know a given operation is the correct one. When students do addition problems, they are combining amounts; for subtraction they are finding the difference between two numbers; with multiplication they are finding the total when there are several equal amounts; and with division they have a total amount that is being divided into equal groups.

Problem solving is a part of daily life. To become good problem solvers, students need to recognize when a new problem is similar to a problem they have already solved. Instead of treating every problem they encounter as new, students can build on their previous experiences with problems and develop strategies to solve similar problems. Knowing they have successfully completed similar problems will help students become confident problem solvers.

Students have solved a variety of problems using the four basic operations: addition, subtraction, multiplication, and division. When they see a new problem, they need to first decide which operation should be used to solve it. Then they can write a number sentence to solve the problem.

Materials to Gather

SUPPLIED

Add or Subtract to Solve activity page

Multiply or Divide to Solve activity page

▶ Common Errors and Misconceptions

- Students might have difficulty solving nonstandard problems, problems requiring multiple steps, or problems with extra information. Avoid introducing students to techniques that work for one-step problems but do not work for multistep problems, such as associating key words with particular operations.

- Students might quickly read through a problem and immediately begin to compute with the numbers, often choosing the wrong operation because they did not take time to read through and understand the context of the problem. Students need to learn to use "slow-down" mechanisms that can help them concentrate on thoroughly understanding a problem before they solve it.

GET READY Create Silly Story Problems

OFFLINE
5 min

Students will create humorous multiplication and division story problems. They will not solve the problems, but they will explain how they know which operation to use to solve them.

There are no materials to gather for this activity.

1. **Say:** You know how to solve many kinds of story problems and you have written your own story problems. You are going to make up silly story problems and tell which operation, multiplication or division, to use to solve the problems.

2. Discuss with students how multiplication and division story problems are different. Multiplication problems often describe combining equal groups to find a total while division problems separate a total into equal groups.

3. Write the numbers 3, 5, 300, and 500. Explain to students that they will use these numbers to make up a story problem that can be solved using multiplication, and then make up a problem that can be solved using division.

4. Tell students that their problems should be about banana slugs, elves, or another subject they find interesting or humorous. Share the following examples with students:

   - 3 elves each had 500 banana slugs for lunch. How many banana slugs came to lunch in all?

   - 300 banana slugs are spread out evenly at 5 tables. How many banana slugs are seated at each table?

5. Explain to students that they do not need to solve their story problem or write a number sentence. Have them simply say their story problem and explain how they know which operation to use to solve it.

6. If time permits, have students make up an addition or a subtraction problem.

Objectives

- Write and solve addition or subtraction number sentences to represent problem-solving situations with sums and minuends up through 1,000.

- Create a story problem that can be represented by a multiplication number sentence.

- Create a story problem that can be represented by a division number sentence.

Tips

If you wish, change the numbers and use this type of activity during car rides or around the dinner table.

LEARN Add or Subtract to Solve

OFFLINE **15**min

Objectives

- Determine whether addition, subtraction, multiplication, or division is the appropriate operation to use to solve a story problem and solve the problem.

Students will identify the correct operation and number sentence that can be used to solve an addition or subtraction story problem. They will write the number sentence and solve the problem. Have students turn to the Add or Subtract to Solve activity page in their Activity Book and read the directions with them.

Students should copy the problems from the Activity Book into their Math Notebook as necessary and solve them there.

1. To start, ask students how they know whether to add or subtract when they do story problems. **Example:** You add when you combine groups and subtract when you take some away or want to find out how much more one group has than the other.

2. Read each of the following situations to students. Ask them whether they would add or subtract to solve the problem. Have them explain how they know which operation to use. Have students focus on the operation for these four problems rather than solving them.

   - Kelly kayaked 14 miles. Brian kayaked 11 miles. How many more miles did Kelly kayak than Brian? Subtract to find the difference.

   - There are 453 campers are eating in the dining hall. 278 campers are eating hamburgers. The rest are eating hot dogs. How many campers are eating hot dogs? Subtract the number of people eating hamburgers from the total to find out how many are eating hot dogs.

   - There are 143 campers who want to kayak in the lake. Everyone who kayaks needs a paddle. There are 121 paddles. How many more paddles are needed so that everyone can kayak? Subtract to find out how many more are needed.

   - Kelly has 21 pieces of gum. She gives 14 pieces away. How many pieces does Kelly have left? Subtract the number given away from the total number of pieces (separation from a group).

3. Read the Worked Example on the activity page with students. Have them answer the questions in the Solution.

   - What are you asked to find in the story problem? the number of adults who visited the park Thursday

   - Would a picture or model help you understand the problem? **Example:** Yes, you could draw a long bar to show the total. Underneath, you could draw shorter bars to show the number of children and the number of adults, which you don't know yet.

1,984 people	
1,237 children	? adults

   - Which operation will you use? subtraction

   - How do you know that you should use that operation? because you have to find the difference between the number of adults and the number of children

   - What number sentence will you use to solve the story problem? $1,984 - 1,237 = ?$

4. Have students read Problem 1. Guide students to answer each question from the Worked Example as it relates to Problem 1.

- What am you asked to find in the story problem? the number of people at the park after it started raining
- Would a picture or model help you understand the problem? **Example:** No, you don't need a picture or model. You will use just the numbers.
- Which operation will you use? subtraction
- How do you know that you should use that operation? **Example:** In the problem, you take some away from a group; you know you have to subtract to find the remaining amount.
- What number sentence will you use to solve the story problem? 2,756 − 1,284 = ?

5. Have students write the number sentence and subtract to answer the question.

6. Have students solve Problems 2–5 on their own. They should identify the operation, the number sentence, and the solution for each problem in their Math Notebook.

Choose the Correct Operation (A)
Add or Subtract to Solve

Worked Examples

Asking yourself problem-solving questions can help you work through addition and subtraction story problems.

PROBLEM A total of 1,984 people visited the park on Thursday. There were 1,237 children and the rest were adults. How many adults visited the park on Thursday? Tell which operation to use to solve the problem. Then solve.

SOLUTION Ask yourself the following questions:
- What are you asked to find in the story problem?
- Would a picture or model help you understand the problem?
- Which operation will you use?
- How do you know that you should use that operation?
- What number sentence will you use to solve the story problem?

Find the difference between the total and one part. Draw a chart to help you understand the problem.

1,984 people	
1,237 children	? adults

Subtract to find the answer. 1,984 − 1,237 = 747

ANSWER There were 747 adults who visited the park on Thursday.

Tell which operation to use to solve the problem. Then solve.

1. On Friday, 2,756 people were at the park. When it started to rain, 1,284 people left.

   How many people were still at the park?
   subtraction; 2,756 − 1,284 = 1,472

2. On Saturday, 3,245 people visited the amusement park. On Sunday, 2,876 people visited the park.

   How many people visited the park over the weekend?
   addition; 3,245 + 2,876 = 6,121

3. At the popcorn stand, 765 bags of buttered popcorn and 592 bags of caramel popcorn were sold.

   How many bags of popcorn were sold in all?
   addition; 765 + 592 = 1,357

4. There were 852 people who rode the Ferris wheel and 975 who rode the carousel.

   How many more people rode the carousel than the Ferris wheel? **subtraction; 975 − 852 = 123**

5. There were 173 tickets sold for the bumper cars in the morning and 58 tickets sold in the afternoon.

   How many tickets in all were sold for the bumper cars?
   addition; 173 + 58 = 231

OFFLINE
15 min

LEARN Multiply or Divide to Solve

Objectives

- Determine whether addition, subtraction, multiplication, or division is the appropriate operation to use to solve a story problem and solve the problem.

Students will identify the correct operation and number sentence to use to solve a multiplication or division story problem. They will write the number sentence and solve the problem.

1. Ask students to share an example of a story problem that is solved using multiplication. **Example:** I had 3 fish tanks. Each tank had 9 fish in it. I bought a bigger tank so that I could put all the fish together. How many fish are in the bigger tank?

2. Share the following division situations with students. Ask students to explain why they can use division to solve each problem. (Students do not have to solve the problem or to identify which problems involve separating and which involve sharing.) Answers should include that division involves separating objects into equal groups or sharing a group equally.

- Kelly is packing lunches. She has 32 candies. She puts 4 candies in each lunch. How many lunches does Kelly pack?
- Kelly and Brian share 24 baseball cards equally. How many cards does each person get?
- Brian bakes 18 brownies to take to play practice. Each person eats 2 brownies until all the brownies are eaten. How many people eat brownies?

3. Have students turn to the Multiply or Divide to Solve activity page in their Activity Book. Read the Worked Example with students. Have them answer the questions in the Solution.

- What are you asked to find in the story problem? the total number of squares in the quilt
- Would a picture or model help you understand the problem? **Example:** Yes, you could make a sketch of 9 rows with 12 squares in each row
- Which operation will you use? multiplication
- How do you know that you should use that operation? because there are 9 equal groups of 12
- What number sentence will you use to solve the story problem? $9 \times 12 = ?$

4. Have students read Problem 1. Guide students to answer each question from the Worked Example as it relates to Problem 1.

- What are you asked to find in the story problem? how many days it will take to sell all the paintbrushes
- Would a picture or model help you understand the problem? **Example:** No, you don't need a picture or model; you can just use the numbers.
- Which operation will you use? division
- How do you know that you should use that operation? **Example:** You know the total number of objects and the number in each group; you know that you can use division to find the total number of equal groups.
- What number sentence will you use to solve the story problem? $258 \div 6 = ?$

5. Have students write the number sentence and divide to answer the question.

6. Have students solve Problems 2–5 on their own. They should identify the operation, the number sentence, and the solution in their Math Notebook.

7. Have students look at Problems 2 and 4 for similarities in the language. Guide them to see that both problems ask them to find a total or to combine parts.

8. Then have students look at Problems 1, 3, and 5 for similarities. Guide them to see that all three problems involve dividing a whole into equal parts or equally sharing a total.

9. Point out that both multiplication and division problems use some of the same words, such as *each*. Tell students that looking for specific words will not indicate which operation to use. Explain that identifying the overall meaning of the story problem will indicate which operation to use.

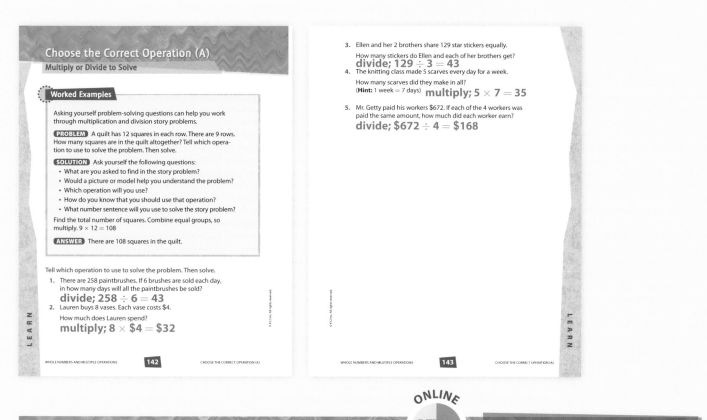

Choose the Correct Operation (A)
Multiply or Divide to Solve

Worked Examples

Asking yourself problem-solving questions can help you work through multiplication and division story problems.

PROBLEM A quilt has 12 squares in each row. There are 9 rows. How many squares are in the quilt altogether? Tell which operation to use to solve the problem. Then solve.

SOLUTION Ask yourself the following questions:
- What are you asked to find in the story problem?
- Would a picture or model help you understand the problem?
- Which operation will you use?
- How do you know that you should use that operation?
- What number sentence will you use to solve the story problem?

Find the total number of squares. Combine equal groups, so multiply. 9 × 12 = 108

ANSWER There are 108 squares in the quilt.

Tell which operation to use to solve the problem. Then solve.

1. There are 258 paintbrushes. If 6 brushes are sold each day, in how many days will all the paintbrushes be sold?
   divide; 258 ÷ 6 = 43
2. Lauren buys 8 vases. Each vase costs $4.

   How much does Lauren spend?
   multiply; 8 × $4 = $32

3. Ellen and her 2 brothers share 129 star stickers equally.

   How many stickers do Ellen and each of her brothers get?
   divide; 129 ÷ 3 = 43
4. The knitting class made 5 scarves every day for a week.

   How many scarves did they make in all?
   (**Hint:** 1 week = 7 days) **multiply; 5 × 7 = 35**
5. Mr. Getty paid his workers $672. If each of the 4 workers was paid the same amount, how much did each worker earn?
   divide; $672 ÷ 4 = $168

WHOLE NUMBERS AND MULTIPLE OPERATIONS **142** CHOOSE THE CORRECT OPERATION (A)

WHOLE NUMBERS AND MULTIPLE OPERATIONS **143** CHOOSE THE CORRECT OPERATION (A)

LEARN Identify the Operation and Solve

ONLINE 15 min

Objectives

- Determine whether addition, subtraction, multiplication, or division is the appropriate operation to use to solve a story problem and solve the problem.

Students will decide which operation—addition, subtraction, multiplication, or division—is appropriate to use to solve a story problem. Then they will create the number sentence to solve the story problem and solve.

You should sit with students as they complete this activity. Ask the following questions as students work to solve each story problem:

- What are you asked to find in the story problem?
- Would a picture or model help you understand the problem?
- Which operation will you use?
- How do you know that you should use that operation?
- What number sentence will you use to solve the story problem?

TRY IT Choose the Operation and Solve

ONLINE 10 min

Objectives

- Determine whether addition, subtraction, multiplication, or division is the appropriate operation to use to solve a story problem and solve the problem.

Students will complete an online Try It. If necessary, read the directions, problems, and answer choices to students and help them with keyboard or mouse operations.

Choose the Correct Operation (B)

Lesson Overview

Skills Update	5 minutes	ONLINE
LEARN Explain Thinking About Solutions	15 minutes	OFFLINE
LEARN Solve Circus Story Problems	20 minutes	OFFLINE
TRY IT Choose the Operation at Camp	10 minutes	OFFLINE
CHECKPOINT	10 minutes	ONLINE

▶ Lesson Objectives

Determine whether addition, subtraction, multiplication, or division is the appropriate operation to use to solve a story problem and solve the problem.

▶ Prerequisite Skills

- Write and solve addition or subtraction number sentences to represent problem-solving situations with sums and minuends up through 1,000.
- Create a story problem that can be represented by a multiplication number sentence.
- Create a story problem that can be represented by a division number sentence.

▶ Content Background

Students will continue to learn to identify which operation—addition, subtraction, multiplication, or division—is appropriate to use to solve a story problem and then solve the problem. They should be able to explain why they know a given operation is the correct one. When students do addition problems, they are combining amounts; for subtraction they are finding the difference between two numbers; with multiplication they are finding the total when there are several equal amounts; and with division, they have a total amount that is being divided into equal groups.

Problem solving is a part of daily life. To become good problem solvers, students need to recognize when a new problem is similar to a problem they have already solved. Instead of treating every problem they encounter as new, students can build on their previous experiences with problems and develop strategies to solve similar problems. Knowing they have successfully completed similar problems will help students become confident problem solvers.

Students have solved a variety of problems using the four basic operations: addition, subtraction, multiplication, and division. When they see a new problem, they need to first decide which operation should be used to solve it. Then they can write a number sentence to solve the problem.

Materials to Gather

SUPPLIED

Explain Thinking About Solutions
  activity page

Solve Circus Story Problems
  activity page

Choose the Operation at Camp
  activity page

▶ Common Errors and Misconceptions

- Students might have difficulty solving nonstandard problems, problems requiring multiple steps, or problems with extra information. Avoid introducing students to techniques that work for one-step problems but do not work for multistep problems, such as associating key words with particular operations.

- Students might quickly read through a problem and immediately begin to compute with the numbers, often choosing the wrong operation because they did not take time to read through and understand the context of the problem. Students need to learn to use "slow-down" mechanisms that can help them concentrate on thoroughly understanding a problem before they solve it.

OFFLINE
15 min

LEARN Explain Thinking About Solutions

Students will explain their thinking to solve a story problem. They will solve the problem and label the answer.

1. Have students turn to the Explain Thinking About Solutions activity page in their Activity Book. Read the Worked Example with them.

2. Discuss the problem-solving questions students should ask themselves as they work to solve story problems.
   - What are you asked to find in the story problem?
   - Would a picture or model help you understand the problem?
   - Which operation will you use?
   - How do you know that you should use that operation?
   - What number sentence will you use to solve the story problem?

   Point out to students how the solution to the Worked Example addresses all the problem-solving questions. Also point out that the question asked for a cost and thus the answer had to be a dollar amount. Tell students that a number alone wouldn't have been enough to answer the question. A statement that includes a label is needed to explain and give meaning to the number.

3. Read Problem 1 with students. Ask students the problem-solving questions listed in Step 2, and have them answer. Make sure they understand how to find the information in the story problem to answer each question. Have them write and solve the number sentence in their Math Notebook.

4. Read Problem 2 with students. Have students tell you the problem-solving questions they would ask and answer. Then have them write and solve the number sentence in their Math Notebook.

5. Repeat Step 4 for Problem 3.

Objectives

- Determine whether addition, subtraction, multiplication, or division is the appropriate operation to use to solve a story problem and solve the problem.

Tips

Write the questions from Step 2 on an index card for students to use as a reference when solving story problems.

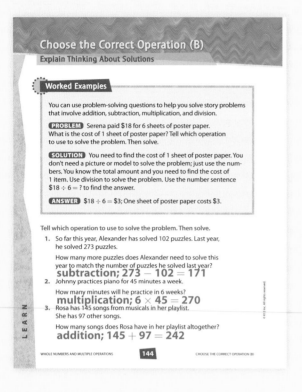

Choose the Correct Operation (B)
Explain Thinking About Solutions

Worked Examples

You can use problem-solving questions to help you solve story problems that involve addition, subtraction, multiplication, and division.

PROBLEM Serena paid $18 for 6 sheets of poster paper. What is the cost of 1 sheet of poster paper? Tell which operation to use to solve the problem. Then solve.

SOLUTION You need to find the cost of 1 sheet of poster paper. You don't need a picture or model to solve the problem; just use the numbers. You know the total amount and you need to find the cost of 1 item. Use division to solve the problem. Use the number sentence $18 ÷ 6 = ?$ to find the answer.

ANSWER $18 ÷ 6 = 3; One sheet of poster paper costs $3.

Tell which operation to use to solve the problem. Then solve.

1. So far this year, Alexander has solved 102 puzzles. Last year, he solved 273 puzzles.

    How many more puzzles does Alexander need to solve this year to match the number of puzzles he solved last year?
    subtraction; $273 - 102 = 171$
2. Johnny practices piano for 45 minutes a week.

    How many minutes will he practice in 6 weeks?
    multiplication; $6 × 45 = 270$
3. Rosa has 145 songs from musicals in her playlist. She has 97 other songs.

    How many songs does Rosa have in her playlist altogether?
    addition; $145 + 97 = 242$

WHOLE NUMBERS AND MULTIPLE OPERATIONS   144   CHOOSE THE CORRECT OPERATION (B)

LEARN Solve Circus Story Problems

OFFLINE 20min

Objectives

- Determine whether addition, subtraction, multiplication, or division is the appropriate operation to use to solve a story problem and solve the problem.

Students will identify the correct operation and number sentence to solve a story problem. They will write the number sentence and label the answer.

1. To begin, review with students the problem-solving questions they can use to solve story problems:

    - What are you asked to find in the story problem?
    - Would a picture or model help you understand the problem?
    - Which operation will you use?
    - How do you know that you should use that operation?
    - What number sentence will you use to solve the story problem?

2. Have students turn to the Solve Circus Story Problems activity page in their Activity Book. Read the Worked Example with them.

    Say: The solution to this problem shows how the problem-solving questions were used. One of those questions is "Which operation will you use?" When you have a story problem, how do you decide which operation to use?
    Example: You read the problem; think about what the question is asking; and decide whether to add, subtract, multiply, or divide.

    Tell students that these steps will help them solve any story problem.

3. Work with students to solve Problems 1–4. Encourage them to think about how to solve each problem by asking and answering the problem-solving questions. If they are having trouble deciding which operation to use, they should read the problem, think about what question is being asked, draw a picture if necessary, and decide whether they will add, subtract, multiply or divide to answer the question.

4. Have students review their solutions and check that the answer to Problem 3 has a label.

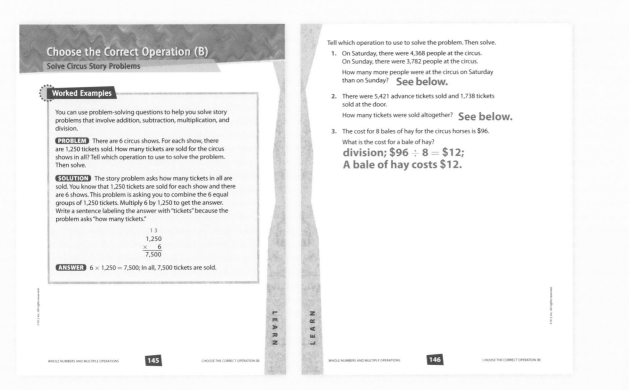

Worked Examples

You can use problem-solving questions to help you solve story problems that involve addition, subtraction, multiplication, and division.

PROBLEM There are 6 circus shows. For each show, there are 1,250 tickets sold. How many tickets are sold for the circus shows in all? Tell which operation to use to solve the problem. Then solve.

SOLUTION The story problem asks how many tickets in all are sold. You know that 1,250 tickets are sold for each show and there are 6 shows. This problem is asking you to combine the 6 equal groups of 1,250 tickets. Multiply 6 by 1,250 to get the answer. Write a sentence labeling the answer with "tickets" because the problem asks "how many tickets."

$$\begin{array}{r} 1\ 3 \\ 1{,}250 \\ \times\quad 6 \\ \hline 7{,}500 \end{array}$$

ANSWER $6 \times 1{,}250 = 7{,}500$; In all, 7,500 tickets are sold.

Tell which operation to use to solve the problem. Then solve.

1. On Saturday, there were 4,368 people at the circus. On Sunday, there were 3,782 people at the circus.

   How many more people were at the circus on Saturday than on Sunday? **See below.**

2. There were 5,421 advance tickets sold and 1,738 tickets sold at the door.

   How many tickets were sold altogether? **See below.**

3. The cost for 8 bales of hay for the circus horses is $96.

   What is the cost for a bale of hay?

   division; $96 ÷ 8 = $12;
   A bale of hay costs $12.

Additional Answers

1. subtraction; $4{,}368 - 3{,}782 = 586$; There were 586 more people at the circus on Saturday.

2. addition; $5{,}421 + 1{,}738 = 7{,}159$; In all, 7,159 tickets were sold.

OFFLINE
10 min

TRY IT Choose the Operation at Camp

Objectives

Students will practice determining whether to add, subtract, multiply, or divide to solve a story problem and then solve the problem. Have students turn to the Choose the Operation at Camp activity page in their Activity Book and read the directions with them.

Students should copy the problems from the Activity Book into their Math Notebook as necessary and solve them there.

- Determine whether addition, subtraction, multiplication, or division is the appropriate operation to use to solve a story problem and solve the problem.

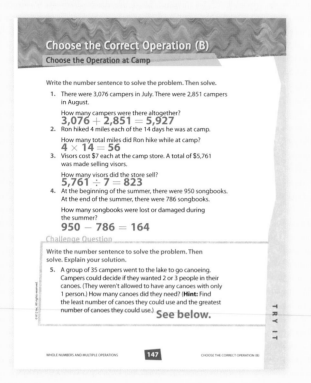

Additional Answers

5. They would need at least 12 canoes and at most 17 canoes.

   Explanation: $35 \div 3 = 11 \text{ r } 2$

   If they put 3 people in each canoe, they would need at least 12 canoes.

   11 canoes would have 3 people and 1 canoe would have 2 people.

   Explanation: $35 \div 2 = 17 \text{ r } 1$

   If they put 2 people in each canoe, they would need at most 17 canoes.

   16 canoes would have 2 people and 1 canoe would have 3 people.

CHECKPOINT

ONLINE **10**min

Students will complete an online Checkpoint. If necessary, read the directions, problems, and answer choices to students and help them with keyboard or mouse operations.

Objectives

- Determine whether addition, subtraction, multiplication, or division is the appropriate operation to use to solve a story problem and solve the problem.

Use More Than One Operation (A)

▶ Lesson Objectives

Solve a story problem involving two or more operations.

▶ Prerequisite Skills

Determine whether addition, subtraction, multiplication, or division is the appropriate operation to use to solve a story problem and solve the problem.

▶ Content Background

Students will learn to solve a problem with multiple steps and involving more than one operation.

Problem solving is a part of daily life. To become good problem solvers, students need to recognize when a new problem is similar to a problem they have already solved. Instead of treating every problem they encounter as new, students can build on their previous experiences with problems and develop strategies to solve similar problems. Knowing they have successfully completed similar problems will help students become confident problem solvers.

Students have solved a wide variety of story problems using the four basic operations: addition, subtraction, multiplication, and division. They will now use their problem-solving skills to solve problems that involve more than one operation.

▶ Common Errors and Misconceptions

- Students might have difficulty solving nonstandard problems, problems requiring multiple steps, or problems with extra information. Avoid introducing students to techniques that work for one-step problems but do not work for multistep problems, such as associating key words with particular operations.
- Students might quickly read through a problem and immediately begin to compute with the numbers, often choosing the wrong operation because they did not take time to read through and understand the context of the problem. Students need to learn to use "slow-down" mechanisms that can help them concentrate on thoroughly understanding a problem before they solve it.

Materials to Gather

SUPPLIED

Problems with More Than One Step activity page

GET READY Choose the Operation

ONLINE 5 min

Objectives

- Determine whether addition, subtraction, multiplication, or division is the appropriate operation to use to solve a story problem and solve the problem.

Students will choose the correct operation to solve a story problem and then solve it.

LEARN Problems with More Than One Step

OFFLINE 20 min

Objectives

- Solve a story problem involving two or more operations.

Students will solve story problems using two or more operations.

1. Have students turn to the Problems with More Than One Step activity page in their Activity Book. Read the Worked Example with them. Have students answer the problem-solving questions aloud. Make sure they understand how the answer was reached before continuing.

2. Read Problem 1 with students. Ask them to explain their thinking about how they would solve the problem. Encourage them to share the problem-solving questions and answers they use to work through solving the problem.

3. Have students solve Problem 1. Emphasize the importance of including a label in the answer. Remind students that labels explain and give meaning to the answers.

4. Have students solve Problems 2–4 on their own. Students should record their answers in their Math Notebook.

Use More Than One Operation (A)
Problems with More Than One Step

Worked Examples

You can solve story problems with two or more operations.

PROBLEM Stella has 2 bags of marbles. There are 6 marbles in each bag. She gets 4 more marbles.

How many marbles does she have in all?

SOLUTION Ask yourself the following questions:

- What are you asked to find in the problem?
- What facts are given?
- Would a picture or model help you understand the problem?
- How are you going to solve the problem?
- Do you need to use more than one operation in this problem?
- What are the different steps you need to take to solve this problem?
- Which operations should you use? Why?

You need to find how many marbles Stella has in all. She starts with some marbles (2 bags of 6 marbles) and then gets more (4). Multiply $2 \times 6 = 12$ to find how many marbles she has at the beginning. Then add the marbles she gets to find the total number of marbles. $12 + 4 = 16$

ANSWER $2 \times 6 = 12$; $12 + 4 = 16$; Stella has 16 marbles in all.

WHOLE NUMBERS AND MULTIPLE OPERATIONS   **148**   USE MORE THAN ONE OPERATION (A)

Solve.

1. Brian and Kelly are 8 years old. Each bought an admission pass to the zoo for $6 and a box of animal crackers for $3.
   How much money did they spend in all?   **They spent $18 in all.**

2. There are 2 boxes of chalk and 8 pieces of chalk in each box.
   If there are 4 children drawing with chalk, how many pieces of chalk will each child get?   **Each child will get 4 pieces of chalk.**

3. Ed bought 3 cartons of eggs at the store. There are 18 eggs in each carton. He also bought a carton of 6 eggs.
   How many eggs does Ed have altogether?   **Ed has 60 eggs altogether.**

4. There are 3 birds' nests in the tree. Each nest had 5 eggs.
   If 3 eggs have already hatched, how many eggs are left still to hatch?   **There are 12 eggs left to hatch.**

WHOLE NUMBERS AND MULTIPLE OPERATIONS   **149**   USE MORE THAN ONE OPERATION (A)

LEARN Problem Solving at the Carousel

ONLINE 20min

Objectives

- Solve a story problem involving two or more operations.

Students will use information in a chart to practice solving story problems that involve more than one step and more than one operation. They should do the calculations in their Math Notebook and enter the answers online.

Tips Encourage students to use the problem-solving questions to help them solve the story problems.

TRY IT Problems with Two or More Operations

ONLINE 10min

Objectives

- Solve a story problem involving two or more operations.

Students will complete an online Try It. If necessary, read the directions, problems, and answer choices to students and help them with keyboard or mouse operations.

Use More Than One Operation (B)

Lesson Overview

GET READY Solve Problems at the Circus	5 minutes	ONLINE
LEARN Problem-Solving Questions	20 minutes	OFFLINE
TRY IT More Than One Operation	25 minutes	OFFLINE
CHECKPOINT	10 minutes	ONLINE

▶ Lesson Objectives

Solve a story problem involving two or more operations.

▶ Prerequisite Skills

Determine whether addition, subtraction, multiplication, or division is the appropriate operation to use to solve a story problem and solve the problem.

Materials to Gather

SUPPLIED

Problem-Solving Questions activity page

More Than One Operation activity page

▶ Content Background

Students will continue to learn to solve a problem with multiple steps and involving more than one operation.

Problem solving is a part of daily life. To become good problem solvers, students need to recognize when a new problem is similar to a problem they have already solved. Instead of treating every problem they encounter as new, students can build on their previous experiences with problems and develop strategies to solve similar problems. Knowing they have successfully completed similar problems will help students become confident problem solvers.

Students have solved a wide variety of story problems using the four basic operations: addition, subtraction, multiplication, and division. They will now use their problem-solving skills to solve problems that involve more than one operation.

▶ Common Errors and Misconceptions

- Students might have difficulty solving nonstandard problems, problems requiring multiple steps, or problems with extra information. Avoid introducing students to techniques that work for one-step problems but do not work for multistep problems, such as associating key words with particular operations.

- Students might quickly read through a problem and immediately begin to compute with the numbers, often choosing the wrong operation because they did not take time to read through and understand the context of the problem. Students need to learn to use "slow-down" mechanisms that can help them concentrate on thoroughly understanding a problem before they solve it.

GET READY Solve Problems at the Circus

Objectives

- Determine whether addition, subtraction, multiplication, or division is the appropriate operation to use to solve a story problem and solve the problem.

Students will complete an online activity to practice choosing the correct operation to solve a story problem. Then students will solve story problems.

LEARN Problem-Solving Questions

Objectives

- Solve a story problem involving two or more operations.

Students will use problem-solving questioning to help them solve story problems involving two or more operations.

1. Review with students the problem-solving questions they can use to solve story problems:
   - What are you asked to find in the problem?
   - What facts are given?
   - Would a picture or model help you solve the problem?
   - How are you going to solve this problem?
   - Do you need to use more than one operation for this problem?
   - What are the different steps you need to take to solve this problem?
   - Which operations should you use? Why?

2. Have students turn to the Problem-Solving Questions activity page in their Activity Book. Read the Worked Example with them. Point out that some of the problem-solving questions are answered in the solution. Make sure students understand how the answer was reached before continuing with the story problems. They should copy the problems from the Activity Book into their Math Notebook as necessary and solve them there.

3. Read Problem 1 with students. Ask students to explain their thinking about how they would solve the problem. Encourage them to share the problem-solving questions and answers they use to work through solving the problem.

4. Have students solve Problem 1. Emphasize the importance of including a label in the answer. Remind students that labels explain and give meaning to the answers.

5. Have students solve Problems 2 and 3 on their own. They should record their answers in their Math Notebook.

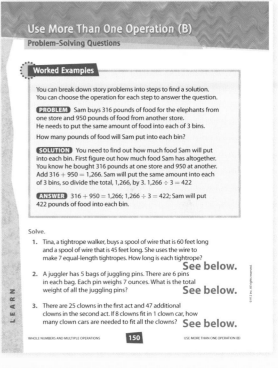

Use More Than One Operation (B)
Problem-Solving Questions

Worked Examples

You can break down story problems into steps to find a solution. You can choose the operation for each step to answer the question.

PROBLEM Sam buys 316 pounds of food for the elephants from one store and 950 pounds of food from another store. He needs to put the same amount of food into each of 3 bins.

How many pounds of food will Sam put into each bin?

SOLUTION You need to find out how much food Sam will put into each bin. First figure out how much food Sam has altogether. You know he bought 316 pounds at one store and 950 at another. Add 316 + 950 = 1,266. Sam will put the same amount into each of 3 bins, so divide the total, 1,266, by 3. 1,266 ÷ 3 = 422

ANSWER 316 + 950 = 1,266; 1,266 ÷ 3 = 422; Sam will put 422 pounds of food into each bin.

Solve.

1. Tina, a tightrope walker, buys a spool of wire that is 60 feet long and a spool of wire that is 45 feet long. She uses the wire to make 7 equal-length tightropes. How long is each tightrope? **See below.**

2. A juggler has 5 bags of juggling pins. There are 6 pins in each bag. Each pin weighs 7 ounces. What is the total weight of all the juggling pins? **See below.**

3. There are 25 clowns in the first act and 47 additional clowns in the second act. If 8 clowns fit in 1 clown car, how many clown cars are needed to fit all the clowns? **See below.**

WHOLE NUMBERS AND MULTIPLE OPERATIONS   150   USE MORE THAN ONE OPERATION (B)

Additional Answers

1. Each tightrope is 15 feet long.
2. The pins weigh 210 ounces altogether.
3. The clowns need 9 clown cars.

TRY IT More Than One Operation

Objectives

- Solve a story problem involving two or more operations.

Students will practice solving story problems with more than one operation. Have students turn to the More Than One Operation activity page in their Activity Book and read the directions with them.

Students should copy the problems from the Activity Book into their Math Notebook as necessary and solve them there.

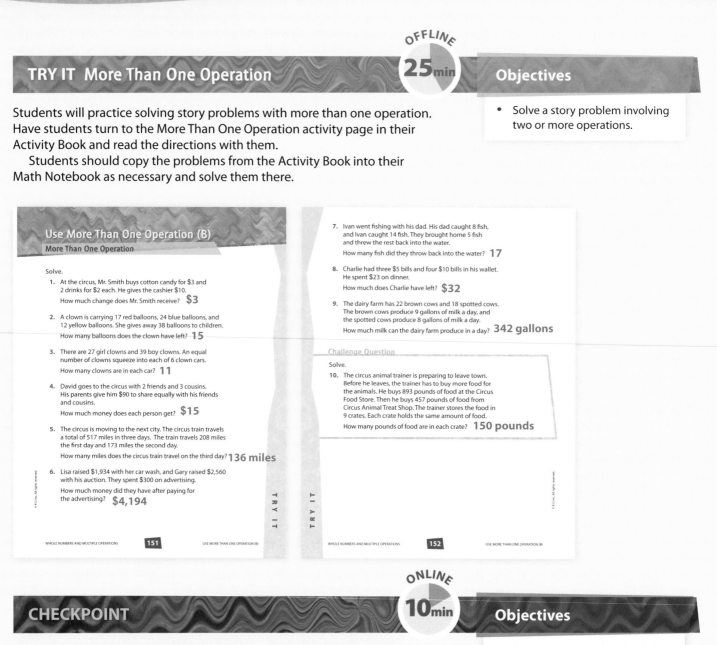

Use More Than One Operation (B)
More Than One Operation

Solve.

1. At the circus, Mr. Smith buys cotton candy for $3 and 2 drinks for $2 each. He gives the cashier $10.
   How much change does Mr. Smith receive? **$3**

2. A clown is carrying 17 red balloons, 24 blue balloons, and 12 yellow balloons. She gives away 38 balloons to children.
   How many balloons does the clown have left? **15**

3. There are 27 girl clowns and 39 boy clowns. An equal number of clowns squeeze into each of 6 clown cars.
   How many clowns are in each car? **11**

4. David goes to the circus with 2 friends and 3 cousins. His parents give him $90 to share equally with his friends and cousins.
   How much money does each person get? **$15**

5. The circus is moving to the next city. The circus train travels a total of 517 miles in three days. The train travels 208 miles the first day and 173 miles the second day.
   How many miles does the circus train travel on the third day? **136 miles**

6. Lisa raised $1,934 with her car wash, and Gary raised $2,560 with his auction. They spent $300 on advertising.
   How much money did they have after paying for the advertising? **$4,194**

7. Ivan went fishing with his dad. His dad caught 8 fish, and Ivan caught 14 fish. They brought home 5 fish and threw the rest back into the water.
   How many fish did they throw back into the water? **17**

8. Charlie had three $5 bills and four $10 bills in his wallet. He spent $23 on dinner.
   How much does Charlie have left? **$32**

9. The dairy farm has 22 brown cows and 18 spotted cows. The brown cows produce 9 gallons of milk a day, and the spotted cows produce 8 gallons of milk a day.
   How much milk can the dairy farm produce in a day? **342 gallons**

Challenge Question

Solve.

10. The circus animal trainer is preparing to leave town. Before he leaves, the trainer has to buy more food for the animals. He buys 893 pounds of food at the Circus Food Store. Then he buys 457 pounds of food from Circus Animal Treat Shop. The trainer stores the food in 9 crates. Each crate holds the same amount of food.
    How many pounds of food are in each crate? **150 pounds**

TRY IT

CHECKPOINT

Objectives

- Solve a story problem involving two or more operations.

Students will complete an online Checkpoint. If necessary, read the directions, problems, and answer choices to students and help them with keyboard or mouse operations.

Unit Review

UNIT REVIEW Look Back	10 minutes	**ONLINE**
UNIT REVIEW Checkpoint Practice	50 minutes	**ONLINE**
⏩ **UNIT REVIEW** Prepare for the Checkpoint		

▶ Unit Objectives

This lesson reviews the following objectives:

- Use the order of operations to evaluate an expression.
- Determine whether addition, subtraction, multiplication, or division is the appropriate operation to use to solve a story problem and solve the problem.
- Solve a story problem involving two or more operations.

▶ Advance Preparation

In this lesson, students will have an opportunity to review previous activities in the Whole Numbers and Multiple Operations unit. Look at the suggested activities in Unit Review: Prepare for the Checkpoint online and gather any needed materials.

Materials to Gather

There are no materials to gather for this lesson.

UNIT REVIEW Look Back

ONLINE **10** min

Students will review key concepts from the unit to prepare for the Unit Checkpoint.

Objectives

- Review unit objectives.

UNIT REVIEW Checkpoint Practice

ONLINE **50** min

Students will complete an online Checkpoint Practice to prepare for the Unit Checkpoint. If necessary, read the directions, problems, and answer choices to students. Have students answer the problems on their own. Review any missed problems with students.

Objectives

- Review unit objectives.

⏩ UNIT REVIEW Prepare for the Checkpoint

What you do next depends on how students performed in the previous activity, Unit Review: Checkpoint Practice. If students had difficulty with any of the problems, complete the appropriate review activity listed in the table online.

Unit Checkpoint

| **UNIT CHECKPOINT** Online | 60 minutes | **ONLINE** |

Unit Objectives

This lesson assesses the following objectives:

- Use the order of operations to evaluate an expression.
- Determine whether addition, subtraction, multiplication, or division is the appropriate operation to use to solve a story problem and solve the problem.
- Solve a story problem involving two or more operations.

Materials to Gather

There are no materials to gather for this lesson.

UNIT CHECKPOINT Online

ONLINE
60min

Objectives

- Assess unit objectives.

Students will complete the Unit Checkpoint online. If necessary, read the directions, problems, and answer choices to students and help them with keyboard or mouse operations.

Geometry

▶ Unit Objectives

- Identify right angles in geometric figures or everyday objects.
- Identify the measure of an angle in a geometric figure or an everyday object as greater than or less than a right angle.
- Identify, describe, and classify a polygon according to the number of its sides.
- Identify attributes of isosceles, equilateral, and right triangles.
- Identify attributes of parallelograms, rectangles, and squares.
- Identify and describe common solid geometric figures.
- Classify common solid geometric figures.
- Determine solid objects that could be combined to create a given solid object.

▶ Big Ideas

- Geometric figures can be described and classified by the shapes of their faces and by how many faces, sides, edges, or vertices they have.
- Shapes can be constructed from other shapes.

▶ Unit Introduction

In this unit, students will learn about both two-dimensional and three-dimensional geometric figures. They will learn to see those figures in the world and will learn how to describe with mathematical language the many attributes of the figures. They will learn that square corners are right angles, and they'll recognize when an angle is greater than, less than, or equal to a right angle.

Students will use their shape blocks and an online geoboard to learn to describe and classify polygons according to the number of sides. They will identify attributes of triangles and will learn to recognize isosceles, equilateral, and right triangles. They'll also identify attributes of parallelograms, rectangles, and squares. Finally they will look at three-dimensional solid figures, including spheres, cones, cylinders, rectangular solids, and triangular and rectangular pyramids. Students will learn to identify the solids and describe them by the number and shape of their faces and the number of vertices. They will also see how three-dimensional figures can be put together to make other figures.

▶ Keywords

angle
angle measure
attributes
base of a figure
cone
cube
cylinder
degree
edge
equilateral
equilateral triangle

face
intersecting lines
isosceles triangle
line
parallel
parallel lines
parallelogram
plane figure
polygon
prism
quadrilateral
ray

rectangle
rectangular prism
rectangular pyramid
right angle
rotate
scalene triangle
side of a polygon
solid figure
sphere
square
triangular prism
triangular pyramid
vertex (plural: vertices)

Right Angles and Other Angles

Lesson Overview

Skills Update	5 minutes	ONLINE
GET READY Name That Shape	5 minutes	OFFLINE
LEARN Recognize Right Angles	15 minutes	OFFLINE
LEARN Greater Than, Less Than a Right Angle	10 minutes	ONLINE
LEARN Geoboard Fun	10 minutes	ONLINE
TRY IT Right Angles	10 minutes	ONLINE
CHECKPOINT	5 minutes	ONLINE

▶ Lesson Objectives

- Identify right angles in geometric figures or everyday objects.
- Identify the measure of an angle in a geometric figure or an everyday object as greater than or less than a right angle.

▶ Prerequisite Skills

Classify plane figures according to similarities and differences, such as triangle, square, rectangle, circle, oval.

▶ Content Background

Students will learn to identify right angles in geometric figures and everyday objects. They will also learn to identify angles by comparing them to the measures of a right angle and deciding if they are greater than, less than, or equal to a right angle.

Avoid using the words *bigger* and *smaller* with students. Do not use phrases like "the angle is bigger/smaller" or "the opening is bigger/smaller." Those terms and phrases lead students to incorrectly assume that an angle with longer sides has a greater measure.

In geometry, students use the terms *lines*, *rays*, and *angles*.

line   ray   angle

An angle is made of two rays that share an endpoint, called a *vertex*.

vertex

The rays of the angle are called the *sides* of the angle. When the sides of an angle form a square corner, the angle is called a *right angle* and can be marked with a square corner marker. An angle that is less than a right angle is called an *acute angle*. An angle that is greater than a right angle is called an *obtuse angle*.

Materials to Gather

SUPPLIED

blocks – A, B, C, D, E, F, G, H, I, J, K, L, M, N (3 of each)

ALSO NEEDED

index card

household objects – pipe cleaner, 2 drinking straws

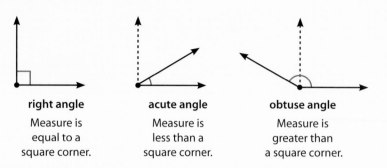

right angle	acute angle	obtuse angle
Measure is equal to a square corner.	Measure is less than a square corner.	Measure is greater than a square corner.

Angles are measured by how much of a rotation has been made between the sides. The rotation is measured in degrees, and a right angle (an angle with a square corner) is 90 degrees.

▶ Common Errors and Misconceptions

- Students might not recognize angles as important parts of figures.
- Students might focus on the length of the line segments that form an angle's sides, the tilt of the top line segment, the area enclosed by the sides, or the proximity of the two sides rather than look at the actual size of the angle. For example, students might indicate that in the two triangles shown here, angle A is smaller than angle X.

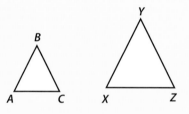

GET READY Name That Shape

Students will review the names of shapes and their attributes. Gather the blocks.

1. Lay out the blocks in random order.
2. Have students sort the blocks by shape.
3. As students pick up each block, ask them to explain how they know that the block has that particular shape. Encourage them to use math vocabulary. Explanations may include the following:

   - A circle is round (A, B blocks).
   - A triangle has 3 sides (F, H, J, K blocks).
   - A rectangle has 4 sides and square corners (C, D, E, G blocks).
   - A square has 4 equal sides and square corners (E, G blocks).
   - A trapezoid has 4 sides. Two of the sides are parallel (M blocks). (Students might describe *parallel* without using the exact term. They will learn it in future lessons.)
   - A rhombus has 4 equal sides (L, G blocks).
   - A hexagon has 6 sides (N block).
   - A parallelogram has 4 sides. Both pairs of opposite sides are parallel (L, I blocks). (Students may or may not recognize this shape. The shape will be covered in future lessons.)

Objectives

- Classify plane figures according to similarities and differences, such as triangle, square, rectangle, circle, oval.

Tips

Remind students that this activity is a review. If they do not remember the names or attributes of the shapes, reinforce vocabulary along with the shapes' sides and angles.

LEARN Recognize Right Angles

Students will learn the definition of an angle. They will identify a right angle in everyday objects and geometric figures. They will recognize angles that are less than a right angle and greater than a right angle.

Gather the blocks, index card, pipe cleaner, and drinking straws.

1. Define an angle as a corner where two lines meet. Tell students that they will learn about angles and that angles are all around them.

2. Have students hold their index finger and thumb straight up in the air, and then move their thumb away from their index finger gradually. Explain that students are making angles with greater and greater measures.

3. Take one of the blocks, choose a vertex, and have students trace that angle with their finger. Students should use their finger to move out from the vertex along one side of the block, then go back to that vertex and trace along the other side. Point out that students are tracing an angle on the block. Repeat the process on paper. Trace a block and have students trace an angle by choosing a vertex and tracing along the two sides that extend from that vertex.

4. Model more examples of angles on the blocks by pointing out where two sides meet to form an angle. Allow time for students to identify other angles on the blocks. Point out that the circle has no angles.

5. Show students a square and ask what kind of shape could fit in its corners. squares

   Tell students that the angles on the square are called *right angles*. Explain that a right angle is an angle that forms when two lines meet to form a square corner.

6. Ask students to find another shape with right angles and to point out two sides that make a right angle. Students should choose a different rectangular piece or one of the right triangles and point to two sides that meet to form a right angle or square.

7. Give students an index card and ask if it has right angles. Yes

   Draw two lines on the card, very close to the edge, with arrows. Put a square corner marker in the corner to show a right angle. Write "right angle" near the corner of the card. Tell students that all the corners of the card are right angles and that sometimes people use the square corner marker to show that there is a right angle.

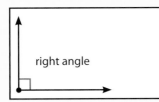

right angle

8. **Say:** We can use the index card to check whether an angle is a right angle.

   Hold the card up to the corner of a rectangular block. Point out how the corners match, which shows the right angle in the rectangle. Have students match the card to something in the room that has a right angle such as a book, a cabinet door, or the corner of a rectangular or square table.

9. Give students one minute to go around the room and point out as many right angles as possible. Students should use the index card to help them recognize objects with right angles. Explain that the lengths of the sides of an object do not matter. Any object that has a square corner has a right angle. A big poster on a wall has a right angle, and a small index card has a right angle.

Objectives

- Identify right angles in geometric figures or everyday objects.
- Identify the measure of an angle in a geometric figure or an everyday object as greater than or less than a right angle.

Tips

If you wish, substitute a twist tie for the pipe cleaner in this activity.

10. Show students an analog clock or watch. Discuss two times when a clock shows a right angle, 3:00 and 9:00.

11. Have students use a pipe cleaner to make a right angle. Have them check that their right-angle pipe cleaner is a right angle by wrapping it around the corner of a table or laying one side on the top of a table and having the other side go down over the edge of the table. They can also check their angle using the index card.

12. Have students open and close the angle to show angles greater than a right angle and less than a right angle. Have them put straws on the end of the bent pipe cleaner to show that the lengths of the sides of the angle don't affect the measure of the angle.

LEARN Greater Than, Less Than a Right Angle

ONLINE 10 min

Students will learn that an angle is made up of two rays that share a vertex. They will identify angles as right angles, as angles that are greater than right angles, and as angles that are less than right angles.

Objectives

- Identify right angles in geometric figures or everyday objects.
- Identify the measure of an angle in a geometric figure or an everyday object as greater than or less than a right angle.

LEARN Geoboard Fun

ONLINE 10 min

Students will use the Geoboard Learning Tool to create shapes that have right angles, angles greater than 90 degrees, and angles less than 90 degrees.

Objectives

- Identify right angles in geometric figures or everyday objects.
- Identify the measure of an angle in a geometric figure or an everyday object as greater than or less than a right angle.

DIRECTIONS FOR USING THE GEOBOARD LEARNING TOOL

1. Click Lesson Mode. If necessary, click Menu and Help to review the instructions for the learning tool.

2. To make the angles, have students use two rubber bands. Have them make a 90-degree angle, or right angle, by following these steps:
   - Drag a rubber band and make a vertical segment of any length.
   - Drag another rubber band and make a horizontal segment that connects to an end of the first rubber band to make a right angle.

3. Have students make the following angles:
   - An angle that measures less than 90 degrees
   - An angle that measures greater than 90 degrees

4. Now have students make shapes that have different types of angles. To make the shapes, they will use one rubber band. Have students make these shapes:
   - A 4-sided shape that has 4 right angles
   - A 5-sided shape that has 2 right angles (If students have difficulty, they can make a 4-sided shape and stretch one side. Refer to the illustration for an example.)
   - A triangle with 1 right angle and 2 angles less than 90 degrees

Students' angles and shapes should be similar to the following:

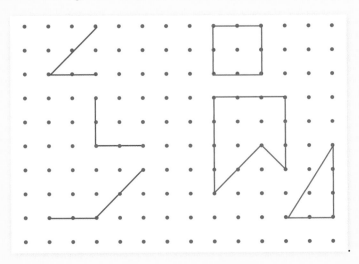

TRY IT Right Angles

Students will complete an online Try It. If necessary, read the directions, problems, and answer choices to students and help them with keyboard or mouse operations.

Objectives

- Identify right angles in geometric figures or everyday objects.
- Identify the measure of an angle in a geometric figure or an everyday object as greater than or less than a right angle.

CHECKPOINT

Students will complete an online Checkpoint. If necessary, read the directions, problems, and answer choices to students and help them with keyboard or mouse operations.

Objectives

- Identify right angles in geometric figures or everyday objects.
- Identify the measure of an angle in a geometric figure or an everyday object as greater than or less than a right angle.

Identify and Classify Polygons

Lesson Overview

Skills Update	5 minutes	ONLINE
GET READY Play a Shape Game	5 minutes	OFFLINE
LEARN Toothpick Polygons	20 minutes	OFFLINE
LEARN Create and Identify Polygons	10 minutes	ONLINE
TRY IT Name Polygons	10 minutes	OFFLINE
CHECKPOINT	10 minutes	ONLINE

▶ Lesson Objectives

Identify, describe, and classify a polygon according to the number of its sides.

▶ Prerequisite Skills

- Identify and describe plane figures according to the number of sides and vertices, such as triangle, square, rectangle, circle, oval.
- Classify plane figures according to similarities and differences, such as triangle, square, rectangle, circle, oval.

▶ Content Background

In this lesson, students will learn to identify, describe, and classify common geometric shapes according to the number of straight sides. They will learn the names for common polygons up through 10 sides.

Students are familiar with a variety of shapes. They will learn that all straight-sided, closed figures are called polygons and that *polygon* means "many-sided figure." A polygon is classified by its number of sides. Students know that all 3-sided figures are triangles. They may also know that 4-sided figures have different names, such as quadrilateral, parallelogram, square, rhombus, rectangle, and trapezoid. Students will learn that the term *quadrilateral* is used to describe all 4-sided figures. They will learn the names for other common polygons, such as the 5-sided pentagon, the 6-sided hexagon, and other polygons up through 10 sides.

When students use the online Geoboard Learning Tool, they will see the words *convex* and *concave*. At this level, it's sufficient to just mention to students that a concave figure "caves in," whereas a convex figure does not.

A figure that lies on a flat surface, or in two dimensions, is called a *plane figure*. Plane figures include those with straight sides (polygons) as well as those with curved sides, such as circles. It's important to use the term *plane figure* with students, but they are not required to use the term.

▶ Common Errors and Misconceptions

- Students might misinterpret which characteristics define a shape. For example, they may see a triangle that has three equal sides and think that all triangles must have three equal sides. Actually, any shape with only three sides is a triangle.

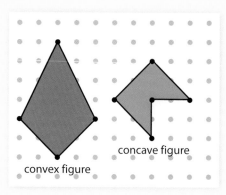

convex figure

concave figure

- Students might not recognize that a shape might be positioned different ways. For example, students might not recognize that the second shape shown here is a square.

- Students might inappropriately use *converse reasoning* when classifying shapes. For example, they might say, "All squares have 4 sides. This shape has 4 sides, so it must be a square."

▶ Advance Preparation
Print the Dot Paper.

▶ Safety
Supervise students as they work with toothpicks, paper clips, and other pointy items.

GET READY Play a Shape Game

OFFLINE
5min

Students will play the game Guess My Shape to identify, describe, and classify plane figures according to the number of sides and vertices.
Gather the blocks.

1. Hide a block in your hand.

   Say: I'm hiding a block. You can ask Yes and No questions about its attributes to guess which block it is. You can ask about the shape's sides and vertices and the types of angles, but you may not ask about its color. And you can ask if it's a certain shape only once, when you're certain what shape it is.

2. Guide students to ask questions such as the following:
   - Does it have exactly 3 sides?
   - Does it have a square corner?
   - Does it have a right angle?
   - Does it have a vertex?
   - Does it have a curved side?
   - Are all sides equal?
   - Is it big?
   - Does it have more than 3 sides?

3. Have students ask questions until they know which block you are hiding. They should state the shape of the block. Uncover the block to show whether they gave the correct answer.

4. Repeat Steps 1–3 two or three times as time allows. Trade roles so students choose the block and you ask the questions.

Objectives

- Identify and describe plane figures according to the number of sides and vertices, such as triangle, square, rectangle, circle, oval.

- Classify plane figures according to similarities and differences, such as triangle, square, rectangle, circle, oval.

Tips

Explain to students that a shape with more than 3 sides, such as a square, has 3 sides, but not exactly 3 sides. Guide students to ask about attributes that narrow the possibilities.

LEARN Toothpick Polygons
OFFLINE
20min

Students will use toothpicks to construct polygons with 3 through 10 sides. They will create shape flash cards.
Gather the toothpicks, blocks, and index cards.

Objectives

- Identify, describe, and classify a polygon according to the number of its sides.

1. Tell students that they have seen many shapes and will now learn more about how to describe them. Ask students to use three toothpicks to make a closed shape. Explain that a closed shape is like a fence with no openings.

   Ask: What shape did you make? triangle

   Ask students to identify each side of the triangle. Have them feel a side with their finger and realize that when they reach a corner, or vertex, it's the beginning of a new side. Ask students to point out a vertex where 2 sides meet.

2. Break some toothpicks and make two more triangles of different shapes. Show one with a right angle. Show the triangles in different orientations so that they're turned in different ways.

   Ask: How do you know that all of these shapes are triangles? They all have 3 sides.

   Tell students that any closed figure with exactly 3 sides is called a triangle. Point out that *tri–* means 3 and that a triangle has 3 angles. Ask students what other words they can think of that start with *tri–*. Examples: tricycle, tripod, triplets

3. Have students write "triangle" on one side of an index card. Then on the other side of the card, have them draw a small picture of a triangle with a 3 inside it. Place the card above the toothpick triangles. Leave the triangles in place.

4. Give students four toothpicks and have them make a 4-sided closed figure.

   Ask: What shape did you make? square or rhombus

   Remind students that a rhombus has 4 equal sides but it doesn't have to have right angles like a square.

5. Break some toothpicks and have students use different-sized pieces to make two more 4-sided figures.

   Tell students that there is a special word to describe all 4-sided figures that are closed and have no lines that cross. That word is *quadrilateral*. *Quad–* means 4 and *–lateral* means "side"; *quadrilateral* means "4-sided." Ask students what other words they can think of that start with *quad–*. Example: quadruplets

6. Have students write "quadrilateral" on one side of an index card. Then on the other side of the card, have them draw a small picture of a quadrilateral with a 4 inside it. Place the card above the toothpick quadrilaterals.

   Say: A quadrilateral is any closed figure that has 4 sides that don't cross over each other. So squares, rhombuses, trapezoids, rectangles, and all other 4-sided figures are quadrilaterals.

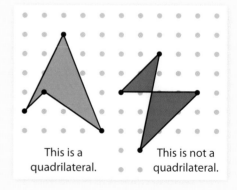

This is a quadrilateral.   This is not a quadrilateral.

7. Draw the figure shown that is closed and has no lines that cross. Explain to students that quadrilaterals can also have sides that "cave in." As long as a closed figure has 4 straight sides and the lines don't cross each other, it's a quadrilateral.

8. Have students continue to create toothpick figures, learn the correct names, and make shape flash cards for the following figures:

   • Pentagon – 5-sided closed figure

   • Hexagon – 6-sided closed figure

   • Septagon – 7-sided closed figure (*Heptagon* is another name for a 7-sided closed figure.)

   • Octagon – 8-sided closed figure

   • Nonagon – 9-sided closed figure

   • Decagon – 10-sided closed figure

9. Tell students that there is one word to describe all closed figures with straight sides. That word is *polygon*. Have students say "polygon." Explain that *polygon* means "many-sided." Have students write the word "polygon" on an index card and place it above all the toothpick figures.

Ask: Which of the figures you made or drew are polygons? all of them

Explain that polygons are made of straight lines that don't cross and that connect to make a closed figure.

10. Have students look at the blocks. Ask the following questions. Allow students to look at their index cards for help.

- Which blocks are polygons? all except the circles

- Which are triangles? F, H, J, K

- Which are quadrilaterals? C, D, E, G, I, L, M

- What other type of polygon do we have among the blocks? hexagon: N block

11. Encourage students to practice memorizing the names of polygons by using their shape flash cards.

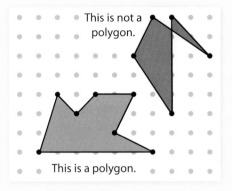

This is not a polygon.

This is a polygon.

 ONLINE **10**min

LEARN Create and Identify Polygons

Students will use the Geoboard Learning Tool to create and name polygons. Remind students that a polygon is a closed figure with straight sides that don't cross each other. Remind them that they have learned the names of many types of polygons.

DIRECTIONS FOR USING THE GEOBOARD LEARNING TOOL

1. Click Lesson Mode. If necessary, click Menu and Help to review the instructions for the learning tool.

2. Have students make a shape, such as a triangle, on the Geoboard.

3. Have students click Show Info to see the name of the shape. Point out the word *concave* or *convex* next to the shape's name. Tell students that a shape is concave if it "caves in" or has an inward dent. Otherwise, it is convex. (Students at this level are not expected to remember those names.)

4. Have students make the following polygons on one screen:

- triangle: green
- quadrilateral: blue
- pentagon: orange
- hexagon: red
- septagon: yellow
- octagon: purple
- nonagon: blue
- decagon: green

Here are sample polygons:

triangle   quadrilateral   pentagon   hexagon   septagon   octagon   nonagon   decagon

Students can decide how they want each figure to look as long as it has the correct number of sides and is a polygon. The color names are a key for you to use in identifying the sample polygons in the illustration. Students can use any color for any polygon. Remember that their polygons can look different from these polygons.

Objectives

- Identify, describe, and classify a polygon according to the number of its sides.

Tips

Allow students to use Dot Paper printouts to create their own polygon designs offline.

TRY IT Name Polygons

Objectives

- Identify, describe, and classify a polygon according to the number of its sides.

Students will practice identifying, describing, and classifying a polygon according to the number of sides it has. Gather the Dot Paper. Have students turn to the Name Polygons activity page in their Activity Book and read the directions with them.

Students should copy the problems from the Activity Book into their Math Notebook as necessary and solve them there.

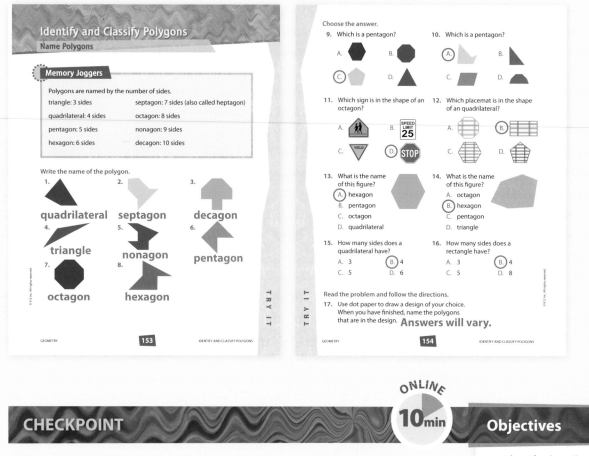

Identify and Classify Polygons
Name Polygons

Memory Joggers

Polygons are named by the number of sides.

triangle: 3 sides   septagon: 7 sides (also called heptagon)

quadrilateral: 4 sides   octagon: 8 sides

pentagon: 5 sides   nonagon: 9 sides

hexagon: 6 sides   decagon: 10 sides

Write the name of the polygon.

1. quadrilateral
2. septagon
3. decagon
4. triangle
5. nonagon
6. pentagon
7. octagon
8. hexagon

Choose the answer.

9. Which is a pentagon? C.

10. Which is a pentagon? A.

11. Which sign is in the shape of an octagon? D. STOP

12. Which placemat is in the shape of an quadrilateral? B.

13. What is the name of this figure?
   A. hexagon
   B. pentagon
   C. octagon
   D. quadrilateral

14. What is the name of this figure?
   A. octagon
   B. hexagon
   C. pentagon
   D. triangle

15. How many sides does a quadrilateral have?
   A. 3   B. 4
   C. 5   D. 6

16. How many sides does a rectangle have?
   A. 3   B. 4
   C. 5   D. 8

Read the problem and follow the directions.

17. Use dot paper to draw a design of your choice. When you have finished, name the polygons that are in the design. **Answers will vary.**

GEOMETRY   153 / 154   IDENTIFY AND CLASSIFY POLYGONS

CHECKPOINT

Objectives

- Identify, describe, and classify a polygon according to the number of its sides.

Students will complete an online Checkpoint. If necessary, read the directions, problems, and answer choices to students and help them with keyboard or mouse operations.

Triangles

▶ Lesson Objectives

Identify attributes of isosceles, equilateral, and right triangles.

▶ Prerequisite Skills

Identify and describe plane figures according to the number of sides and vertices, such as triangle, square, rectangle, circle, oval.

▶ Content Background

Students will learn to identify different types of triangles.

Isosceles triangles have at least 2 equal sides.

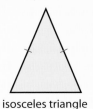

isosceles triangle

Equilateral triangles have 3 equal sides.

equilateral triangle

An equilateral triangle is a special type of isosceles triangle, but students should name a triangle as equilateral if all 3 sides are the same length.

Right triangles have a right angle.

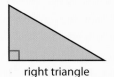

right triangle

Materials to Gather

SUPPLIED

blocks – A, B, C, D, E, F, G, H, I, J, K, L, M, N (1 of each)

Dot Paper (printout)

Isometric Dot Paper (printout)

ALSO NEEDED

index cards – 6

scissors, pointed-end safety

household objects – 6 toothpicks

Students will use two types of dot paper—regular dot paper and isometric dot paper—to draw polygons. On isometric dot paper, the dots are in a triangular pattern where each dot is 1 unit from the dots that surround it. An equilateral triangle with a side unit of 1 is the smallest triangle that can be shown on isometric dot paper. This paper is designed so that it's easy to draw equilateral triangles and parallelograms that have equal side lengths but are not squares (nonsquare rhombuses).

On regular dot paper that uses a square grid pattern, a square is the smallest polygon that has side lengths of 1 unit. Notice that the distance between diagonal points on the regular dot paper is greater than 1 unit. This makes it difficult to draw an equilateral triangle on this paper.

The Geoboard Learning Tool has options to use these different types of grids.

square grid   isometric grid

▶ Common Errors and Misconceptions

Students might misinterpret which characteristics define a shape. For example, they may see a triangle that has three equal sides and think that all triangles must have three equal sides. Actually, any shape with only three sides is a triangle.

▶ Advance Preparation

Print the Dot Paper and Isometric Dot Paper.

▶ Safety

Supervise students as they work with toothpicks, paper clips, and other pointy items.

Make sure students handle the scissors carefully and be sure to store them in a safe place.

OFFLINE
5min

GET READY Shape Comparison

Students will sort shapes into groups of triangles and quadrilaterals and will describe the differences among the shapes in each group.

Gather the blocks.

1. Lay out the blocks in random order.

2. **Ask:** What is a 3-sided figure called? triangle

3. Have students make a pile of all the triangles and describe the differences between them. They may notice that some are big, some are small, some have right angles, some have sides that are the same length, and some have sides that are different lengths.

Objectives

- Identify and describe plane figures according to the number of sides and vertices, such as triangle, square, rectangle, circle, oval.

4. **Ask:** What is a 4-sided figure called? quadrilateral

5. Have students make a pile of all the quadrilaterals and describe the differences between them. They may notice that some are squares, some are rectangles, some are rhombuses, some are parallelograms, some have sides that are all the same length, and some have opposite sides that are the same length.

6. Explain to students that they might know more words to describe quadrilaterals and that in this lesson, they will learn more ways to describe the different types of triangles.

LEARN Attributes of Three Triangles

OFFLINE
25 min

Students will learn to identify right, isosceles, and equilateral triangles and describe their attributes.

Gather the blocks, index cards, toothpicks, and scissors, and the two types of dot paper.

RIGHT TRIANGLES

1. **Say:** You know about different types of triangles. Now let's learn new ways to describe and group them.

   Have students cut a diagonal from the bottom edge to the side edge of an index card as shown.

   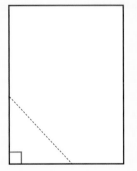

   Ask students to explain what they notice about the angles in the triangle. Guide students to see that one of the angles is a right angle. Have students draw a square corner marker on the triangle to show the right angle.

2. Have students identify the blocks that are right triangles. F, H, J

   Tell students that these triangles are called right triangles because they have a right angle in them. Have students write "right triangle" on one side of an index card. On the other side, have them draw a picture of a right triangle with a square corner marker to signify the right angle.

3. Emphasize that the lengths of the sides of a right angle do not affect the angle. Therefore, a triangle of any size that has a right angle is a right triangle. Have students match up the right angles on the F, H, and J blocks to model that any size triangle that has a right angle is a right triangle.

   As time permits, have students draw right triangles on the Dot Paper (square grid).

Objectives

- Identify attributes of isosceles, equilateral, and right triangles.

Tips

Draw dotted lines on the index cards to show students where to cut. Students may need to lay the toothpicks on the index card and trace the equilateral triangle.

ISOSCELES TRIANGLES

4. Give students a new index card. Have them fold the card in half and cut a diagonal line from the bottom right to the left side as shown.

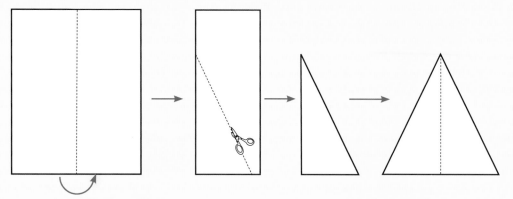

Ask students to explain what they notice about the sides of the triangle. Guide them to see that 2 of the sides are the same length. Turn the triangle so that it has a different orientation. Some students have difficulty seeing that 2 sides of a triangle are the same length if the triangle is turned at an odd angle.

5. Have students identify the triangle blocks that have 2 sides the same length. F, H, J, K

Students can check to see that the sides of one triangle are equal by comparing them to the same side of another triangle. Tell them that triangles that have 2 equal-length sides are called isosceles triangles. Have them write "isosceles triangle" on one side of an index card. On the other side, have students draw a picture of an isosceles triangle.

As time permits, have students draw isosceles triangles on the Dot Paper (square grid or isometic grid).

6. Ask: What are the names of the two special triangles? What makes them special? A right triangle has a right angle, and an isosceles triangle has at least 2 equal sides.

7. Have students identify the blocks that are both right triangles and isosceles triangles. F, H, J

EQUILATERAL TRIANGLES

8. Tell students there is one more special triangle. Explain that this triangle has 3 sides that have equal lengths. Give students three toothpicks. Have them create a triangle with the toothpicks.

Ask students to explain what they notice about the sides of the triangle. Guide them to see that the 3 sides of the triangle have the same length. Have them look at the triangle from different orientations. Some students have difficulty seeing that a triangle is equilateral if the triangle is at an odd angle.

9. Have students identify the triangle block that has 3 equal sides. K

Tell students this triangle is called an equilateral triangle because it has 3 equal-length sides. Have them write "equilateral triangle" on one side of an index card. On the other side, have students draw a picture of an equilateral triangle.

As time permits, have students draw equilateral triangles on Isometric Dot Paper. As a challenge, have them draw an equilateral triangle on Dot Paper (square grid).

10. Present the following questions to students and allow them to share their answers:

- Are all equilateral triangles isosceles triangles? Guide students to see that since isosceles triangles have at least 2 equal sides and equilateral triangles have 3 equal sides, all equilateral triangles are isosceles triangles.

- Can an equilateral triangle be a right triangle? Use toothpicks to show students that this is not possible. A right angle made with two toothpicks cannot be closed to make a triangle with a third toothpick because the third toothpick is too short.

11. Review that *equilateral* means "equal-sided." Tell students that just as there are equilateral triangles, there are also equilateral polygons. Any polygon with all equal sides is called an equilateral polygon. Examples are the square and hexagon blocks.

12. Summarize and review right, isosceles, and equilateral triangles and their attributes.

LEARN Three Types of Triangles

 ONLINE **10**min

Objectives

- Identify attributes of isosceles, equilateral, and right triangles.

Students will identify right, isosceles, and equilateral triangles using marks such as a square corner marker to signify a right angle in a right triangle, or tick marks to signify the equal sides of an isosceles or equilateral triangle. Help students recognize that the triangles can be turned so that equal sides or right angles are not as easy to see.

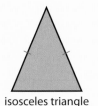

isosceles triangle

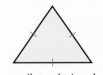

equilateral triangle

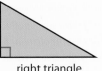

right triangle

Tips

If students have difficulty recognizing isosceles triangles or right triangles when they are turned in an odd way, take the blocks and turn them in an odd way and have students practice picking out which are right triangles, isosceles triangles, and equilateral triangles.

TRY IT Triangle Practice

ONLINE **10**min

Objectives

- Identify attributes of isosceles, equilateral, and right triangles.

Students will complete an online Try It. If necessary, read the directions, problems, and answer choices to students and help them with keyboard or mouse operations.

CHECKPOINT

 ONLINE **10**min

Objectives

- Identify attributes of isosceles, equilateral, and right triangles.

Students will complete an online Checkpoint. If necessary, read the directions, problems, and answer choices to students and help them with keyboard or mouse operations.

Parallelograms

▶ Lesson Objectives

Identify attributes of parallelograms, rectangles, and squares.

▶ Prerequisite Skills

Identify and describe plane figures according to the number of sides and vertices, such as triangle, square, rectangle, circle, oval.

▶ Content Background

Students will learn how to identify parallelograms. They will recognize that rectangles are special parallelograms and squares are special rectangles.

Polygons are classified by the number of sides they have. Quadrilaterals are polygons with 4 sides. Among quadrilaterals are parallelograms. Parallelograms have parallel opposite sides that are equal in length. Identify a parallelogram by looking at the sides and the angles. Rectangles, rhombuses, and squares are special types of parallelograms. The illustration shows the relationship between the sides and angles in different types of parallelograms. Notice the tick marks. Sides with one tick mark have the same length and those with two tick marks have the same length. The square in the corner indicates a right angle.

A square is not only a square but also a rectangle, a rhombus, and a parallelogram. A rectangle is always a parallelogram, but it is only a square when its sides are equal. A rhombus is always a parallelogram, but it is only a square when its angles are right angles.

▶ Common Errors and Misconceptions

- Students might misinterpret which characteristics define a shape. For example, they may see a triangle that has three equal sides and think that all triangles must have three equal sides. Actually, any shape with only three sides is a triangle.

Materials to Gather

SUPPLIED

blocks – A, B, C, D, E, F, G, H, I, J, K, L, M, N (2 of each)

Dot Paper (printout)

Isometric Dot Paper (printout)

Parallelogram Practice activity page

ALSO NEEDED

index cards – 4

paper, printer – 1 sheet

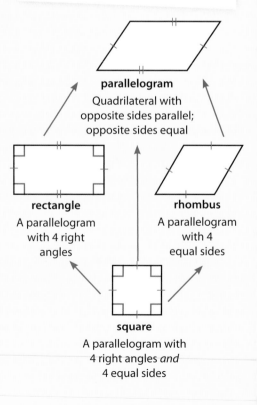

parallelogram
Quadrilateral with opposite sides parallel; opposite sides equal

rectangle
A parallelogram with 4 right angles

rhombus
A parallelogram with 4 equal sides

square
A parallelogram with 4 right angles *and* 4 equal sides

- Students might not recognize that a shape might be positioned different ways. For example, students might not recognize that the second shape is a square.

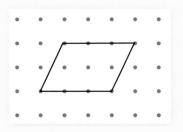

- Students might inappropriately use *converse reasoning* when classifying shapes. For example, they might say, "All squares have 4 sides. This shape has 4 sides, so it must be a square."

▶ Advance Preparation

Print the Dot Paper and Isometric Dot Paper.
  Draw a parallelogram on the Dot Paper.

GET READY Shape Design

ONLINE
5min

Students will use polygons to make a design on the online Geoboard. Have students look at both the isometric grid and the regular grid before starting their design.
  Students can use their ideas from this activity to create further designs on the Dot Paper and Isometric Dot Paper.

DIRECTIONS FOR USING THE GEOBOARD LEARNING TOOL

1. Click Lesson Mode. If necessary, click Menu and Help to review the instructions for the learning tool.
2. Have students make a complex figure on the Geoboard. Encourage students to use as many of the following shapes as possible to create their design: square, rectangle, rhombus, triangle, pentagon, hexagon, septagon, octagon, nonagon, decagon, and right triangle. Students may use either the isometric grid or the regular grid.
3. Have students identify and describe the figures in their design by name and attributes.

Objectives

- Identify and describe plane figures according to the number of sides and vertices, such as triangle, square, rectangle, circle, oval.

Tips

Sit with students during the activity. Ask them to explain how they know the name of each figure in their design.

LEARN What Is a Parallelogram?

Students will learn the attributes of parallelograms. They will identify and sort special types of parallelograms (rhombuses, rectangles, and squares).

Gather the parallelogram you have drawn on the Dot Paper, blocks, and index cards.

1. Remind students that polygons are closed figures with straight sides and no lines crossing. Tell them that in this lesson, they're going to look more closely at 4-sided polygons. Explain that 4-sided polygons are called *quadrilaterals*.

2. Introduce the term *parallel lines*. Give examples of parallel lines such as the lines on binder paper or the rails on a train track. Have the students draw parallel lines on the dot paper. Then have them describe parallel lines in their own words and tell where they see them in the world. Guide students to understand that parallel lines never cross and provide additional examples: top and bottom of windows, doors, and some furniture; the tracks of skiers and the tracks of a car after it goes through a puddle; and the 10-yard lines of a football field. Conclude by telling students that anywhere there are rectangles, there are parallel lines.

3. Have students draw a rectangle and a square on separate index cards. Remind them that these are both quadrilaterals. Have them note that opposite sides have the same length and are parallel.

4. Show students the parallelogram on the Dot Paper. Have them tell the number of sides in the shape. 4

   Ask: Are any of the lines parallel? Yes, the opposite sides

   Ask: Are any of the sides the same length? Yes, opposite sides

   Explain that the shape is a parallelogram.

   Say: A parallelogram is a special quadrilateral. Its opposite sides are parallel and equal in length.

   Have students write "parallelogram" on one side of an index card and draw a picture of a parallelogram on the other side.

   Ask: Is a rectangle a parallelogram? Yes

   Ask: Are all parallelograms rectangles? No, some parallelograms look like they are slanting to the side and don't have right angles like a rectangle.

5. Show students the trapezoid block (M block) without naming it. Ask if it is a parallelogram and have students explain why or why not. Students should notice that the trapezoid has only one set of parallel sides. To be a parallelogram, the other two sides would also need to be parallel.

6. Have students sort the parallelogram-shaped blocks. Display a rhombus (L block). Ask students to describe the shape according to number of sides, lengths of sides, and parallel lines. 4 sides, all sides equal in length, opposite sides are parallel

   Explain that this shape is a rhombus.

   Say: A rhombus is a quadrilateral with 4 equal sides.

   Have students write "rhombus" on one side of an index card and draw a picture of a rhombus on the other side.

7. Ask the following questions and have students explain their answers:
   - Is a rhombus a parallelogram? Yes, opposite sides are parallel.
   - Are all parallelograms rhombuses? No, only those with all sides the same length.
   - Can a rhombus be a rectangle? Yes, if all angles are right angles.
   - Can a rhombus be a square? Yes, if all angles are right angles.
   - Are all rhombuses squares? No, some rhombuses do not have right angles.

8. Ask the following questions and have students explain their answers:
   - Is a square a parallelogram? Yes, it has opposite sides that are parallel and of equal length.
   - Is a square a rectangle? Yes, it has 4 right angles.
   - Is a square a rhombus? Yes, it has 4 equal-length sides.

   Remind students that a shape with sides of equal length is equilateral, and that squares and rhombuses are equilateral polygons.

9. Have students find as many different-shaped rectangles as they can among the blocks and put them near the rectangle card. If necessary, remind students that squares are rectangles. C, D, E, G

   Leave the rectangles in place and have students find different-shaped rhombuses and put them near the rhombus card. E, G, L

   Ask students if there are any blocks that are both rectangles and rhombuses. squares (E and G blocks)

10. Turn a blank sheet of printer paper horizontally. Draw the diagram shown.Use the diagram to organize the blocks. Point to the appropriate section of the diagram to emphasize each step of the directions.
    Say: Put rectangles in the left oval labeled "rectangles" and rhombuses in the right oval labeled "rhombuses." If there are shapes that are both rectangles and rhombuses, put them in the center where the two ovals overlap.

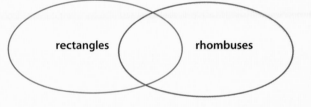

11. Have students sort the blocks into the diagram. Have them describe which type of blocks go into the overlapping section. the blocks that are squares, because they are rectangles and rhombuses

    Tell students that this type of diagram is called a *Venn diagram* and it is sometimes used to sort objects.

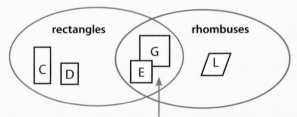

objects that are rectangles and rhombuses

LEARN Side Lengths of Parallelograms

ONLINE 10min

Objectives

Students will practice making lines parallel. They will then review attributes parallelograms and the special parallelograms, including the following:
- Rectangles: parallelograms with all right angles
- Squares: parallelograms with all right angles *and* all sides equal

- Identify attributes of parallelograms, rectangles, and squares.

TRY IT Parallelogram Practice

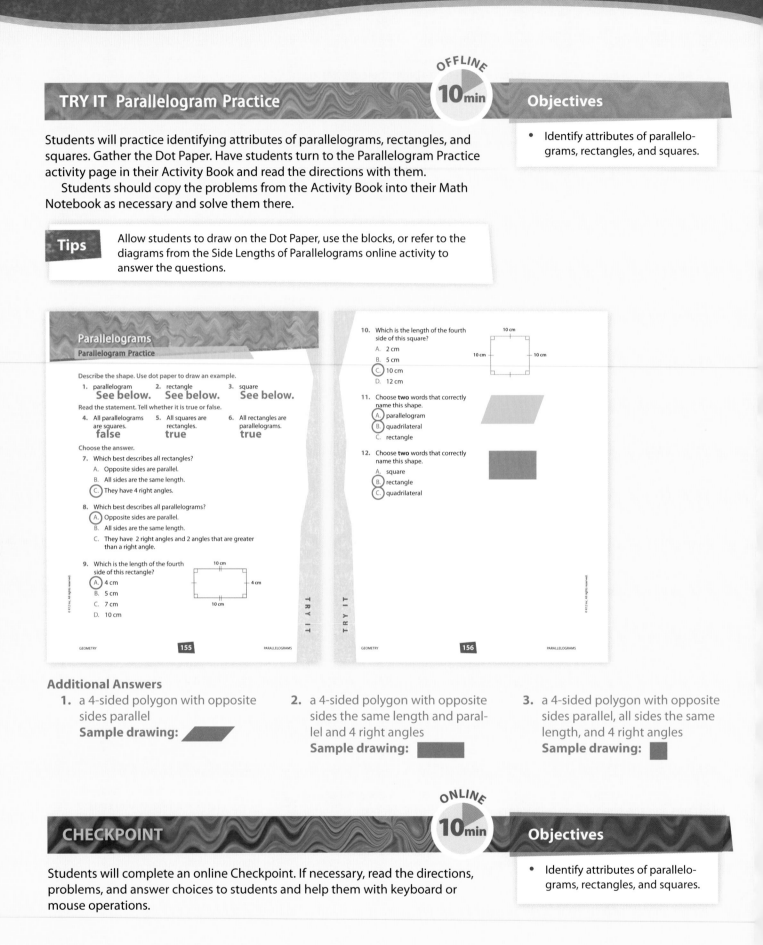

OFFLINE 10 min

Objectives

- Identify attributes of parallelograms, rectangles, and squares.

Students will practice identifying attributes of parallelograms, rectangles, and squares. Gather the Dot Paper. Have students turn to the Parallelogram Practice activity page in their Activity Book and read the directions with them.

Students should copy the problems from the Activity Book into their Math Notebook as necessary and solve them there.

Tips Allow students to draw on the Dot Paper, use the blocks, or refer to the diagrams from the Side Lengths of Parallelograms online activity to answer the questions.

Parallelograms
Parallelogram Practice

Describe the shape. Use dot paper to draw an example.

1. parallelogram **See below.**
2. rectangle **See below.**
3. square **See below.**

Read the statement. Tell whether it is true or false.

4. All parallelograms are squares. **false**
5. All squares are rectangles. **true**
6. All rectangles are parallelograms. **true**

Choose the answer.

7. Which best describes all rectangles?
   A. Opposite sides are parallel.
   B. All sides are the same length.
   C. They have 4 right angles.

8. Which best describes all parallelograms?
   A. Opposite sides are parallel.
   B. All sides are the same length.
   C. They have 2 right angles and 2 angles that are greater than a right angle.

9. Which is the length of the fourth side of this rectangle?
   A. 4 cm
   B. 5 cm
   C. 7 cm
   D. 10 cm

10. Which is the length of the fourth side of this square?
   A. 2 cm
   B. 5 cm
   C. 10 cm
   D. 12 cm

11. Choose **two** words that correctly name this shape.
   A. parallelogram
   B. quadrilateral
   C. rectangle

12. Choose **two** words that correctly name this shape.
   A. square
   B. rectangle
   C. quadrilateral

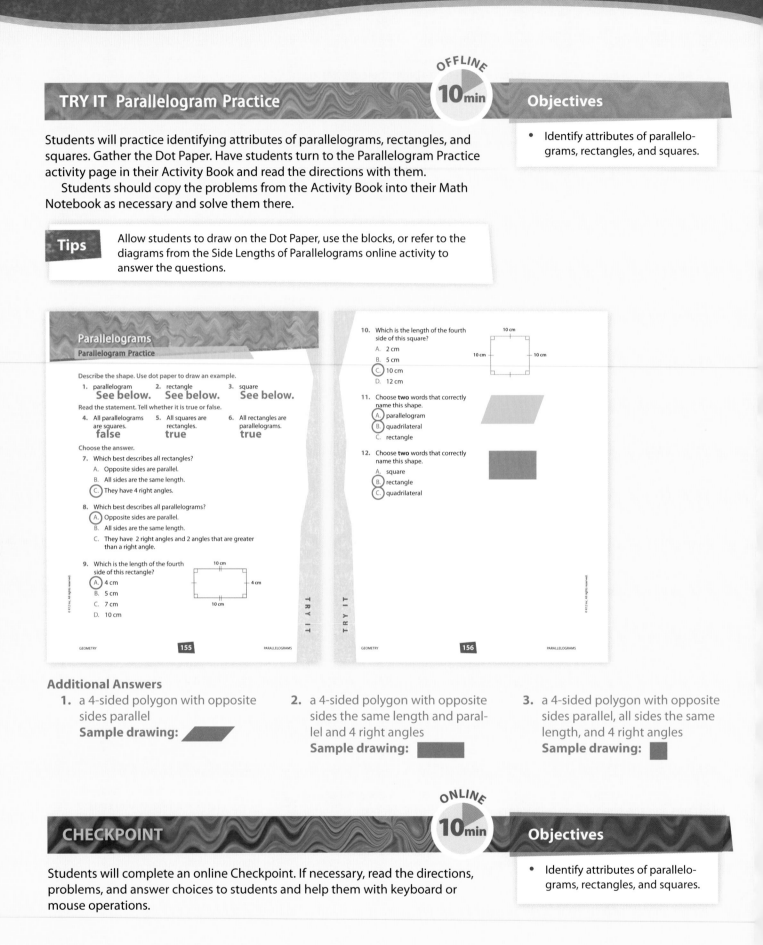

GEOMETRY **155** PARALLELOGRAMS

GEOMETRY **156** PARALLELOGRAMS

Additional Answers

1. a 4-sided polygon with opposite sides parallel
   Sample drawing:

2. a 4-sided polygon with opposite sides the same length and parallel and 4 right angles
   Sample drawing:

3. a 4-sided polygon with opposite sides parallel, all sides the same length, and 4 right angles
   Sample drawing:

CHECKPOINT

ONLINE 10 min

Objectives

- Identify attributes of parallelograms, rectangles, and squares.

Students will complete an online Checkpoint. If necessary, read the directions, problems, and answer choices to students and help them with keyboard or mouse operations.

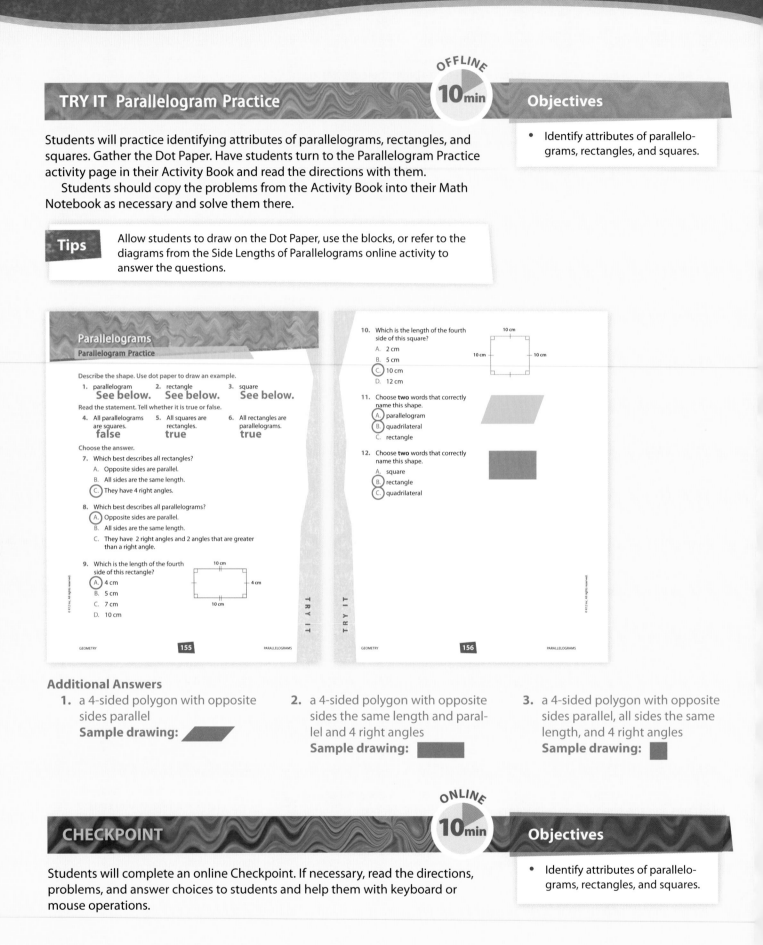

Identify and Classify Solids

Lesson Overview

Skills Update	5 minutes	ONLINE
GET READY Describe Solids	10 minutes	OFFLINE
LEARN Attributes of Solids	15 minutes	OFFLINE
LEARN Identify and Sort Solids	10 minutes	ONLINE
TRY IT Classify Solids	10 minutes	OFFLINE
CHECKPOINT	10 minutes	ONLINE

▶ Lesson Objectives

- Identify and describe common solid geometric figures.
- Classify common solid geometric figures.

▶ Prerequisite Skills

Describe solid figures according to the number and shape of faces, such as sphere, pyramid, cube, rectangular prism.

▶ Content Background

In this lesson, students will learn to identify, describe, and classify common solid geometric figures.

Solid figures are three-dimensional shapes such as cubes, pyramids, or cones. Many common objects have the shape of solid figures. A baseball is a sphere and a juice can is a cylinder.

Solid figures have faces, edges, and vertices. A face is the flat, traceable part of a solid. A sphere is curved and does not have any flat parts; a sphere has no faces. A cylinder has both flat parts and curved parts. The faces are circles the same size. The curved part is not a face, but simply a curved surface. One or more of the faces of a solid can also be considered the base. A cone has one face, a circle, which is also its base.

One type of solid is a prism. Prisms have two bases that are polygons of the same size and shape. A rectangular prism has a base that is a rectangle. Because squares are rectangles, a cube is a rectangular prism. If the base of a prism is a triangle, it is called a triangular prism. Prisms can have other kinds of polygons as the base, such as hexagonal or octagonal prisms. The prisms that students will study in this lesson are all right prisms. The faces of these prisms, which are not the bases, are all rectangles (including squares).

Another type of solid figure is a pyramid. Pyramids have one base that is a polygon, such as a triangle, square, rectangle, or other polygon. Like the prism, the shape of its base names the pyramid. If the base is a triangle, the pyramid is called a triangular pyramid. If the base is a rectangle, the pyramid is called a rectangular pyramid. A pyramid with a hexagon base is a hexagonal pyramid, and a pyramid with an octagon base is an octagonal pyramid. The faces that are not the base of the pyramid are all triangles. The edges from the vertices of the base meet at a single vertex.

Materials to Gather

SUPPLIED

blocks – P, Q, R, S, T, U, V

Attributes of Solids activity page

Classify Solids activity page

ALSO NEEDED

household objects – everyday objects shaped like solids, bag (large enough to hold blocks and everyday objects)

▶ Common Errors and Misconceptions

- Students might misinterpret which characteristics define a shape. For example, they may see a triangle that has three equal sides and think that all triangles must have three equal sides. Actually, any shape with only three sides is a triangle.

- Students might not recognize that a shape might be positioned different ways. For example, students might not recognize that the second shape is a square.

- Students might inappropriately use *converse reasoning* when classifying shapes. For example, they might say, "All squares have 4 sides. This shape has 4 sides, so it must be a square."

▶ Advance Preparation

- For the Get Ready: Describe Solids activity, gather everyday objects shaped like solids, such as a ball for a sphere, a small can for a cylinder, a small box for a rectangular prism, and a party hat for a cone.

- For the Learn: Attributes of Solids activity, gather everyday objects shaped like geometric solids, such as a round piece of fruit for a sphere, a small can or a straw for a cylinder, and a small box for a rectangular prism. Find a bag that is large enough to hold the objects and the P, Q, R, S, T, U, and V blocks.

▶ Safety

Supervise students when they are working with the geometric solid blocks. These blocks have sharp corners.

GET READY Describe Solids

OFFLINE
10 min

Objectives

- Describe solid figures according to the number and shape of faces, such as sphere, pyramid, cube, rectangular prism.

Students will describe three-dimensional shapes and identify them using their sense of touch as well as their sense of sight.

Gather the blocks, bag, and everyday objects.

1. Display the blocks. Have students describe each shape. Guide them to use the words *edge*, *vertex*, *face*, and *base* in the descriptions. Discuss the names of the different solids.

P	Q	R	S	T	U	V
cube	rectangular prism	square pyramid	triangular pyramid	cone	cylinder	sphere

2. Place the blocks in a bag with the everyday objects.

3. Have students close their eyes, reach into the bag, and touch one object. Have them describe the shape of its bases and faces and then tell what geometric shape they think it is. Then have students remove the object from the bag to check if they were correct.

4. Repeat Step 3 several times.

5. Have students look around the room (and out the window) to identify or think of other everyday objects that are three-dimensional geometric shapes. A full moon is a sphere and most boxes are rectangular prisms. A thick paperback book could be a rectangular prism, a wastepaper basket could be a cylinder, and an ice-cream cone or party hat could be a cone.

LEARN Attributes of Solids

Objectives

- Identify and describe common solid geometric figures.

Tips

Have students touch each face, edge, or vertex on the blocks or objects as they count.

Students will identify and describe three-dimensional geometric objects and will learn about the attributes of each type of solid.

Gather the blocks and everyday objects. Have students turn to the Attributes of Solids activity page in their Activity Book and read the directions with them. Students should copy the problems from the activity page into their Math Notebook as necessary and solve them there.

1. **Say:** Every geometric solid has its own characteristics, or attributes. We use these attributes to name and identify the geometric solids.

2. Point to different solids to review the terms *face* (flat surface) and *edge* (where two faces meet or a face meets a curved surface). Show a cone, a cylinder, and a sphere and point to the curved surfaces. Discuss how some solids have curved surfaces while other solids have only flat surfaces. Show a cone, a cube, and a triangular pyramid. Have students point to a vertex on each solid. Point out that a cone has 1 vertex while a cube has 8 vertices.

3. Have students look at the first solid in the chart on the activity page— a cone. Discuss with students everyday examples of cones, such as party hats and ice-cream cones. Guide them to supply the missing answers from the chart to identify the attributes of a cone. 1 face, 1 edge, 1 curved surface, 1 vertex

   Explain that in a picture, the lines on either side where the curved surface goes around to the back of the cone look like an edge but they aren't, because an edge is a flat surface touching another surface. The only edge in a cone is where the flat circle, the base, meets the cone's curved surface.

4. Continue with the next two solids listed in the chart—a cylinder and a sphere. Discuss everyday examples of each shape and then guide students in supplying the missing answers from the chart. cylinder – 2 circular faces, 2 edges, 1 curved surface, 0 vertices; sphere – 0 faces, 0 edges, 1 curved surface, 0 vertices

5. Display examples of a cube and a rectangular prism.

   Say: Prisms have two special faces that are the same size and shape. These two faces can be any kind of polygon. These two faces are called bases.

   Explain that a prism has rectangular faces that join two bases. Mention that a square is just a special rectangle and that a prism could have two square bases.

6. Show the cube. Point out that all the faces are squares. Tell students that a cube is a special rectangular prism, just as a square is a special kind of rectangle.

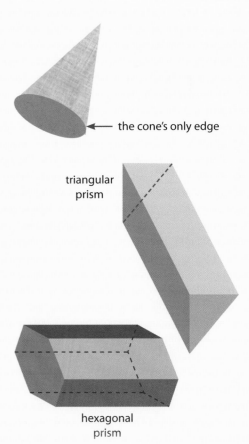

← the cone's only edge

triangular prism

hexagonal prism

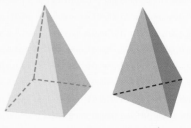

square pyramid

triangular pyramid

7. Explain that the two bases of a prism can be any polygons that are the same size and shape. Tell students that there can be triangular prisms or hexagonal prisms.

8. Guide students to supply the missing answers from the chart for the rectangular prism and the cube. Remember that the bases are just special faces and are counted as faces of the solid. 6 faces, 12 edges, 0 curved surfaces, 8 vertices

9. Display the two pyramids.

   Say: Pyramids have one base that is a polygon, such as a triangle, square, rectangle, hexagon, or other polygon. Like the prism, the shape of its base names the pyramid.

10. Point to each pyramid and have students name the shape of the bases. Explain that the faces that are not the base are all triangles. Guide students to supply the missing answers from the chart for the pyramids. square pyramid – 5 faces, 8 edges, 0 curved surfaces, 5 vertices; triangular pyramid – 4 faces, 6 edges, 0 curved surfaces, 4 vertices

11. After students have supplied all the missing information in the chart, use the following questions to summarize the activity:

    • Why do the cube and the rectangular prism have the same number of faces, edges, and vertices? The cube is just a special rectangular prism where all faces are squares.

    • Why do the pyramids have different numbers of faces, edges, and vertices? The base of a pyramid can be different shapes. If the base is a triangle, there will be 3 faces plus the base or 4 faces altogether, 4 vertices, and 6 edges. If the base is a rectangle or square, it will have 4 faces plus the base or 5 faces altogether, 5 vertices, and 8 edges.

    • Why does a sphere have no faces, edges, or vertices? A sphere has only a single curved surface.

Identify and Classify Solids
Attributes of Solids

Worked Examples

You can count the faces, edges, curved surfaces, and vertices of solids.

PROBLEM 1 How many faces, edges, curved surfaces, and vertices does a cube have?

SOLUTION

❶ Faces are flat surfaces. The cube has 6 flat surfaces.

❷ Edges are where faces meet. The cube has 12 edges.

❸ Curved surfaces are not flat. The cube does not have any curved surfaces.

❹ Vertices are corners. The cube has 8 vertices.

ANSWER The cube has 6 faces, 12 edges, 0 curved surfaces, and 8 vertices.

PROBLEM 2 How many faces, edges, curved surfaces, and vertices does a sphere have?

SOLUTION

❶ Faces are flat surfaces. The sphere does not have any flat surfaces.

❷ Edges are where faces meet. The sphere does not have any edges.

❸ Curved surfaces are not flat. The sphere has 1 curved surface.

❹ Vertices are corners. The sphere does not have any vertices.

ANSWER The sphere has 0 flat surfaces, 0 edges, 1 curved surface, and 0 vertices.

L E A R N

Write the missing numbers of faces, edges, curved surfaces, and vertices.

	Solids	Faces	Edges	Curved Surfaces	Vertices
1.	cone	1	1	1	1
2.	cylinder	2	2	1	0
3.	sphere	0	0	1	0
4.	rectangular prism	6	12	0	8
5.	cube	6	12	0	8
6.	square pyramid	5	8	0	5
7.	triangular pyramid	4	6	0	4

L E A R N

LEARN Identify and Sort Solids

In this activity, students will identify solid figures by name and sort them by kind.

Objectives

- Identify and describe common solid geometric figures.
- Classify common solid geometric figures.

TRY IT Classify Solids

Students will practice identifying, describing, and classifying solids. Have students turn to the Classify Solids activity page in their Activity Book and read the directions with them.

Students should copy the problems from the Activity Book into their Math Notebook as necessary and solve them there.

Objectives

- Identify and describe common solid geometric figures.
- Classify common solid geometric figures.

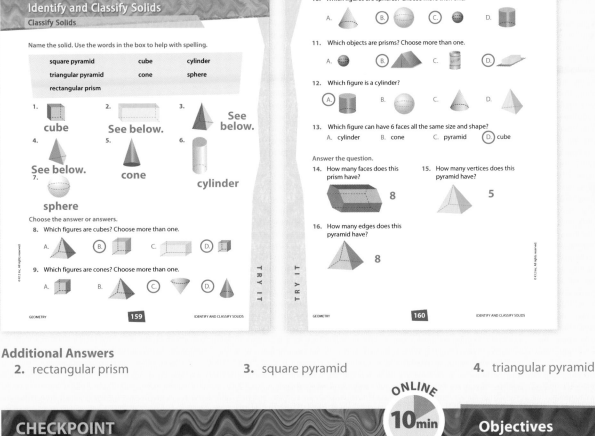

Additional Answers

2. rectangular prism
3. square pyramid
4. triangular pyramid

CHECKPOINT

Students will complete an online Checkpoint. If necessary, read the directions, problems, and answer choices to students and help them with keyboard or mouse operations.

Objectives

- Identify and describe common solid geometric figures.
- Classify common solid geometric figures.

Combine Solids to Create New Shapes

Lesson Overview

Skills Update	5 minutes	ONLINE
GET READY Combine Figures	10 minutes	ONLINE
LEARN Combine Solids	15 minutes	OFFLINE
LEARN Identify Parts	10 minutes	ONLINE
TRY IT Together and Apart	10 minutes	OFFLINE
CHECKPOINT	10 minutes	ONLINE

▶ Lesson Objectives
Determine solid objects that could be combined to create a given solid object.

▶ Prerequisite Skills
Put geometric figures together to form other geometric figures.

▶ Content Background
Students will learn to put solids together to make other shapes and recognize the solid objects that are combined to create a given solid object.

Solid figures are three-dimensional shapes such as cubes, pyramids, or cones. Many common objects have the shape of solid figures. A baseball is a sphere and a juice can is a cylinder.

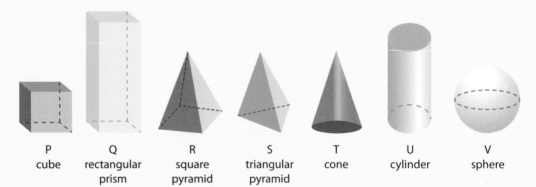

P	Q	R	S	T	U	V
cube	rectangular prism	square pyramid	triangular pyramid	cone	cylinder	sphere

Solid figures have faces, edges, and vertices. A face is the flat, traceable part of a solid. A sphere is curved and does not have any flat parts; a sphere has no faces. A cylinder has both flat parts and curved parts. The faces are circles the same size. The curved part is not a face, but simply a curved surface. One or more of the faces of a solid can also be considered the base. A cone has one face, a circle, which is also its base.

One type of solid is a prism. Prisms have two bases that are polygons of the same size and shape. A rectangular prism has a base that is a rectangle. Because squares are rectangles, a cube is a rectangular prism. If the base of a prism is a triangle, it's called a triangular prism. Prisms can have other kinds of polygons as the base, such as hexagonal or octagonal prisms. The prisms that students will study in this lesson are all right prisms. The faces of these prisms that are not the bases are all rectangles (including squares).

Another type of solid figure is a pyramid. Pyramids have one base that is a polygon, such as a triangle, square, rectangle, or other polygon. Like the prism, the shape of its base names the pyramid. If the base is a triangle, the pyramid is called a triangular pyramid. If the base is a rectangle, the pyramid is called a rectangular pyramid. A pyramid with a hexagon base is a hexagonal pyramid, and a pyramid with an octagon base is an octagonal pyramid. The faces that are not the base of the pyramid are all triangles. The edges from the vertices of the base meet at a single vertex.

The world is made up of geometric shapes—such as the sphere seen in an orange, the rectangular prism seen in a skyscraper, and the cylinder in an oatmeal box. Seeing an object made up of combined shapes and being able to identify those shapes and how they go together expands geometric awareness.

▶ Common Errors and Misconceptions

- Students might misinterpret which characteristics define a shape. For example, they may see a triangle that has three equal sides and think that all triangles must have three equal sides. Actually, any shape with only three sides is a triangle.

- Students might not recognize that a shape might be positioned different ways. For example, students might not recognize that the second shape is a square.

- Students might inappropriately use *converse reasoning* when classifying shapes. For example, they might say, "All squares have 4 sides. This shape has 4 sides, so it must be a square."

▶ Safety

Supervise students when they are working with the geometric solid blocks. These blocks have sharp corners.

GET READY Combine Figures

Objectives

- Put geometric figures together to form other geometric figures.

Students will use the online Pattern Blocks Learning Tool to combine plane figures to make new plane figures.

DIRECTIONS FOR USING THE PATTERN BLOCKS LEARNING TOOL

1. Click Free Play. Then read the instructions, and click Start.

2. Drag two green triangles to the canvas. Show students how to rotate the triangles using the Rotate arrows.

3. **Say:** Put the triangles together to make another shape.

   Ask: What shape did you make? rhombus

4. Click the broom to clear the triangles.

5. Have students make several more shapes from pattern-block pieces or create one larger design from many shapes. Ask them to describe the pieces used and resulting shapes. If students are having difficulty, you can suggest that they make one or more of the following:

   - Rectangle (combine two squares)
   - Parallelogram (combine two rhombuses)
   - Hexagon (combine two trapezoids).

LEARN Combine Solids

Objectives

- Determine solid objects that could be combined to create a given solid object.

Students will combine two or more solid shapes to create other solid shapes. Gather the blocks.

1. **Say:** You can put together two or more shapes to create another shape.

2. Model putting a square pyramid on top of a cube to make an object that resembles a house.

   Say: I put the square base of the pyramid on top of a square face of the cube.

   Emphasize the use of geometric terms when describing the blocks.

3. Give students several minutes to explore combining shapes. Have them describe how they are combining the shapes. Encourage them to use math vocabulary to describe the solid figures they use to make other shapes.

4. Discuss with students shapes that cannot be put together, such as the vertex of a cone and a sphere.

5. Have students make a list of solid shapes that are often combined in their environment. Lists might include a sphere and a cone to make an ice-cream cone, and a triangular prism and a rectangular prism to make a barn.

Tips

Encourage students to combine the blocks and small everyday objects shaped like solids to create new shapes.

LEARN Identify Parts

Objectives

- Determine solid objects that could be combined to create a given solid object.

Students will identify the solids that were combined to create a solid object. Encourage students to name the objects that combine to make other objects.

TRY IT Together and Apart

OFFLINE
10 min

Objectives

- Determine solid objects that could be combined to create a given solid object.

Students will practice combining solids to make other shapes and recognizing the solid objects that are combined to create a given figure. Have students turn to the Together and Apart activity page in their Activity Book and read the directions with them.

Students should copy the problems from the Activity Book into their Math Notebook as necessary and solve them there.

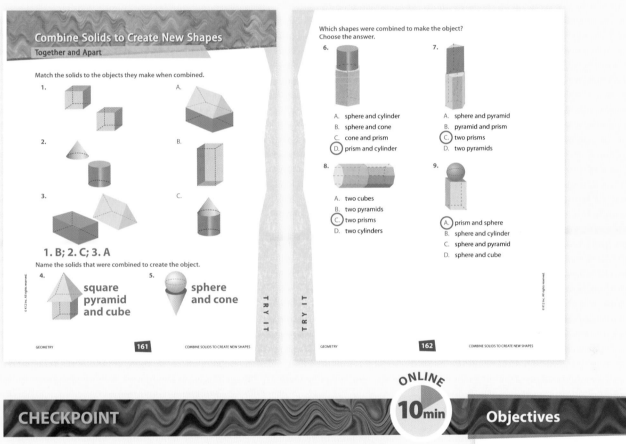

Combine Solids to Create New Shapes
Together and Apart

Match the solids to the objects they make when combined.

1.

A.

2.

B.

3.

C.

1. B; 2. C; 3. A

Name the solids that were combined to create the object.

4. **square pyramid and cube**

5. **sphere and cone**

GEOMETRY 161 COMBINE SOLIDS TO CREATE NEW SHAPES

Which shapes were combined to make the object? Choose the answer.

6.
- A. sphere and cylinder
- B. sphere and cone
- C. cone and prism
- (D.) prism and cylinder

7.
- A. sphere and pyramid
- B. pyramid and prism
- (C.) two prisms
- D. two pyramids

8.
- A. two cubes
- B. two pyramids
- (C.) two prisms
- D. two cylinders

9.
- (A.) prism and sphere
- B. sphere and cylinder
- C. sphere and pyramid
- D. sphere and cube

GEOMETRY 162 COMBINE SOLIDS TO CREATE NEW SHAPES

CHECKPOINT

ONLINE
10 min

Objectives

- Determine solid objects that could be combined to create a given solid object.

Students will complete an online Checkpoint. If necessary, read the directions, problems, and answer choices to students and help them with keyboard or mouse operations.

Unit Review

Lesson Overview

UNIT REVIEW Look Back	10 minutes	ONLINE
UNIT REVIEW Checkpoint Practice	50 minutes	ONLINE
▣ **UNIT REVIEW** Prepare for the Checkpoint		

▶ Unit Objectives

This lesson reviews the following objectives:

- Identify right angles in geometric figures or everyday objects.
- Identify the measure of an angle in a geometric figure or an everyday object as greater than or less than a right angle.
- Identify, describe, and classify a polygon according to the number of its sides.
- Identify attributes of isosceles, equilateral, and right triangles.
- Identify attributes of parallelograms, rectangles, and squares.
- Identify and describe common solid geometric figures.
- Classify common solid geometric figures.
- Determine solid objects that could be combined to create a given solid object.

Materials to Gather

There are no materials to gather for this lesson.

▶ Advance Preparation

In this lesson, students will have an opportunity to review previous activities in the Geometry unit. Look at the suggested activities in Unit Review: Prepare for the Checkpoint online and gather any needed materials.

UNIT REVIEW Look Back

ONLINE **10min**

Students will review key concepts from the unit to prepare for the Unit Checkpoint.

Objectives

- Review unit objectives.

UNIT REVIEW Checkpoint Practice

ONLINE **50min**

Students will complete an online Checkpoint Practice to prepare for the Unit Checkpoint. If necessary, read the directions, problems, and answer choices to students. Have students answer the problems on their own. Review any missed problems with students.

Objectives

- Review unit objectives.

▣ UNIT REVIEW Prepare for the Checkpoint

What you do next depends on how students performed in the previous activity, Unit Review: Checkpoint Practice. If students had difficulty with any of the problems, complete the appropriate review activity listed in the table online.

Unit Checkpoint

UNIT CHECKPOINT Online .... 60 minutes | **ONLINE**

▶ Unit Objectives

This lesson assesses the following objectives:

- Identify right angles in geometric figures or everyday objects.
- Identify the measure of an angle in a geometric figure or an everyday object as greater than or less than a right angle.
- Identify, describe, and classify a polygon according to the number of its sides.
- Identify attributes of isosceles, equilateral, and right triangles.
- Identify attributes of parallelograms, rectangles, and squares.
- Identify and describe common solid geometric figures.
- Classify common solid geometric figures.
- Determine solid objects that could be combined to create a given solid object.

Materials to Gather

There are no materials to gather for this lesson.

UNIT CHECKPOINT Online

ONLINE 60min

Students will complete the Unit Checkpoint online. If necessary, read the directions, problems, and answer choices to students and help them with keyboard or mouse operations.

Objectives

- Assess unit objectives.

Decimals and Money

▶ Unit Objectives

- Identify decimal place values through thousandths.
- Solve a story problem involving addition or subtraction of money amounts in decimal notation.
- Solve a story problem involving multiplication or division of money amounts in decimal notation.

▶ Big Ideas

The use of letters, numbers, and mathematical symbols makes possible the translation of complex situations or long word statements into concise mathematical sentences or expressions.

▶ Unit Introduction

In this unit, students will extend their knowledge of the number system and learn decimal place value to thousandths. They will use models to understand the meaning of decimal numbers, learn how to represent numbers with decimals, and relate decimals to the decimals' fraction representations. Students will use their experience with money to add, subtract, multiply, and divide decimal amounts by single-digit whole numbers.

▶ Keywords

decimal
decimal notation
decimal place value

decimal point
hundredths

tenths
thousandths

Decimal Place Values

Skills Update	5 minutes	ONLINE
GET READY Whole Number Place Value	10 minutes	ONLINE
LEARN Place Value to the Thousandths	10 minutes	ONLINE
LEARN Identify and Read Decimals	15 minutes	OFFLINE
TRY IT Place and Value of Decimal Numbers	10 minutes	OFFLINE
CHECKPOINT	10 minutes	ONLINE

▶ Lesson Objectives

Identify decimal place values through thousandths.

▶ Prerequisite Skills

- Use decimal notation for money.
- Identify the place value for each digit in whole numbers through 10,000.

▶ Content Background

In this lesson, students will learn to identify the place and value of digits in decimal numbers through thousandths.

Decimal numbers are a natural extension of whole numbers. Whole number place values increase by a factor of 10 in each position to the left of the ones. The place-value names are ones, tens, hundreds, thousands, and so forth. Decimal numbers are to the right of the the decimal point. Decimals indicate fractional parts of a whole with place-value names of tenths, hundredths, thousandths, and so forth.

Decimal numbers are simply different representations for their equivalent fractions and mixed numbers. Saying and thinking about decimal numbers correctly promotes a strong and necessary understanding of place value. When students say a decimal number, they will learn to say the word *and* to signal the placement of the decimal. For example, they would read 1.35 as "1 and 35 hundredths." Similarly, students should think about the equivalent fraction representation when they say a decimal number. For example, $1\frac{35}{100}$ is the fraction equivalent of 1.35. It is also important for students to think about the equivalent representation of $1\frac{35}{100}$ as they say the decimal number.

Materials to Gather

SUPPLIED

Decimal Place-Value Chart to Thousandths (printout)

Place and Value of Decimal Numbers activity page

Students will become familiar with and use a place-value chart, such as the one shown here, to identify and understand decimal numbers.

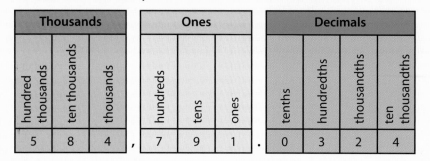

Thousands			Ones			Decimals			
hundred thousands	ten thousands	thousands	hundreds	tens	ones	tenths	hundredths	thousandths	ten thousandths
5	8	4	7	9	1	0	3	2	4

▶ Common Errors and Misconceptions

- Students might use incorrect rules that do not apply as they learn to add and subtract decimal numbers. Therefore, use decimal grids and number line models to remind students of the meaning of decimal addition and subtraction.

- Students might not see the relationship between the models (such as place-value charts and number lines) and the procedures for adding and subtracting decimals. Once they begin to use symbols without models, students might apply memorized rules without thinking about the reasons for the procedures.

▶ Advance Preparation

Print the Decimal Place-Value Chart to Thousandths.

GET READY Whole Number Place Value　ONLINE **10**min

Students will identify the place and value of digits in whole numbers through 10,000.

Objectives

- Identify the place value for each digit in whole numbers through 10,000.

LEARN Place Value to the Thousandths　ONLINE **10**min

Students will learn the names and meanings of the decimal place-value positions through thousandths. They will see that on a place-value chart, starting with the highest value on the left, they divide each place value by 10 to get the value of the place to the right.

Objectives

- Identify decimal place values through thousandths.

- In the ten thousands place, divide 10,000 by 10 to get 1,000 (the value of the thousands place).
- Divide 1,000 by 10 to get 100 as the value of the hundreds place.
- Divide 100 by 10 to get 10 as the value of the tens place.
- Divide 10 by 10 to get 1 as the value of the ones place.

When students get to the ones place, the pattern continues. The ones place is 1 whole.

- Divide 1 whole by 10 to get $\frac{1}{10}$ as the value of the tenths place to the right.

- Write "1 tenth" as 0.1. Always place a zero in front of the decimal number when there is no digit in the ones place.

Continuing the pattern:

- Divide 0.1 by 10 to get 1 hundredth in the hundredths place; $\frac{1}{100}$ is written 0.01 as a decimal.
- Divide 0.01 by 10 to get 1 thousandth in the thousandths place; $\frac{1}{1,000}$ is written 0.001 as a decimal.

Encourage students to watch the animations several times to understand this important idea.

LEARN Identify and Read Decimals

OFFLINE 15 min

Students will identify the value of digits in a decimal number and learn to read decimal numbers.

Gather the Decimal Place-Value Chart to Thousandths.

Objectives

- Identify decimal place values through thousandths.

DECIMAL PLACE VALUE

1. Write the number 253 in the place-value chart and have students read it aloud. two hundred fifty-three

   Have students identify the place value of each digit in the number. 2 is in the hundreds place, 5 is in the tens place, 3 is in the ones place

2. Explain that just as the value of a whole number depends on its place value, the value of a decimal number depends on its place value. Review each decimal place value in the chart—tenths, hundredths, and thousandths. Also point out the decimal point and remind students that the decimal point separates the whole, or ones place, from the tenths place.

3. Write 1.436 in the chart. Ask students to identify the place value of each digit in the number. 1 is in the ones place, 4 is in the tenths place, 3 is in the hundredths place, 6 is in the thousandths place

   Repeat twice with the following numbers:

   - 3.809 3 is in the ones place, 8 is in the tenths place, 0 is in the hundredths place, 9 is in the thousandths place
   - 2.716 2 is in the ones place, 7 is in the tenths place, 1 is in the hundredths place, 6 is in the thousandths place

ten thousands	thousands	,	hundreds	tens	ones	.	tenths	hundredths	thousandths
			2	5	3				
					1	.	4	3	6
					3	.	8	0	9
					2	.	7	1	6

VALUE OF A DIGIT IN ITS PLACE

4. Refer to the number 253 in the place-value chart. Identify the values of each digit in the number. (The value of the 2 is 200, the value of the 5 is 50, and the value of the 3 is 3.) Emphasize that the place value of each digit determines its value.

5. Refer to the number 1.436 in the place-value chart.

   Ask: What is the value of the digit 4 in 1.436?

   Guide students to see that since the 4 is in the tenths place, its value is 4 tenths. Have them write 0.4 and read it as "four tenths." Have them identify and write the value of the digits 3 and 6 in 1.436. Students should explain that the value of the 3 is 3 hundredths, 0.03, and the value of the 6 is 6 thousandths, 0.006.

6. Have students identify the value of each digit in 3.809 and 2.716. Encourage them to use the place-value chart labels to help them determine each digit's value.

- **3.809** the value of the 3 is 3 ones; the value of the 8 is 8 tenths; the value of the 0 is 0 hundredths; the value of the 9 is 9 thousandths

- **2.716** the value of the 2 is 2 ones; the value of the 7 is 7 tenths; the value of the 1 is 1 hundredth; the value of the 6 is 6 thousandths

7. Remind students that the decimal point separates the whole-number part from the decimal part. Explain that to read a decimal number, they first read the whole-number part (if there is one), then say *and* for the decimal point, and then read the decimal part, followed by the name of the final place value. If students have difficulty saying the names, have them practice saying "tens, tenTHS, hundreds, hundredTHS, thousands, thousandTHS" so they can hear the difference.

- Explain that if the number ends in the tenths place, say "tenths" at the end.
  Write 1.4 in the place-value chart and say "one and four tenths."

- Explain that if the number ends in the hundredths place, say "hundredths" at the end.
  Write 1.35 in the place-value chart and say "one and thirty-five hundredths."

- Explain that if the number ends in the thousandths place, say "thousandths" at the end.
  Write 1.562 in the place-value chart and say "one and five hundred sixty-two thousandths."

8. In the place-value chart, write the numbers 2.853, 6.71, and 3.9. Have students read the numbers aloud.

- **2.853** two and eight hundred fifty-three thousandths

- **6.71** six and seventy-one hundredths

- **3.9** three and nine tenths

ten thousands	thousands	,	hundreds	tens	ones	.	tenths	hundredths	thousandths
					2	.	8	5	3
					6	.	7	1	
					3	.	9		

TRY IT Place and Value of Decimal Numbers

OFFLINE 10 min

Objectives

- Identify decimal place values through thousandths.

Students will practice identifying the place and value of digits in decimal numbers through thousandths. Have students turn to the Place and Value of Decimal Numbers activity page in their Activity Book and read the directions with them.

Students should copy the problems from the Activity Book into their Math Notebook as necessary and solve them there.

Decimal Place Values

Place and Value of Decimal Numbers

Choose the answer.

1. Which number has a 6 in the tenths place?
   A. 50.06   (B.) 58.6
   C. 63.589   D. 73.536

2. Which number has a 3 in the hundredths place?
   (A.) 286.63   B. 386.72
   C. 472.123   D. 521.38

3. Which number has a 4 in the thousandths place?
   A. 38.84   (B.) 56.234
   C. 183.432   D. 4,195.38

4. Which digit is in the hundredths place in the number 2,758.492?
   A. 2   B. 4
   C. 7   (D.) 9

5. Which digit is in the tenths place in the number 854.397?
   (A.) 3   B. 4
   C. 5   D. 9

6. Which shows 8 thousandths written as a decimal?
   (A.) 0.008   B. 0.08
   C. 0.8   D. 8,000.0

Answer the question.

7. Which digit is in the tenths place in the number 469.283?
   2

8. Which digit is in the hundredths place in the number 1,207.639?
   3

Write the place value of the digit 4 in the number.

9. 5.426   10. 3.954   11. 4.267   12. 0.348
   tenths   **thousandths**   **ones**   **hundredths**

Write the value of the digit 8 in the number.

13. 0.985   14. 2.832   15. 1.008
   0.08 or   **0.8 or**   **0.008 or**
   8 hundredths   **8 tenths**   **8 thousandths**

DECIMALS AND MONEY   **163**   DECIMAL PLACE VALUES

TRY IT

CHECKPOINT

ONLINE 10 min

Objectives

- Identify decimal place values through thousandths.

Students will complete an online Checkpoint. If necessary, read the directions, problems, and answer choices to students and help them with keyboard or mouse operations.

Money in Decimal Notation

▶ Lesson Objectives

Solve a story problem involving addition or subtraction of money amounts in decimal notation.

▶ Prerequisite Skills

Identify decimal place values through thousandths.

▶ Content Background

Students will learn to solve story problems involving addition or subtraction of money amounts in decimal notation.

Avoid using "can't take away" with students. Do not say, "You can't take away 4 from 3." Instead say, "There aren't enough pennies in the hundredths place to take away 4 pennies, so regroup 1 dime in the tenths place." Also avoid using a rote rule that says to line up the decimal points before adding or subtracting. This leads to answers that don't have a true meaning to students.

Students will use their knowledge of place value to add and subtract money amounts. They will learn to add digits with the same place value by using money as a model, thinking of hundredths as pennies, tenths as dimes, and ones as dollars.

▶ Advance Preparation

Print the Decimal Place-Value Chart to Thousandths.

Materials to Gather

SUPPLIED

Decimal Place-Value Chart to Thousandths (printout)

Add or Subtract Money Amounts activity page

Solve Money Story Problems activity page

GET READY Decimal Place Values 10min

Objectives

- Identify decimal place values through thousandths

Students will identify the value and place value of digits in decimal numbers through thousandths.

LEARN Add or Subtract Money Amounts

Objectives

- Solve a story problem involving addition or subtraction of money amounts in decimal notation.

Students will work to solve story problems that involve addition and subtraction of money amounts. Students will add and subtract amounts that include dollars, dimes, and pennies.

Gather the Decimal Place-Value Chart to Thousandths.

1. Review the place-value chart. Remind students that when going from left to right on the place-value chart, they divide each place value by 10 to get the value of the place to the right. Emphasize that dividing by 10 to the right of the ones place leads to the decimal place values of tenths, hundredths, and thousandths.

2. Write 2.14 in the place-value chart. Have students read the decimal number as "two and fourteen hundredths."

3. Explain that a common use of decimal numbers is representing amounts of money. Write a dollar symbol to the left of the 2 in the place-value chart. Tell students to think of the ones place as the $1 bills. Write "$1 bills" beside *ones*. Explain that dividing the ones, or dollars, by 10 leads to the next place value to the right.

    Say: Divide 1 dollar into 10 equal parts. How much is in each part? 10 cents or 1 dime

    Tell students that the tenths place can be thought of as dimes. Write "dimes" beside *tenths*.

    Say: Divide 1 dime into 10 equal parts. How much is in each part? 1 cent or 1 penny

    Tell students to think of the hundredths place as pennies and write "pennies" beside *hundredths*.

    Be sure students understand that there is no coin to represent the thousandths place.

4. Tell students that when reading decimal numbers as money, they say the dollar amount first, say *"and"* for the decimal point, and then say the cents amount. Have students read the money amount aloud as "two dollars and fourteen cents."

5. Explain that thinking of place value as dollars, dimes, and pennies can help students understand how to add and subtract decimals and money amounts. Read the following problem:

    - Sam has 426 stamps. He buys 253 more stamps at the stamp show. How many stamps does Sam have now?

    Have students write the problem vertically and add.

6. Have students turn to the Add or Subtract Money Amounts activity page in their Activity Book. Direct students' attention to the Worked Examples. Read Problem 1 with students.

    Ask: How do you know that you need to add the numbers in this problem? because the problem says to combine amounts

    Point out that this problem is similar to the problem about stamps in Step 5. In that problem, students lined up numbers of the same place value, then added.

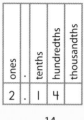

$2\frac{14}{100}$

two *and* fourteen hundredths

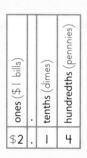

$$\begin{array}{r} 426 \\ + 253 \\ \hline 679 \end{array}$$

7. Read the Solution with students. Have them write the problem in their Math Notebook, then add. Make sure they lined up numbers of the same place value in the same column. Also make sure they included the dollar symbols and decimal points. Ask students how many dollars, dimes, and pennies Sam has altogether. 6 dollars, 7 dimes, and 9 pennies

8. Have them read the sum aloud. six dollars and seventy-nine cents

   Place your finger over the dollar symbol in the sum in the Worked Example. Have the students read the decimal number 6.79 as "six and seventy-nine hundredths." Point out that with the dollar symbol, they say it in dollars and cents, and without the dollar symbol, they say it as whole numbers and fractions.

9. Read Problem 2 with students.

   Ask: How do you solve this problem? subtract, because the problem asks how much is left after one amount is taken away from another amount

10. Read the Solution with students. Have them write the numbers in their Math Notebook, then subtract. Make sure they lined up numbers of the same place value in the same column. Also make sure they included the dollar symbols and decimal points. Ask students how many dollars, dimes, and pennies the scouts have left. 86 dollars, 4 dimes, and 2 pennies

11. Have them read the answer aloud. eighty-six dollars and forty-two cents

    Place your finger over the dollar symbol in the difference in the Worked Example. Have the students read the decimal number 86.42 as "eighty-six and forty-two hundredths."

12. Work with students to solve the remaining problems. Read Problem 1 in the problem set with them. Guide them to see that they need to add to solve the problem. Have them write the problem vertically. Be sure they write the numbers of the same place value in the same column. Remind students to start by adding the pennies, then the dimes, and then the dollars. This problem requires regrouping. Students should be familiar with regrouping, but guide them to regroup 10 pennies for 1 dime and 10 dimes for 1 dollar.

    Have students add to solve the problem. Have them read the sum aloud. nine dollars and twenty-five cents

13. Read Problem 2 in the problem set with students. Guide them to see that they need to subtract to solve the problem.

    Have them write the problem vertically. Point out that they should line up the dollar symbols.

14. For additional practice, give students a blank copy of the Decimal Place-Value Chart to Thousandths. Read aloud the number "sixteen and eighty-seven hundredths." Have students write the number in the chart. Make sure they placed all the numbers in the correct columns. Repeat this step with the following numbers:

    • seventy-seven and seventy-seven hundredths
    • one hundred one and fifteen hundredths
    • three thousand and nine hundredths

ten thousands	thousands	,	hundreds	tens	ones	.	tenths	hundredths	thousandths
				1	6	.	8	7	
				7	7	.	7	7	
			1	0	1	.	1	5	
	3	,	0	0	0	.	0	9	

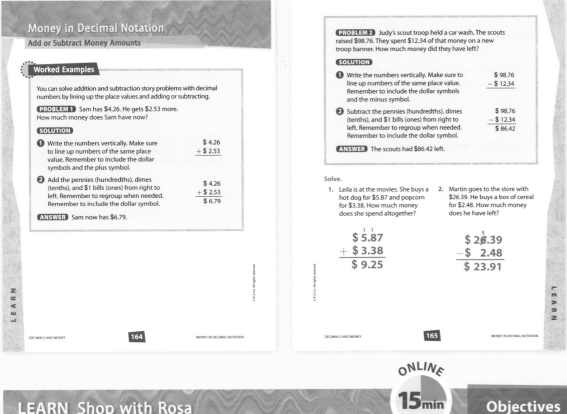

Money in Decimal Notation
Add or Subtract Money Amounts

Worked Examples

You can solve addition and subtraction story problems with decimal numbers by lining up the place values and adding or subtracting.

PROBLEM 1 Sam has $4.26. He gets $2.53 more. How much money does Sam have now?

SOLUTION

❶ Write the numbers vertically. Make sure to line up numbers of the same place value. Remember to include the dollar symbols and the plus symbol.

$$\begin{array}{r} \$\,4.26 \\ +\ \$\,2.53 \\ \hline \end{array}$$

❷ Add the pennies (hundredths), dimes (tenths), and $1 bills (ones) from right to left. Remember to regroup when needed. Remember to include the dollar symbol.

$$\begin{array}{r} \$\,4.26 \\ +\ \$\,2.53 \\ \hline \$\,6.79 \end{array}$$

ANSWER Sam now has $6.79.

PROBLEM 2 Judy's scout troop held a car wash. The scouts raised $98.76. They spent $12.34 of that money on a new troop banner. How much money did they have left?

SOLUTION

❶ Write the numbers vertically. Make sure to line up numbers of the same place value. Remember to include the dollar symbols and the minus symbol.

$$\begin{array}{r} \$\,98.76 \\ -\ \$\,12.34 \\ \hline \end{array}$$

❷ Subtract the pennies (hundredths), dimes (tenths), and $1 bills (ones) from right to left. Remember to regroup when needed. Remember to include the dollar symbol.

$$\begin{array}{r} \$\,98.76 \\ -\ \$\,12.34 \\ \hline \$\,86.42 \end{array}$$

ANSWER The scouts had $86.42 left.

Solve.

1. Leila is at the movies. She buys a hot dog for $5.87 and popcorn for $3.38. How much money does she spend altogether?

$$\begin{array}{r} \overset{1\ \ 1}{\$\ 5.87} \\ +\ \$\ 3.38 \\ \hline \$\ 9.25 \end{array}$$

2. Martin goes to the store with $26.39. He buys a box of cereal for $2.48. How much money does he have left?

$$\begin{array}{r} \$\ 2\overset{5}{\cancel{6}}.39 \\ -\ \$\ \ 2.48 \\ \hline \$\ 23.91 \end{array}$$

LEARN Shop with Rosa

ONLINE 15 min

Students will solve addition and subtraction story problems involving money. They will use place value and regrouping strategies to solve problems.

Tips — Remind students that they should add or subtract each place value with like place values. They should add or subtract hundredths to hundredths, tenths to tenths, and ones to ones, regrouping when necessary.

Objectives

- Solve a story problem involving addition or subtraction of money amounts in decimal notation.

TRY IT Solve Money Story Problems

Students will practice solving addition and subtraction story problems involving money amounts. Reinforce the importance of decimal place value and writing the dollar symbol and decimal point in each answer. Have students turn to the Solve Money Story Problems activity page in their Activity Book and read the directions with them.

Students should copy the problems from the Activity Book into their Math Notebook as necessary and solve them there.

Objectives

- Solve a story problem involving addition or subtraction of money amounts in decimal notation.

Tips

Remind students to add or subtract like place values starting from the right with hundredths, then tenths, then ones.

Money in Decimal Notation
Solve Money Story Problems

Solve.

1. Ava is at the store with $16.00. She buys a new doll for $12.75. How much money does Ava have left? **$3.25**

2. Thomas worked as a pet sitter for three weeks. He earned $15.50, $10.75, and $20.25. How much money did Thomas earn in all? **$46.50**

Choose the answer.

3. Carlos bought a notebook for $3.24, a pencil for $1.79, and an eraser for $2.23. What was the total cost of these three items?

   A. $6.26   B. $6.16   C. $7.16   (D.) $7.26

4. Manuel bought toothpaste for $5.49 and a toothbrush for $2.99. What was the total cost of the two items?

   A. $2.50   B. $7.38   C. $8.38   (D.) $8.48

5. Jia bought a frame for $19.44 and a piece of art for $24.75. What was the cost of the two items?

   (A.) $44.19   B. $43.19   C. $33.19   D. $5.31

6. Cari bought a ball for $2.49. She gave the cashier $3.00. How much money did she get back?

   (A.) $0.51   B. $0.61   C. $1.49   D. $5.49

TRY IT

Money Story Problems (A)

Lesson Overview

Skills Update	5 minutes	ONLINE
GET READY Select the Operation	5 minutes	ONLINE
LEARN Multiply Money Amounts	15 minutes	ONLINE
LEARN Aquarium Story Problems	25 minutes	OFFLINE
TRY IT Money Stories and Multiplication	10 minutes	OFFLINE

▶ Lesson Objectives

Solve a story problem involving multiplication or division of money amounts in decimal notation.

▶ Prerequisite Skills

- Use decimal notation for money.
- Determine whether addition, subtraction, multiplication, or division is the appropriate operation to use to solve a story problem and solve the story problem.

▶ Content Background

Students will learn how to solve story problems in which they multiply amounts of money using the dollar symbol and a decimal point.

Students have added money amounts using decimal notation. They have seen that when the amounts in the hundredths place (pennies) and the tenths place (dimes) are added, the decimal point stays between the ones and the tenths place. When learning about multiplying money amounts using decimal notation, students will first use repeated addition to find the answer. This helps them to see that multiplication is simply repeated addition and makes it easier for them to know where to place the decimal point in the answer. As long as students think about each place value, there will be no question as to where the decimal point goes. For example, in a problem like the one shown here, students will notice that when they add 9 five times, it's the same as multiplying 5×9. Notice that in the example, whether students add 9 pennies five times or multiply 5×9 pennies, they get 45 pennies. This amount is regrouped to become 4 dimes and 5 pennies.

Materials to Gather

SUPPLIED

Aquarium Story Problems activity page

Money Stories and Multiplication activity page

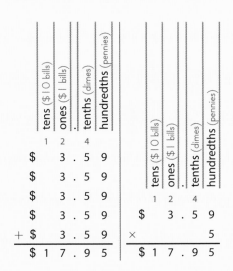

▶ Common Errors and Misconceptions

- Students might use incorrect rules that do not apply as they learn to multiply and divide decimal numbers. To remind students of the meaning of decimal multiplication and division, make connections to everyday situations familiar to them.
- Students might not see the relationship between the models (such as decimal grids) and the procedures for multiplying and dividing decimals. Once they begin to use symbols without models, students might apply memorized rules without thinking about the reasons for the procedures.

GET READY Select the Operation

ONLINE 5 min

Students will select which operation to use to solve story problems involving money amounts. When students see the problem about the 9 reference books, remind them that it's more efficient to multiply the cost by 9 than to add the cost 9 times. Encourage students to explain how they know what operation to use to solve each problem. Students will not solve the problems but will identify the operation that would be used to solve the problem.

Objectives

- Use decimal notation for money.
- Determine whether addition, subtraction, multiplication, or division is the appropriate operation to use to solve a story problem and solve the problem.

LEARN Multiply Money Amounts

ONLINE 15 min

Students will learn to multiply using decimals and will solve multiplication story problems using money amounts. Encourage students to explain why each step on the screen is correct.

Tips Have students work the example on paper as they see it worked out on the screen.

Objectives

- Solve a story problem involving multiplication or division of money amounts in decimal notation.

LEARN Aquarium Story Problems

OFFLINE 25 min

Students will solve multiplication story problems that involve money amounts in decimal notation. Have students turn to the Aquarium Story Problems activity page in their Activity Book and read the directions with them.

Students should copy the problems from the Activity Book into their Math Notebook as necessary and solve them there.

1. Direct students' attention to the Worked Example on the activity page. Read the problem with them. Ask them why multiplication is used to solve this problem. Each ticket is the same price.

2. Remind students that multiplying money amounts written as decimal numbers is done using the same steps as in multiplying whole numbers. Tell them that they can think of the hundredths as pennies, the tenths as dimes, and the ones as dollars.

3. Read the solution and the answer with students.

4. Have students solve the remaining problems on the Activity Book page. For each problem, have them explain what the problem is asking and tell how they will solve it. Then work through the computation together. Reinforce writing the dollar symbol and decimal point in the answers.

Tips Have students use grid paper or lined paper turned sideways to record their work, which helps them keep the place values aligned.

Objectives

- Solve a story problem involving multiplication or division of money amounts in decimal notation.

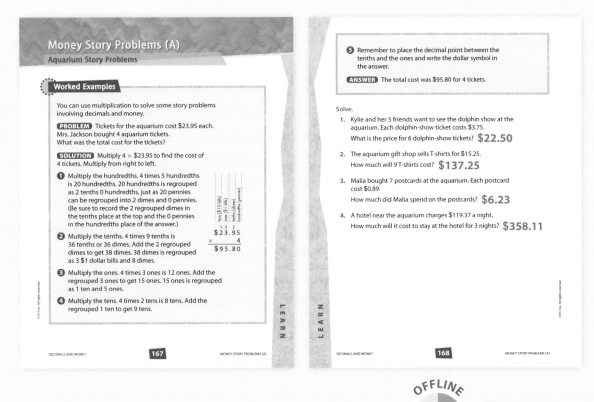

Money Story Problems (A)
Aquarium Story Problems

Worked Examples

You can use multiplication to solve some story problems involving decimals and money.

PROBLEM Tickets for the aquarium cost $23.95 each. Mrs. Jackson bought 4 aquarium tickets. What was the total cost for the tickets?

SOLUTION Multiply 4 × $23.95 to find the cost of 4 tickets. Multiply from right to left.

❶ Multiply the hundredths. 4 times 5 hundredths is 20 hundredths. 20 hundredths is regrouped as 2 tenths 0 hundredths, just as 20 pennies can be regrouped into 2 dimes and 0 pennies. (Be sure to record the 2 regrouped dimes in the tenths place at the top and the 0 pennies in the hundredths place of the answer.)

❷ Multiply the tenths. 4 times 9 tenths is 36 tenths or 36 dimes. Add the 2 regrouped dimes to get 38 dimes. 38 dimes is regrouped as 3 $1 dollar bills and 8 dimes.

❸ Multiply the ones. 4 times 3 ones is 12 ones. Add the regrouped 3 ones to get 15 ones. 15 ones is regrouped as 1 ten and 5 ones.

❹ Multiply the tens. 4 times 2 tens is 8 tens. Add the regrouped 1 ten to get 9 tens.

```
      1 3 2
    $ 2 3 . 9 5
  ×           4
    $ 9 5 . 8 0
```

❺ Remember to place the decimal point between the tenths and the ones and write the dollar symbol in the answer.

ANSWER The total cost was $95.80 for 4 tickets.

Solve.

1. Kylie and her 5 friends want to see the dolphin show at the aquarium. Each dolphin-show ticket costs $3.75.
   What is the price for 6 dolphin-show tickets? **$22.50**

2. The aquarium gift shop sells T-shirts for $15.25.
   How much will 9 T-shirts cost? **$137.25**

3. Malia bought 7 postcards at the aquarium. Each postcard cost $0.89.
   How much did Malia spend on the postcards? **$6.23**

4. A hotel near the aquarium charges $119.37 a night.
   How much will it cost to stay at the hotel for 3 nights? **$358.11**

TRY IT Money Stories and Multiplication

OFFLINE 10 min

Students will practice multiplying money amounts to solve story problems. Have students turn to the Money Stories and Multiplication activity page in their Activity Book and read the directions with them.

Students should copy the problems from the Activity Book into their Math Notebook as necessary and solve them there.

Objectives

- Solve a story problem involving multiplication or division of money amounts in decimal notation.

Tips

Have students use grid paper or lined paper turned sideways to help them keep the place values aligned.

Money Story Problems (A)
Money Stories and Multiplication

Solve.

1. Tina bought 3 cat toys at the pet store. Each cat toy cost $4.67. How much did Tina spend on cat toys? **$14.01**

2. The pet store is having a sale on large bags of dog food. 1 large bag costs $21.85. What is the cost for 5 large bags of dog food? **$109.25**

3. Sophie bought 6 kitchen chairs. Each chair cost $48.79. How much did Sophie spend on chairs? **$292.74**

Choose the answer.

4. Mira bought 7 oranges. Each orange cost $0.49. How much did Mira spend on oranges?

   A. $0.07   B. $0.70   C. $2.83   (D.) $3.43

Money Story Problems (B)

Lesson Overview

GET READY Picnic Time	10 minutes	ONLINE
LEARN Model Money Division	10 minutes	ONLINE
LEARN Divide Money Amounts	10 minutes	ONLINE
LEARN Zoo Story Problems	20 minutes	OFFLINE
TRY IT Money Stories and Division	10 minutes	OFFLINE

▶ Lesson Objectives

Solve a story problem involving multiplication or division of money amounts in decimal notation.

▶ Prerequisite Skills

- Use decimal notation for money.
- Determine whether addition, subtraction, multiplication, or division is the appropriate operation to use to solve a story problem and solve the story problem.

▶ Content Background

Students will learn how to solve story problems in which they divide amounts of money using the dollar symbol and a decimal point.

Avoid using the phrase "goes into" as in "5 goes into $40.00" when discussing division. Instead say "$40.00 divided by 5" or "5 divides $40.00."

Students have learned the meaning of division and the division algorithm (the steps to solving a longer division problem). They have learned about decimals and will apply what they know about division and place value to divide monetary amounts using decimal notation. Students will learn to see the place values of tenths and hundredths as dimes and pennies in monetary amounts. As they multiply or divide, they will learn that if they think of dividing each place value by the whole-number divisor, they will be able to understand the placement of the decimal point in the quotient.

By working with place value, students will be able to take advantage of a shortcut for recording division in which they record their division process as shown here. With this method, they divide each digit by the divisor and record the results, regrouping any leftover numbers into the next place value as shown. Following this method will help students stay focused on the meaning of the division rather than on the rote steps of recording long division.

Materials to Gather

SUPPLIED

Zoo Story Problems activity page

Money Stories and Division activity page

▶ Common Errors and Misconceptions

- Students might use incorrect rules that do not apply as they learn to multiply and divide decimal numbers. To remind students of the meaning of decimal multiplication and division, make connections to everyday situations familiar to them.

- Students might not see the relationship between the models (such as decimal grids) and the procedures for multiplying and dividing decimals. Once they begin to use symbols without models, students might apply memorized rules without thinking about the reasons for the procedures.

GET READY Picnic Time

ONLINE 10 min

Students will solve story problems involving money Have students do the calculations in their notebooks and enter the answers on-screen. Encourage them to explain how they are finding the amounts and how they know where the decimal goes in the answer.

Objectives

- Use decimal notation for money.
- Determine whether addition, subtraction, multiplication, or division is the appropriate operation to use to solve a story problem and solve the story problem.

LEARN Model Money Division

ONLINE 10 min

Students will review multiplying money amounts. They will model dividing money amounts. You can use the chart shown here to review place value with students.

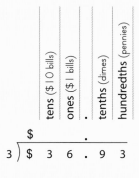

Objectives

- Solve a story problem involving multiplication or division of money amounts in decimal notation.

Tips

Students can easily divide three $10 bills, six $1 bills, nine dimes, and three pennies among three people. Emphasize that writing the division problem is just a way to record the results.

LEARN Divide Money Amounts

ONLINE 10 min

Students will learn to divide using decimals and will solve a division story problem using money amounts.

Objectives

- Solve a story problem involving multiplication or division of money amounts in decimal notation.

LEARN Zoo Story Problems

Students will solve division story problems that involve money amounts in decimal notation. Have students turn to the Zoo Story Problems activity page in their Activity Book and read the directions with them.

Students should copy the problems from the Activity Book into their Math Notebook as necessary and solve them there.

1. Read the problem from the Worked Example with students. Ask why division is used to solve this problem. We know the total cost for 5 tickets, so we divide to find the cost of each ticket.

   Remind students that the steps for dividing money amounts written as decimal numbers are the same as those for dividing whole numbers.

2. Read the Solution with students. Have them write out the problem, step by step, as you go over it with them.

3. Have students think about the place values as money to help them understand the division. In Step 4, it may be easier for students to think of dividing 47 dimes into 5 equal groups. They would then realize that 45 of the dimes would have been used and 2 dimes left to regroup into pennies.

   Note that the shortcut method of division is used here to help students focus on dividing the amount in each place-value position. When dividing by a one-digit number, this method is easier than writing down all the steps of the standard algorithm.

4. Have students solve the remaining problems on the Activity Book page. For each problem, have students explain what the problem is asking and how they will solve the problem. Then work through the computation together. Reinforce writing the dollar symbol and decimal point in the answers.

Objectives

- Solve a story problem involving multiplication or division of money amounts in decimal notation.

Tips

Have students use grid paper or lined paper turned sideways to record their work, which helps them keep the place values aligned.

Money Story Problems (B)
Zoo Story Problems

Worked Examples

You can use division to solve some story problems involving decimals and money.

PROBLEM Mr. Roth buys 5 tickets to the zoo. Each ticket costs the same amount. He spends a total of $59.75. How much does each ticket cost?

SOLUTION Divide $59.75 by 5 to find the cost of each ticket. Divide, starting with the greatest place value and moving left to right from the tens to the ones, then the tenths, and finally the hundredths.

1. Divide the tens. 5 tens divided by 5 is 1 ten. Record the 1 in the tens place. There are no tens left over.

2. Divide the ones. 9 ones divided by 5 is 1, with 4 ones left over. Record the 1 in the ones place. Regroup the 4 ones as 40 tenths. Show the 40 tenths with a small 4 in the tenths place. There are now 47 tenths.

3. Place the decimal point between the ones place and the tenths place in the answer.

4. Divide the tenths. 47 tenths divided by 5 is 9, with 2 tenths left over. Record the 9 in the tenths place. Regroup the 2 tenths as 20 hundredths. Show the 20 hundredths with a small 2 in the hundredths place. There are now 25 hundredths.

5. Divide the hundredths. 25 hundredths divided by 5 is 5 hundredths with no hundredths left over. Record the 5 in the hundredths place. Write the dollar symbol in the answer.

ANSWER Each ticket costs $11.95.

Solve.

1. 4 friends have a total of $48.60 to spend at the zoo. If they share the money equally, how much will each person get? **$12.15**

2. Erin bought 3 animal plush toys at the zoo gift shop. She spent a total of $21.45. Each animal plush toy was the same price. What is the price of 1 animal plush toy? **$7.15**

3. Mr. Roth and his family stayed at the hotel near the zoo. The total cost for their 3-night stay was $391.53. What was the cost for 1 night? **$130.51**

TRY IT Money Stories and Division

Students will practice dividing money amounts to solve story problems. Have students turn to the Money Stories and Division activity page in their Activity Book and read the directions with them.

Students should copy the problems from the Activity Book into their Math Notebook as necessary and solve them there.

- Solve a story problem involving multiplication or division of money amounts in decimal notation.

Tips

Have students use grid paper or lined paper turned sideways to help them keep the place values aligned.

Money Story Problems (B)
Money Stories and Division

Solve.

1. Monique rented a bike for $15.99 for 3 hours. How much did Monique spend for each hour? **$5.33**

2. The soccer team paid $247.26 for 6 new uniforms. How much did each uniform cost? **$41.21**

Choose the answer.

3. Alexander spent a total of $64.26 for 6 identical bunches of flowers. How much did each bunch of flowers cost?

   A. $1.71   (B.) $10.71   C. $17.10   D. $385.56

4. Walter rented a car for $875.25 for 9 days. How much did the car cost each day?

   (A.) $97.25   B. $97.50   C. $7,235.85   D. $62.87

TRY IT

DECIMALS AND MONEY   **172**   MONEY STORY PROBLEMS (B)

Money Story Problems (C)

Lesson Overview

GET READY Decimal Number Review	10 minutes	ONLINE
LEARN Two-Step Money Story Problems	10 minutes	ONLINE
LEARN Art Club Story Problems	20 minutes	OFFLINE
TRY IT Money Stories	10 minutes	OFFLINE
CHECKPOINT	10 minutes	ONLINE

▶ Lesson Objectives

Solve a story problem involving multiplication or division of money amounts in decimal notation.

▶ Prerequisite Skills

- Use decimal notation for money.
- Determine whether addition, subtraction, multiplication, or division is the appropriate operation to use to solve a story problem and solve the problem.

Materials to Gather

SUPPLIED

Art Club Story Problems activity page

Money Stories activity page

▶ Content Background

Students have added, subtracted, multiplied, and divided money amounts. The activities in this lesson focus on applying these skills to solve story problems that involve more than one computation. When a story problem has a two-step solution, the order of completing the steps may be important. For example, a person buys 3 shirts priced at $4.50 each and pays with a $20 bill. To find the amount of change, students should first multiply 3 × $4.50 and then subtract the product from $20.00 to get $6.50. Notice that in this example, the money amount, $20, was rewritten with additional place values. Students can add a decimal point and zeros to any whole-number dollar amount without changing its value.

▶ Common Errors and Misconceptions

- Students might use incorrect rules that do not apply as they learn to multiply and divide decimal numbers. To remind students of the meaning of decimal multiplication and division, make connections to everyday situations familiar to them.
- Students might not see the relationship between the models (such as decimal grids) and the procedures for multiplying and dividing decimals. Once they begin to use symbols without models, students might apply memorized rules without thinking about the reasons for the procedures.

GET READY Decimal Number Review

Objectives

Students will identify the place value of digits in decimal numbers. They will also solve story problems involving multiplication and division of money amounts. Have students work the problems on paper and enter their answers on-screen.

- Use decimal notation for money.
- Determine whether addition, subtraction, multiplication, or division is the appropriate operation to use to solve a story problem and solve the problem.

LEARN Two-Step Money Story Problems

Objectives

Students will learn to solve two-step story problems that involve adding, subtracting, multiplying, or dividing money amounts. Encourage students to explain why each step of the solution is correct.

- Solve a story problem involving multiplication or division of money amounts in decimal notation.

LEARN Art Club Story Problems

Objectives

Students will solve story problems that involve money amounts in decimal notation. The problems have two steps. Have students turn to the Art Club Story Problems activity page in their Activity Book and read the directions with them.

Students should copy the problems from the Activity Book into their Math Notebook as necessary and solve them there.

- Solve a story problem involving multiplication or division of money amounts in decimal notation.

1. Read the Worked Example aloud to students. Point out that this is a two-step problem. Point out that the total cost is shared among three friends. Guide students to see that they must first multiply the number of jars by the cost of each jar to find the total cost. Ask students to copy the problem into their Math Notebook as you work through each step.

2. Point to Step 1. Ask students to multiply $3.27 by 5.

   Ask: In which places do you need to regroup? all three places

   Remind students to record the decimal point and dollar symbol in the answer.

3. Point to Step 2. Explain that division is used to share a value equally. Ask students to divide $16.35 by 3. Guide students as they divide each place value, moving from left to right. Discuss placing the decimal point between the ones and the tenths and writing the dollar symbol in the answer.

4. Have students solve the remaining problems on the Activity Book page. For each problem, have students explain what the problem is asking and tell how they will solve each step. Then work through the computation together. Reinforce writing the dollar symbol and decimal point in the answers.

Tips

Have students use grid paper or lined paper turned sideways to record their work, which helps them keep the place values aligned.

Worked Examples

You can solve two-step problems using multiplication and division with money amounts.

PROBLEM The art club wanted to buy 5 jars of paint at $3.27 a jar. Three members of the club said they would share the cost. How much did each person have to pay?

SOLUTION Break down the problem into steps and solve each step.

❶ Multiply to find the total cost of 5 jars of paint at $3.27 each.

$$\begin{array}{r} \overset{1\ 3}{\$\ 3.27} \\ \times\qquad 5 \\ \hline \$16.35 \end{array}$$

❷ Divide the total cost by 3 to see how much each person had to pay.

$$\begin{array}{r} \$\ 5.45 \\ 3)\overline{\$16.35} \end{array}$$

ANSWER Each person had to pay $5.45.

Solve.

1. Mr. Mathews ordered 8 boxes of markers for $3.25 each and a package of construction paper for $5.70. What was the total amount of his order?

   See below.

2. Lisa spent a total of $46.00 at the art store. She bought a set of colored pencils for $31.60 and spent the rest on 6 tubes of glue. How much did each tube of glue cost?

   See below.

L E A R N

Additional Answers

1. **Step 1:** Multiply 8 × $3.25 to find the total cost of the 8 boxes of markers.

   $$\begin{array}{r} \overset{2\ 4}{\$\ 3.25} \\ \times\qquad 8 \\ \hline \$\ 26.00 \end{array}$$

   Step 2: Add the cost of the construction paper ($5.70) to the total cost of the markers.

   $$\begin{array}{r} \$\ 26.00 \\ +\ \$\ \ 5.70 \\ \hline \$\ 31.70 \end{array}$$

   The total cost was $31.70.

2. **Step 1:** Subtract the cost of colored pencils from the total cost to find the cost of the glue.

   $$\begin{array}{r} \overset{5}{\$\ 46.00} \\ -\ \$\ 31.60 \\ \hline \$\ 14.40 \end{array}$$

   Step 2: Divide the cost of the glue by 6 to find the cost of each tube.

   $$\begin{array}{r} \$\ \ 2.40 \\ 6)\overline{\$\ 14.40} \end{array}$$

   Each tube of glue cost $2.40.

TRY IT Money Stories

Students will practice multiplying and dividing money amounts to solve story problems. Have students turn to the Money Stories activity page in their Activity Book and read the directions with them.

Students should copy the problems from the Activity Book into their Math Notebook as necessary and solve them there.

Objectives

- Solve a story problem involving multiplication or division of money amounts in decimal notation.

Tips

Have students use grid paper or lined paper turned sideways to help them keep the place values aligned.

Money Story Problems (C)
Money Stories

Solve.

1. Jazmyne buys 5 pounds of apples for $1.89 a pound and a watermelon for $7.49. How much does Jazmyne spend on fruit? **$16.94**

2. Christine bought 4 hair clips and 3 hair bands. Each hair clip cost $0.28. Each hair band cost $0.93. How much did Christine spend altogether? **$3.91**

Choose the answer.

3. James bought 4 pairs of socks and 3 shirts. Each pair of socks cost $3.45. Each shirt cost $25.56. How much did James spend altogether?

   A. $29.01   B. $90.48   C. $112.59   D. $203.07

TRY IT

DECIMALS AND MONEY   **174**   MONEY STORY PROBLEMS (C)

CHECKPOINT

Students will complete an online Checkpoint. If necessary, read the directions, problems, and answer choices to students and help them with keyboard or mouse operations.

Objectives

- Solve a story problem involving multiplication or division of money amounts in decimal notation.

- Solve a story problem involving addition or subtraction of money amounts in decimal notation.

Unit Review

Lesson Overview

UNIT REVIEW Look Back	10 minutes	**ONLINE**
UNIT REVIEW Checkpoint Practice	50 minutes	**ONLINE**
⊡ **UNIT REVIEW** Prepare for the Checkpoint		

▶ Unit Objectives

This lesson reviews the following objectives:

- Identify decimal place values through thousandths.
- Solve a story problem involving addition or subtraction of money amounts in decimal notation.
- Solve a story problem involving multiplication or division of money amounts in decimal notation.

Materials to Gather

There are no materials to gather for this lesson.

▶ Advance Preparation

In this lesson, students will have an opportunity to review previous activities in the Decimals and Money unit. Look at the suggested activities in Unit Review: Prepare for the Checkpoint online and gather any needed materials.

UNIT REVIEW Look Back

ONLINE 10min

Students will review key concepts from the unit to prepare for the Unit Checkpoint.

Objectives

- Review unit objectives.

UNIT REVIEW Checkpoint Practice

ONLINE 50min

Students will complete an online Checkpoint Practice to prepare for the Unit Checkpoint. If necessary, read the directions, problems, and answer choices to students. Have students answer the problems on their own. Review any missed problems with students.

Objectives

- Review unit objectives.

⊡ UNIT REVIEW Prepare for the Checkpoint

What you do next depends on how students performed in the previous activity, Unit Review: Checkpoint Practice. If students had difficulty with any of the problems, complete the appropriate review activity listed in the table online.

Unit Checkpoint

UNIT CHECKPOINT Online   60 minutes   **ONLINE**

▶ Unit Objectives

This lesson assesses the following objectives:

- Identify decimal place values through thousandths.
- Solve a story problem involving addition or subtraction of money amounts in decimal notation.
- Solve a story problem involving multiplication or division of money amounts in decimal notation.

Materials to Gather

There are no materials to gather for this lesson.

UNIT CHECKPOINT Online

ONLINE 60min

Students will complete the Unit Checkpoint online. If necessary, read the directions, problems, and answer choices to students and help them with keyboard or mouse operations.

Objectives

- Assess unit objectives.

Fractions and Probability

▶ Unit Objectives

- Explain that a fraction can be used to represent part of a set, the relationship of a part to a whole, and a rational number on the number line.
- Write the fraction represented by a drawing that shows parts of a set or parts of a whole.
- Use a sketch to represent a fraction.
- Compare and order unit fractions, such as $\frac{1}{4}$, and fractions with like denominators, such as $\frac{2}{5}$ and $\frac{4}{5}$, by using objects or sketches.
- Use objects or sketches to solve a simple story problem involving addition or subtraction of fractions.
- Solve and simplify an addition or subtraction problem involving fractions with like denominators.
- Explain that a simple fraction and a decimal amount can represent the same quantity.
- Identify whether specific events are certain, likely, unlikely, or impossible.
- Identify and systematically record the possible outcomes for a simple event.
- Summarize and display the results of a probability experiment in a clear and organized way.
- Use the results of a probability experiment to predict future events.

▶ Big Ideas

- Fractions represent the ratio of a part to a whole, including a part of a set to the whole set.
- A rational number (a fraction) is any number that can be written as a ratio of one integer to another integer.

▶ Unit Opener

In this unit, students will explore fractions, decimals, and early probability concepts. They will explain that fractions can be seen as part of a whole, such as when they have half a cookie; part of a set of objects, such as when they think of half of the cupcakes on the plate; or as a rational number on the number line. Students will recognize that the number above the fraction bar is the numerator and the number below the fraction bar is the denominator. They will recognize that as the denominator gets greater, the fractional pieces become smaller, and they will recognize that a fraction such as $\frac{1}{5}$ is less than $\frac{1}{4}$. Students will learn the relationship between fractions and decimals and explain that a fraction and a decimal can represent the same quantity. They will look at simple notions of probability, identifying whether specific events are certain, likely, unlikely, or impossible. They will identify and record possible outcomes for a simple event. They will learn about tally charts, line plots, and bar graphs, and they will use the results of a probability experiment to predict future events.

▶ Keywords

decimal	fractions with like	mixed number
denominator	denominators	numerator
equivalent fractions	fractions with unlike	outcomes
fraction	denominators	predict an outcome
fraction bar	improper fraction	probability

Represent and Name Fractions (A)

Skills Update	5 minutes	ONLINE
GET READY Fraction Meanings and Names	5 minutes	ONLINE
LEARN Name and Show Parts of a Whole	20 minutes	ONLINE
LEARN Name and Show Parts of a Set	15 minutes	ONLINE
TRY IT Name Fractions	15 minutes	OFFLINE

▶ Lesson Objectives

- Explain that a fraction can be used to represent part of a set, the relationship of a part to a whole, and a rational number on the number line.
- Write the fraction represented by a drawing that shows parts of a set or parts of a whole.
- Use a sketch to represent a fraction.

▶ Prerequisite Skills

- Demonstrate that a fraction can represent the relationship of equal parts to a whole or parts of a set.
- Demonstrate how fractions and whole numbers can be plotted on a number line.
- Generate fraction representations (for example, show $\frac{2}{3}$ of a shape or $\frac{2}{3}$ of a set of objects or $\frac{2}{3}$ of an interval on a number line).
- Write the fraction represented by a drawing that shows parts of a set or parts of a whole.

▶ Content Background

Students will learn that a fraction can represent part of a set, the relationship of a part to a whole, and a rational number on the number line. They will draw a sketch to show a fraction and write the fraction represented by a drawing. Avoid using the term *rational numbers* with students.

Fractions are numbers that can represent whole numbers and parts of a whole. Fractions can be shown as parts of a whole, parts of a set, or as a location on a number line.

Although a fraction can represent many different relationships, a fraction as part of a whole is most familiar. A set of 3 slices of 8 equal-sized slices in a whole pizza is a part-of-a-whole comparison written as $\frac{3}{8}$. If there is a combination of 1 whole pizza and 3 equal-sized slices of another 8-slice pizza of the same size, the part-of-a-whole comparison is $1\frac{3}{8}$. Remember that when discussing fractions as a part of a whole, all the parts must be the same size and shape, and all the wholes must also be the same size and shape.

Materials to Gather

SUPPLIED

Name Fractions activity page

Numbers that have a whole and a fraction are called mixed numbers. The mixed number $1\frac{3}{8}$ can also be written as an improper fraction. Since 1 whole is $\frac{8}{8}$, $1\frac{3}{8}$ would be $\frac{8}{8}$ plus $\frac{3}{8}$, or $\frac{11}{8}$. When the numerator is greater than the denominator, the fraction is called an improper fraction.

$\frac{3}{4}$	$1\frac{3}{4}$	$\frac{7}{4}$
fraction	mixed number	improper fraction

Fractions can also represent part of a set. For example, a set may be a group of 4 children playing soccer, 2 girls and 2 boys, with 3 of the players dressed in red and 1 player dressed in white. Although the children are not all the same size, each child is 1 out of the 4 children, so each child is $\frac{1}{4}$ of the group. The denominator (the number below the fraction bar) shows how many objects are in the whole group. The numerator (the number above the fraction bar) shows how many of these objects have the same given feature. The fraction of children that are boys is $\frac{2}{4}$, and the fraction of children dressed in red is $\frac{3}{4}$.

Fractions are a part of the larger set of rational numbers. Every rational number has a specific location along the number line. For example, $\frac{3}{4}$ is located at the point exactly $\frac{3}{4}$ of the distance from 0 to 1 on the number line, and $5\frac{3}{8}$ is located at the point exactly $\frac{3}{8}$ of the distance from 5 to 6.

Although students will most often see fractions written with a horizontal fraction bar in math, such as $\frac{2}{3}$ or $5\frac{5}{6}$, they will occasionally see a diagonal fraction bar, such as 2/3 or 5 5/6. Students will very likely see the diagonal fraction bar in everyday experiences, but be sure they understand that using the horizontal fraction bar in their work makes problems involving fractions easier to interpret and solve.

▶ Common Errors and Misconceptions

- Students might view the numerator and denominator of a fraction as separate, isolated numbers that can be operated on independently. This may lead to students "memorizing" rather than understanding fraction algorithms, and then using them incorrectly.

- Students might not understand the difference between fractions and whole numbers. Fractions are parts of whole numbers. Examples of fractions include $\frac{4}{5}$, $\frac{7}{100}$, and $2\frac{1}{2}$. Examples of whole numbers include 4, 6, and 10. Whole numbers may be written as fractions, but always with a denominator of 1, such as $\frac{4}{1}$, $\frac{6}{1}$, or $\frac{10}{1}$.

- Students might have difficulty understanding how different models represent fractions because they often see fractions represented as parts of circles—for example, pie and pizza illustrations. They might not recognize, for example, that the following models all represent the fraction $\frac{3}{5}$.

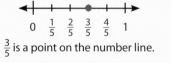

$\frac{3}{5}$ is a point on the number line.

$\frac{3}{5}$ of the shapes are triangles.

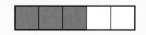

$\frac{3}{5}$ of the rectangle is shaded.

- Students might think that a fraction always represents the size of a part of a whole, number of items in a set, or a location on the number line, and so might not understand that a fraction can also represent a relationship, such as a quotient or a ratio of one quantity to another.

- Students might think that a fraction compares one part to another part rather than recognizing that a fraction compares one part to the whole.

GET READY Fraction Meanings and Names

ONLINE 5 min

Students will review the meaning of fractions. They also will name fractions as equal parts of a whole.

Objectives

- Demonstrate that a fraction can represent the relationship of equal parts to a whole or parts of a set.
- Write the fraction represented by a drawing that shows parts of a set or parts of a whole.

LEARN Name and Show Parts of a Whole

ONLINE 20 min

Students will identify the fraction that names the shaded part of a whole. They will recognize that the whole must have equal-sized parts. They will also see that the numerator shows the number of parts shaded and the denominator shows the number of parts in a whole. Students will use the Different Ways to Show Fractions learning tool to practice illustrating fractions to describe parts of a whole. They will learn that a number greater than 1 can be a mixed number, or it can be written as an improper fraction. For example, $1\frac{2}{3}$ can also be written as $\frac{5}{3}$.

Objectives

- Explain that a fraction can be used to represent part of a set, the relationship of a part to a whole, and a rational number on the number line.
- Write the fraction represented by a drawing that shows parts of a set or parts of a whole.
- Use a sketch to represent a fraction.

DIRECTIONS FOR USING THE DIFFERENT WAYS TO SHOW FRACTIONS LEARNING TOOL

1. Click Parts of a Whole.
2. Click the + symbol in the lower right of the screen three times to divide the square into four equal parts.

   Say: The square is one whole. It's divided into four equal parts. So each part equals one-fourth.

3. Have students click one part of the square to color it.

   Ask: What fraction did you show? one-fourth

   Ask: How do you know that this fraction shows one-fourth? The whole is divided into four parts. One of the parts is green.

4. Point to the fraction $\frac{1}{4}$ on the screen, and explain how the 1 represents the green parts and the 4 represents the total parts in the whole.

5. Have students click another part of the square so that two parts are green.

   Say: Now two out of four parts are green. So the fraction changed to two-fourths. The bottom number, 4, stayed the same because the whole is still divided into four parts.

6. Have students click a third part and note how the fraction changed. Then have them click the fourth part.

   Say: Now four out of four parts are green. The fraction changed to four-fourths. Four-fourths is equal to one whole.

7. Have students click each green part again to clear the fraction. They should watch how the fraction changes from $\frac{4}{4}$ to $\frac{3}{4}$ to $\frac{2}{4}$ to $\frac{1}{4}$ to $\frac{0}{4}$.

8. Repeat the activity with thirds and sixths. Students may choose another shape than the square, if they'd like. As students color each part, have them explain why the top number of the fraction, the numerator, is changing and the bottom number, the denominator, is not.

Tips	Have students count the number of parts in each shape. Write that number as the denominator (the number below the fraction bar) before focusing on the number of shaded parts.

LEARN Name and Show Parts of a Set

ONLINE **15**min

Objectives

- Explain that a fraction can be used to represent part of a set, the relationship of a part to a whole, and a rational number on the number line.
- Write the fraction represented by a drawing that shows parts of a set or parts of a whole.
- Use a sketch to represent a fraction.

Students will identify various fractions that name parts of a set. They will see that if they have 5 marbles and 3 of them are red, they can say that $\frac{3}{5}$ of the marbles are red. Students will use the Different Ways to Show Fractions learning tool to practice illustrating fractions to describe parts of a set.

DIRECTIONS FOR USING THE DIFFERENT WAYS TO SHOW FRACTIONS LEARNING TOOL

1. Click Parts of a Set.

2. Click the + symbol under the frog until there are four frogs in the set.

   Say: There are four frogs in the set. Each frog equals one-fourth of the set. Notice that zero frogs are green.

3. Have students click one frog to color it.

   Ask: What fraction did you show? one-fourth

   Ask: How do you know that this fraction shows one-fourth? The set has four frogs. One of the frogs is green.

4. Point to the fraction $\frac{1}{4}$ on the screen, and explain how the 1 represents the green frog and the 4 represents the total number of frogs in the set. Point to the phrase *1 of 4* below the fraction and explain that this means one of four frogs in the set is green.

5. Have students click another frog so that two frogs are green.

   Say: Now two out of four frogs are green. So the fraction changed to two-fourths. The bottom number, 4, stayed the same because the set still has four frogs.

6. Have students click a third frog and note how the fraction changed. Then have them click the fourth frog.

   Say: Now four out of four frogs are green. The fraction changed to four-fourths. Four-fourths is equal to the whole set.

7. Have students click each green frog again to clear the fraction. They should watch how the fraction changes from $\frac{4}{4}$ to $\frac{3}{4}$ to $\frac{2}{4}$ to $\frac{1}{4}$ to $\frac{0}{4}$.

8. Repeat the activity with thirds and sixths. Students may choose another item than the frog, if they'd like. As students color each part, have them explain why the top number of the fraction, the numerator, is changing and the bottom number, the denominator, is not.

TRY IT Name Fractions

Objectives

Students will practice representing and naming fractions. Have students turn to the Name Fractions activity page in their Activity Book and read the directions with them.

Students should copy the problems from the Activity Book into their Math Notebook as necessary and solve them there.

- Explain that a fraction can be used to represent part of a set, the relationship of a part to a whole, and a rational number on the number line.
- Write the fraction represented by a drawing that shows parts of a set or parts of a whole.
- Use a sketch to represent a fraction.

Represent and Name Fractions (A)

Name Fractions

Match the sketch to its fraction name.

$\frac{6}{7}$ $\frac{8}{5}$

$1\frac{2}{3}$ $2\frac{1}{4}$

$\frac{2}{3}$ $\frac{7}{8}$

1. $1\frac{2}{3}$ 1 whole

2. $2\frac{1}{4}$ 1 whole

3. $\frac{6}{7}$

4. $\frac{2}{3}$

5. $\frac{7}{8}$

6. $\frac{8}{5}$ 1 whole

Choose the answer.

7. Jeff said that this model shows $2\frac{3}{8}$ shaded.
Eliza said that this model shows $\frac{19}{8}$ shaded.
Who is correct?   1 whole

A. Jeff   B. Eliza   C. both Jeff and Eliza

FRACTIONS AND PROBABILITY   **175**   REPRESENT AND NAME FRACTIONS (A)

TRY IT

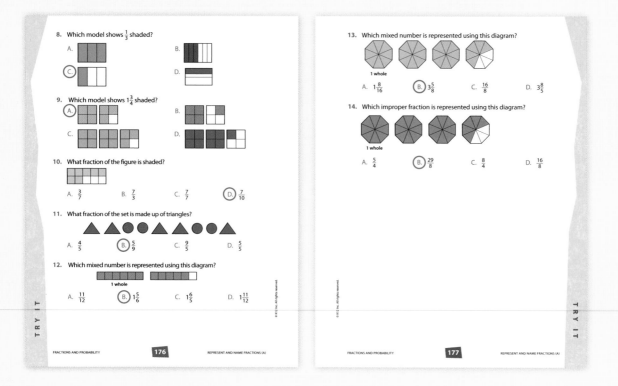

8. Which model shows $\frac{1}{3}$ shaded?

A.   B.

C.   D.

9. Which model shows $1\frac{3}{4}$ shaded?

A.   B.

C.   D.

10. What fraction of the figure is shaded?

A. $\frac{3}{7}$ B. $\frac{7}{3}$ C. $\frac{7}{7}$ D. $\frac{7}{10}$

11. What fraction of the set is made up of triangles?

A. $\frac{4}{5}$ B. $\frac{5}{9}$ C. $\frac{9}{5}$ D. $\frac{5}{5}$

12. Which mixed number is represented using this diagram?

1 whole

A. $\frac{11}{12}$ B. $1\frac{5}{6}$ C. $1\frac{6}{5}$ D. $1\frac{11}{12}$

13. Which mixed number is represented using this diagram?

1 whole

A. $1\frac{8}{16}$ B. $3\frac{5}{8}$ C. $\frac{16}{8}$ D. $3\frac{8}{5}$

14. Which improper fraction is represented using this diagram?

1 whole

A. $\frac{5}{4}$ B. $\frac{29}{8}$ C. $\frac{8}{4}$ D. $\frac{16}{8}$

TRY IT

Represent and Name Fractions (B)

Lesson Overview

GET READY Write Fractions	10 minutes	ONLINE
LEARN Fractions on a Number Line	25 minutes	OFFLINE
TRY IT Represent Fractions	15 minutes	OFFLINE
CHECKPOINT	10 minutes	ONLINE

▶ Lesson Objectives

- Explain that a fraction can be used to represent part of a set, the relationship of a part to a whole, and a rational number on the number line.
- Write the fraction represented by a drawing that shows parts of a set or parts of a whole.
- Use a sketch to represent a fraction.

▶ Prerequisite Skills

- Demonstrate that a fraction can represent the relationship of equal parts to a whole or parts of a set.
- Demonstrate how fractions and whole numbers can be plotted on a number line.
- Generate fraction representations (for example, show $\frac{2}{3}$ of a shape or $\frac{2}{3}$ of a set of objects or $\frac{2}{3}$ of an interval on a number line).
- Write the fraction represented by a drawing that shows parts of a set or parts of a whole.

▶ Content Background

Students will continue to learn that a fraction can represent part of a set, the relationship of a part to a whole, and a rational number on the number line. They will draw a sketch to show a fraction and write the fraction represented by a drawing. Avoid using the term *rational numbers* with students.

Fractions are numbers that can represent whole numbers and parts of a whole. Fractions can be shown as parts of a whole, parts of a set, or as a location on a number line.

Although a fraction can represent many different relationships, a fraction as part of a whole is most familiar. A set of 3 slices of 8 equal-sized slices in a whole pizza is a part-of-a-whole comparison written as $\frac{3}{8}$. If there is a combination of 1 whole pizza and 3 equal-sized slices of another 8-slice pizza of the same size, the part-of-a-whole comparison is $1\frac{3}{8}$. Remember that when discussing fractions as a part of a whole, all the parts must be the same size and shape, and all the wholes must also be the same size and shape.

Numbers that have a whole and a fraction are called mixed numbers. The mixed number $1\frac{3}{8}$ can also be written as an improper fraction. Since 1 whole is $\frac{8}{8}$,

Materials to Gather

SUPPLIED

number lines from Number Line Creator Tool

Represent Fractions activity page

$1\frac{3}{8}$ would be $\frac{8}{8}$ plus $\frac{3}{8}$, or $\frac{11}{8}$. When the numerator is greater than the denominator, the fraction is called an improper fraction.

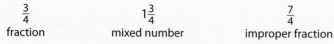

$$\frac{3}{4}$$
fraction

$$1\frac{3}{4}$$
mixed number

$$\frac{7}{4}$$
improper fraction

Fractions can also represent part of a set. For example, a set may be a group of 4 children playing soccer, 2 girls and 2 boys, with 3 of the players dressed in red and 1 player dressed in white. Although the children are not all the same size, each child is 1 out of the 4 children, so each child is $\frac{1}{4}$ of the group. The denominator (the number below the fraction bar) shows how many objects are in the whole group. The numerator (the number above the fraction bar) shows how many of these objects have the same given feature. The fraction of the children that are boys is $\frac{2}{4}$, and the fraction of children dressed in red is $\frac{3}{4}$.

Fractions are a part of the larger set of rational numbers. Every rational number has a specific location along the number line. For example, $\frac{3}{4}$ is located at the point exactly $\frac{3}{4}$ of the distance from 0 to 1 on the number line, and $5\frac{3}{8}$ is located at the point exactly $\frac{3}{8}$ of the distance from 5 to 6.

Although students will most often see fractions written with a horizontal fraction bar in math, such as $\frac{2}{3}$ or $5\frac{5}{6}$, they will occasionally see a diagonal fraction bar, such as 2/3 or 5 5/6. Students will very likely see the diagonal fraction bar in everyday experiences, but be sure they understand that using the horizontal fraction bar in their work makes problems involving fractions easier to interpret and solve.

 ## Common Errors and Misconceptions

- Students might view the numerator and denominator of a fraction as separate, isolated numbers that can be operated on independently. This may lead to students "memorizing" rather than understanding fraction algorithms, and then using them incorrectly.

- Students might not understand the difference between fractions and whole numbers. Fractions are parts of whole numbers. Examples of fractions include $\frac{4}{5}$, $\frac{7}{100}$, and $2\frac{1}{2}$. Examples of whole numbers include 4, 6, and 10. Whole numbers may be written as fractions, but always with a denominator of 1, such as $\frac{4}{1}$, $\frac{6}{1}$, or $\frac{10}{1}$.

- Students might have difficulty understanding how different models represent fractions because they often see fractions represented as parts of circles—for example, pie and pizza illustrations. They might not recognize, for example, that the following models all represent the fraction $\frac{3}{5}$.

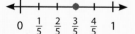

$\frac{3}{5}$ is a point on the number line.

$\frac{3}{5}$ of the shapes are triangles.

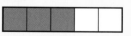

$\frac{3}{5}$ of the rectangle is shaded.

- Students might think that a fraction always represents the size of a part of a whole, number of items in a set, or a location on the number line, and so might not understand that a fraction can also represent a relationship, such as a quotient or a ratio of one quantity to another.

- Students might think that a fraction compares one part to another part rather than recognizing that a fraction compares one part to the whole.

▶ Advance Preparation

Use the Number Line Creator Tool to make nine number lines, three to a page.
Print the number lines.

DIRECTIONS FOR USING THE NUMBER LINE CREATOR TOOL

To create number lines for thirds:

1. Set Range:	2. Select Options:	3. Print Number Line:
• Start Number Line at: 0 • End Number Line at: 4	• Tick Marks: ones, thirds • Labels: ones • Label Format: fractions	• Page Orientation: landscape • Number Lines per Sheet: 3

To create number lines for fourths:

1. Set Range:	2. Select Options:	3. Print Number Line:
• Start Number Line at: 0 • End Number Line at: 4	• Tick Marks: ones, fourths • Labels: ones • Label Format: fractions	• Page Orientation: landscape • Number Lines per Sheet: 3

To create number lines for tenths:

1. Set Range:	2. Select Options:	3. Print Number Line:
• Start Number Line at: 0 • End Number Line at: 2	• Tick Marks: ones, tenths • Labels: ones • Label Format: fractions	• Page Orientation: landscape • Number Lines per Sheet: 3

ONLINE
10min

GET READY   Write Fractions

Students will review number lines and fractions on the number line. Remind them that a fraction is a special kind of number used to show amounts less than 1.

On the number line a fraction, such as $\frac{3}{4}$, can be seen as marking a point three-fourths of the distance from 0 to 1.

Objectives

- Demonstrate how fractions and whole numbers can be plotted on a number line.
- Write the fraction represented by a drawing that shows parts of a set or parts of a whole.

LEARN Fractions on a Number Line

- Explain that a fraction can be used to represent part of a set, the relationship of a part to a whole, and a rational number on the number line.

- Write the fraction represented by a drawing that shows parts of a set or parts of a whole.

- Use a sketch to represent a fraction.

Students will label fractions, improper fractions, and mixed numbers on a number line. Gather the printed number lines from the Number Line Creator Tool.

1. Tell students that fractions can be shown on a number line. Give them the sheet of number lines that have the tick marks for thirds. Remind students that they have seen whole numbers on a number line.

2. Have students imagine that the tick marks show the hops that a miniature frog would have to take to get to 1.

   Ask: How many hops would it take to get to 1? 3

   Ask: How much of the distance would the frog go with each hop? $\frac{1}{3}$

   Ask: How far would the frog go in 3 hops? $\frac{3}{3}$ or 1

3. Guide students to find and label the fractions on the number line. $\frac{1}{3}$, $\frac{2}{3}$, $\frac{3}{3}$, $\frac{4}{3}$, and so on

   Then have students count aloud, saying both the fraction and whole number. $\frac{1}{3}$, $\frac{2}{3}$, $\frac{3}{3}$ equals 1; $\frac{4}{3}$, $\frac{5}{3}$, $\frac{6}{3}$ equals 2; and so on

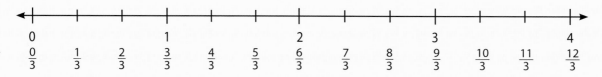

4. Tell students that a number line can be divided into different numbers of equal sections to show different fractions.

   Say: If there were four sections between each whole number, the number line would be divided into fourths and each tick mark would show $\frac{1}{4}$.

5. Give students the sheet of number lines that have the tick marks for fourths. Have students look at one of these lines and explain why it shows fourths even though there are only three tick marks between each whole number. It shows fourths because there are four sections. The tick marks are $\frac{1}{4}$, $\frac{2}{4}$, and $\frac{3}{4}$ and the fourth tick mark is $\frac{4}{4}$ or 1.

6. Guide students to find and label the fractions on the number line and say each one. $\frac{1}{4}$, $\frac{2}{4}$, $\frac{3}{4}$, $\frac{4}{4}$ equals 1; $\frac{5}{4}$, $\frac{6}{4}$, $\frac{7}{4}$, $\frac{8}{4}$ equals 2; and so on

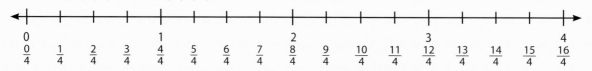

7. Refer to the number line that the students marked in thirds. Guide students to write the mixed numbers for the improper fractions on a new number line marked in thirds. Have students count aloud by thirds again from 0 to 4, using mixed numbers. $\frac{1}{3}$, $\frac{2}{3}$, $\frac{3}{3}$ equals 1; $1\frac{1}{3}$, $1\frac{2}{3}$, $1\frac{3}{3}$ equals 2; $2\frac{1}{3}$, $2\frac{2}{3}$, $2\frac{3}{3}$ equals 3; and so on

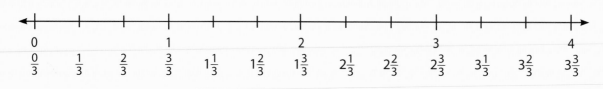

8. After students are comfortable counting, ask them to locate the following fractions on the number line: $\frac{2}{3}$, $1\frac{1}{3}$, and $2\frac{2}{3}$.

9. Have students go back to the number line they labeled in fourths. Have them label a new fourths number line with mixed numbers. $\frac{1}{4}$, $\frac{2}{4}$, $\frac{3}{4}$, $\frac{4}{4}$ equals 1; $1\frac{1}{4}$, $1\frac{2}{4}$, $1\frac{3}{4}$, $1\frac{4}{4}$ equals 2; $2\frac{1}{4}$, $2\frac{2}{4}$, $2\frac{3}{4}$, $2\frac{4}{4}$ equals 3; and so on

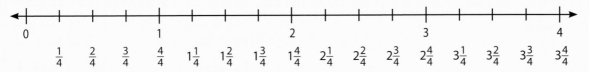

10. Give students the sheet of number lines that have the tick marks for tenths. Have them label a line with fractions. Then have them read aloud the numbers on the number line. Have students label a new tenths line with mixed numbers. As time permits, say various fractions, mixed numbers, and improper fractions and have students find them on the number line. For mixed numbers, have students say the fraction as an improper fraction.

Remind students that they have now seen fractions as part of a whole, part of a set, and as a number on the number line.

Tips	Have students look at the two number lines they marked in thirds and remind them that while improper fractions and mixed numbers look very different, numbers such as $\frac{4}{3}$ and $1\frac{1}{3}$ stand for exactly the same amount, just as $\frac{3}{3}$ and 1 stand for the same amount.

OFFLINE

15 min

TRY IT Represent Fractions

Students will practice sketching the same fraction in multiple ways—as part of a whole, as part of a set, and as a number on a number line. They will practice identifying fractions sketched in multiple ways. Have students turn to the Represent Fractions activity page in their Activity Book and read the directions with them.

Students should copy the problems from the Activity Book into their Math Notebook as necessary and solve them there.

Objectives

- Explain that a fraction can be used to represent part of a set, the relationship of a part to a whole, and a rational number on the number line.

- Write the fraction represented by a drawing that shows parts of a set or parts of a whole.

- Use a sketch to represent a fraction.

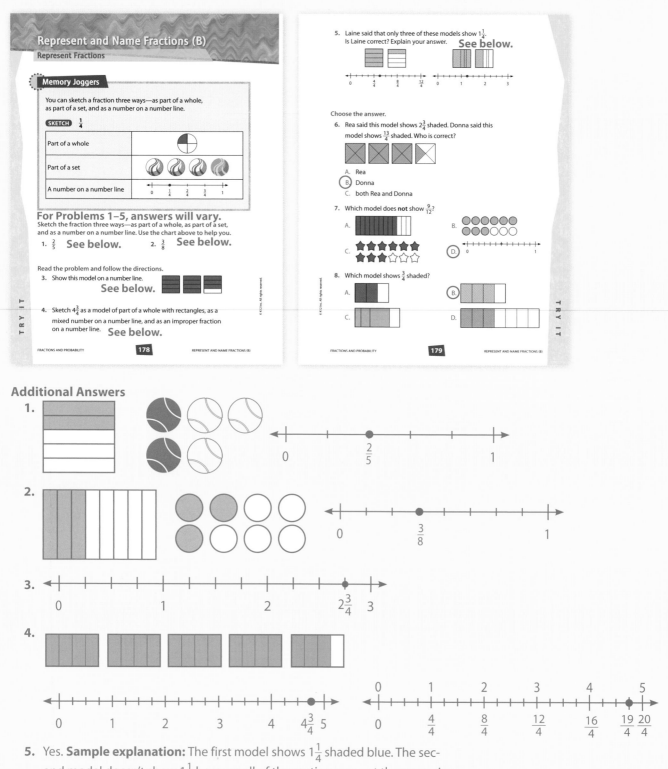

Represent and Name Fractions (B)

Represent Fractions

Memory Joggers

You can sketch a fraction three ways—as part of a whole, as part of a set, and as a number on a number line.

SKETCH $\frac{1}{4}$

Part of a whole	
Part of a set	
A number on a number line	

For Problems 1–5, answers will vary.
Sketch the fraction three ways—as part of a whole, as part of a set, and as a number on a number line. Use the chart above to help you.

1. $\frac{2}{5}$ **See below.**   2. $\frac{3}{8}$ **See below.**

Read the problem and follow the directions.

3. Show this model on a number line.
   See below.

4. Sketch $4\frac{3}{4}$ as a model of part of a whole with rectangles, as a mixed number on a number line, and as an improper fraction on a number line.   **See below.**

5. Laine said that only three of these models show $1\frac{1}{4}$. Is Laine correct? Explain your answer.   **See below.**

Choose the answer.

6. Rea said this model shows $2\frac{3}{4}$ shaded. Donna said this model shows $\frac{13}{4}$ shaded. Who is correct?

   A. Rea
   B. Donna
   C. both Rea and Donna

7. Which model does **not** show $\frac{9}{12}$?

   A.   B.
   C.   D.

8. Which model shows $\frac{3}{4}$ shaded?

   A.   B.
   C.   D.

Additional Answers

1.

2.

3.

4.

5. Yes. **Sample explanation:** The first model shows $1\frac{1}{4}$ shaded blue. The second model doesn't show $1\frac{1}{4}$ because all of the sections are not the same size and same shape. The first number line shows a dot at $\frac{5}{4}$, which is the same as $1\frac{1}{4}$. The second number line shows a dot at $1\frac{1}{4}$.

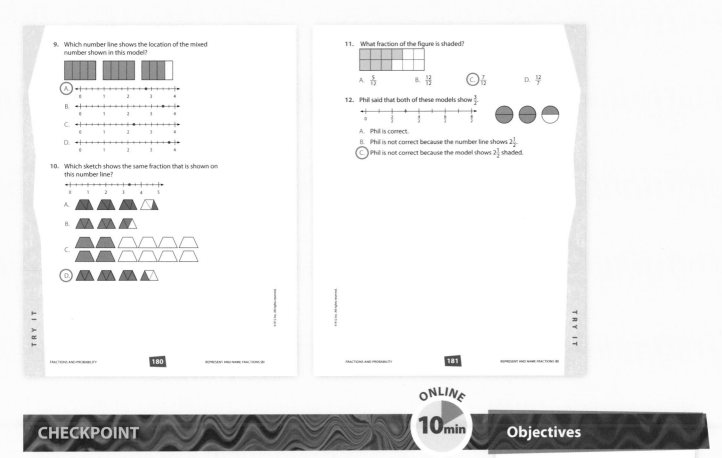

9. Which number line shows the location of the mixed number shown in this model?

10. Which sketch shows the same fraction that is shown on this number line?

11. What fraction of the figure is shaded?

A. $\frac{5}{12}$ B. $\frac{12}{12}$ C. $\frac{7}{12}$ D. $\frac{12}{7}$

12. Phil said that both of these models show $\frac{3}{2}$.

A. Phil is correct.

B. Phil is not correct because the number line shows $2\frac{1}{2}$.

C. Phil is not correct because the model shows $2\frac{1}{2}$ shaded.

TRY IT

ONLINE
10 min

CHECKPOINT

Students will complete an online Checkpoint. If necessary, read the directions, problems, and answer choices to students and help them with keyboard or mouse operations.

Objectives

- Explain that a fraction can be used to represent part of a set, the relationship of a part to a whole, and a rational number on the number line.

- Write the fraction represented by a drawing that shows parts of a set or parts of a whole.

- Use a sketch to represent a fraction.

Compare and Order Fractions (A)

Lesson Overview

Skills Update	5 minutes	ONLINE
GET READY Identify and Order Fractions	5 minutes	ONLINE
LEARN Compare Fractions on a Number Line	20 minutes	ONLINE
LEARN Fractions and Fraction Strips	20 minutes	ONLINE
TRY IT Compare Fractions	10 minutes	OFFLINE

▶ Lesson Objectives

Compare and order unit fractions, such as $\frac{1}{4}$, and fractions with like denominators, such as $\frac{2}{5}$ and $\frac{4}{5}$, by using objects or sketches.

▶ Prerequisite Skills

Use concrete objects or given drawings to compare unit fractions from $\frac{1}{12}$ to $\frac{1}{2}$.

▶ Content Background

Students will learn to identify and compare fractions with like and unlike denominators using $<$, $>$, and $=$.

    Students will use the comparison symbols of $<$, $>$, and $=$ to compare fractions. The denominator, or the number below the fraction bar, of a fraction tells how many equal pieces the whole has been divided into. It is important for students to understand that as the denominator increases, the size of each piece decreases.

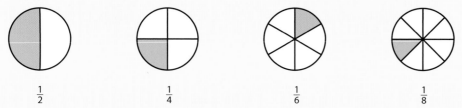

$$\frac{1}{2} \qquad \frac{1}{4} \qquad \frac{1}{6} \qquad \frac{1}{8}$$

> ### Materials to Gather
>
> **SUPPLIED**
>
> Compare Fractions activity page

▶ Common Errors and Misconceptions

- Students might view the numerator and denominator of a fraction as separate, isolated numbers that can be operated on independently. This may lead to students "memorizing" rather than understanding fraction algorithms, and then using them incorrectly.

- Students might not understand the difference between fractions and whole numbers. Fractions are parts of whole numbers. Examples of fractions include $\frac{4}{5}$, $\frac{7}{100}$, and $2\frac{1}{2}$. Examples of whole numbers include 4, 6, and 10. Whole numbers may be written as fractions, but always with a denominator of 1, such as $\frac{4}{1}$, $\frac{6}{1}$, or $\frac{10}{1}$.

- Students might have difficulty understanding how different models represent fractions because they often see fractions represented as parts of circles—for example, pie and pizza illustrations. They might not recognize, for example, that the following models all represent the fraction $\frac{3}{5}$.

$\frac{3}{5}$ is a point on the number line. $\frac{3}{5}$ of the shapes are triangles. $\frac{3}{5}$ of the rectangle is shaded.

- Students might think that a fraction always represents the size of a part of a whole, number of items in a set, or a location on the number line, and so might not understand that a fraction can also represent a relationship, such as a quotient or a ratio of one quantity to another.

- Students might think that a fraction compares one part to another part rather than recognizing that a fraction compares one part to the whole.

GET READY Identify and Order Fractions

ONLINE 5min

Students will compare and order unit fractions. Unit fractions have 1 in the numerator. Students will see that with unit fractions, the greater the denominator, the less value the fraction has. Help them recognize that the denominator, below the fraction bar, tells how many parts are in a whole and the numerator, above the fraction bar, tells how many parts are shaded.

Objectives

- Use concrete objects or given drawings to compare unit fractions from $\frac{1}{12}$ to $\frac{1}{2}$.

LEARN Compare Fractions on a Number Line

ONLINE 20min

Students will use the Different Ways to Show Fractions Learning Tool to see that unit fractions (fractions that have 1 in the numerator), such as $\frac{1}{2}, \frac{1}{3}, \frac{1}{4}$, can be compared by looking at the denominator. The greater the denominator, the less value the unit fraction has. Students will also see that when two fractions have the same denominator, such as $\frac{3}{12}$ and $\frac{5}{12}$, the fraction with the greater numerator has the greater value. The fraction $\frac{5}{12}$ is greater than $\frac{3}{12}$ because $\frac{5}{12}$ has more twelfths.

Objectives

- Compare and order unit fractions, such as $\frac{1}{4}$, and fractions with like denominators, such as $\frac{2}{5}$ and $\frac{4}{5}$, by using objects or sketches.

DIRECTIONS FOR USING THE DIFFERENT WAYS TO SHOW FRACTIONS LEARNING TOOL

1. Click Parts of a Whole.
2. Click Show Number Line.
3. Have students click the square to show one whole.

   Say: Fractions can be shown as part of a whole or as a number on the number line.

4. Have students click the + symbol in the lower right of the screen a few times and watch the number line.

   Ask: What happens to the number line as you click the + symbol? It gets divided into more and more sections that are smaller.

   Ask: What happens to the denominator as you click the + symbol? It increases with each click.

   Ask: What happens to the square? It gets more parts.

5. Have students watch the number line as they click the + symbol until the denominator is 12.

   Say: What happens to the sections on the number line as the denominator increases? The sections get smaller.

6. Have students do the following:
   - Click the – symbol in the lower right until the denominator is back to 1. See that the sections of the number line get bigger.
   - Click the square to show 1. See how the number line shows 1.
   - Click the + symbol to show halves. Click $\frac{1}{2}$ of the square. Notice how the number line shows $\frac{1}{2}$.

   Ask: Is $\frac{1}{2}$ greater than or less than 1 whole? less

7. Click the + symbol to show thirds and then click one section of the square to show $\frac{1}{3}$.

   Ask: Is $\frac{1}{3}$ greater than or less than $\frac{1}{2}$? less

8. Repeat Step 7 to show the unit fractions $\frac{1}{4}, \frac{1}{5}, \frac{1}{6}, \ldots$ to $\frac{1}{12}$. Each time, ask students whether the current fraction is greater than or less than the previous fraction. It will always be less than the previous fraction, which they will be able to see as they watch the number line.

   Remind students that when the denominator is greater, the parts are smaller. So if they compare fractions that have a 1 in the numerator, they can always say that the fraction with the greatest denominator will have the least value.

9. Look at $\frac{1}{12}$ on the number line. Have students click two more sections of the square to show $\frac{3}{12}$ and notice that $\frac{3}{12}$ is to the right of $\frac{1}{12}$ on the number line.

   Ask: Which is greater: $\frac{3}{12}$ or $\frac{1}{12}$? $\frac{3}{12}$

10. Have students click a few more parts to show $\frac{5}{12}$.

    Ask: Which is greater: $\frac{3}{12}$ or $\frac{5}{12}$? $\frac{5}{12}$

    Ask: Without making the fraction, answer this question: Which would be greater, $\frac{5}{12}$ or $\frac{7}{12}$, and how do you know? The answer is $\frac{7}{12}$, because it has more twelfths, and because it's to the right on the number line.

    Say: When two fractions have the same denominator, the fraction with the greater numerator has the greater value.

ONLINE

20min

LEARN Fractions and Fraction Strips

Objectives

Students will use the Fraction Strips Learning Tool to compare unit fractions and fractions with the same denominator. After they use the learning tool, they will put fractions in order from least to greatest and from greatest to least.

- Compare and order unit fractions, such as $\frac{1}{4}$, and fractions with like denominators, such as $\frac{2}{5}$ and $\frac{4}{5}$, by using objects or sketches.

DIRECTIONS FOR USING THE FRACTION STRIPS LEARNING TOOL

1. Read the instructions, and click Start.
2. Click the equivalent chart reference icon in the lower-left corner of the screen to show students the many combinations of fractions that are equivalent to a whole, or 1.

3. **Say:** The top fraction strip represents a whole, or 1. Look at the fraction strips below 1.

   Ask: How many one-thirds $\left(\frac{1}{3}\right)$ are equal to 1 whole? 3 one-thirds

   Ask: How many one-twelfths $\left(\frac{1}{12}\right)$ are equal to 1 whole? 12 one-twelfths

4. **Say:** Since $\frac{3}{3}$ and $\frac{12}{12}$ both equal 1 whole, we know that $\frac{12}{12}$ and $\frac{3}{3}$ are equal to each other. They have the same value.

   Click the X in the upper-right corner of the chart to close it.

5. Tell students that they will use the fraction strips to compare fractions. Have students drag a 1-whole strip from the top bar to the top of the screen's left section.

6. Next have students drag a $\frac{1}{2}$ strip under the 1 whole.

   Ask: Which fraction is greater? 1 whole

7. Repeat Step 6 with each fraction strip. Have students line up the strips from greatest to least, one under the other. Have them state each comparison.

   Example: $\frac{1}{6}$ is less than $\frac{1}{5}$ $\left(\text{or } \frac{1}{5} \text{ is greater than } \frac{1}{6}\right)$.

   Remind students that the greater the denominator, the smaller each part of the whole is.

8. Have students use the middle section to compare $\frac{5}{8}$ and $\frac{3}{8}$. Have them drag five $\frac{1}{8}$ strips, and underneath those strips, drag three $\frac{1}{8}$ strips.

   Ask: How do $\frac{5}{8}$ and $\frac{3}{8}$ compare with each other? $\frac{5}{8}$ is more than $\frac{3}{8}$ $\left(\text{or } \frac{3}{8} \text{ is less than } \frac{5}{8}\right)$.

9. Do a few more. Have students compare $\frac{3}{12}$ and $\frac{6}{12}$; have them compare $\frac{2}{6}$ and $\frac{4}{6}$.

   Say: When you compare two fractions with the same denominator, the number in the numerator determines which fraction is greater.

OFFLINE

10 min

TRY IT Compare Fractions

Students will practice identifying and comparing fractions as part of a whole and as a location on a number line. They will use $<$, $>$, or $=$ to compare fractions. Have students turn to the Compare Fractions activity page in their Activity Book and read the directions with them.

Students should copy the problems from the Activity Book into their Math Notebook as necessary and solve them there.

Objectives

- Compare and order unit fractions, such as $\frac{1}{4}$, and fractions with like denominators, such as $\frac{2}{5}$ and $\frac{4}{5}$, by using objects or sketches.

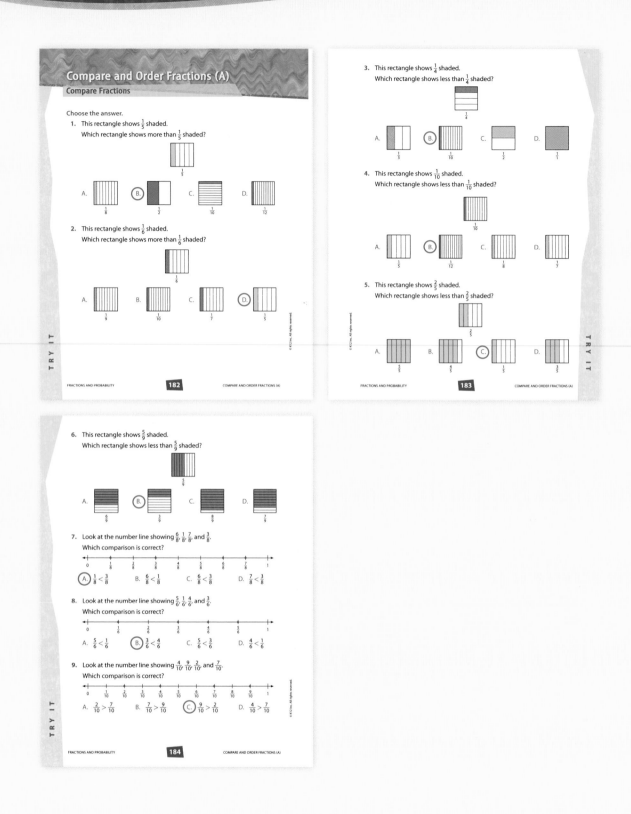

Compare and Order Fractions (A)
Compare Fractions

Choose the answer.

1. This rectangle shows $\frac{1}{5}$ shaded.
   Which rectangle shows more than $\frac{1}{5}$ shaded?

   $\frac{1}{5}$

   A. $\frac{1}{8}$ B. $\frac{1}{2}$ C. $\frac{1}{10}$ D. $\frac{1}{12}$

2. This rectangle shows $\frac{1}{6}$ shaded.
   Which rectangle shows more than $\frac{1}{6}$ shaded?

   $\frac{1}{6}$

   A. $\frac{1}{9}$ B. $\frac{1}{10}$ C. $\frac{1}{7}$ D. $\frac{1}{5}$

3. This rectangle shows $\frac{1}{4}$ shaded.
   Which rectangle shows less than $\frac{1}{4}$ shaded?

   $\frac{1}{4}$

   A. $\frac{1}{3}$ B. $\frac{1}{10}$ C. $\frac{1}{2}$ D. $\frac{1}{1}$

4. This rectangle shows $\frac{1}{10}$ shaded.
   Which rectangle shows less than $\frac{1}{10}$ shaded?

   $\frac{1}{10}$

   A. $\frac{1}{5}$ B. $\frac{1}{12}$ C. $\frac{1}{8}$ D. $\frac{1}{7}$

5. This rectangle shows $\frac{2}{5}$ shaded.
   Which rectangle shows less than $\frac{2}{5}$ shaded?

   $\frac{2}{5}$

   A. $\frac{5}{5}$ B. $\frac{4}{5}$ C. $\frac{1}{5}$ D. $\frac{3}{5}$

6. This rectangle shows $\frac{5}{9}$ shaded.
   Which rectangle shows less than $\frac{5}{9}$ shaded?

   $\frac{5}{9}$

   A. $\frac{6}{9}$ B. $\frac{3}{9}$ C. $\frac{8}{9}$ D. $\frac{7}{9}$

7. Look at the number line showing $\frac{6}{8}, \frac{1}{8}, \frac{7}{8},$ and $\frac{3}{8}$.
   Which comparison is correct?

   A. $\frac{1}{8} < \frac{3}{8}$ B. $\frac{6}{8} < \frac{1}{8}$ C. $\frac{6}{8} < \frac{3}{8}$ D. $\frac{7}{8} < \frac{3}{8}$

8. Look at the number line showing $\frac{5}{6}, \frac{1}{6}, \frac{4}{6},$ and $\frac{3}{6}$.
   Which comparison is correct?

   A. $\frac{5}{6} < \frac{1}{6}$ B. $\frac{3}{6} < \frac{4}{6}$ C. $\frac{5}{6} < \frac{3}{6}$ D. $\frac{4}{6} < \frac{1}{6}$

9. Look at the number line showing $\frac{4}{10}, \frac{9}{10}, \frac{2}{10},$ and $\frac{7}{10}$.
   Which comparison is correct?

   A. $\frac{2}{10} > \frac{7}{10}$ B. $\frac{7}{10} > \frac{9}{10}$ C. $\frac{9}{10} > \frac{2}{10}$ D. $\frac{4}{10} > \frac{7}{10}$

Compare and Order Fractions (B)

Lesson Overview		
LEARN Compare with Fraction Strips	15 minutes	OFFLINE
LEARN Use Number Lines to Compare Fractions	20 minutes	OFFLINE
TRY IT Compare and Order with Models	15 minutes	OFFLINE
CHECKPOINT	10 minutes	ONLINE

▶ Lesson Objectives

Compare and order unit fractions, such as $\frac{1}{4}$, and fractions with like denominators, such as $\frac{2}{5}$ and $\frac{4}{5}$, by using objects or sketches.

▶ Prerequisite Skills

Use concrete objects or given drawings to compare unit fractions from $\frac{1}{12}$ to $\frac{1}{2}$.

▶ Content Background

Students will continue to learn to identify and compare fractions with like and unlike denominators using $<$, $>$, or $=$.

Students will use the comparison symbols of $<$, $>$, or $=$ to compare fractions. The denominator, or the number below the fraction bar, of a fraction tells how many equal pieces the whole has been divided into. It is important for students to understand that as the denominator increases, the size of each piece decreases.

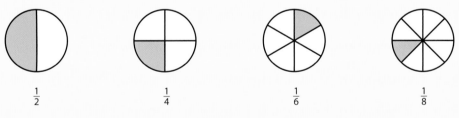

$$\frac{1}{2} \qquad \frac{1}{4} \qquad \frac{1}{6} \qquad \frac{1}{8}$$

Materials to Gather

SUPPLIED

Fraction Strips (printout)

Whole to Twelfths Number Lines (printout)

Use Number Lines to Compare Fractions activity page

Compare and Order with Models activity page

ALSO NEEDED

straightedge

▶ Common Errors and Misconceptions

- Students might view the numerator and denominator of a fraction as separate, isolated numbers that can be operated on independently. This may lead to students "memorizing" rather than understanding fraction algorithms, and then using them incorrectly.

- Students might not understand the difference between fractions and whole numbers. Fractions are parts of whole numbers. Examples of fractions include $\frac{4}{5}$, $\frac{7}{100}$, and $2\frac{1}{2}$. Examples of whole numbers include 4, 6, and 10. Whole numbers may be written as fractions, but always with a denominator of 1, such as $\frac{4}{1}$, $\frac{6}{1}$, or $\frac{10}{1}$.

- Students might have difficulty understanding how different models represent fractions because they often see fractions represented as parts of circles—for example, pie and pizza illustrations. They might not recognize, for example, that the following models all represent the fraction $\frac{3}{5}$.

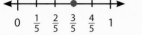  

$\frac{3}{5}$ is a point on the number line. $\frac{3}{5}$ of the shapes are triangles. $\frac{3}{5}$ of the rectangle is shaded.

- Students might think that a fraction always represents the size of a part of a whole, number of items in a set, or a location on the number line, and so might not understand that a fraction can also represent a relationship, such as a quotient or a ratio of one quantity to another.

- Students might think that a fraction compares one part to another part rather than recognizing that a fraction compares one part to the whole.

▶ Advance Preparation

Print the Fraction Strips and the Whole to Twelfths Number Lines.

| **LEARN Compare with Fraction Strips** | OFFLINE **15**min | **Objectives** |

Students will use fraction strips to compare and order fractions using <, >, or =. They will also use fraction strips to order fractions from least to greatest and from greatest to least.

Gather the Fraction Strips printout.

1. Introduce the fraction strips to students. Explain that the first row shows one whole and each row after that shows fractions of a whole. Mention that the fraction strips do not include elevenths.

2. Have students look at the second row. Tell them that this row shows $\frac{1}{2}$ two times. Ask them how many halves it takes to make a whole. 2

   Have students look at the third row. Tell them that this row shows $\frac{1}{3}$ three times. Ask them how many thirds it takes to make a whole. 3

3. Repeat Step 2 for each remaining row on the printout. Make sure students understand that if a row shows fourths, there are 4 parts that make a whole and if a row shows twelfths, there are 12 parts that make a whole. Emphasize that as the denominator increases, the fraction sections get smaller.

4. Explain how to use fraction strips to compare fractions, as follows:

   - Have students look at the fraction strips and identify the $\frac{1}{3}$ strip and the $\frac{1}{4}$ strip. Then ask which is greater, $\frac{1}{3}$ or $\frac{1}{4}$. $\frac{1}{3}$

   - Emphasize that if a whole is divided into 3 equal parts, the parts are bigger than if a whole is divided into 4 equal parts.

   - Have students find a fraction that is less than $\frac{1}{4}$. Students should identify any fraction below $\frac{1}{4}$ $\left(\frac{1}{5}, \frac{1}{6}, \frac{1}{7}, \frac{1}{8}, \frac{1}{9}, \frac{1}{10}, \text{ or } \frac{1}{12}\right)$ as less than $\frac{1}{4}$. Explain that these fraction pieces are all smaller than $\frac{1}{4}$.

   - Explain that you can go straight up or down on the fraction strips to find fractions that are equal to one another.

Objectives

- Compare and order unit fractions, such as $\frac{1}{4}$, and fractions with like denominators, such as $\frac{2}{5}$ and $\frac{4}{5}$, by using objects or sketches.

Say: Look at $\frac{1}{2}$. The fraction $\frac{1}{2}$ is equal to $\frac{2}{4}$. Find other fractions equal to $\frac{1}{2}$.

$\frac{3}{6}, \frac{4}{8}, \frac{5}{10},$ and $\frac{6}{12}$

5. Ask students to use the fraction strips to compare these fractions:

- $\frac{1}{8}$? $\frac{1}{4}$ $<$
- $\frac{1}{2}$? $\frac{1}{8}$ $>$
- $\frac{1}{12}$? $\frac{1}{3}$ $<$
- $\frac{1}{6}$? $\frac{1}{10}$ $>$
- $\frac{1}{5}$? $\frac{1}{4}$ $<$
- $\frac{1}{12}$? $\frac{1}{2}$ $<$

6. Have students use the fraction strips to order the following fractions:

- $\frac{1}{4}, \frac{1}{2}, \frac{1}{3}$ least to greatest $\frac{1}{4}, \frac{1}{3}, \frac{1}{2}$
- $\frac{1}{6}, \frac{1}{12}, \frac{1}{4}$ greatest to least $\frac{1}{4}, \frac{1}{6}, \frac{1}{12}$

LEARN Use Number Lines to Compare Fractions   OFFLINE 20 min

Objectives

- Compare and order unit fractions, such as $\frac{1}{4}$, and fractions with like denominators, such as $\frac{2}{5}$ and $\frac{4}{5}$, by using objects or sketches.

Students will use number lines to compare fractions.
Gather the Whole to Twelfths Number Lines printout and the straightedge (index card or ruler).

1. Introduce the stacked number lines to students. Explain that the stacked number lines are similar to fraction strips. The difference is that here the fractions are just points on a number line, not part of a whole strip.

 Say: All the points shown here exist on every number line. However, if they all appeared on the same line, they'd be too close together to see clearly. The stacked number lines are a way to see the points separately.

2. Point out that each number line goes from 0 to 1 and that along the right side are all the fractions that equal 1 whole. Emphasize that the fractions equal to 1 whole are all equal, or equivalent, fractions. Have students point to 1 whole on the bottom strip. Then have them move their finger up to $\frac{1}{2}, \frac{1}{3}, \frac{1}{4}$, continuing up to $\frac{1}{12}$. Students will see that these unit fractions decrease in value as the denominator increases.

3. Tell students that the stacked number line is another way to compare fractions to identify greater, lesser, or equal fractions. Show students how to use a straight-edge to see fractions that have the same value. Line up a straightedge with the line showing fractions that equal $\frac{1}{2}$. By lining up the straightedge with a given fraction, students can tell which fractions are greater than, less than, or equal to the given fraction.

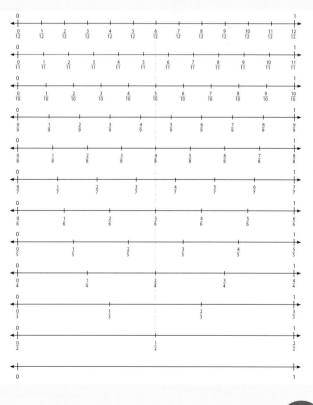

4. Read the first Worked Example with students. Then have students complete Problems 1–8, referring to the Worked Example as needed. Students may use the Whole to Twelfths Number Lines printout.

5. Read the second Worked Example with students. Then have students complete Problems 9–14, referring to the Worked Example as needed. Students may use the Whole to Twelfths Number Lines printout.

6. Have students complete Problems 15–19. Have them explain how they solved the problems.

Compare and Order Fractions (B)
Use Number Lines to Compare Fractions

Worked Examples

You can use number lines to compare fractions.

PROBLEM 1 Compare the fractions. Use $<$, $>$, or $=$.

$\frac{7}{12}$? $\frac{11}{12}$

SOLUTION

Since both fractions are twelfths (they both have 12 in the denominator), you know that 7 twelfths is less than 11 twelfths. You can also locate $\frac{7}{12}$ and $\frac{11}{12}$ on the twelfths number line. The numbers on the number line get greater as you move to the right. The fraction $\frac{11}{12}$ is to the right of $\frac{7}{12}$. So $\frac{7}{12}$ is less than $\frac{11}{12}$.

ANSWER $\frac{7}{12} < \frac{11}{12}$

Compare the fractions. Use $<$, $>$, or $=$.

1. $\frac{1}{3}$? $\frac{2}{3}$ $<$

2. $\frac{6}{8}$? $\frac{3}{8}$ $>$

3. $\frac{4}{5}$? $\frac{1}{5}$ $>$

4. $\frac{1}{4}$? $\frac{2}{4}$ $<$

5. $\frac{3}{6}$? $\frac{2}{6}$ $>$

6. $\frac{9}{10}$? $\frac{5}{10}$ $>$

7. $\frac{4}{11}$? $\frac{8}{11}$ $<$

8. $\frac{8}{12}$? $\frac{2}{12}$ $>$

Worked Examples

You can use number lines to order fractions.

PROBLEM 2 Order the fractions from least to greatest.

$\frac{3}{4}$, $\frac{2}{4}$

SOLUTION

Since both fractions are fourths (they both have 4 in the denominator), you know that 2 fourths is less than 3 fourths. On the number line you can see that $\frac{2}{4}$ is to the left of $\frac{3}{4}$, so $\frac{2}{4}$ is less than $\frac{3}{4}$.

ANSWER $\frac{2}{4}$, $\frac{3}{4}$

Order the fractions from least to greatest.

9. $\frac{4}{6}$, $\frac{5}{6}$ $\frac{4}{6}$, $\frac{5}{6}$

10. $\frac{11}{12}$, $\frac{10}{12}$ $\frac{10}{12}$, $\frac{11}{12}$

11. $\frac{6}{10}$, $\frac{5}{10}$, $\frac{7}{10}$ $\frac{5}{10}$, $\frac{6}{10}$, $\frac{7}{10}$

12. $\frac{3}{3}$, $\frac{1}{3}$, $\frac{2}{3}$ $\frac{1}{3}$, $\frac{2}{3}$, $\frac{3}{3}$

13. $\frac{5}{8}$, $\frac{4}{8}$, $\frac{3}{8}$ $\frac{3}{8}$, $\frac{4}{8}$, $\frac{5}{8}$

14. $\frac{2}{12}$, $\frac{5}{12}$, $\frac{7}{12}$ $\frac{2}{12}$, $\frac{5}{12}$, $\frac{7}{12}$

Use the number lines showing $\frac{1}{3}$, $\frac{1}{4}$, $\frac{1}{6}$, and $\frac{1}{10}$ to solve Problems 15–19.

Compare the fractions. Use $<$, $>$, or $=$.

15. $\frac{1}{3}$? $\frac{1}{6}$ $>$

16. $\frac{1}{10}$? $\frac{1}{4}$ $<$

17. $\frac{1}{6}$? $\frac{2}{6}$ $<$

Order the fractions from least to greatest.

18. $\frac{1}{6}$, $\frac{1}{10}$, $\frac{1}{4}$ $\frac{1}{10}$, $\frac{1}{6}$, $\frac{1}{4}$

19. $\frac{1}{3}$, $\frac{1}{4}$, $\frac{1}{6}$ $\frac{1}{6}$, $\frac{1}{4}$, $\frac{1}{3}$

TRY IT Compare and Order with Models

OFFLINE
15 min

Students will practice comparing and ordering fractions with like and unlike denominators. They will use stacked number lines and illustrations to make the comparisons. Have students turn to the Compare and Order with Models activity page in their Activity Book and read the directions with them.

Students should copy the problems from the Activity Book into their Math Notebook as necessary and solve them there.

Objectives

- Compare and order unit fractions, such as $\frac{1}{4}$, and fractions with like denominators, such as $\frac{2}{5}$ and $\frac{4}{5}$, by using objects or sketches.

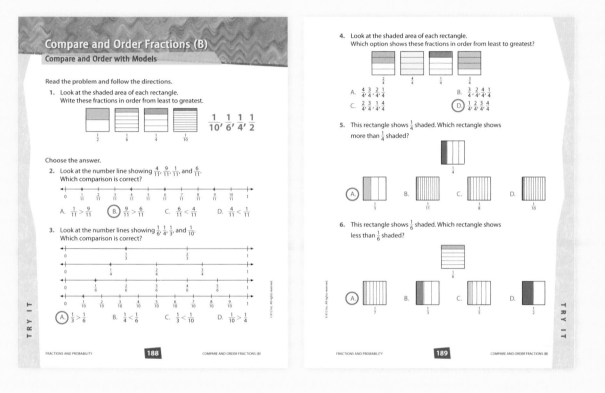

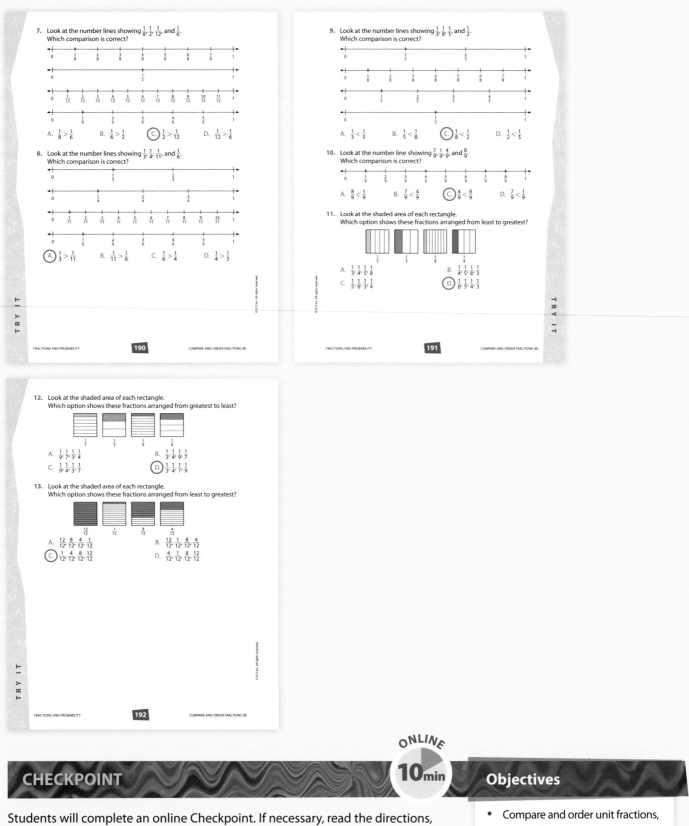

7. Look at the number lines showing $\frac{1}{8}$, $\frac{1}{2}$, $\frac{1}{12}$, and $\frac{1}{6}$.
Which comparison is correct?

A. $\frac{1}{8} > \frac{1}{6}$ B. $\frac{1}{6} > \frac{1}{2}$ C. $\frac{1}{2} > \frac{1}{12}$ D. $\frac{1}{12} > \frac{1}{6}$

8. Look at the number lines showing $\frac{1}{3}$, $\frac{1}{4}$, $\frac{1}{11}$, and $\frac{1}{6}$.
Which comparison is correct?

A. $\frac{1}{3} > \frac{1}{11}$ B. $\frac{1}{11} > \frac{1}{6}$ C. $\frac{1}{6} > \frac{1}{4}$ D. $\frac{1}{4} > \frac{1}{3}$

9. Look at the number lines showing $\frac{1}{3}$, $\frac{1}{8}$, $\frac{1}{5}$, and $\frac{1}{2}$.
Which comparison is correct?

A. $\frac{1}{3} < \frac{1}{5}$ B. $\frac{1}{5} < \frac{1}{8}$ C. $\frac{1}{8} < \frac{1}{2}$ D. $\frac{1}{2} < \frac{1}{5}$

10. Look at the number line showing $\frac{7}{9}$, $\frac{1}{9}$, $\frac{4}{9}$, and $\frac{8}{9}$.
Which comparison is correct?

A. $\frac{8}{9} < \frac{1}{9}$ B. $\frac{7}{9} < \frac{4}{9}$ C. $\frac{4}{9} < \frac{8}{9}$ D. $\frac{7}{9} < \frac{1}{9}$

11. Look at the shaded area of each rectangle.
Which option shows these fractions arranged from least to greatest?

A. $\frac{1}{3}$, $\frac{1}{5}$, $\frac{1}{8}$, $\frac{1}{4}$ B. $\frac{1}{4}$, $\frac{1}{5}$, $\frac{1}{8}$, $\frac{1}{3}$
C. $\frac{1}{5}$, $\frac{1}{8}$, $\frac{1}{3}$, $\frac{1}{4}$ D. $\frac{1}{8}$, $\frac{1}{5}$, $\frac{1}{4}$, $\frac{1}{3}$

12. Look at the shaded area of each rectangle.
Which option shows these fractions arranged from greatest to least?

A. $\frac{1}{9}$, $\frac{1}{7}$, $\frac{1}{3}$, $\frac{1}{4}$ B. $\frac{1}{3}$, $\frac{1}{4}$, $\frac{1}{9}$, $\frac{1}{7}$
C. $\frac{1}{9}$, $\frac{1}{4}$, $\frac{1}{3}$, $\frac{1}{7}$ D. $\frac{1}{3}$, $\frac{1}{4}$, $\frac{1}{7}$, $\frac{1}{9}$

13. Look at the shaded area of each rectangle.
Which option shows these fractions arranged from least to greatest?

A. $\frac{12}{12}$, $\frac{8}{12}$, $\frac{4}{12}$, $\frac{1}{12}$ B. $\frac{12}{12}$, $\frac{1}{12}$, $\frac{8}{12}$, $\frac{4}{12}$
C. $\frac{1}{12}$, $\frac{4}{12}$, $\frac{8}{12}$, $\frac{12}{12}$ D. $\frac{4}{12}$, $\frac{1}{12}$, $\frac{8}{12}$, $\frac{12}{12}$

TRY IT

CHECKPOINT

ONLINE
10 min

Objectives

Students will complete an online Checkpoint. If necessary, read the directions, problems, and answer choices to students and help them with keyboard or mouse operations.

- Compare and order unit fractions, such as $\frac{1}{4}$, and fractions with like denominators, such as $\frac{2}{5}$ and $\frac{4}{5}$, by using objects or sketches.

Model Fraction Story Problems

Lesson Overview

GET READY Show the Fraction	10 minutes	**OFFLINE**
LEARN Use Drawings for Fraction Stories	15 minutes	**OFFLINE**
LEARN Sketch to Solve Fraction Problems	15 minutes	**OFFLINE**
TRY IT Draw Fraction Story Problems	10 minutes	**OFFLINE**
CHECKPOINT	10 minutes	**ONLINE**

▶ Lesson Objectives

Use objects or sketches to solve a simple story problem involving addition or subtraction of fractions.

▶ Prerequisite Skills

- Use a sketch to represent a given fraction.
- Demonstrate and explain the meaning of addition as putting together or combining sets.
- Demonstrate and explain the meaning of subtraction as taking away.

▶ Content Background

Students will learn how to use objects, number lines, and sketches to model and solve story problems involving addition and subtraction of fractions.

Avoid using the term *mixed fraction* with students. Use the more common term *mixed number*.

Students will learn to add and subtract fractions with like denominators such as $\frac{2}{6} + \frac{3}{6} = \frac{5}{6}$. To foster understanding, students first should model the addition without writing anything down. They will easily see that two-sixths plus three-sixths equals five-sixths. By gaining a conceptual understanding of computing with fractions, students will avoid the common rote error of simply adding the numerators and denominators. They will know from the models that they are adding sixths and that the total will be five-sixths, which is written $\frac{5}{6}$.

▶ Common Errors and Misconceptions

- Students might view the numerator and denominator of a fraction as separate, isolated numbers that can be operated on independently. This may lead to students "memorizing" rather than understanding fraction algorithms, and then using them incorrectly.
- Students might not understand the difference between fractions and whole numbers. Fractions are parts of whole numbers. Examples of fractions include $\frac{4}{5}$, $\frac{7}{100}$, and $2\frac{1}{2}$. Examples of whole numbers include 4, 6, and 10. Whole numbers may be written as fractions, but always with a denominator of 1, such as $\frac{4}{1}$, $\frac{6}{1}$, or $\frac{10}{1}$.

Materials to Gather

SUPPLIED

blocks – N (1), K (6)

Use Drawings for Fraction Stories activity page

Sketch to Solve Fraction Problems activity page

Draw Fraction Story Problems activity page

ALSO NEEDED

index cards – 2

- Students might have difficulty understanding how different models represent fractions because they often see fractions represented as parts of circles—for example, pie and pizza illustrations. They might not recognize, for example, that the following models all represent the fraction $\frac{3}{5}$.

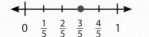  

$\frac{3}{5}$ is a point on the number line. $\frac{3}{5}$ of the shapes are triangles. $\frac{3}{5}$ of the rectangle is shaded.

- Students might think that a fraction always represents the size of a part of a whole, number of items in a set, or a location on the number line, and so might not understand that a fraction can also represent a relationship, such as a quotient or a ratio of one quantity to another.

- Students might think that a fraction compares one part to another part rather than recognizing that a fraction compares one part to the whole.

▶ Advance Preparation

Trace a hexagon (N block) on two different index cards and make dashed lines as shown.

GET READY Show the Fraction

OFFLINE
10 min

Objectives

Students will use their shape blocks to represent fractions and show how to combine fraction pieces to add and take away fraction pieces to subtract.
  Gather the hexagon (N block), triangles (K blocks), and prepared index cards.

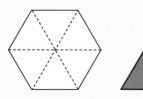

- Use a sketch to represent a given fraction.

- Demonstrate and explain the meaning of addition as putting together or combining sets.

- Demonstrate and explain the meaning of subtraction as taking away.

1. Show the hexagon block and explain that in this activity, the hexagon block will be equal to 1. Have students cover the hexagon with the 6 triangles.

   Ask: What fraction of the hexagon is 1 triangle? $\frac{1}{6}$

2. Show an index card with the traced hexagon. Ask students to show $\frac{2}{6}$ with blocks on the hexagon and explain how they know it is $\frac{2}{6}$. Students should put 2 triangles on the hexagon drawing and explain that since 6 equal triangles make up the whole hexagon, showing 2 of the 6 triangles is $\frac{2}{6}$.

3. Keep the $\frac{2}{6}$ together but slide them off the card. Ask students to show $\frac{3}{6}$ on the card with different triangles. They should place 3 triangles on the hexagon.

4. Remind students that addition is the same as combining groups. Explain that this idea is true for whole numbers and for fractions. Point to the model for $\frac{2}{6}$ and the model for $\frac{3}{6}$.

   Say: We have $\frac{2}{6}$ and $\frac{3}{6}$. Combine the triangles on the card to show adding the two fractions. Count the triangles.

   Ask: What is $\frac{2}{6}$ plus $\frac{3}{6}$? $\frac{5}{6}$

5. Remind students that subtraction is the same as taking away. Explain that this idea is true for whole numbers and for fractions. Point to the model of $\frac{5}{6}$. Ask students to model $\frac{5}{6}$ minus $\frac{2}{6}$. Students should take away 2 of the triangles, leaving 3 triangles, or $\frac{3}{6}$.

   Ask: What is $\frac{5}{6}$ minus $\frac{2}{6}$? $\frac{3}{6}$

6. Have students sketch each of the above problems in their Math Notebook.

7. Guide students to see that when adding or subtracting fractions, they are combining or taking away a certain number of the same-sized fraction pieces, so they can view it as adding sixths or subtracting sixths. In either case, they add or subtract the numerators. The denominators (sixths) just tell them what size parts they are adding or subtracting.

$$\frac{2}{6} + \frac{3}{6} = \frac{5}{6}$$

$$\frac{5}{6} - \frac{2}{6} = \frac{3}{6}$$

LEARN Use Drawings for Fraction Stories

OFFLINE
15 min

Students will use number lines and sketches to solve simple story problems involving addition and subtraction of fractions. Have students turn to the Use Drawings for Fraction Stories activity page in their Activity Book and read the directions with them.

Students should copy the problems from the Activity Book into their Math Notebook as necessary and solve them there.

1. Read the Worked Example with students. Point to the number line. Explain that the number line is divided into sixths, so each jump on the number line is $\frac{1}{6}$. Place your finger on the 0 mark. Jump forward to $\frac{3}{6}$, and then jump $\frac{4}{6}$ more to $\frac{7}{6}$.

   Say: First I jumped $\frac{3}{6}$, and then I jumped 4 more sixths to show adding $\frac{4}{6}$. The mark where I landed, $\frac{7}{6}$, shows the sum of $\frac{3}{6}$ and $\frac{4}{6}$.

2. Direct students' attention to the number sentence, $\frac{3}{6} + \frac{4}{6} = \frac{7}{6}$. Explain that $\frac{7}{6}$ is the same as 1 whole and $\frac{1}{6}$, or $1\frac{1}{6}$. Tell students that when the sum is a fraction greater than 1, they should write the answer as a mixed number like $1\frac{1}{6}$ instead of an improper fraction like $\frac{7}{6}$. Reinforce the fact that the denominator just tells what size pieces they're adding, so the denominator doesn't change.

3. Have students read Problem 1. Ask them how to solve the problem. They should realize that they need to add $\frac{3}{6}$ and $\frac{2}{6}$ find how far the grasshopper jumps. Have them model the problem on the number line. Students should jump to $\frac{3}{6}$ and then jump forward two more tick marks to $\frac{5}{6}$. Then have students write the addition number sentence for the problem as $\frac{3}{6} + \frac{2}{6} = \frac{5}{6}$.

Objectives

- Use objects or sketches to solve a simple story problem involving addition or subtraction of fractions.

Tips

Review adding and subtracting whole numbers on a number line. If students have difficulty with adding and subtracting fractions, try using the shape blocks to model and solve the fraction addition and subtraction problems.

4. Read Problem 2 with students. Have students do a quick sketch of the fence in their Math Notebook. Explain that the picture shows a fence with 7 equal sections.

   Ask: How much of the fence does each section make up? $\frac{1}{7}$

   Have students model the problem by shading $\frac{2}{7}$ of the sketch one color and $\frac{3}{7}$ of the sketch a different color. Ask students to use the model to find the sum of $\frac{2}{7} + \frac{3}{7}$. Encourage students to count the number of shaded equal sections. Have them write the addition number sentence for the problem as $\frac{2}{7} + \frac{3}{7} = \frac{5}{7}$.

5. Have students read Problem 3 and explain how to solve the problem by adding the mixed numbers. Point out that they should add the whole numbers first. Have students explain how they showed the addition on the number line. Students should jump to $2\frac{3}{5}$ and then jump $1\frac{1}{5}$ more to land on $3\frac{4}{5}$. Have students write the number sentence for the problem as $2\frac{3}{5} + 1\frac{1}{5} = 3\frac{4}{5}$.

$$\begin{array}{r} 2\frac{3}{5} \\ + 1\frac{1}{5} \\ \hline 3\frac{4}{5} \end{array}$$

6. Read Problem 4 with students. Ask them how to solve the problem. They should point out that this is a subtraction problem. Explain how to model subtraction on the number line. Students should start with the first number and jump backward the amount of the second number. Have them use the number line shown to model the problem and find the answer. They should start at $\frac{5}{8}$ and jump back $\frac{3}{8}$ to land on $\frac{2}{8}$. Have students write the subtraction number sentence for the problem as $\frac{5}{8} - \frac{3}{8} = \frac{2}{8}$.

7. Have students work through Problem 5 and explain how they showed the subtraction. Students should cover up or take away $\frac{1}{4}$ yard in the model, leaving $2\frac{2}{4}$ yards. Have students write the subtraction number sentence for the problem as $2\frac{3}{4} - \frac{1}{4} = 2\frac{2}{4}$.

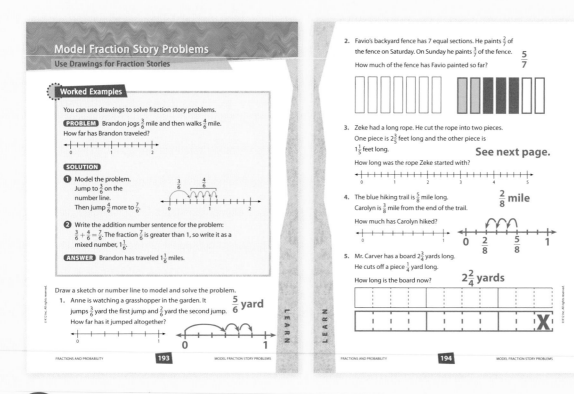

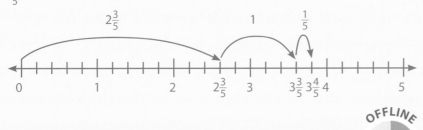

LEARN Sketch to Solve Fraction Problems

OFFLINE
15min

Objectives

- Use objects or sketches to solve a simple story problem involving addition or subtraction of fractions.

Students will add and subtract fractions to solve story problems. They also will answer questions about solving the problems. Have students turn to the Sketch to Solve Fraction Problems activity page in their Activity Book and read the directions with them.

Students should copy the problems from the Activity Book into their Math Notebook as necessary and solve them there.

1. Read the Worked Example with students. Make sure they understand how the sketch relates to the problem.

2. Have students read Problem 1 and identify the given information and what they need to find. Guide students to make a number line to model the problem.

   Say: Turn your notebook sideways and draw a line across the page, so your line is crossing the printed lines on your notebook page. The lines on the page make evenly spaced marks. To make a number line marked in fifths, make a mark for 0 and then mark the first blue line $\frac{1}{5}$, and then mark $\frac{2}{5}$, $\frac{3}{5}$, $\frac{4}{5}$, and $\frac{5}{5}$ (or 1). Make sure that $\frac{5}{5}$ and 1 are the same point on the number line. Continue adding numbers $1\frac{1}{5}$, $1\frac{2}{5}$ … through 3.

   Ask: If the number line is the trail, where is the end of the trail? $2\frac{4}{5}$
   Have students place a dot on $2\frac{4}{5}$. Walk them through the problem by asking the following questions:

   - How will you show the amount Aaron jogged so far? Start at 0. Move forward $1\frac{3}{5}$.

   - How can you find how much farther Aaron has left to jog? Count how far it is from $1\frac{3}{5}$ to $2\frac{4}{5}$. Starting at $1\frac{3}{5}$ students should count forward by fifths to get to $2\frac{4}{5}$. They will count forward $\frac{6}{5}$ or $1\frac{1}{5}$. Aaron has $1\frac{1}{5}$ miles left to jog.
     Tell students that they found the difference by counting forward from $1\frac{3}{5}$ to $2\frac{4}{5}$.

3. Have students complete Problems 2 and 3. Guide students as they work through the problems by asking the following questions:

   - What information do you know?

   - Do you need to add or subtract?

   - How can you model the problem?

   - Will you use a number line or a drawing?

   - How will you use your sketch to find the answer?

   - What is the answer?

In Problem 2, the ribbon problem, have students show a number line to 3 divided into sixths. Students can place a dot at $2\frac{5}{6}$ and make 4 jumps backward to take away the $\frac{4}{6}$ yard of ribbon that was used. This gives the answer of $2\frac{1}{6}$ yards of ribbon left.

In Problem 3, help students draw 2 circles and divide them into 8 pieces by drawing lines to cut them in half, then in fourths, and then in eighths. Have students shade first $\frac{7}{8}$ and then $\frac{2}{8}$ to get $\frac{9}{8}$ altogether. Help students see that $\frac{9}{8}$ is $\frac{8}{8}$, or 1 whole, plus $\frac{1}{8}$ more. Have students explain how the picture and the fractions represent the same amount.

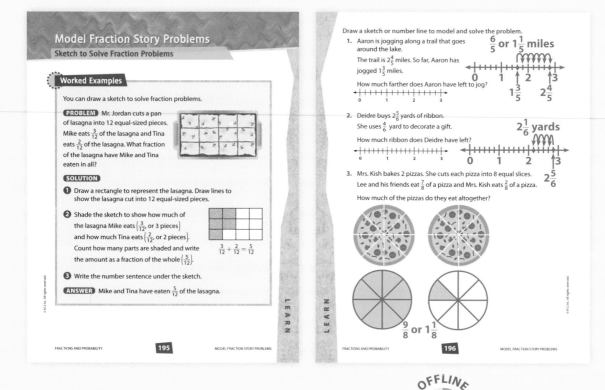

TRY IT Draw Fraction Story Problems

OFFLINE
10 min

Objectives

- Use objects or sketches to solve a simple story problem involving addition or subtraction of fractions.

Students will practice using objects or sketches to solve simple story problems involving adding and subtracting fractions. Have students turn to the Draw Fraction Story Problems activity page in their Activity Book and read the directions with them.

Students should copy the problems from the Activity Book into their Math Notebook as necessary and solve them there.

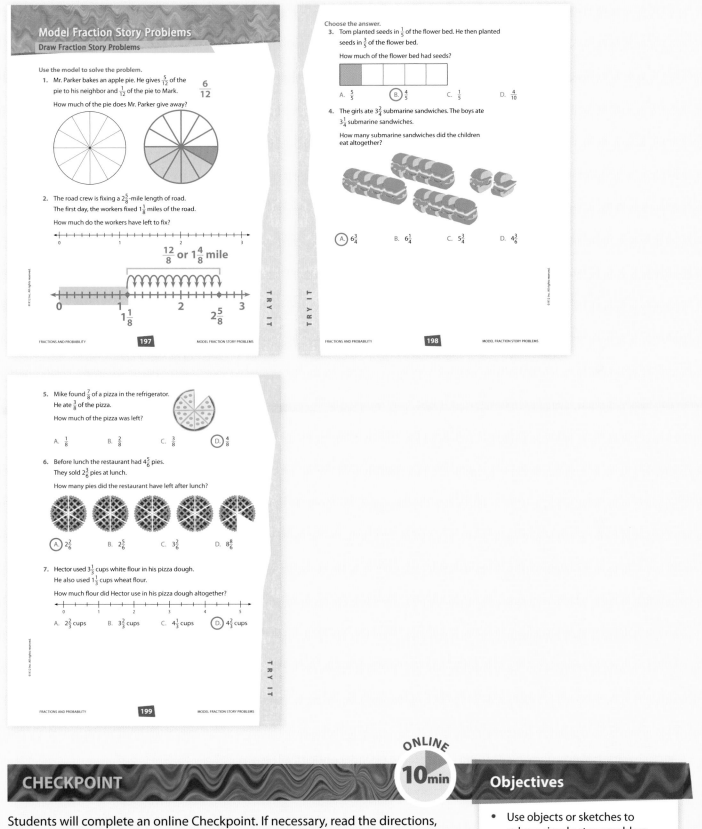

Model Fraction Story Problems
Draw Fraction Story Problems

Use the model to solve the problem.

1. Mr. Parker bakes an apple pie. He gives $\frac{5}{12}$ of the pie to his neighbor and $\frac{1}{12}$ of the pie to Mark.

   How much of the pie does Mr. Parker give away?

   $\frac{6}{12}$

2. The road crew is fixing a $2\frac{5}{8}$-mile length of road. The first day, the workers fixed $1\frac{1}{8}$ miles of the road.

   How much do the workers have left to fix?

   $\frac{12}{8}$ or $1\frac{4}{8}$ mile

FRACTIONS AND PROBABILITY 197 MODEL FRACTION STORY PROBLEMS

TRY IT

Choose the answer.

3. Tom planted seeds in $\frac{1}{5}$ of the flower bed. He then planted seeds in $\frac{3}{5}$ of the flower bed.

   How much of the flower bed had seeds?

   A. $\frac{5}{5}$ B. $\frac{4}{5}$ C. $\frac{1}{5}$ D. $\frac{4}{10}$

4. The girls ate $3\frac{2}{4}$ submarine sandwiches. The boys ate $3\frac{1}{4}$ submarine sandwiches.

   How many submarine sandwiches did the children eat altogether?

   A. $6\frac{3}{4}$ B. $6\frac{1}{4}$ C. $5\frac{3}{4}$ D. $4\frac{3}{6}$

FRACTIONS AND PROBABILITY 198 MODEL FRACTION STORY PROBLEMS

TRY IT

5. Mike found $\frac{7}{8}$ of a pizza in the refrigerator. He ate $\frac{3}{8}$ of the pizza.

   How much of the pizza was left?

   A. $\frac{1}{8}$ B. $\frac{2}{8}$ C. $\frac{3}{8}$ D. $\frac{4}{8}$

6. Before lunch the restaurant had $4\frac{5}{6}$ pies. They sold $2\frac{3}{6}$ pies at lunch.

   How many pies did the restaurant have left after lunch?

   A. $2\frac{2}{6}$ B. $2\frac{5}{6}$ C. $3\frac{2}{6}$ D. $8\frac{8}{6}$

7. Hector used $3\frac{1}{3}$ cups white flour in his pizza dough. He also used $1\frac{1}{3}$ cups wheat flour.

   How much flour did Hector use in his pizza dough altogether?

   A. $2\frac{2}{3}$ cups   B. $3\frac{2}{3}$ cups   C. $4\frac{1}{3}$ cups   D. $4\frac{2}{3}$ cups

FRACTIONS AND PROBABILITY 199 MODEL FRACTION STORY PROBLEMS

TRY IT

ONLINE 10min

CHECKPOINT

Students will complete an online Checkpoint. If necessary, read the directions, problems, and answer choices to students and help them with keyboard or mouse operations.

Objectives

- Use objects or sketches to solve a simple story problem involving addition or subtraction of fractions.

MODEL FRACTION STORY PROBLEMS **381**

Add and Subtract Like Fractions

Lesson Overview

Skills Update	5 minutes	ONLINE
GET READY Freddy Frog and Fractions	5 minutes	ONLINE
LEARN Add and Subtract Fractions	15 minutes	OFFLINE
LEARN Solve Fraction Story Problems	10 minutes	OFFLINE
TRY IT Solve and Simplify	15 minutes	OFFLINE
CHECKPOINT	10 minutes	ONLINE

▶ Lesson Objectives

Solve and simplify an addition or subtraction problem involving fractions with like denominators.

▶ Prerequisite Skills

Use objects or sketches to solve a simple story problem involving addition or subtraction of fractions.

▶ Content Background

Students will solve addition and subtraction problems that involve like fractions, or fractions that have the same denominator, such as $\frac{1}{4} + \frac{3}{4} = \frac{4}{4}$ or $\frac{1}{8} + \frac{3}{8} = \frac{4}{8}$. They will simplify the answers to addition and subtraction problems.

Students have solved story problems that involve adding and subtracting fractions and will now simplify the solution. When a solution is simplified, it means that the fraction is written in the simplest form as a fraction, whole number, or mixed number. For example, $\frac{4}{4}$ would be written as 1, and $\frac{6}{4}$ would be written as $1\frac{2}{4}$. The mixed number $1\frac{2}{4}$ is then written in simplest form as $1\frac{1}{2}$. Students will also learn to simplify improper fractions in which the numerator is greater than the denominator, such as $\frac{23}{6}$. They will think about this in terms of how many wholes $\left(\frac{6}{6}\right)$ they can make from the improper fraction. They will discover that $\frac{6}{6} + \frac{6}{6} + \frac{6}{6} + \frac{5}{6} = \frac{23}{6}$, so $\frac{23}{6}$ is the same as 3 wholes and $\frac{5}{6}$ or $3\frac{5}{6}$.

▶ Common Errors and Misconceptions

- Students might view the numerator and denominator of a fraction as separate, isolated numbers that can be operated on independently. This may lead to students "memorizing" rather than understanding fraction algorithms, and then using them incorrectly.

Materials to Gather

SUPPLIED

Fraction Strips (printout)

Solve Fraction Story Problems activity page

Solve and Simplify activity page

ALSO NEEDED

straightedge

- Students might not understand the difference between fractions and whole numbers. Fractions are parts of whole numbers. Examples of fractions include $\frac{4}{5}$, $\frac{7}{100}$, and $2\frac{1}{2}$. Examples of whole numbers include 4, 6, and 10. Whole numbers may be written as fractions, but always with a denominator of 1, such as $\frac{4}{1}$, $\frac{6}{1}$, or $\frac{10}{1}$.

- Students might have difficulty understanding how different models represent fractions because they often see fractions represented as parts of circles—for example, pie and pizza illustrations. They might not recognize, for example, that the following models all represent the fraction $\frac{3}{5}$.

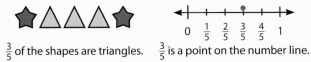

$\frac{3}{5}$ of the rectangle is shaded. $\frac{3}{5}$ of the shapes are triangles. $\frac{3}{5}$ is a point on the number line.

- Students might think that a fraction always represents the size of a part of a whole, number of items in a set, or a location on the number line, and so might not understand that a fraction can also represent a relationship, such as a quotient or a ratio of one quantity to another.

- Students might think that a fraction compares one part to another part rather than recognizing that a fraction compares one part to the whole.

▶ Advance Preparation

Print the Fraction Strips.

GET READY Freddy Frog and Fractions

ONLINE 5 min

Objectives

Students will use a number line to solve simple story problems involving addition of fractions. Before they solve the first problem, have them practice with their finger hopping $\frac{3}{8} + \frac{4}{8}$ to get $\frac{7}{8}$. Then have them hop $\frac{5}{8}$ more to get to $\frac{12}{8}$ or $1\frac{4}{8}$. Students should get comfortable with jumps that go beyond 1.

- Use objects or sketches to solve a simple story problem involving addition or subtraction of fractions.

Tips	Review how to use a number line to add and subtract. Stress moving forward to add and moving backward to subtract.

LEARN Add and Subtract Fractions

OFFLINE 15 min

Objectives

Students will add and subtract like fractions. They will use fraction strips to simplify the answer.

Gather the Fraction Strips and straightedge (index card or ruler).

- Solve and simplify an addition or subtraction problem involving fractions with like denominators.

ADD AND SUBTRACT FRACTIONS

1. Tell students that they have added and subtracted fractions using models, such as number lines or sketches. Now they'll add and subtract fractions without using models. Explain that the fractions in each problem will be *like fractions*: they'll have the same denominator.

2. Write $\frac{1}{5} + \frac{2}{5}$. Have students say the problem aloud. one-fifth plus two-fifths
Explain that the denominator shows that equal-sized parts, fifths, are being
added. So 1 fifth plus 2 fifths simply equals 3 fifths. Write $\frac{1}{5} + \frac{2}{5} = \frac{3}{5}$. Ask
students if they can think of a rule that would help them add like fractions.
Add the numerators and leave the denominator unchanged.

3. Have students find the following sums. Allow them to draw models if
necessary, but encourage them to simply add the numerators.
   - $\frac{3}{8} + \frac{2}{8}$ $\frac{5}{8}$
   - $\frac{3}{12} + \frac{4}{12}$ $\frac{7}{12}$

4. Write $\frac{5}{8} - \frac{2}{8}$. Explain that as with addition, the denominator in a subtraction
problem shows the type of equal-sized parts. Have students say the problem
aloud with the answer. five-eighths minus two-eighths equals three-eighths
Write $\frac{5}{8} - \frac{2}{8} = \frac{3}{8}$.

5. Have students find the following differences. Allow them to draw models if
necessary, but encourage them to simply subtract the numerators.
   - $\frac{4}{10} - \frac{1}{10}$ $\frac{3}{10}$
   - $\frac{3}{9} - \frac{2}{9}$ $\frac{1}{9}$

SIMPLIFY FRACTIONS WITH FRACTION STRIPS

6. Explain that sometimes after adding or subtracting fractions, the sum or
difference can be written in a simpler way. Show this example: $\frac{3}{8} + \frac{1}{8} = \frac{4}{8}$.
Circle the sum, $\frac{4}{8}$. Ask students if there are other fractions that are equal to $\frac{4}{8}$.
Guide students to find the fraction strip that shows eighths and put a
straightedge vertically at $\frac{4}{8}$. Point out that $\frac{3}{6}, \frac{5}{10}, \frac{6}{12}, \frac{2}{4}$, and $\frac{1}{2}$ are all equal
to $\frac{4}{8}$. Ask which of the equal fractions is made up of the fewest number of
pieces. $\frac{1}{2}$

   Write $\frac{4}{8} = \frac{1}{2}$. Explain that $\frac{1}{2}$ uses the fewest number of fraction pieces, so $\frac{4}{8}$
   written in simplest form is $\frac{1}{2}$.

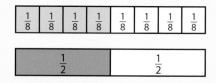

7. Have students add $\frac{1}{6} + \frac{1}{6}$ and write the answer in simplest form.
   $\frac{1}{6} + \frac{1}{6} = \frac{2}{6}$ and $\frac{2}{6} = \frac{1}{3}$

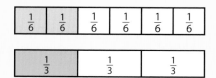

8. Have students subtract $\frac{5}{8} - \frac{3}{8}$. Guide them to first subtract the numerators
to find the difference of $\frac{2}{8}$. Then guide them to use the fraction strips and
straightedge to see that $\frac{2}{8}$ is equal to $\frac{1}{4}$. Emphasize that because $\frac{1}{4}$ has fewer
pieces, it is the simplest form of $\frac{2}{8}$. Write $\frac{5}{8} - \frac{3}{8} = \frac{2}{8}$ and
$\frac{2}{8} = \frac{1}{4}$, so $\frac{5}{8} - \frac{3}{8} = \frac{1}{4}$.

9. Have students subtract $\frac{5}{6} - \frac{1}{6}$ and write the answer in simplest form.
   $\frac{5}{6} - \frac{1}{6} = \frac{4}{6}$ and $\frac{4}{6} = \frac{2}{3}$

ADD AND SUBTRACT MIXED NUMBERS

10. Explain that when students add and subtract mixed numbers, they should write the problems vertically so that they can line up the whole-number parts and the fraction parts.

11. Have students write $1\frac{1}{4} + 2\frac{1}{4}$ vertically. Have them first add the whole-number parts: $1 + 2 = 3$. Then have them add the fraction parts: $\frac{1}{4} + \frac{1}{4} = \frac{2}{4}$. Write the sum, $3\frac{2}{4}$.

    Have students use the fraction strips to simplify the answer. Explain that the whole number, 3, is already in simplest form. Students should find that the fraction part, $\frac{2}{4}$, can be simplified to $\frac{1}{2}$.

$$\begin{array}{r} 1\frac{1}{4} \\ + 2\frac{1}{4} \\ \hline 3\frac{2}{4} = 3\frac{1}{2} \end{array}$$

12. Guide students to subtract $3\frac{9}{10} - 1\frac{3}{10}$. Have them write the problem vertically, subtract the whole numbers, subtract the fractions, and simplify the answer.

$$\begin{array}{r} 3\frac{9}{10} \\ - 1\frac{3}{10} \\ \hline 2\frac{6}{10} = 2\frac{3}{5} \end{array}$$

SIMPLIFY IMPROPER FRACTIONS

13. Explain that an improper fraction is not in simplest form. Improper fractions can always be changed to mixed numbers or whole numbers. If the sum or difference of fractions is an improper fraction, students should change the improper fraction to a mixed number or whole number.

14. Write $\frac{3}{4} + \frac{7}{4}$ and have students find the sum. $\frac{10}{4}$

    Point out that the answer is an improper fraction because the numerator is greater than the denominator. Guide students to write the improper fraction as a mixed number. Explain that $\frac{4}{4}$ equals 1 whole. Ask them how many wholes can be made with $\frac{10}{4}$. Guide them to find the answer by making groups of 4 fourths that equal 1.

$$\frac{10}{4} = \frac{4}{4} + \frac{4}{4} + \frac{2}{4} = 1 + 1 + \frac{2}{4} = 2 + \frac{2}{4} = 2\frac{2}{4} = 2\frac{1}{2}$$

15. Have students add $\frac{1}{3} + \frac{5}{3}$ and simplify the answer.

$$\frac{1}{3} + \frac{5}{3} = \frac{6}{3} = \frac{3}{3} + \frac{3}{3} = 1 + 1 = 2$$

LEARN Solve Fraction Story Problems

OFFLINE 10 min

Students will solve story problems that involve adding and subtracting fractions. They will use fraction strips to help them simplify their answers. Gather the Fraction Strips and straightedge. Have students turn to the Solve Fraction Story Problems activity page in their Activity Book and read the directions with them.

Students should copy the problems from the Activity Book into their Math Notebook as necessary and solve them there.

1. Read the Worked Example with students. Point out that this problem is a two-step problem. First they must add to find the total amount of pizza eaten, and then they must subtract that amount from the whole.

    Remind students that when subtracting fractions with like denominators, they just subtract the numerators (the denominator tells the number of pieces in the whole).

    Point out that the answer, $\frac{2}{6}$, was not in simplest form. Have students use the fraction strips and straightedge to see that $\frac{2}{6} = \frac{1}{3}$.

Objectives

- Solve and simplify an addition or subtraction problem involving fractions with like denominators.

Tips

Encourage students to draw pictures or sketches to help them visualize the problems.

2. Have students read Problem 1. Ask students whether they'll add or subtract to solve and how they know this. add; I need to find the distance altogether.

Have students write the number sentence $\frac{3}{10} + \frac{5}{10} = \underline{\hphantom{xx}}$. Remind them that when the denominators are the same, they just add the numerators and keep the denominator.

Ask: What is the sum of $\frac{3}{10}$ plus $\frac{5}{10}$? $\frac{8}{10}$

Ask students if the sum is in simplest form. Encourage them to use the fraction strips to simplify $\frac{8}{10}$ to $\frac{4}{5}$.

3. Guide students to complete Problems 2 and 3. Ask questions such as the following:

- What information do you know?
- Do you need to add or subtract?
- What is the answer?
- Is the answer in simplest form?
- Is the answer an improper fraction?
- How do you simplify an improper fraction?

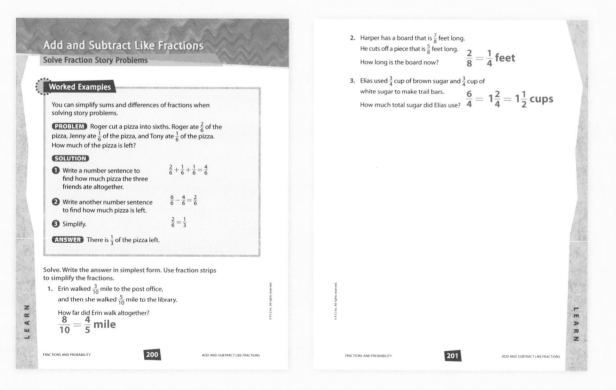

Add and Subtract Like Fractions
Solve Fraction Story Problems

Worked Examples

You can simplify sums and differences of fractions when solving story problems.

PROBLEM Roger cut a pizza into sixths. Roger ate $\frac{2}{6}$ of the pizza, Jenny ate $\frac{1}{6}$ of the pizza, and Tony ate $\frac{1}{6}$ of the pizza. How much of the pizza is left?

SOLUTION

1. Write a number sentence to find how much pizza the three friends ate altogether. $\quad \frac{2}{6} + \frac{1}{6} + \frac{1}{6} = \frac{4}{6}$

2. Write another number sentence to find how much pizza is left. $\quad \frac{6}{6} - \frac{4}{6} = \frac{2}{6}$

3. Simplify. $\quad \frac{2}{6} = \frac{1}{3}$

ANSWER There is $\frac{1}{3}$ of the pizza left.

Solve. Write the answer in simplest form. Use fraction strips to simplify the fractions.

1. Erin walked $\frac{3}{10}$ mile to the post office, and then she walked $\frac{5}{10}$ mile to the library.

How far did Erin walk altogether?
$\frac{8}{10} = \frac{4}{5}$ **mile**

2. Harper has a board that is $\frac{7}{8}$ feet long. He cuts off a piece that is $\frac{5}{8}$ feet long. How long is the board now? $\quad \frac{2}{8} = \frac{1}{4}$ **feet**

3. Elias used $\frac{3}{4}$ cup of brown sugar and $\frac{3}{4}$ cup of white sugar to make trail bars. How much total sugar did Elias use? $\quad \frac{6}{4} = 1\frac{2}{4} = 1\frac{1}{2}$ **cups**

LEARN

TRY IT Solve and Simplify

Students will practice adding and subtracting fractions and using fractions strips to simplify their answers. Gather the Fraction Strips and straightedge. Have students turn to the Solve and Simplify activity page in their Activity Book and read the directions with them.

Students should copy the problems from the Activity Book into their Math Notebook as necessary and solve them there.

- Solve and simplify an addition or subtraction problem involving fractions with like denominators.

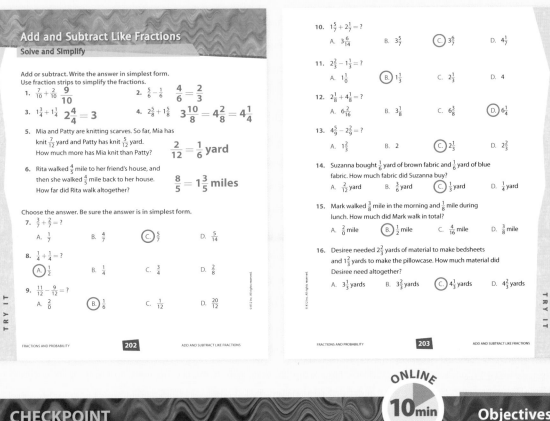

CHECKPOINT

Students will complete an online Checkpoint. If necessary, read the directions, problems, and answer choices to students and help them with keyboard or mouse operations.

- Solve and simplify an addition or subtraction problem involving fractions with like denominators.

Fractions and Decimals (A)

GET READY Identify Fractions and Decimals	5 minutes	ONLINE
LEARN Equal Fractions and Decimals	10 minutes	ONLINE
LEARN Represent Fractions as Decimal Numbers	30 minutes	ONLINE
TRY IT Different Ways to Show the Same Thing	15 minutes	OFFLINE

▶ Lesson Objectives

Explain that a simple fraction and a decimal amount can represent the same quantity.

▶ Prerequisite Skills

- Identify decimal place values through thousandths.
- Write the fraction represented by a drawing that shows parts of a set or parts of a whole.

▶ Content Background

Students will learn how to show the decimal equivalent of fractions, such as $\frac{1}{10}$, $\frac{3}{100}$, and $\frac{5}{1,000}$.

Fractions and decimals have a mathematical connection that is key to understanding how to represent numbers. Decimal numbers are an alternative way to write fractional parts of a whole in terms of tenths, hundredths, thousandths, and so on. Decimal numbers are simply different representations for their equivalent fractions and mixed numbers. Saying and thinking about decimal numbers correctly promotes a strong and necessary understanding of place value and fractions. When students say a decimal number such as 1.35, they will learn to say "1 and 35 hundredths." The word *and* signals the placement of the decimal. Students should think about the equivalent representation of $1\frac{35}{100}$ as they say the decimal number and should be able to visualize the meaning with a visual representation as shown in the illustration. They should be able to read the name of the decimal and recognize the difference between *hundreds* and *hundredths*.

When saying a decimal number such as 0.52, students should say "fifty-two hundredths," not "zero point fifty-two." When students say *point*, they are not focusing on the place value, which is critical to their understanding. It is important to model the correct way to read decimals.

▶ Common Errors and Misconceptions

- Students might view the numerator and denominator of a fraction as separate, isolated numbers that can be operated on independently. This may lead to students "memorizing" rather than understanding fraction algorithms, and then using them incorrectly.

Materials to Gather

SUPPLIED

Fractions and Decimal Equivalents (printout)

Different Ways to Show the Same Thing activity page

- Students might not understand the difference between fractions and whole numbers. Fractions are parts of whole numbers. Examples of fractions include $\frac{4}{5}$, $\frac{7}{100}$, and $2\frac{1}{2}$. Examples of whole numbers include 4, 6, and 10. Whole numbers may be written as fractions, but always with a denominator of 1, such as $\frac{4}{1}$, $\frac{6}{1}$, or $\frac{10}{1}$.

- Students might have difficulty understanding how different models represent fractions because they often see fractions represented as parts of circles—for example, pie and pizza illustrations. They might not recognize, for example, that the following models all represent the fraction $\frac{3}{5}$.

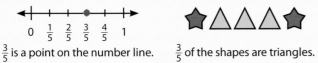

$\frac{3}{5}$ is a point on the number line.

$\frac{3}{5}$ of the shapes are triangles.

$\frac{3}{5}$ of the rectangle is shaded.

- Students might think that a fraction always represents the size of a part of a whole, number of items in a set, or a location on the number line, and so might not understand that a fraction can also represent a relationship, such as a quotient or a ratio of one quantity to another.

- Students might think that a fraction compares one part to another part rather than recognizing that a fraction compares one part to the whole.

▶ Advance Preparation

Print the Fractions and Decimal Equivalents printout.

GET READY Identify Fractions and Decimals

ONLINE **5**min

Objectives

Students will review the decimal place values of tenths, hundredths, and thousandths. They will then identify the decimal number that has the same value as a given fraction.

- Identify decimal place values through thousandths.
- Write the fraction represented by a drawing that shows parts of a set or parts of a whole.

LEARN Equal Fractions and Decimals

ONLINE **10**min

Objectives

Students will complete a decimal number when given the fraction, word form, and grid representation of the number.

- Explain that a simple fraction and a decimal amount can represent the same quantity.

LEARN Represent Fractions as Decimal Numbers

ONLINE **30**min

Objectives

Students will show equivalent fractions and decimals in this online activity. First they will see a Grid Learning Tool Preview. Then they will use the hundred grid as 1 whole and will shade tenths, halves, fifths, and fourths.
    Gather the Fractions and Decimal Equivalents printout.

DIRECTIONS FOR USING THE GRID LEARNING TOOL

1. Tell students that they can represent fractions on the grid. There are 100 squares that can be thought of as 1 whole; when they shade a portion of the grid, they're shading a fraction of the whole.

2. Have students shade one column on the grid.

   Say: There are 10 columns. You've shaded one column. One column is one-tenth of the whole, so you've shaded the fraction $\frac{1}{10}$. And since there are 100 squares, 10 of which you shaded, you have also shaded ten-hundredths, or $\frac{10}{100}$.

   Ask: How do you write $\frac{1}{10}$ as a decimal? 0.1

   Ask: How do you write $\frac{10}{100}$ as a decimal? 0.10

3. Have students shade each remaining column, one at a time, naming the corresponding tenths and hundredths fractions as they go. $\frac{2}{10}$ and $\frac{20}{100}$, $\frac{3}{10}$ and $\frac{30}{100}$, and so on

4. Give students the Fractions and Decimal Equivalents printout and have them complete the Tenths table.

5. Have students clear the squares they've shaded. Repeat Steps 2–4 for the Halves, then Fifths, and then Fourths tables. For halves, students should shade 5 columns (5 tenths), which is 50 squares (50 hundredths). For fifths, students should shade 20 squares at a time. For fourths, guide students to shade 25 squares at a time as two columns of 10 (2 tenths) and 5 squares of an adjacent column (5 hundredths). Make sure students understand they show a fourth of the whole square when they shade 25 of the hundred squares. Ask students if they can shade the square to show fourths in a different way. If necessary, point out that one way is to color each half of the square and then make each half into two colors to get 4 equal parts in the traditional pattern as shown below.

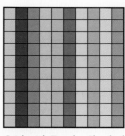

Grid with Tenths Shaded

Grid Showing One-Half

Grid Showing One-Fifth

Grid Showing Fifths Shaded

Grid Showing Fourths Shaded as 2 Tenths and 5 Hundredths

Grid Showing Fourths as $\frac{25}{100}$ Arranged in Traditional Pattern

Fractions and Decimal Equivalents

Fractions and Decimals for Tenths			
Fraction (in tenths)	Decimal equivalent (in tenths)	Fraction (in hundredths)	Decimal equivalent (in hundredths)
$\frac{1}{10}$	0.1	$\frac{10}{100}$	0.10
$\frac{2}{10}$	0.2	$\frac{20}{100}$	0.20
$\frac{3}{10}$	0.3	$\frac{30}{100}$	0.30
$\frac{4}{10}$	0.4	$\frac{40}{100}$	0.40
$\frac{5}{10}$	0.5	$\frac{50}{100}$	0.50
$\frac{6}{10}$	0.6	$\frac{60}{100}$	0.60
$\frac{7}{10}$	0.7	$\frac{70}{100}$	0.70
$\frac{8}{10}$	0.8	$\frac{80}{100}$	0.80
$\frac{9}{10}$	0.9	$\frac{90}{100}$	0.90
$\frac{10}{10}$	1.0	$\frac{100}{100}$	1.00

Fractions and Decimals for Halves				
Fraction	Fraction (in tenths)	Decimal equivalent (in fifths)	Fraction (in hundredths)	Decimal equivalent (in hundredths)
$\frac{1}{2}$	$\frac{5}{10}$	0.5	$\frac{50}{100}$	0.50
$\frac{2}{2}$	$\frac{10}{10}$	1.0	$\frac{100}{100}$	1.00

Fractions and Decimals for Fifths				
Fraction	Fraction (in tenths)	Decimal equivalent (in tenths)	Fraction (in hundredths)	Decimal equivalent (in hundredths)
$\frac{1}{5}$	$\frac{2}{10}$	0.2	$\frac{20}{100}$	0.20
$\frac{2}{5}$	$\frac{4}{10}$	0.4	$\frac{40}{100}$	0.40
$\frac{3}{5}$	$\frac{6}{10}$	0.6	$\frac{60}{100}$	0.60
$\frac{4}{5}$	$\frac{8}{10}$	0.8	$\frac{80}{100}$	0.80
$\frac{5}{5}$	$\frac{10}{10}$	1.0	$\frac{100}{100}$	1.00

Fractions and Decimals for Fourths		
Fraction	Fraction (in hundredths)	Decimal equivalent (in hundredths)
$\frac{1}{4}$	$\frac{25}{100}$	0.25
$\frac{2}{4}$	$\frac{50}{100}$	0.50
$\frac{3}{4}$	$\frac{75}{100}$	0.75
$\frac{4}{4}$	$\frac{100}{100}$	1.00

TRY IT Different Ways to Show the Same Thing

Objectives

- Explain that a simple fraction and a decimal amount can represent the same quantity.

Students will practice writing fractions and decimals that are equivalent. Have students turn to the Different Ways to Show the Same Thing activity page in their Activity Book and read the directions with them.

Students should copy the problems from the Activity Book into their Math Notebook as necessary and solve them there.

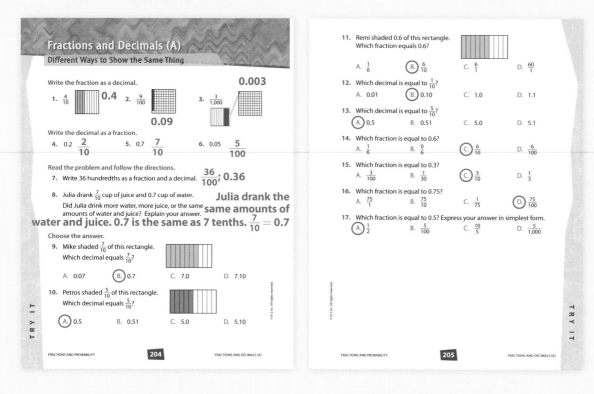

Fractions and Decimals (A)

Different Ways to Show the Same Thing

Write the fraction as a decimal.

1. $\frac{4}{10}$ **0.4**   2. $\frac{9}{100}$ **0.09**   3. $\frac{3}{1,000}$ **0.003**

Write the decimal as a fraction.

4. 0.2 **$\frac{2}{10}$**   5. 0.7 **$\frac{7}{10}$**   6. 0.05 **$\frac{5}{100}$**

Read the problem and follow the directions.

7. Write 36 hundredths as a fraction and a decimal. **$\frac{36}{100}$; 0.36**

8. Julia drank $\frac{7}{10}$ cup of juice and 0.7 cup of water. Did Julia drink more water, more juice, or the same amounts of water and juice? Explain your answer. **Julia drank the same amounts of water and juice. 0.7 is the same as 7 tenths. $\frac{7}{10} = 0.7$**

Choose the answer.

9. Mike shaded $\frac{7}{10}$ of this rectangle. Which decimal equals $\frac{7}{10}$?

   A. 0.07   (B.) 0.7   C. 7.0   D. 7.10

10. Petros shaded $\frac{5}{10}$ of this rectangle. Which decimal equals $\frac{5}{10}$?

   (A.) 0.5   B. 0.51   C. 5.0   D. 5.10

11. Remi shaded 0.6 of this rectangle. Which fraction equals 0.6?

   A. $\frac{1}{6}$ (B.) $\frac{6}{10}$ C. $\frac{6}{1}$ D. $\frac{60}{1}$

12. Which decimal is equal to $\frac{1}{10}$?

   A. 0.01   (B.) 0.10   C. 1.0   D. 1.1

13. Which decimal is equal to $\frac{5}{10}$?

   (A.) 0.5   B. 0.51   C. 5.0   D. 5.1

14. Which fraction is equal to 0.6?

   A. $\frac{1}{6}$ B. $\frac{0}{6}$ (C.) $\frac{6}{10}$ D. $\frac{6}{100}$

15. Which fraction is equal to 0.3?

   A. $\frac{3}{100}$ B. $\frac{1}{30}$ (C.) $\frac{3}{10}$ D. $\frac{1}{3}$

16. Which fraction is equal to 0.75?

   A. $\frac{75}{1}$ B. $\frac{75}{10}$ C. $\frac{1}{75}$ (D.) $\frac{75}{100}$

17. Which fraction is equal to 0.5? Express your answer in simplest form.

   (A.) $\frac{1}{2}$ B. $\frac{5}{100}$ C. $\frac{10}{5}$ D. $\frac{5}{1,000}$

TRY IT

Fractions and Decimals (B)

Lesson Overview

LEARN Number Line Fractions and Decimals	20 minutes	**ONLINE**
LEARN Write a Fraction as a Decimal	15 minutes	**ONLINE**
TRY IT Same Amount in Fraction and Decimal	15 minutes	**OFFLINE**
CHECKPOINT	10 minutes	**ONLINE**

▶ Lesson Objectives

Explain that a simple fraction and a decimal amount can represent the same quantity.

▶ Prerequisite Skills

- Identify decimal place values through thousandths.
- Write the fraction represented by a drawing that shows parts of a set or parts of a whole.

▶ Content Background

Students will continue to learn how to show the decimal equivalent of fractions, such as $\frac{1}{10}$, $\frac{3}{100}$, and $\frac{5}{1,000}$.

Fractions and decimals have a mathematical connection that is key to understanding how to represent numbers. Decimal numbers are an alternative way to write fractional parts of a whole in terms of tenths, hundredths, thousandths, and so on. Decimal numbers are simply different representations for their equivalent fractions and mixed numbers. Saying and thinking about decimal numbers correctly promotes a strong and necessary understanding of place value and fractions. When students say a decimal number such as 1.35, they will learn to say "1 and 35 hundredths." The word *and* signals the placement of the decimal.

Students should think about the equivalent representation of $1\frac{35}{100}$ as they say the decimal number and should be able to visualize the meaning with a visual representation as shown in the illustration. They should be able to read the name of the decimal and recognize the difference between *hundreds* and *hundredths*.

When saying a decimal number such as 0.52, students should say "fifty-two hundredths," not "zero point fifty-two." When students say *point*, they are not focusing on the place value, which is critical to their understanding. It is important to model the correct way to read decimals.

Materials to Gather

SUPPLIED

Fraction Strips (optional printout)

Same Amount in Fraction and Decimal activity page

▶ Common Errors and Misconceptions

- Students might view the numerator and denominator of a fraction as separate, isolated numbers that can be operated on independently. This may lead to students "memorizing" rather than understanding fraction algorithms, and then using them incorrectly.

- Students might not understand the difference between fractions and whole numbers. Fractions are parts of whole numbers. Examples of fractions include $\frac{4}{5}$, $\frac{7}{100}$, and $2\frac{1}{2}$. Examples of whole numbers include 4, 6, and 10. Whole numbers may be written as fractions, but always with a denominator of 1, such as $\frac{4}{1}$, $\frac{6}{1}$, or $\frac{10}{1}$.

- Students might have difficulty understanding how different models represent fractions because they often see fractions represented as parts of circles—for example, pie and pizza illustrations. They might not recognize, for example, that the following models all represent the fraction $\frac{3}{5}$.

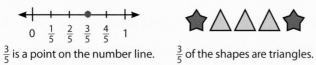  

$\frac{3}{5}$ is a point on the number line. $\frac{3}{5}$ of the shapes are triangles. $\frac{3}{5}$ of the rectangle is shaded.

- Students might think that a fraction always represents the size of a part of a whole, number of items in a set, or a location on the number line, and so might not understand that a fraction can also represent a relationship, such as a quotient or a ratio of one quantity to another.

- Students might think that a fraction compares one part to another part rather than recognizing that a fraction compares one part to the whole.

LEARN Number Line Fractions and Decimals

ONLINE
20min

Objectives

- Explain that a simple fraction and a decimal amount can represent the same quantity.

Students will learn that fractions and decimals can represent the same quantity. They will see fraction and decimal equivalencies on models and number lines.

DIRECTIONS FOR USING THE DIFFERENT WAYS TO SHOW FRACTIONS LEARNING TOOL

1. Click Parts of a Whole.
2. Click the + symbol in the lower right of the screen 9 times to divide the square into 10 equal parts.
3. Have students click three parts of the square to color them. Point out that the fraction changes to match the model.
4. Have students click Show Number Line. Have them click some sections of the model to select and deselect them. Point out that the number line changes each time to match the model.
5. Have students click Show Equivalent Fraction Chart. Have them make the fraction $\frac{2}{10}$ with the model (shading 2 out of the 10 sections). Have students roll over the orange bars in the fraction chart. They will see the equivalent fractions for $\frac{2}{10}$. They'll also see that the model changes to match those equivalent fractions.
6. Have students write the fraction $\frac{1}{2}$ in their Math Notebook. Have them show the fraction on the on-screen model (clicking the − symbol until the square is divided into two parts). Have them color one part of the model. They'll see the fraction and its equivalents on-screen. In their Math Notebook, have students write the following: the equivalent fraction in hundredths, the decimal equivalents, and the equivalent fraction in tenths. $\frac{50}{100}$, 0.50, 0.5, $\frac{5}{10}$

Tips

Have students make a memory tool by shading squares on grid paper to model fractions. Then have them write the equivalent fractions and decimals next to the models.

Note: Students will also see other fraction equivalents for $\frac{1}{2}$, but for this activity they need to write only the equivalents in hundredths and tenths.

7. Repeat Step 6 with the following fractions:

- $\frac{1}{4}$ $\frac{25}{100}$, 0.25
- $\frac{3}{4}$ $\frac{75}{100}$, 0.75
- $\frac{1}{5}$ $\frac{20}{100}$, 0.20, 0.2, $\frac{2}{10}$
- $\frac{2}{5}$ $\frac{40}{100}$, 0.40, 0.4, $\frac{4}{10}$
- $\frac{3}{5}$ $\frac{60}{100}$, 0.60, 0.6, $\frac{6}{10}$
- $\frac{4}{5}$ $\frac{80}{100}$, 0.80, 0.8, $\frac{8}{10}$
- $\frac{5}{5}$ $\frac{100}{100}$, 1

LEARN Write a Fraction as a Decimal

ONLINE 15 min

Students will practice matching equivalent fractions and decimals. They'll use on-screen flash cards to practice the most common fraction and decimal equivalencies. Students may want to refer to the equivalent fractions they wrote in their Math Notebook in the previous Learn.

Objectives

- Explain that a simple fraction and a decimal amount can represent the same quantity.

TRY IT Same Amount in Fraction and Decimal

OFFLINE 15 min

Students will practice naming fractions and decimals that represent the same quantity. Have students turn to the Same Amount in Fraction and Decimal activity page in their Activity Book and read the directions with them.

Students should copy the problems from the Activity Book into their Math Notebook as necessary and solve them there.

Tips Allow students to use fraction strips to help them simplify and find equivalent fractions and decimals.

Fractions and Decimals (B)
Same Amount in Fraction and Decimal

Write the number as a fraction.

1. 0.7 $\dfrac{7}{10}$

2. 0.25 $\dfrac{25}{100}$

3. 0.02 $\dfrac{2}{100}$

Write the number as a decimal.

4. $\dfrac{2}{5}$ **0.4**

5. $\dfrac{1}{2}$ **0.5**

6. $\dfrac{3}{4}$ **0.75**

Write the number as a decimal in tenths and hundredths.
Write the equivalent fractions for those decimals.

7. $\dfrac{1}{2}$
See below.

8. $\dfrac{1}{5}$
See below.

9. $\dfrac{4}{5}$
See below.

Read the problem and follow the directions.

10. Draw a number line that shows $\dfrac{2}{4}$.

Write a fraction and a decimal that equal $\dfrac{2}{4}$.

See below.

11. Write 3 tenths as a fraction and as a decimal. Use a number line to show why they represent the same quantity.

See below.

12. Johnny and Winnie are weaving placemats. Johnny has completed 0.4 of his placemat and Winnie has completed $\dfrac{2}{5}$ of her placemat. Who has the least amount left to weave? Explain. **They have the same amount left to weave because 0.4 is equal to $\dfrac{2}{5}$.**

Choose the answer.

13. Which decimal is equal to $\dfrac{7}{10}$?

A. 0.07   B. 0.071   C. (0.7)   D. 0.71

14. Which decimal is equal to $\dfrac{3}{5}$?

A. (0.6)   B. 6.0   C. 0.35   D. 3.5

15. Which fraction is equal to 0.25?

A. $\dfrac{25}{10}$ B. $\dfrac{1}{25}$ C. $\dfrac{10}{25}$ D. $\left(\dfrac{25}{100}\right)$

16. Which fraction is equal to 0.6?
Express your answer in simplest form.

A. $\dfrac{6}{1}$ B. $\dfrac{5}{3}$ C. $\left(\dfrac{3}{5}\right)$ D. $\dfrac{1}{6}$

17. Which decimal is equal to $\dfrac{4}{5}$?

A. 4.0, because this is the same as $\dfrac{4}{10}$, which simplifies to $\dfrac{4}{5}$

B. 8.0, because this is the same as $\dfrac{8}{10}$, which simplifies to $\dfrac{4}{5}$

C. 0.8, because this is the same as $\dfrac{8}{10}$, which simplifies to $\dfrac{4}{5}$

D. 0.4, because this is the same as $\dfrac{4}{10}$, which simplifies to $\dfrac{4}{5}$

Additional Answers

7. $0.5, \dfrac{5}{10}, 0.50, \dfrac{50}{100}$

8. $0.2, \dfrac{2}{10}, 0.20, \dfrac{20}{100}$

9. $0.8, \dfrac{8}{10}, 0.80, \dfrac{80}{100}$

10. Students should draw a number line divided into fourths and show $\dfrac{2}{4}$ at the halfway point between 0 and 1. Answers may include $\dfrac{1}{2}, \dfrac{5}{10}$, or $\dfrac{50}{100}$; and 0.5 or 0.50.

11. Students should draw a number line divided into tenths and show $\dfrac{3}{10}$ and 0.3 at the third tick mark between 0 and 1.

CHECKPOINT

ONLINE 10 min

Students will complete an online Checkpoint. If necessary, read the directions, problems, and answer choices to students and help them with keyboard or mouse operations.

Objectives

- Explain that a simple fraction and a decimal amount can represent the same quantity.

Probability

▶ Lesson Objectives

Identify whether specific events are certain, likely, unlikely, or impossible.

▶ Content Background

In this lesson, students will learn to describe the likelihood of an event occurring as certain, likely, unlikely, or impossible. This is an introductory lesson on probability.

In order for students to understand the concepts that form the foundation of mathematical probability, they must first learn about the likelihood of something happening or not happening. By using the image of a number line between and including 0 and 1, students will begin to visually position given events between 0 (impossible) and 1 (certain), as shown in the illustration.

Students will not do formal probability at this level but will learn to identify potential outcomes and consider whether they are certain, likely, unlikely, or impossible. When they determine actual probability values, they will discover that probabilities that are not impossible or certain are expressed as fractions between 0 and 1, sometimes also expressed as decimals and percents.

The probability of an event occurring is not the same as the odds that an event will occur. The terms *probability* and *odds* should not be used interchangeably. If the probability of an event is $\frac{3}{5}$, the odds are 3 to 2.

Materials to Gather

There are no materials to gather for this lesson.

LEARN Certain, Likely, Unlikely, Impossible

ONLINE **20**min

Students will learn about probability and consider whether the likelihood of an event occurring is certain, likely, unlikely, or impossible. They will also learn to identify equally likely outcomes, such as flipping heads or tails with a coin.

Objectives

- Identify whether specific events are certain, likely, unlikely, or impossible.

LEARN Outcomes

Students will describe the probability of an event occurring as certain, likely, unlikely, or impossible.

- Identify whether specific events are certain, likely, unlikely, or impossible.

TRY IT What Is the Probability?

Students will complete an online Try It. If necessary, read the directions, problems, and answer choices to students and help them with keyboard or mouse operations.

- Identify whether specific events are certain, likely, unlikely, or impossible.

CHECKPOINT

Students will complete an online Checkpoint. If necessary, read the directions, problems, and answer choices to students and help them with keyboard or mouse operations.

- Identify whether specific events are certain, likely, unlikely, or impossible.

Identify, Record, and Display Outcomes

Lesson Overview

Skills Update	5 minutes	ONLINE
GET READY Compare Data	5 minutes	ONLINE
LEARN Chart the Outcomes	10 minutes	ONLINE
LEARN Data Display	20 minutes	OFFLINE
TRY IT Find the Outcome	10 minutes	OFFLINE
CHECKPOINT	10 minutes	ONLINE

▶ Lesson Objectives

- Identify and systematically record the possible outcomes for a simple event.
- Summarize and display the results of a probability experiment in a clear and organized way.

▶ Prerequisite Skills

- Systematically record numerical data.
- Identify whether specific events are certain, likely, unlikely, or impossible.
- Represent the same data set with more than one representation, such as a tally, picture graph, or bar graph.

Materials to Gather

SUPPLIED

blocks – E (4 yellow, 3 blue)

Data Display (printout)

Find the Outcome activity page

ALSO NEEDED

household objects – paper bag, coin

▶ Content Background

Students will learn to record data from probability experiments as tally marks in tally charts and then represent that information in line plots and bar graphs.

It is important for students to understand the possible outcomes in a situation and represent these outcomes as data in a clear and organized way. They will learn to use tally marks, tally charts, line plots, and bar graphs as tools for collecting, recording, and displaying data.

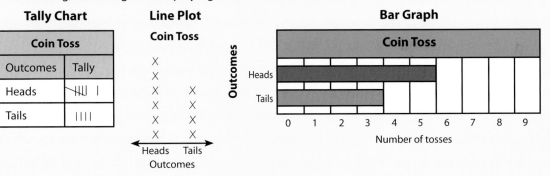

When analyzing probability problems, students should be able to list the possible outcomes of each event. Diagrams and tables are effective ways to organize possible outcomes. Students should also be able to state whether the probability of each event is likely, unlikely, impossible, or certain.

▶ Advance Preparation

Print the Data Display printout.

GET READY Compare Data

ONLINE 5 min

Students will see data in a picture graph and will identify the tally chart and bar graph that show the same data. Point out that the charts show the same data different ways. In the picture graph, students count the symbols to see how many people prefer a certain type of fruit. In the tally chart, they count the tally marks. In the bar graph, they look at the numbers to the left of the bars.

Objectives

- Systematically record numerical data.
- Identify whether specific events are certain, likely, unlikely, or impossible.
- Represent the same data set with more than one representation, such as a tally, picture graph, or bar graph.

LEARN Chart the Outcomes

ONLINE 10 min

Students will learn to identify possible outcomes for tossing a coin, rolling a number cube, and spinning a spinner. They will also identify outcomes that are not possible for spinning a spinner or rolling a number cube. They'll see that it's impossible to land on a color that isn't on the spinner or to land on a number that isn't on the cube. Toward the end of the activity, students will use an online spinner do a probability experiment. They will see how the data from the experiment are displayed in a tally chart and bar graph.

Objectives

- Identify and systematically record the possible outcomes for a simple event.
- Summarize and display the results of a probability experiment in a clear and organized way.

DIRECTIONS FOR USING THE TALLY CHARTS AND BAR GRAPHS LEARNING TOOL

1. Click Begin.
2. Have students spin the spinner until one outcome has 10 tally marks.
3. Explain to students that it's important to collect, record, and organize the data from probability experiments in a way that can be easily understood by others.

LEARN Data Display

OFFLINE 20 min

Students will gather data and complete a tally chart, a line plot, and a vertical bar graph (a graph with bars that are vertical rather than horizontal).
  Gather the E blocks, paper bag, and Data Display printout.

Objectives

- Identify and systematically record the possible outcomes for a simple event.
- Summarize and display the results of a probability experiment in a clear and organized way.

1. Give students the Data Display printout. Tell them that in this activity, they'll carry out an experiment and record the results in the tally chart, line plot, and bar graph on the printout.
2. Have students place the yellow and blue squares in the paper bag.
3. Ask students to identify the possible outcomes when picking 1 square out of the bag. Student should explain that picking a yellow square or a blue square are the possible outcomes.

Tell students that since there are 4 yellow squares out of 7 squares total, the chance of picking a yellow square is 4 out of 7. Relate this to fractions by saying that the chance of picking a yellow square is $\frac{4}{7}$.

4. Have students draw 1 square out of the bag. Have them record the result in the tally chart in the printout. Students should then place the square back in the bag and draw again. They should repeat this step until they have made a total of 10 draws.

5. Have students use the data in the tally chart to complete the line plot.

6. Have students use the data in the tally chart to complete the bar graph. The graph will have vertical bars showing how many yellow squares and blue squares were drawn.

7. **Say:** The the line plot and the bar graph show the same data. However, you must count the Xs to determine values on the line plot and use the scale to determine the value of each bar on the bar graph.

OFFLINE
10 min

TRY IT Find the Outcome

Students will practice identifying the outcomes and the data of different probability experiments, such as tossing a coin, spinning a spinner, and rolling a number cube. Gather the coin. Have students turn to the Find the Outcome activity page in their Activity Book and read the directions with them.

Students should copy the problems from the Activity Book into their Math Notebook as necessary and solve them there.

Objectives

- Identify and systematically record the possible outcomes for a simple event.

- Summarize and display the results of a probability experiment in a clear and organized way.

Identify, Record, and Display Outcomes
Find the Outcome

Memory Joggers

Here are some different ways to show the outcome of a probability experiment:

TALLY CHART

Experiment: Squares from a Bag	
Color of squares	Tally
Green	IIII
Red	IIII II
Blue	IIII
Yellow	III

LINE PLOT

Experiment: Squares from a Bag

HORIZONTAL BAR GRAPH

Experiment: Squares from a Bag

VERTICAL BAR GRAPH

Experiment: Squares from a Bag

Read the problem and follow the directions.

1. Toss a coin 10 times. Record the results (heads or tails) on a tally chart.

Answers will vary.

Coin Toss Results	
Outcomes	Tally
Heads	
Tails	

Choose the answer.

2. Which outcome is **not** possible if the spinner is spun once?
   A. green
   B. blue
   C. orange
   D. red

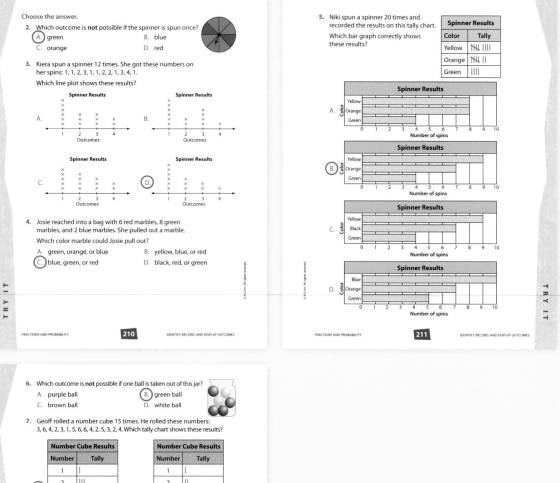

3. Kiera spun a spinner 12 times. She got these numbers on her spins: 1, 1, 2, 3, 1, 1, 2, 2, 1, 3, 4, 1.

   Which line plot shows these results?

   A.
   Spinner Results
   Outcomes 1 2 3 4

   B.
   Spinner Results
   Outcomes 1 2 3 4

   C.
   Spinner Results
   Outcomes 1 2 3 4

   D.
   Spinner Results
   Outcomes 1 2 3 4

4. Josie reached into a bag with 6 red marbles, 8 green marbles, and 2 blue marbles. She pulled out a marble.

   Which color marble could Josie pull out?
   A. green, orange, or blue
   B. yellow, blue, or red
   C. blue, green, or red
   D. black, red, or green

5. Niki spun a spinner 20 times and recorded the results on this tally chart.

   Which bar graph correctly shows these results?

Spinner Results	
Color	Tally
Yellow	卌 ||||
Orange	卌 ||
Green	||||

   A.
   Spinner Results
   Color: Yellow, Orange, Green
   Number of spins 0–10

   B.
   Spinner Results
   Color: Yellow, Orange, Green
   Number of spins 0–10

   C.
   Spinner Results
   Color: Yellow, Black, Green
   Number of spins 0–10

   D.
   Spinner Results
   Color: Blue, Orange, Green
   Number of spins 0–10

6. Which outcome is **not** possible if one ball is taken out of this jar?
   A. purple ball
   B. green ball
   C. brown ball
   D. white ball

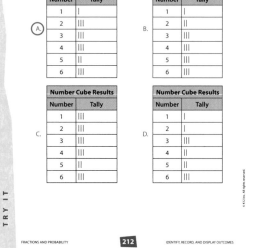

7. Geoff rolled a number cube 15 times. He rolled these numbers: 3, 6, 4, 2, 3, 1, 5, 6, 6, 4, 2, 5, 3, 2, 4. Which tally chart shows these results?

   A.

Number Cube Results	
Number	Tally
1		
2				
3				
4				
5			
6				

   B.

Number Cube Results	
Number	Tally
1		
2			
3				
4				
5				
6				

   C.

Number Cube Results	
Number	Tally
1				
2				
3				
4				
5			
6				

   D.

Number Cube Results	
Number	Tally
1		
2		
3				
4			
5			
6				

TRY IT

CHECKPOINT

Students will complete an online Checkpoint. If necessary, read the directions, problems, and answer choices to students and help them with keyboard or mouse operations.

Use Data to Make Predictions

Lesson Overview

Skills Update	5 minutes	ONLINE
GET READY Compare Tally Charts and Bar Graphs	5 minutes	ONLINE
LEARN Squares from a Bag	20 minutes	OFFLINE
LEARN What Will Happen Next?	10 minutes	OFFLINE
TRY IT Make a Prediction	10 minutes	OFFLINE
CHECKPOINT	10 minutes	ONLINE

▶ Lesson Objectives

Use the results of a probability experiment to predict future events.

▶ Prerequisite Skills

Summarize and display the results of a probability experiment in a clear and organized way.

▶ Content Background

Students will learn to use the results of a probability experiment to predict future events. For example, they can look at the results of drawing a colored square from a bag to predict the chance of certain colored squares being pulled from the bag in the future.

Although students will not do formal probability at this level, it is important that they understand that the likelihood of something happening or not happening can be described as impossible, unlikely, likely, or certain. When they determine actual probability values, they will discover that probabilities that are not impossible or certain are expressed as fractions between 0 and 1, sometimes as decimals and as percents.

The probability of an event occurring is not the same as the odds that an event will occur. The terms *probability* and *odd* should not be used interchangeably. If the probability of an event is $\frac{3}{5}$, the odds are 3 to 2.

In this lesson, students will record the results of probability experiments in tally charts, line plots, and bar graphs. Avoid using the term *bar chart* with students. The term *bar graph* is the correct term.

▶ Advance Preparation

Place the 15 blue and 2 red squares in a bag. Do not let students see how many of each color are in the bag.

Draw two copies of this chart in students' Math Notebook:

Experiment: Squares from a Bag	
Color of squares	Tally

GET READY Compare Tally Charts and Bar Graphs

Students will look at data in a tally chart and choose the bar graph that displays the tally chart data correctly.

Objectives

- Summarize and display the results of a probability experiment in a clear and organized way.

LEARN Squares from a Bag

Students will do a probability experiment by selecting colored squares out of a bag. They will use the results to predict what would happen if they continued the experiment.

   Gather the prepared bag of squares. Students will write tally marks on the chart you drew in their Math Notebook.

Objectives

- Use the results of a probability experiment to predict future events.

1. Discuss how past experiences are often used to predict future events. For example, if a family lives in a place where summer days are usually hot, they can be pretty sure it will not snow in the summer. If a girl wants to run into a friend at the park, she might go at the most popular times. She wouldn't expect to run into her friend if she went to the park at 6:00 in the morning. It's possible, but not likely.

2. **Say:** A dog had several litters of puppies in the past. There were three or four puppies in each litter. How many puppies would you expect the dog to have in the next litter? three or four puppies

   Ask students to explain how they made this prediction. Students might say that they know that each of the previous litters had three or four puppies and they used what they know about the past to predict what might happen in the future.

3. Show students the bag.

   Say: There are at least two colors of squares in this bag. Let's do an experiment where you draw squares from the bag 20 times and record the outcomes. Then you'll use that information to predict what will happen if you repeat the experiment. After that, you'll repeat the experiment and compare those results to your prediction.

4. Have students draw a square from the bag, record the color, and place a tally mark on the tally chart. Have them return the square to the bag. Have them repeat this 19 times for a total of 20 tally marks.

5. At the end of the experiment, ask students to discuss and explain the results. They may find that they drew a blue square more often than a red one.

6. Have students predict the results if they drew squares from the bag 20 more times. Most likely, students will predict that they would continue to draw a greater number of blue squares.

7. Repeat the experiment. Have students choose a square from the bag 20 times and record the outcomes in the second tally chart. At the end of the experiment, have students review the data and explain if their prediction was correct.

8. Show students the squares from the bag. Ask them to compare the number of blue squares and the number of red squares. Talk about how the number of blue and red squares affected the results of the experiment. Also, discuss how the information that there are 15 blue squares and 2 red squares helps confirm their predictions.

LEARN What Will Happen Next?

OFFLINE
10 min

Objectives

- Use the results of a probability experiment to predict future events.

Students will use results from probability experiments, displayed in tally charts, line plots, and bar graphs, to make predictions about future events. Have students turn to the What Will Happen Next? activity page in their Activity Book and read the directions with them.

Students should copy the problems from the Activity Book into their Math Notebook as necessary and solve them there.

1. Read the Worked Example with students. Have them look at the spinner. Point out that the section labeled Yo-yos takes up half the space on the spinner; it's much larger than the other three sections. Have students summarize the problem in their own words.

2. Guide students through Problems 1–3. For each problem, discuss the results of the experiment. Have students use the results shown in the charts and graphs to make predictions about future events. Use the following questions to guide students:

   - Which outcome occurred the most?
   - Which outcome occurred the least?
   - If this experiment were repeated, which outcome would be most likely and least likely to occur?

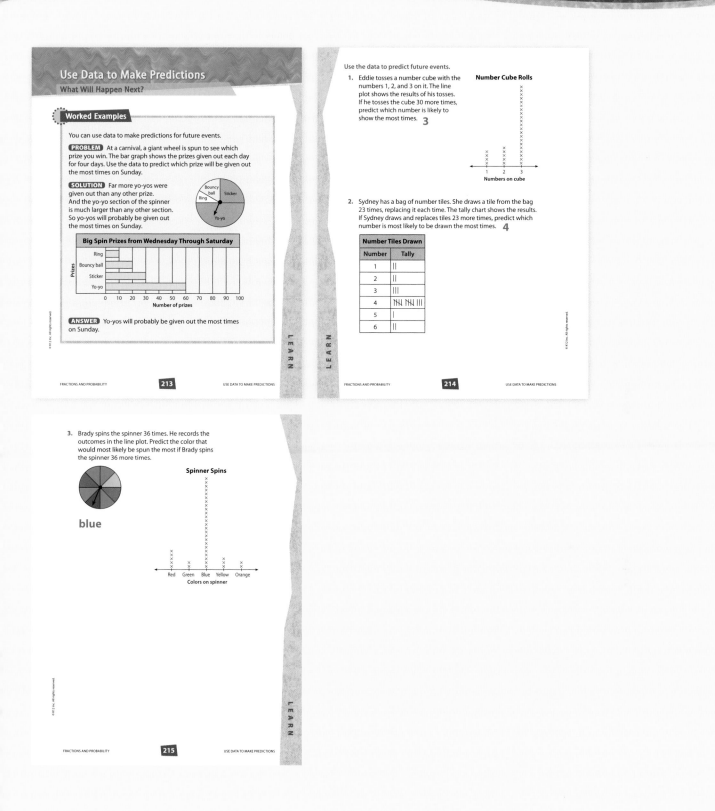

Use Data to Make Predictions

What Will Happen Next?

Worked Examples

You can use data to make predictions for future events.

PROBLEM At a carnival, a giant wheel is spun to see which prize you win. The bar graph shows the prizes given out each day for four days. Use the data to predict which prize will be given out the most times on Sunday.

SOLUTION Far more yo-yos were given out than any other prize. And the yo-yo section of the spinner is much larger than any other section. So yo-yos will probably be given out the most times on Sunday.

Big Spin Prizes from Wednesday Through Saturday

ANSWER Yo-yos will probably be given out the most times on Sunday.

Use the data to predict future events.

1. Eddie tosses a number cube with the numbers 1, 2, and 3 on it. The line plot shows the results of his tosses. If he tosses the cube 30 more times, predict which number is likely to show the most times. **3**

2. Sydney has a bag of number tiles. She draws a tile from the bag 23 times, replacing it each time. The tally chart shows the results. If Sydney draws and replaces tiles 23 more times, predict which number is most likely to be drawn the most times. **4**

Number Tiles Drawn

Number	Tally
1	II
2	II
3	III
4	TNL TNL III
5	I
6	II

3. Brady spins the spinner 36 times. He records the outcomes in the line plot. Predict the color that would most likely be spun the most if Brady spins the spinner 36 more times.

blue

LEARN

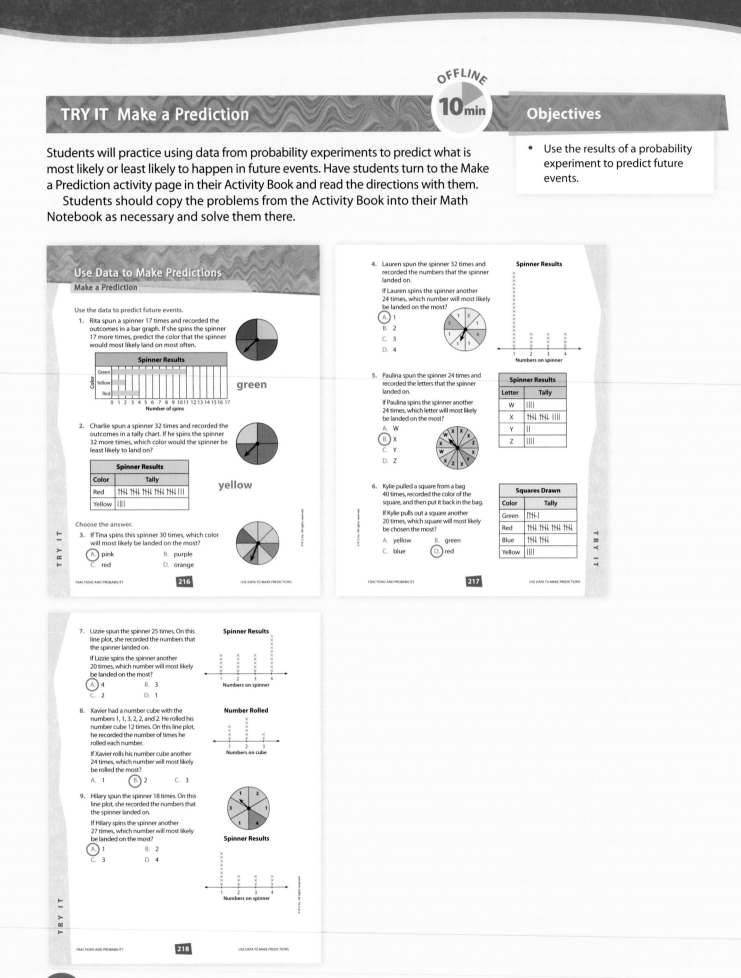

TRY IT Make a Prediction

OFFLINE
10 min

Objectives

- Use the results of a probability experiment to predict future events.

Students will practice using data from probability experiments to predict what is most likely or least likely to happen in future events. Have students turn to the Make a Prediction activity page in their Activity Book and read the directions with them.

Students should copy the problems from the Activity Book into their Math Notebook as necessary and solve them there.

Use Data to Make Predictions
Make a Prediction

Use the data to predict future events.

1. Rita spun a spinner 17 times and recorded the outcomes in a bar graph. If she spins the spinner 17 more times, predict the color that the spinner would most likely land on most often.

Spinner Results

Color	Number of spins
Green	
Yellow	
Red	

0 1 2 3 4 5 6 7 8 9 10 11 12 13 14 15 16 17
Number of spins

green

2. Charlie spun a spinner 32 times and recorded the outcomes in a tally chart. If he spins the spinner 32 more times, which color would the spinner be least likely to land on?

Spinner Results

Color	Tally
Red	|||| |||| |||| |||| |||| |||
Yellow	||||

yellow

Choose the answer.

3. If Tina spins this spinner 30 times, which color will most likely be landed on the most?

(A.) pink   B. purple
C. red   D. orange

FRACTIONS AND PROBABILITY   **216**   USE DATA TO MAKE PREDICTIONS

---

4. Lauren spun the spinner 32 times and recorded the numbers that the spinner landed on.

If Lauren spins the spinner another 24 times, which number will most likely be landed on the most?

(A.) 1
B. 2
C. 3
D. 4

Spinner Results

Numbers on spinner

5. Paulina spun the spinner 24 times and recorded the letters that the spinner landed on.

If Paulina spins the spinner another 24 times, which letter will most likely be landed on the most?

A. W
(B.) X
C. Y
D. Z

Spinner Results

Letter	Tally
W	||||
X	|||| |||| ||||
Y	||
Z	||||

6. Kylie pulled a square from a bag 40 times, recorded the color of the square, and then put it back in the bag.

If Kylie pulls out a square another 20 times, which square will most likely be chosen the most?

A. yellow   B. green
C. blue   (D.) red

Squares Drawn

Color	Tally
Green	||||-|
Red	|||| |||| |||| ||||
Blue	|||| ||||
Yellow	||||

FRACTIONS AND PROBABILITY   **217**   USE DATA TO MAKE PREDICTIONS

---

7. Lizzie spun the spinner 25 times. On this line plot, she recorded the numbers that the spinner landed on.

If Lizzie spins the spinner another 20 times, which number will most likely be landed on the most?

(A.) 4   B. 3
C. 2   D. 1

Spinner Results

Numbers on spinner

8. Xavier had a number cube with the numbers 1, 1, 3, 2, 2, and 2. He rolled his number cube 12 times. On this line plot, he recorded the number of times he rolled each number.

If Xavier rolls his number cube another 24 times, which number will most likely be rolled the most?

A. 1   (B.) 2   C. 3

Number Rolled

Numbers on cube

9. Hilary spun the spinner 18 times. On this line plot, she recorded the numbers that the spinner landed on.

If Hilary spins the spinner another 27 times, which number will most likely be landed on the most?

(A.) 1   B. 2
C. 3   D. 4

Spinner Results

Numbers on spinner

FRACTIONS AND PROBABILITY   **218**   USE DATA TO MAKE PREDICTIONS

Objectives

- Use the results of a probability experiment to predict future events.

Students will complete an online Checkpoint. If necessary, read the directions, problems, and answer choices to students and help them with keyboard or mouse operations.

Unit Review

Lesson Overview		
UNIT REVIEW Look Back	10 minutes	**ONLINE**
UNIT REVIEW Checkpoint Practice	50 minutes	**ONLINE**
▶ **UNIT REVIEW** Prepare for the Checkpoint		

▶ Unit Objectives

This lesson reviews the following objectives:

- Explain that a fraction can be used to represent part of a set, the relationship of a part to a whole, and a rational number on the number line.
- Write the fraction represented by a drawing that shows parts of a set or parts of a whole.
- Use a sketch to represent a fraction.
- Compare and order unit fractions, such as $\frac{1}{4}$, and fractions with like denominators, such as $\frac{2}{5}$ and $\frac{4}{5}$, by using objects or sketches.
- Use objects or sketches to solve a simple story problem involving addition or subtraction of fractions.
- Solve and simplify an addition or subtraction problem involving fractions with like denominators.
- Explain that a simple fraction and a decimal amount can represent the same quantity.
- Identify whether specific events are certain, likely, unlikely, or impossible.
- Identify and systematically record the possible outcomes for a simple event.
- Summarize and display the results of a probability experiment in a clear and organized way.
- Use the results of a probability experiment to predict future events.

▶ Advance Preparation

In this lesson, students will have an opportunity to review previous activities in the Fractions and Probability unit. Look at the suggested activities in Unit Review: Prepare for the Checkpoint online and gather any needed materials.

Materials to Gather

There are no materials to gather for this lesson.

UNIT REVIEW Look Back   ONLINE **10**min

Students will review key concepts from the unit to prepare for the Unit Checkpoint.

Objectives

- Review unit objectives.

UNIT REVIEW Checkpoint Practice

Objectives

- Review unit objectives.

Students will complete an online Checkpoint Practice to prepare for the Unit Checkpoint. If necessary, read the directions, problems, and answer choices to students. Have students answer the problems on their own. Review any missed problems with students.

⇥ UNIT REVIEW Prepare for the Checkpoint

What you do next depends on how students performed in the previous activity, Unit Review: Checkpoint Practice. If students had difficulty with any of the problems, complete the appropriate review activity listed in the table online. Tias eosam, nonem dignis evenihi ciantistempe nobis dererum velesec esenis iumquam la cullabo reperior sit ex et quate ne non rernati dolorrum ad que sanist ulparia volute opta nis sum voluptiis ipsam erum quiderf erumque aut officto is voluptasit ipsum restis magnimagnat laut magnat occum quunt dolor aut aut

Unit Checkpoint

Lesson Overview

UNIT CHECKPOINT Online	60 minutes	**ONLINE**

▶ Unit Objectives

This lesson assesses the following objectives:

- Explain that a fraction can be used to represent part of a set, the relationship of a part to a whole, and a rational number on the number line.
- Write the fraction represented by a drawing that shows parts of a set or parts of a whole.
- Use a sketch to represent a fraction.
- Compare and order unit fractions, such as $\frac{1}{4}$, and fractions with like denominators, such as $\frac{2}{5}$ and $\frac{4}{5}$, by using objects or sketches.
- Use objects or sketches to solve a simple story problem involving addition or subtraction of fractions.
- Solve and simplify an addition or subtraction problem involving fractions with like denominators.
- Explain that a simple fraction and a decimal amount can represent the same quantity.
- Identify whether specific events are certain, likely, unlikely, or impossible.
- Identify and systematically record the possible outcomes for a simple event.
- Summarize and display the results of a probability experiment in a clear and organized way.
- Use the results of a probability experiment to predict future events.

Materials to Gather

There are no materials to gather for this lesson.

UNIT CHECKPOINT Online

ONLINE
60min

Objectives

- Assess unit objectives.

Students will complete the Unit Checkpoint online. If necessary, read the directions, problems, and answer choices to students and help them with keyboard or mouse operations.

Measurement: Length and Time

▶ Unit Objectives

- Identify the appropriate tools for measuring the length of an object.
- Identify the appropriate metric or English units for measuring the length of an object.
- Estimate and measure the length of an object to the nearest centimeter.
- Estimate the length of an object to the nearest $\frac{1}{2}$ inch and measure the length to the nearest $\frac{1}{4}$ inch.

- Tell time to the nearest minute.
- Determine elapsed time to the nearest minute.
- Use a calendar to determine elapsed time.

▶ Big Ideas

Measurement is the process of repeatedly using a unit over a quantity to determine how much you have.

▶ Unit Introduction

In this unit, students will explore measurement of length and time. They will start by identifying tools for measuring the length of an object. They will use metric units to estimate measurements and precisely measure to the nearest centimeter. They will use English units to estimate measurements to the nearest half inch and precisely measure to the nearest quarter inch. Students will learn to tell time to the nearest minute and find elapsed time between a starting time and an ending time. They will also study elapsed time from a starting date to an ending date on a calendar.

▶ Keywords

centimeter (cm)
elapsed time
English system of
   measurement
foot (ft)
inch (in.)

kilometer (km)
measurement
meter (m)
metric system of
   measurement

mile (mi)
standard unit
yard (yd)

Tools and Units for Measuring Length

Lesson Overview		
GET READY Measure Height in Feet and Inches	5 minutes	**OFFLINE**
LEARN Different Measurement Tools	5 minutes	**OFFLINE**
LEARN English and Metric Units of Length	15 minutes	**OFFLINE**
LEARN Appropriate Tools and Units	15 minutes	**ONLINE**
TRY IT Choose the Tool and Unit	10 minutes	**ONLINE**
CHECKPOINT	10 minutes	**ONLINE**

▶ Lesson Objectives

- Identify the appropriate tools for measuring the length of an object.
- Identify the appropriate metric or English units for measuring the length of an object.

▶ Prerequisite Skills

Measure the length of objects by repeating a standard unit.

▶ Content Background

Students will learn to identify tools for measuring the length of objects. They will learn the appropriate unit of measure in the metric system of measurement (centimeters, meters, and kilometers) and the English system of measurement (inches, feet, yards, and miles).

Students experience measurement every day. Their clothing and shoes are a particular size. They travel distances by foot, by car, by bus, or on their bicycles. They carry things that are heavy. They tell time and identify what day it is. They know if the weather is hot or cold. All of these experiences require some knowledge of measurement.

In this lesson, the term *length* is used interchangeably to mean length, width, height, or depth. Note that when measurements are abbreviated (cm, m, km, in., ft, yd, and mi), only the abbreviation for *inch* has a period. The period is added to avoid confusion with the word *in*.

Materials to Gather

SUPPLIED

There are no supplied materials to gather for this lesson.

ALSO NEEDED

ruler, dual-scale

tape, masking

▶ Common Errors and Misconceptions

Students often have difficulty giving the correct measure of an object when the object is not aligned with the 0-end of a ruler. For example, they might think that this pencil is 4 inches long because the right end of the pencil aligns with the 4-inch mark. The pencil is actually only 3 inches long because the left end of the pencil aligns with the 1-inch mark.

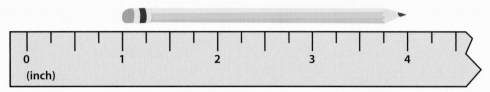

GET READY Measure Height in Feet and Inches

Students will use a ruler to measure their height in feet and inches. Gather the ruler and tape.

1. Show students a 12-inch ruler and point to the inch marks on the ruler.
   Ask: What is the name of each unit on this ruler? inch

2. Point out that the ruler is 12 inches long, and the length of the entire ruler is 1 foot.

3. Have students stand with their backs against a wall. Place the ruler flat on the top of their heads. One end of the ruler should be touching the wall. Place a small piece of masking tape on the wall so that the top edge of the tape is just under the ruler.

4. Guide students to use the ruler to measure their height in feet and inches. Students should place the 0-end of the ruler on the floor and work their way up the wall by repeatedly using the foot unit. Show students how to use a finger to mark the ending point of the first foot. Then have them slide the ruler so the 0-end aligns with their finger as they measure the next foot.

5. Record the number of whole feet. Explain how to add the extra inches that don't make up a whole foot. Help students find their height to the nearest half inch. If students are unfamiliar with reading the half-inch marks on a ruler, explain that a ruler is like a number line; the halfway mark between each inch marks the half-inch point. Have them record their height in feet and inches.

6. Have students record their height in feet and inches in the front of their Math Notebook. Encourage them to use abbreviations, such as 3 ft 10 in. Point out the period in the abbreviation for inches. Add a note that at the end of the year, students can measure their height again and compare the measurements.

Objectives

- Measure the length of objects by repeating a standard unit.

Tips

If students have difficulty marking the end of each foot with a finger, use masking tape to mark each foot.

LEARN Different Measurement Tools

Students will identify different kinds of measurement tools, such as a clock for measuring time and a thermometer for measuring temperature. They will also locate measuring tools in their environment.

There are no materials to gather for this activity.

1. Tell students that they use measurement all the time. Explain that they make informal measurements when they make statements like these:
   - That's a long way to walk.
   - That's so small (or large).
   - That's really heavy.
   - It's very hot (or cold) outside.
   - It's too early.

2. Discuss with students what they are measuring in each of the statements in Step 1. Explain that they are indicating a way to measure distance, size, weight, temperature, and time.

3. Explain that measuring tools are needed to make accurate measurements. Ask students what tool they use for measuring each of the following:
   - **Time** clock or watch
   - **An object's weight** scale
   - **How hot it is outside** thermometer
   - **A person's height or the length of a board** ruler, tape measure, yardstick, or meterstick
   - **How far away something is** map or odometer in a car

   Students may be familiar with a car odometer, but they probably don't know what it's called. You may wish to show students a picture of an odometer.

4. Explain to students that they need the correct tool to measure accurately.

   Say: You cannot measure temperature with a clock or the distance to New York with a thermometer.

5. Have students look around their environment and locate as many measuring tools as they can find. For example, help them locate clocks, measuring cups and spoons, rulers, tape measures, thermometers, and scales.

Objectives

- Identify the appropriate tools for measuring the length of an object.

Tips

Allow students to look at books, magazines, or the Internet for examples of measuring tools.

Car odometers measure miles.

LEARN English and Metric Units of Length

Students will learn about the English and metric units for measuring length, including the inch, foot, yard, mile, centimeter, meter, and kilometer.

Gather the ruler.

1. Discuss with students that if they need to find the length of an object, they must use a measurement tool. Explain that the terms *length* and *width* are used interchangeably at times. For instance, if you have a long table, you might measure the length, but when you want to see if it will fit in a certain place, you might ask "How wide is it?" and refer to the same measure.

   Have students look at some common objects nearby and identify the length and width to see that in some instances, they have to decide which is which.

Objectives

- Identify the appropriate tools for measuring the length of an object.
- Identify the appropriate metric or English units for measuring the length of an object.

2. **Say:** It's important to know the unit you will use to measure the length of an object. Look at the ruler. Notice that one side of the ruler is divided into inches and the other side is divided into centimeters.

3. Explain that the units of length or distance in the English system of measurement are inches, feet, yards, and miles. Have students identify inches on the ruler. Explain that miles measure long distances.

4. Explain that some of the units of length or distance in the metric system of measurement are centimeters, meters, and kilometers. Have students identify centimeters on the ruler. Explain that kilometers measure long distances.

5. Tell students that they have to use a unit, such as an inch or a centimeter, to measure the length of an object.

6. Point to the side of the ruler labeled in inches.

   Ask: What units are on this side of the ruler? inches

7. Guide students to see that the ruler is 12 inches long, which is the same as 1 foot. Have students find one object in the room that is about 1 inch in length and one object that is about 1 foot in length or height.

8. Explain that there is another unit of length in the English system of measurement called a *yard*. If there is a measuring tape or yardstick available, show students 1 yard. Otherwise, measure 3 feet along a table edge, or other piece of furniture, to give students a sense of 1 yard.

9. Explain that, for many people, a yard is about the distance from their nose to the tip of their fingers when they are facing forward with an arm outstretched to the side. Demonstrate this distance for students.

10. Point to the metric side of the ruler labeled in centimeters.

    Ask: What units are on this side of the ruler? centimeters

11. Explain that centimeters are units of the metric system used to measure shorter lengths. Tell students that 100 centimeters equals 1 meter. Explain that 1 meter is about 3 inches longer than 1 yard, so meters and yards are used to measure the same types of objects. Have students find one object in the room that is about 1 centimeter in length and one object that is about 1 meter in length or height.

12. Tell students that the metric system also has a unit called a *decimeter*. A decimeter is the length of 10 centimeters. It is the unit between a centimeter and a meter. Explain that decimeters are not used as frequently as the English system's foot. Instead in the metric system, lengths are usually measured in centimeters or meters.

13. **Say:** We could use *yards* or *meters* to describe the distance we travel in a car or on a train or airplane. But we'd need so many yards or meters that the number would be huge. Instead, we use greater units of measure to describe longer distances. In the English system, we use miles. In the metric system, we use kilometers.

    Go over some familiar distances with students. Discuss about how far it is to the library or to a relative's house, or to other places students commonly visit.

LEARN Appropriate Tools and Units

ONLINE 15min

Students will identify the most appropriate tool and unit of measure for measuring the length of different types of objects, such as the length of a straw or the width of a room.

Objectives

- Identify the appropriate tools for measuring the length of an object.
- Identify the appropriate metric or English units for measuring the length of an object.

TRY IT Choose the Tool and Unit

ONLINE 10min

Students will complete an online Try It. If necessary, read the directions, problems, and answer choices to students and help them with keyboard or mouse operations.

Objectives

- Identify the appropriate tools for measuring the length of an object.
- Identify the appropriate metric or English units for measuring the length of an object.

CHECKPOINT

ONLINE 10min

Students will complete an online Checkpoint. If necessary, read the directions, problems, and answer choices to students and help them with keyboard or mouse operations.

Objectives

- Identify the appropriate tools for measuring the length of an object.
- Identify the appropriate metric or English units for measuring the length of an object.

Estimate and Measure Centimeters

Lesson Overview

GET READY Hand Measurements	10 minutes	OFFLINE
LEARN Round to the Nearest Centimeter	15 minutes	OFFLINE
LEARN Estimate and Measure	15 minutes	OFFLINE
TRY IT Centimeter Measures	10 minutes	OFFLINE
CHECKPOINT	10 minutes	ONLINE

▶ Lesson Objectives

Estimate and measure the length of an object to the nearest centimeter.

▶ Prerequisite Skills

- Identify centimeters on a ruler and measure the length of an object to the nearest centimeter.
- Estimate the length of an object to the nearest inch or centimeter.

▶ Content Background

Students will learn to estimate and measure in centimeters.

Avoid using the words *round up* or *round down* with students. Use *round to the nearest centimeter* instead.

Estimating and measuring objects is an important skill. When judging whether an object will fit in a given space, students estimate the length, width, and height of the object. Then they compare the estimates to the given space to determine if the object will fit. Students often use familiar benchmark measurements when estimating and measuring. They may know that a large paper clip is about 1 centimeter wide, a dime is about 2 centimeters across, and a child's finger is about 1 centimeter wide. Benchmark measurements help students judge the measure of other objects.

Note that when measurements are abbreviated (cm, m, km, in., ft, yd, and mi), only the abbreviation for *inch* has a period. The period is added to avoid confusion with the word *in*.

Materials to Gather

SUPPLIED

Centimeter Ruler (printout)

Round to the Nearest Centimeter activity page

Centimeter Measures activity page

ALSO NEEDED

scissors, adult

ruler, dual-scale

index card

household objects – various lengths (3 objects less than 15 cm, 3 objects between 20 and 30 cm, and 2 objects greater than 30 cm)

▶ Common Errors and Misconceptions

Students often have difficulty giving the correct measure of an object when the object is not aligned with the 0-end of a ruler. For example, they might think that this pencil is 4 inches long because the right end of the pencil aligns with the 4-inch mark. The pencil is actually only 3 inches long because the left end of the pencil aligns with the 1-inch mark.

▶ Advance Preparation

- For the Learn: Round to the Nearest Centimeter activity, print the Centimeter Ruler and cut it out. The printed ruler has decimals and fractions, which students will need for the activity.

- For the Learn: Estimate and Measure activity, gather three household items that are less than 15 centimeters long, three household items that are between 20 and 30 centimeters long, and two household items that are greater than 30 centimeters long.

OFFLINE
10 min

GET READY Hand Measurements

Objectives

- Identify centimeters on a ruler and measure the length of an object to the nearest centimeter.
- Estimate the length of an object to the nearest inch or centimeter.

Students will measure their hand span in centimeters. They will use this measurement as a benchmark to estimate the length, width, or height of objects. Students will compare the estimate to the actual measurement in centimeters.
Gather the index card and ruler.

1. **Say:** When you need to measure an object, you won't always have a measurement tool handy. But if you know the measure of a part of your body, you can use it as a measurement tool.

2. Explain that students will measure their hand span in centimeters and use this measurement to estimate the length, width, and height of objects.

3. Give students the ruler. Have them point to the side of the ruler marked in centimeters (cm). Mention that the abbreviation for *centimeter* and *centimeters* is *cm*. Students may see the abbreviation on rulers and other everyday objects.

4. Have students spread their fingers as wide as they can and place them on the ruler so that their thumb is on the 0-mark. Help students determine their hand span in centimeters.

5. Have students record the measure of their hand span on the index card.

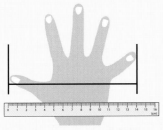

hand span: 14 cm

6. Find an object that is approximately 1 to 3 hand spans long (or wide or high). Have students use their hand span to estimate the length, width, or height of the object.

7. Help students use their hand span to measure the object. Have them place their left hand span on the object to start measuring and then put their right hand span next to it, making sure the hands do not overlap. If the object is more than 2 hand spans long, have students use the first hand to cross over and continue measuring where the second hand span ended. If a student's hand span is 14 cm and the object measured is about 2 hand spans long, add 14 cm plus 14 cm to get an estimate of 28 cm. Most objects won't be an exact number of hand spans. Students will have to estimate how many centimeters the partial hand span is.

8. Have students use the ruler to measure the length of the object in centimeters. Then have them compare their estimate with the actual length.

LEARN Round to the Nearest Centimeter

Students will measure line segments and round the measurements to the nearest centimeter. Mention to students that in most instances when they use measuring devices, they measure things exactly. In this activity, they are making "rough" measurements, so they are rounding to the nearest centimeter. After students finish the activity page, have them measure actual objects to the nearest centimeter.

Gather the cut-out centimeter ruler. Have students turn to the Round to the Nearest Centimeter activity page in their Activity Book and read the directions with them.

Students should copy the problems from the Activity Book into their Math Notebook as necessary and solve them there.

1. Tell students they will be measuring lines to the nearest centimeter. Have them find the edge of the centimeter ruler and point to the centimeter marks on the ruler.

2. Explain that lengths of objects are not usually an exact number of centimeters. When a measurement falls between two centimeters, the measurement rounds to the nearest centimeter. If the measurement falls before the halfway mark, it is rounded to the lesser centimeter. If the measurement falls on or after the halfway mark, it is rounded to the greater centimeter.

3. Have students look at the centimeter and half-centimeter markings on the ruler. Emphasize that the marks on a centimeter ruler are just like those on a number line.

4. Explain how 0.5 on a number line is the same as 1-half centimeter on a centimeter ruler.

   Have students find the 0.5 mark and the $\frac{1}{2}$ cm mark. Guide students to see the relationship between 1.5 and $1\frac{1}{2}$ cm, 2.5 and $2\frac{1}{2}$ cm, 3.5 and $3\frac{1}{2}$ cm, and so on.

5. Have students look at the Worked Example on the activity page. Be sure they understand how to measure the length of a line. Students should align the beginning of the line with the 0-mark of the ruler. Then they should identify the mark on the ruler where the line ends. Review the rules for rounding the length to the nearest centimeter.

6. Have students measure the length of the line in Problem 1. Ask them whether the line ends before the halfway mark or after it. Students should explain that the line ends after the halfway mark so the length, to the nearest centimeter, is 1 cm.

7. Have students complete Problems 2–7. Guide them in measuring each line segment and rounding the measurement to the nearest centimeter.

8. Discuss with students that because the line segment in Problem 3 measures exactly halfway between 4 and 5 centimeters, the length is rounded to the greater centimeter, or 5 cm. Make sure students apply the same rule to Problems 6 and 7.

9. As time allows, have students measure the length of objects of their choice to the nearest centimeter.

Tips

• Remind students to align the beginning of each line with the 0-mark on the ruler.

• Note that many printers scale documents to fit to a printable area by default. Be sure to turn off page scaling so that documents print at 100% of their intended size.

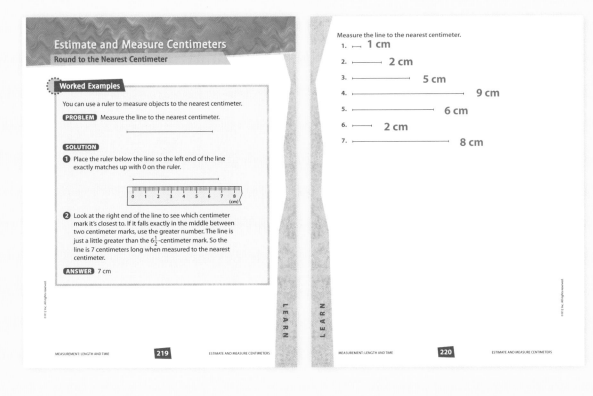

Estimate and Measure Centimeters
Round to the Nearest Centimeter

Worked Examples

You can use a ruler to measure objects to the nearest centimeter.

PROBLEM Measure the line to the nearest centimeter.

SOLUTION

❶ Place the ruler below the line so the left end of the line exactly matches up with 0 on the ruler.

❷ Look at the right end of the line to see which centimeter mark it's closest to. If it falls exactly in the middle between two centimeter marks, use the greater number. The line is just a little greater than the $6\frac{1}{2}$-centimeter mark. So the line is 7 centimeters long when measured to the nearest centimeter.

ANSWER 7 cm

Measure the line to the nearest centimeter.

1.   1 cm
2.   2 cm
3.   5 cm
4.   9 cm
5.   6 cm
6.   2 cm
7.   8 cm

LEARN Estimate and Measure

OFFLINE **15 min**

Objectives

- Estimate and measure the length of an object to the nearest centimeter.

Tips

Review how to round a measurement to the nearest centimeter.

Students will measure everyday objects in centimeters and use these measurements to estimate the measurements of other objects.

Gather the ruler, the index card with the student's hand-span measurement (from the Get Ready activity), and the household objects to measure.

1. Tell students that they will estimate and measure the length of objects to the nearest centimeter. Have students identify the centimeter side of the ruler.

2. Ask students to identify an object that measures about 1 centimeter long. They may suggest a ones cube. Explain that they should think of 1 centimeter as the length of a ones cube, or whatever object they identified, when estimating length.

3. Remind students that when they measure objects, they must match up the beginning of the object with the 0-mark on the ruler. This mark is not on the edge of most rulers, so students must adjust the ruler and the object to align at 0.

4. Show students one of the objects that measures less than 15 centimeters. Tell them which dimension of the object they will measure in centimeters. For example, students might measure the height of a cup.

5. Have students measure the object in centimeters. Remind them that if the length does not measure exactly to a centimeter line, they must round it to the nearest centimeter. If the measurement falls before the halfway mark, they should round to the lesser centimeter. If the measurement falls on or after the halfway mark, they should round to the greater centimeter.

ESTIMATE AND MEASURE CENTIMETERS **423**

6. Have students write the name of the object and its measurement to the nearest centimeter in their Math Notebook. Students may abbreviate *centimeters* as *cm*. Tell them that they now have a known measure and they can use this measure to estimate the length of other objects.

7. Show students the next object that measures less than 15 centimeters. Tell them which dimension of the object they will measure. Have students use a known measure to estimate the measurement of the object. For example, they may know that the height of the cup is 13 cm or the width of a dime is about 2 cm. Students should compare the known measure with the new object to make an estimate.

8. Have students measure the object and record the measurement. Have them compare their estimate with the actual measurement.

9. Repeat Steps 7 and 8 with the third object that's less than 15 centimeters in length.

10. Present the smallest object that has a measure of 20 to 30 centimeters. Have students estimate its length, keeping in mind known measurements. Then have them measure the object with the ruler and compare their estimate with the actual measurement.

11. Have students estimate and measure the remaining items that are 20 to 30 centimeters long. Encourage them to compare and describe their estimates with the actual measurements.

12. Have students look at the index card and note the width of their hand span. Then have them use their hand span to estimate the measure of the two objects that are greater than 30 cm. After estimating, have them measure the objects with the ruler.

TRY IT Centimeter Measures

OFFLINE
10 min

Objectives

- Estimate and measure the length of an object to the nearest centimeter.

Students will practice estimating and measuring items in centimeters. Remind them that when they measure an object to the nearest centimeter, if the measure is exactly to the half-centimeter mark or past that mark, they should round to the greater centimeter. Have students turn to the Centimeter Measures activity page in their Activity Book and read the directions with them.

Students should copy the problems from the Activity Book into their Math Notebook as necessary and solve them there.

Point out to students that sometimes an object is held up to a ruler but isn't aligned with the 0 on the ruler as Problem 2 illustrates. Discuss ways to find the lengths of such objects. Students can count forward from the beginning of the object, or subtract the amount to the left of the object from the length.

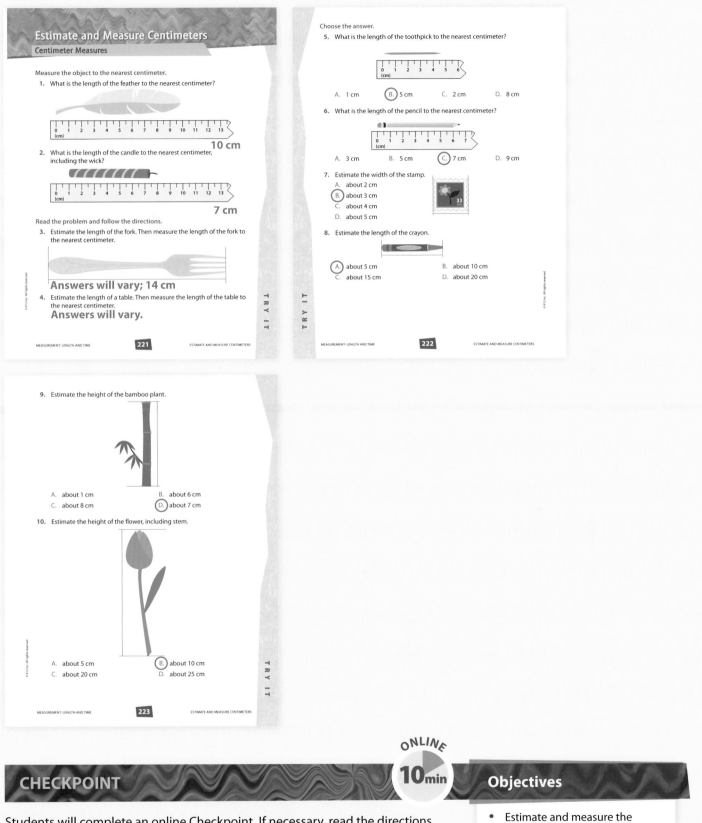

Estimate and Measure Centimeters
Centimeter Measures

Measure the object to the nearest centimeter.

1. What is the length of the feather to the nearest centimeter?

10 cm

2. What is the length of the candle to the nearest centimeter, including the wick?

7 cm

Read the problem and follow the directions.

3. Estimate the length of the fork. Then measure the length of the fork to the nearest centimeter.

Answers will vary; 14 cm

4. Estimate the length of a table. Then measure the length of the table to the nearest centimeter.

Answers will vary.

T R Y   I T

Choose the answer.

5. What is the length of the toothpick to the nearest centimeter?

A. 1 cm   (B.) 5 cm   C. 2 cm   D. 8 cm

6. What is the length of the pencil to the nearest centimeter?

A. 3 cm   B. 5 cm   (C.) 7 cm   D. 9 cm

7. Estimate the width of the stamp.
   A. about 2 cm
   (B.) about 3 cm
   C. about 4 cm
   D. about 5 cm

8. Estimate the length of the crayon.

   (A.) about 5 cm   B. about 10 cm
   C. about 15 cm   D. about 20 cm

T R Y   I T

---

9. Estimate the height of the bamboo plant.

   A. about 1 cm   B. about 6 cm
   C. about 8 cm   (D.) about 7 cm

10. Estimate the height of the flower, including stem.

   A. about 5 cm   (B.) about 10 cm
   C. about 20 cm   D. about 25 cm

T R Y   I T

ONLINE
10 min

CHECKPOINT

Students will complete an online Checkpoint. If necessary, read the directions, problems, and answer choices to students and help them with keyboard or mouse operations.

Objectives

- Estimate and measure the length of an object to the nearest centimeter.

Estimate and Measure Inches (A)

Lesson Overview

GET READY Measure in Inches	10 minutes	OFFLINE
LEARN Measure to the Nearest Quarter Inch	20 minutes	OFFLINE
LEARN Measure Everyday Objects	20 minutes	OFFLINE
TRY IT Find the Nearest Quarter Inch	10 minutes	OFFLINE

▶ Lesson Objectives

Estimate the length of an object to the nearest $\frac{1}{2}$ inch and measure the length to the nearest $\frac{1}{4}$ inch.

▶ Prerequisite Skills

- Identify inches on a ruler and measure the length of an object to the nearest inch.
- Estimate the length of an object to the nearest inch or centimeter.

▶ Content Background

Students will learn to estimate and measure in inches. They will estimate to the nearest half inch and measure to the nearest quarter inch.

Estimating and measuring objects is an important skill. When judging whether an object will fit in a given space, students estimate the length, width, and height of the object. Then they compare the estimates to the given space to determine if the object will fit. Students often use familiar benchmark measurements when estimating and measuring. For instance, they may be familiar with $8\frac{1}{2} \times 11$ inch notebook paper. Students may use this information to estimate the length of an object or judge whether it will fit in a given space.

Note that when measurements are abbreviated (cm, m, km, in., ft, yd, and mi), only the abbreviation for *inch* has a period. The period is added to avoid confusion with the word *in*.

▶ Common Errors and Misconceptions

Students often have difficulty giving the correct measure of an object when the object is not aligned with the 0-end of a ruler. For example, they might think that this pencil is 4 inches long because the right end of the pencil aligns with the 4-inch mark. The pencil is actually only 3 inches long because the left end of the pencil aligns with the 1-inch mark.

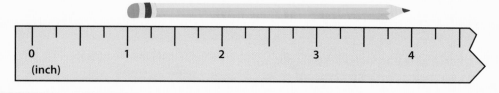

Materials to Gather

SUPPLIED

Measure to the Nearest Quarter Inch activity page

Find the Nearest Quarter Inch activity page

ALSO NEEDED

ruler, dual-scale

index card – 3 by 5 inches (2)

tape, masking

▶ Advance Preparation

Put a piece of masking tape across the length of a ruler in a way that doesn't cover up the inch markings or numbers. Write small labels on the tape to illustrate what the ruler marks mean. Write $\frac{1}{4}$, $\frac{1}{2}$, $\frac{3}{4}$, $1\frac{1}{2}$, and $2\frac{1}{2}$ in the correct places on the ruler. If students have difficulties as you measure during the activity, write more fractions on the tape.

GET READY   Measure in Inches

OFFLINE 10 min

Students will measure the length of an index card to the nearest inch and use that measurement to estimate the length of other objects.
   Gather the ruler and index card.

1. Give students the ruler. Have them point to the side of the ruler marked in inches (in.). Tell them that the abbreviation for *inch* and *inches* is *in.* with a period after it. They may see the abbreviation on rulers and other everyday objects.

2. Give students the index card. Explain that they are to measure the length of the index card to the nearest inch. Remind them that the length is the longer side. Students should determine that the length is 5 inches.

3. Have students gather objects that they think have a measure of about 5 inches. Encourage them to use the index card as a known measure of 5 inches.

4. Explain that students should use the index card to estimate the length, width, or height of the objects. Then have them use the ruler to find the actual length, width, or height. Have them compare their estimates with the actual measurements.

Objectives

- Identify inches on a ruler and measure the length of an object to the nearest inch.
- Estimate the length of an object to the nearest inch or centimeter.

LEARN   Measure to the Nearest Quarter Inch

OFFLINE 20 min

Students will learn how to measure objects to the nearest quarter inch. Gather the ruler marked with fractions. Have students turn to the Measure to the Nearest Quarter Inch activity page in their Activity Book and read the directions with them.
   Students should copy the problems from the Activity Book into their Math Notebook as necessary and solve them there.

1. Ask students what they know about quarters. They may relate quarters to the fraction $\frac{1}{4}$, the coin, or a whole divided into four equal parts. Emphasize that when a whole is divided into quarters, there are four equal parts. Also emphasize that the word *whole* means a unit of measure such as 1 inch. Say that a quarter of an inch is $\frac{1}{4}$ of the way to 1 inch. Tell students they will learn to measure length to the nearest quarter inch.

2. Tell students that the ruler is like a number line that shows halves, fourths, eighths, and even sixteenths. Have students count the small lines between two numbers to see that there are 16 tiny lines that make up a whole. The distance between each small line is one-sixteenth of an inch.

Objectives

- Estimate the length of an object to the nearest $\frac{1}{2}$ inch and measure the length to the nearest $\frac{1}{4}$ inch.

Tips

Remind students to align the beginning of each line with the 0-mark on the ruler.

3. Ask students to point out the half-inch markings on the ruler. Explain that the half-inch marks divide each inch into two equal parts. Point out the quarter-inch marks. Explain that the quarter-inch marks, $\frac{1}{4}, \frac{2}{4}, \frac{3}{4},$ and $\frac{4}{4},$ divide each inch into four equal parts. Emphasize that $\frac{2}{4}$ is equal to $\frac{1}{2}$. Point out the eighth-inch marks and explain that these markings divide each inch into eight equal parts.

4. Tell students that they will measure line segments to the nearest $\frac{1}{4}$ inch. **Ask:** How many $\frac{1}{4}$ inches are in one inch? 4

   Explain that sometimes a line may measure to the $1\frac{2}{4}$ mark on the ruler. Remind students that $1\frac{2}{4}$ inches is the same as $1\frac{1}{2}$ inches, so that particular measure to the nearest quarter inch is $1\frac{1}{2}$ inches. Also, a line might measure $1\frac{4}{4}$ inches. This is the same as 2 inches. Be sure students understand that when measuring to the nearest quarter inch, the answer may not always be given in quarter inches. Sometimes it will be given in halves or wholes.

5. Review how to measure the length of a line. Students should align the beginning of the line with the 0-mark on the ruler. Then they should identify the nearest quarter-inch mark on the ruler where the line ends to determine the length to the nearest quarter inch. Remind students that if a line measures exactly halfway between two quarter-inch marks, they use the greater measure.

6. Direct students' attention to the Worked Example. Read the example with them. Then have them complete Problems 1–6. Guide them in measuring each line segment to the nearest quarter inch.

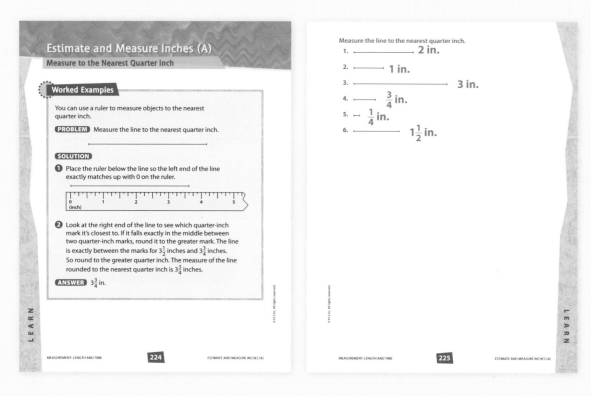

LEARN Measure Everyday Objects

Objectives

- Estimate the length of an object to the nearest $\frac{1}{2}$ inch and measure the length to the nearest $\frac{1}{4}$ inch.

Students will use a known measurement to estimate the measure of other objects. Students will measure the objects to the nearest quarter inch.

Gather the ruler and index card.

1. Review what it means to measure to the nearest quarter inch. Remind students that 4 quarter inches equal 1 whole inch. Also remind them that measurements such as $2\frac{1}{2}$ inches and 3 inches can represent lengths to the nearest quarter inch.

2. Tell students that they will determine known measurements and use them to estimate the length of objects. Then they will measure the objects to the nearest quarter inch and compare their estimates to the actual measurements.

3. Have students find and measure a part of their hand that is about 1 inch and record it on the index card. For example, they may identify the length of part of their thumb, the width of two fingers, or the distance from the tip of the finger to the knuckle.

4. Have students also measure their hand span by spreading their fingers as wide as they can and placing them on the ruler so their thumb is on the 0-mark. Help students determine their hand span and record it on the index card.

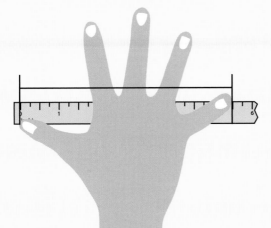

5. Ask students to look at the two measures and try to memorize them. The goal is for students to use a known measure to estimate the length of other objects.

6. Choose an object in the room for students to measure. Have them estimate the measure of its length, width, or height. Remind students to use one of the known measures—the part of the hand they measured or their hand span—to make the estimate.

7. Give students the ruler and have them measure the object to the nearest quarter inch. Check to make sure students measured to the nearest quarter inch correctly.

8. Have students compare their estimate with the actual measure. If students made estimates that are close to the actual measure, have them find a longer object to estimate and measure. If students did not estimate well, have them find another object about the same size to estimate and measure.

9. Have students continue to practice estimating and measuring objects. Make sure they measure different-sized objects and different dimensions (length, width, and height).

TRY IT Find the Nearest Quarter Inch

Students will practice estimating and measuring to the nearest quarter inch. Have students turn to the Find the Nearest Quarter Inch activity page in their Activity Book and read the directions with them.

Students should copy the problems from the Activity Book into their Math Notebook as necessary and solve them there.

Remind students that sometimes an object is held up to a ruler but isn't aligned with the 0-mark on the ruler as Problems 4 and 11 illustrate. Remind students that they can count forward from the beginning of the object, or subtract the amount to the left of the object from the length.

- Estimate the length of an object to the nearest $\frac{1}{2}$ inch and measure the length to the nearest $\frac{1}{4}$ inch.

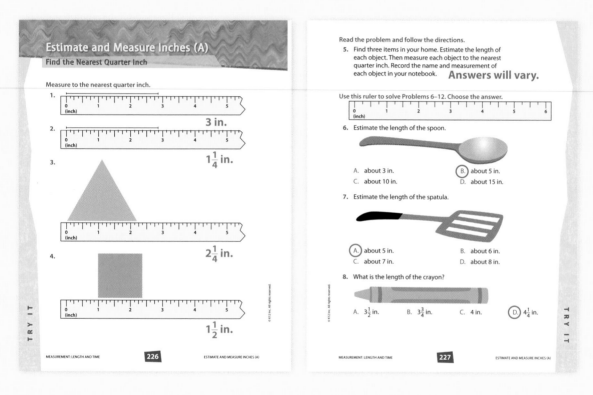

Estimate and Measure Inches (A)
Find the Nearest Quarter Inch

Measure to the nearest quarter inch.

1.
   (inch) 0 1 2 3 4 5
   3 in.

2.
   (inch) 0 1 2 3 4 5
   $1\frac{1}{4}$ in.

3.
   (inch) 0 1 2 3 4 5
   $2\frac{1}{4}$ in.

4.
   (inch) 0 1 2 3 4 5
   $1\frac{1}{2}$ in.

Read the problem and follow the directions.

5. Find three items in your home. Estimate the length of each object. Then measure each object to the nearest quarter inch. Record the name and measurement of each object in your notebook. **Answers will vary.**

Use this ruler to solve Problems 6–12. Choose the answer.
   (inch) 0 1 2 3 4 5 6

6. Estimate the length of the spoon.

   A. about 3 in.   B. about 5 in.
   C. about 10 in.   D. about 15 in.

7. Estimate the length of the spatula.

   A. about 5 in.   B. about 6 in.
   C. about 7 in.   D. about 8 in.

8. What is the length of the crayon?

   A. $3\frac{1}{2}$ in.   B. $3\frac{3}{4}$ in.   C. 4 in.   D. $4\frac{1}{4}$ in.

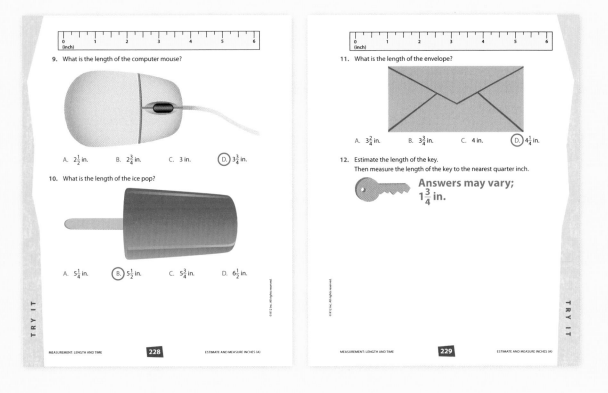

9. What is the length of the computer mouse?

A. $2\frac{1}{2}$ in.   B. $2\frac{3}{4}$ in.   C. 3 in.   (D.) $3\frac{3}{4}$ in.

10. What is the length of the ice pop?

A. $5\frac{1}{4}$ in.   (B.) $5\frac{1}{2}$ in.   C. $5\frac{3}{4}$ in.   D. $6\frac{1}{2}$ in.

11. What is the length of the envelope?

A. $3\frac{2}{4}$ in.   B. $3\frac{3}{4}$ in.   C. 4 in.   (D.) $4\frac{1}{4}$ in.

12. Estimate the length of the key.
Then measure the length of the key to the nearest quarter inch.

Answers may vary;
$1\frac{3}{4}$ **in.**

TRY IT

TRY IT

Estimate and Measure Inches (B)

Lesson Overview

GET READY Draw and Measure Lines	5 minutes	OFFLINE
LEARN Use Hand Spans to Estimate Measures	15 minutes	OFFLINE
LEARN Estimate-and-Measure Game	15 minutes	OFFLINE
TRY IT Measure to a Quarter Inch	15 minutes	OFFLINE
CHECKPOINT	10 minutes	ONLINE

▶ Lesson Objectives

Estimate the length of an object to the nearest $\frac{1}{2}$ inch and measure the length to the nearest $\frac{1}{4}$ inch.

▶ Prerequisite Skills

- Identify inches on a ruler and measure the length of an object to the nearest inch.
- Estimate the length of an object to the nearest inch or centimeter.

▶ Content Background

Students will continue to learn to estimate and measure in inches. They will estimate to the nearest half inch and measure to the nearest quarter inch.

Estimating and measuring objects is an important skill. When judging whether an object will fit in a given space, students estimate the length, width, and height of the object. Then they compare the estimates to the given space to determine if the object will fit. Students often use familiar benchmark measurements when estimating and measuring. For instance, they may be familiar with $8\frac{1}{2} \times 11$ inch notebook paper. Students may use this information to estimate the length of an object or judge whether it will fill a given space.

Note that when measurements are abbreviated (cm, m, km, in., ft, yd, and mi), only the abbreviation for *inch* has a period. The period is added to avoid confusion with the word *in*.

▶ Common Errors and Misconceptions

Students often have difficulty giving the correct measure of an object when the object is not aligned with the 0-end of a ruler. For example, they might think that this pencil is 4 inches long because the right end of the pencil aligns with the 4-inch mark. The pencil is actually only 3 inches long because the left end of the pencil aligns with the 1-inch mark.

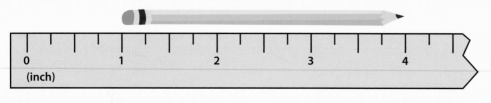

Advance Preparation

On index cards, write the names of readily available objects and a measurable characteristic of each object, such as a pencil's length, a drinking-glass's height, a chair's width, a table's length, a marker's width, and a pair of scissors' widest opening. Students will use them to play a game in which they will estimate the length of objects and then measure the objects.

GET READY Draw and Measure Lines

Students will practice drawing lines of a given length without a measuring tool. They will then measure the lines to check for accuracy.
Gather the ruler.

1. Ask students to draw a line 2 inches long without using a measuring tool.

2. Give students a ruler and have them measure the line. Have students compare the length of their line to the 2-inch mark on the ruler.

3. Repeat Steps 1 and 2 with a 3-inch line.

4. Challenge students to draw longer lines and line lengths ending in half inches as they become more comfortable with the process. Ask them to draw lines that are $2\frac{1}{2}$ and $3\frac{1}{2}$ inches long.

Objectives

- Identify inches on a ruler and measure the length of an object to the nearest inch.

- Estimate the length of an object to the nearest inch or centimeter.

Tips

Remind students to align the beginning of each line with the 0-mark on the ruler.

LEARN Use Hand Spans to Estimate Measures

Students will measure parts of their hand and use those known measurements to estimate the length of other objects.
Gather the ruler.

1. Have students extend their four fingers (index finger through pinky finger) straight out, with all fingers touching. Have them measure the width of these four fingers by holding a ruler with the other hand. Students should measure the width to the nearest half inch.

Objectives

- Estimate the length of an object to the nearest $\frac{1}{2}$ inch and measure the length to the nearest $\frac{1}{4}$ inch.

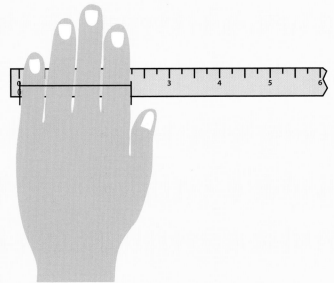

2. Have students record the width of their four fingers and any lesser widths they may find helpful. If students don't already have the other two found measures, their hand span and a 1-inch length such as the width of two fingers, have them record those measurements.

3. Have students gather several objects from their surroundings. Ask them to choose part of an object to measure. Explain that they will use the measurement tools on their hands to estimate the length, width, or height of the object. For example, if students want to find the width of a picture frame, they will estimate by using their hand span. If a hand span is 5 inches and the frame is a little more than 2 hand spans, students may estimate the width to be 11 inches.

4. After students estimate the length, width, or height of the object, have them use a ruler to find the actual measurement to the nearest quarter inch. Students should compare their estimate with the actual measurement.

5. Have students continue practicing estimating and measuring. When they are comfortable with their estimates to the nearest inch, have them estimate measures to the nearest half inch and quarter inch.

LEARN Estimate-and-Measure Game

OFFLINE

15min

Play a game with students to practice estimating and measuring various objects. Students will earn points based on how close their estimate is to the actual measure of the object.

Gather the ruler and labeled index cards.

1. Place the index cards face down in a pile. The first player takes the top card, identifies the object, and estimates the given measurement. If the card says "a pencil's length," students choose whatever pencil they wish. If it says "chair's width," they choose any chair to measure. Remind players to use a known measure (such as a hand span) to estimate. Then the player uses a ruler to find the actual measure of the object. Players get a point for every inch of the actual measure, and they subtract 2 points for each inch that their estimate was off. For instance, if students estimated an object was 2 feet or 24 inches long, and its actual length was 21 inches long, they would be 3 inches off from the actual measure, so they get 21 points minus $2 \times 3 = 6$. So their score would be $21 - 6 = 15$.

Place the card on the bottom of the pile when the turn is over.

2. The next player takes the top card from the pile, identifies the object, estimates the measurement, finds the actual measurement, and calculates the score.

3. Continue playing. The player with the highest score when all the cards have been used is the winner. To continue playing, reuse the cards with the rule that players pick different objects from ones they picked in the previous game.

Objectives

- Estimate the length of an object to the nearest $\frac{1}{2}$ inch and measure the length to the nearest $\frac{1}{4}$ inch.

Tips

Write the points on an index card for each player. Have students help refine the scoring system. They can add bonus points for estimating very close to the actual measurement, or for estimating objects that are greater than 3 hand spans, or for meeting other challenges that come up during the game.

TRY IT Measure to a Quarter Inch

Objectives

Students will practice estimating to the nearest half inch and measuring to the nearest quarter inch. Remind students to adjust their measure if an object is not matched up with the 0-mark on the ruler. Gather the ruler. Have students turn to the Measure to a Quarter Inch activity page in their Activity Book and read the directions with them.

Students should copy the problems from the Activity Book into their Math Notebook as necessary and solve them there.

- Estimate the length of an object to the nearest $\frac{1}{2}$ inch and measure the length to the nearest $\frac{1}{4}$ inch.

Estimate and Measure Inches (B)
Measure to a Quarter Inch

Estimate the measurement. Use a ruler to find the actual measurement to the nearest quarter inch.

1. Length of your favorite book
   Estimate? **Answers**
   Actual? **will vary.**

2. Length of your foot
   Estimate? **Answers**
   Actual? **will vary.**

3. Width of a plate
   Estimate?
   Actual?
   Answers will vary.

4. Length of a desk
   Estimate?
   Actual?
   Answers will vary.

Choose the answer.

5. What is the length of the worm?

   A. $2\frac{1}{4}$ in.   B. 3 in.   C. $3\frac{1}{4}$ in.   D. 4 in.

6. What is the length of the toy train?

   A. 4 in.   B. $4\frac{1}{4}$ in.   C. $4\frac{1}{2}$ in.   D. 5 in.

7. Estimate the length of the dollar bill.

   A.   about 3 in.   B. about 5 in.
   C.   about 10 in.   D. about 15 in.

8. Estimate the length of the milk bottle.

   A.   about $3\frac{1}{2}$ in.   B.   about 4 in.
   C.   about $4\frac{1}{2}$ in.   D.   about 5 in.

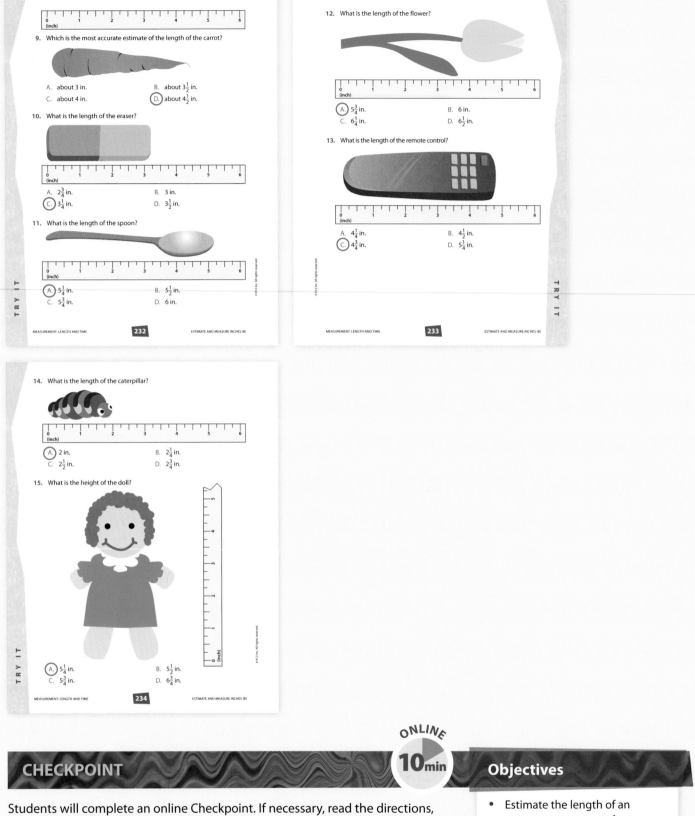

9. Which is the most accurate estimate of the length of the carrot?

A. about 3 in.   B. about $3\frac{1}{2}$ in.
C. about 4 in.   (D.) about $4\frac{1}{2}$ in.

10. What is the length of the eraser?

A. $2\frac{3}{4}$ in.   B. 3 in.
(C.) $3\frac{1}{4}$ in.   D. $3\frac{1}{2}$ in.

11. What is the length of the spoon?

(A.) $5\frac{1}{4}$ in.   B. $5\frac{1}{2}$ in.
C. $5\frac{3}{4}$ in.   D. 6 in.

12. What is the length of the flower?

(A.) $5\frac{3}{4}$ in.   B. 6 in.
C. $6\frac{1}{4}$ in.   D. $6\frac{1}{2}$ in.

13. What is the length of the remote control?

A. $4\frac{1}{4}$ in.   B. $4\frac{1}{2}$ in.
(C.) $4\frac{3}{4}$ in.   D. $5\frac{1}{4}$ in.

14. What is the length of the caterpillar?

(A.) 2 in.   B. $2\frac{1}{4}$ in.
C. $2\frac{1}{2}$ in.   D. $2\frac{3}{4}$ in.

15. What is the height of the doll?

(A.) $5\frac{1}{4}$ in.   B. $5\frac{1}{2}$ in.
C. $5\frac{3}{4}$ in.   D. $6\frac{3}{4}$ in.

CHECKPOINT

ONLINE
10 min

Students will complete an online Checkpoint. If necessary, read the directions, problems, and answer choices to students and help them with keyboard or mouse operations.

Objectives

- Estimate the length of an object to the nearest $\frac{1}{2}$ inch and measure the length to the nearest $\frac{1}{4}$ inch.

Tell Time in Minutes

Lesson Overview

Skills Update	5 minutes	ONLINE
GET READY Time to the Nearest Quarter Hour	5 minutes	ONLINE
LEARN Time to the Nearest Minute	15 minutes	ONLINE
LEARN Read the Time More Than One Way	15 minutes	ONLINE
TRY IT Show and Tell Time	10 minutes	OFFLINE
CHECKPOINT	10 minutes	ONLINE

▶ Lesson Objectives

Tell time to the nearest minute.

▶ Prerequisite Skills

Tell time to the nearest quarter hour.

▶ Content Background

Students will learn to tell time to the nearest minute. They will show and tell time on an analog clock (one with a face and hands) as well as a digital clock.

Materials to Gather

SUPPLIED
Show and Tell Time activity page

GET READY Time to the Nearest Quarter Hour

ONLINE 5 min

Students will work with the Clock Learning Tool to review quarter hours and to tell the time to the nearest quarter hour.

DIRECTIONS FOR USING THE CLOCK LEARNING TOOL

1. Click Begin and choose the following:
   - Click the clock display button.
   - Uncheck the AM/PM box.
   - Uncheck the digital clock box.
2. Drag the minute hand to 15, 30, 45, and 60 to review quarter hours. As you move to each location, discuss the phrases for those quarter hours: *quarter after, half past, quarter to,* and *o'clock.*
3. Drag the minute hand around the clock to show 9:28.
   Ask: What is the time to the nearest quarter hour? Half past nine; 9:30
4. Repeat Step 3 with the following times:
   - **10:02** ten o'clock
   - **8:55** nine o'clock
   - **10:12** quarter after 10; 10:15
   - **10:43** quarter to 11; 10:45

Objectives

- Tell time to the nearest quarter hour.

Tips

Encourage students to say the time in more than one way.

LEARN Time to the Nearest Minute

Students will use the Clock Learning Tool to tell time to the nearest minute. They will say the time two different ways.

DIRECTIONS FOR USING THE CLOCK LEARNING TOOL

1. Click Begin and choose the following:
   - Click the clock display button.
   - Uncheck the digital clock box.
2. Drag the minute hand to set the clock to 12:05.
3. Point to the light blue 5 on the outer ring of the clock. Explain that the light blue numbers on the outer ring of the clock tell how many minutes after the hour it is. Point out that those numbers are like skip counting by 5s.
4. Have students click the speaker button and listen as the time is read.
5. To show students how 12:05 is written and how it would display on a digital clock, choose the following:
   - Click the clock display button.
   - Check the digital clock box.

   Say: Another way to say this time is *5 minutes after 12.*

6. Repeat Steps 2–5 for the following times, allowing students to move the minute hand. Point out the corresponding light blue numbers for each time.
   - **1:25** one twenty-five; 25 minutes after 1
   - **2:40** two forty; 40 minutes after 2
   - **3:55** three fifty-five; 55 minutes after 3
7. Set the clock to exactly 4:00.
8. Have students drag the minute hand very slowly around the clock. Have them look at the time on the digital clock as the minute hand moves. Emphasize that each tick mark on the clock represents one minute. Point out that the time on the digital clock advances by one-minute intervals as they drag the minute hand around the clock. Continue until students get to 4:59 and then finally move to 5:00.
9. Have students click the + button under the minutes on the digital clock. They will find that the minutes display does not necessarily increase by one with every click. Have students verify for themselves that the display on the digital clock matches the time shown on the analog clock.
10. Change the settings again to the following:
    - Click the clock display button.
    - Uncheck the digital clock box.
11. Move the minute hand to the following times. Have students read the time two different ways.
    - **4:37** four thirty-seven; 37 minutes after 4
    - **11:52** eleven fifty-two; 52 minutes after 11
    - **8:49** eight forty-nine; 49 minutes after 8
    - **5:13** five thirteen; 13 minutes after 5

Objectives

- Tell time to the nearest minute.

Tips

Throughout the day, have students look at an analog clock, with hour and minute hands, and state the time.

LEARN Read the Time More Than One Way

Students will use the Clock Learning Tool to learn how to read the time as both the number of minutes after an hour and the number of minutes before the next hour. For example, they'll learn that 2:40 is both *40 minutes after 2* and *20 minutes before* 3. They will show times on an analog clock.

DIRECTIONS FOR USING THE CLOCK LEARNING TOOL

1. Click Begin and choose the following:
   - Click the clock display button.
   - Uncheck the digital clock box.

2. Drag the minute hand around the clock to show 5:45.

   Say: The time shown is 5:45 or 45 minutes after 5. There is another way to say this time. Since the time will be 6:00 in 15 minutes, you can say this time as *15 minutes before 6* or *15 minutes till 6*. You can also say this as *quarter till 6*.

3. Point to the light blue numbers around the outer edge of the clock. Explain that when the minute hand is on one of these multiples of five, students should skip count by 5s to the next hour to see how many minutes there are until that hour.

4. Drag the minute hand back to show 5:40. Have students count the number of minutes before 6.

   Ask: Now that you know how many minutes there are before 6, how do you read this time? 20 minutes before 6; 20 minutes till 6; 40 minutes after 5

5. Drag the minute hand around the clock to show 7:51.

   Say: The time shown is 7:51 or 51 minutes after 7. There is another way to say this time. Since the time will be 8:00 in 9 minutes, you can say this time as *9 minutes before 8* or *9 minutes till 8*. You can see that there are 4 minutes until the next five, which is 7:55, and then 5 more minutes, so altogether there are 9 minutes until 8.

6. Drag the minute hand around the clock to show 10:38.

   Ask: What time is shown? 10:38 or 38 minutes after 10

   Say: There is another way to say this time.
   Ask students how they could figure out how many minutes it is before 11. Students could figure it out in any of the following ways.
   - Start at 38 and count 2 minutes to 40; skip count by 5s, stepping from number to number on the clock (5, 10, 15, 20); then add the 2 minutes to get 22 minutes till 11.
   - Start at 11 o'clock and skip count by 5s going backward on the clock from number to number—5, 10, 15, 20—then 21, 22 to get to 10:38.
   - Count up by 10s from 38 to 60 without using the clock (starting at 38, 48, then 58, and 2 more is 60) to get 22 minutes till 11.
   - Simply subtract 38 minutes from 60 minutes. Since 60 − 38 = 22, the time is 22 minutes before 11, or 22 minutes till 11.

7. Repeat Step 6 with the following times. Allow students to choose the strategy that works best for them to determine the answer.
   - 12:35 35 minutes after 12; 25 minutes before 1; 25 minutes till 1
   - 2:49 49 minutes after 2; 11 minutes before 3; 11 minutes till 3

Objectives
- Tell time to the nearest minute.

Tips
If students have difficulty setting the hands for a particular time, have them use the the digital clock to practice setting times and checking them.

8. Have students drag the minute hand around the clock to show the times in each of the following situations. Then have them press the speaker button to see if they're correct.

   - Serena leaves for swim practice at 4:30 p.m.
   - Alexander arrived at the party at 3:05 p.m.
   - The sun rose this morning at 7:43 a.m.
   - The tide of the ocean is at its lowest today at 9:58 p.m.

9. Have students move the clock hands to show each of the following times. Check their work. The speaker button will give the time in only one way. For instance, it will say, "The time is 7:35." Check that students are comfortable also giving the time as *35 minutes after 7* and *25 minutes before 8*.

   - Rosa left for play rehearsal at 14 minutes after 7. 7:14
   - Johnny left for the park at 10 minutes before 2. 1:50
   - Ron's baseball game ended at 12 minutes till 6. 5:48
   - The moonrise tonight is at 26 minutes after 9. 9:26

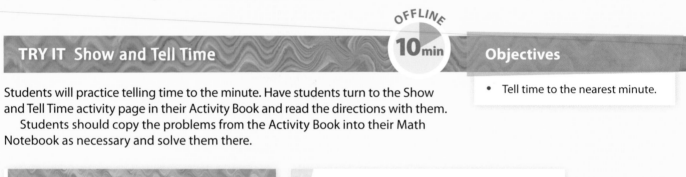

TRY IT Show and Tell Time

OFFLINE **10 min**

Objectives

- Tell time to the nearest minute.

Students will practice telling time to the minute. Have students turn to the Show and Tell Time activity page in their Activity Book and read the directions with them.

Students should copy the problems from the Activity Book into their Math Notebook as necessary and solve them there.

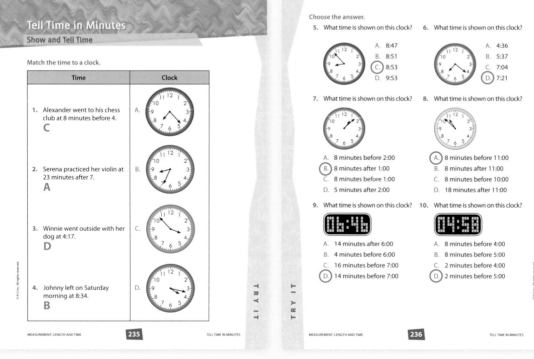

11. Which clock shows the same time as this clock?

12. Which clock shows the same time as this clock?

13. Which clock shows the same time as this clock?

14. Which clock shows the same time as this clock?

TRY IT

TRY IT

ONLINE

10 min

CHECKPOINT

Students will complete an online Checkpoint. If necessary, read the directions, problems, and answer choices to students and help them with keyboard or mouse operations.

Objectives

- Tell time to the nearest minute.

Determine Elapsed Time in Minutes

Lesson Overview

Skills Update	5 minutes	ONLINE
GET READY Passing Time	5 minutes	ONLINE
LEARN Time Spent	20 minutes	ONLINE
LEARN Across A.M. and P.M.	20 minutes	ONLINE
TRY IT How Much Time?	10 minutes	OFFLINE

▶ Lesson Objectives

Determine elapsed time to the nearest minute.

▶ Prerequisite Skills

Determine elapsed time in hours, such as 11:00 a.m. to 4:00 p.m.

▶ Content Background

Students will learn to determine elapsed time. Elapsed time is the amount of time that passes between a starting and ending time. Students will also learn to find the end time of an activity given the start time and the elapsed time.

Elapsed time can include elapsed hours, elapsed days, elapsed months, or other time periods. Students need to understand that when counting to determine elapsed time, such as hours, they count beginning with the hour, day, or month after the starting time. For example, if students are counting how many hours there are between 2:00 p.m. to 7:00 p.m., they begin counting at 3:00—that is, 3:00, 4:00, 5:00, 6:00, 7:00—to find that there are 5 hours between 2:00 p.m. and 7:00 p.m. Similarly, if students want to know the number of months from June to September, they begin counting with July—July, August, September—to find that there are 3 months from June to September. Students should use this counting principle in any type of counting-on situation, either from a number or from another starting point such as time.

▶ Advance Preparation

Print the Time Spent printout and Across A.M. and P.M. printout.

Materials to Gather

SUPPLIED

Time Spent (printout)

Across A.M. and P.M. (printout)

How Much Time? activity page

ONLINE
5min

GET READY Passing Time

Students will determine elapsed time in hours. Explain to students that *elapsed time* is the time that passes between a starting time and an ending time.

Objectives

- Determine elapsed time in hours, such as 11:00 a.m. to 4:00 p.m.

Tips Have students find 3 more than 5 by counting on: 6, 7, 8. Apply this counting-on strategy to find 3 hours after 5:00 by counting on hours: 6:00, 7:00, 8:00.

LEARN Time Spent

Students will use the Clock Learning Tool to learn how to find elapsed times and ending times in story problems. Elapsed time is the amount of time that passes between two times. The story problems in this activity use times that don't cross 12:00 noon or 12:00 midnight, so answers will not include a.m. and p.m.

Gather the Time Spent printout.

- Determine elapsed time to the nearest minute.

DIRECTIONS FOR USING THE CLOCK LEARNING TOOL

1. Click Begin.

2. Explain that elapsed time is the amount of time that passes between a start time and an end time. Tell students that when they know the time an activity starts and the time it ends, they can find the elapsed time.

   Say: Moving the minute hand 1 full circle equals 1 hour. When you figure elapsed time, start by moving the minute hand around the clock 1 full circle for each hour that has passed. Then move the minute hand the number of minutes.

3. Give students the printout and have them read Problem 1.

   - Have students drag the minute hand around the analog clock until the time is 3:10, the starting time in Problem 1.

   - Tell students that they will need to drag the minute hand to 4:55, the ending time, and count forward while doing so.

   - Have them move the minute hand 1 full rotation and count aloud "1 hour." They should make a note on the printout that they have counted 1 hour.

   - For counting 55 minutes, have them first move the minute hand 30 minutes from 4:10 to 4:40. Then have them move the hand and count by 5-minute intervals, starting with 30, until they reach 4:55. They will say, "30, 35, 40, 45" as they reach 4:55 on the clock. Have them make a note on the printout that they counted 45 minutes. They have written 1 hour and 45 minutes as the elapsed time.

   - **Ask:** How long did the movie last? 1 hour and 45 minutes

4. Have students read Problem 2 on the printout and move the clock hands to 9:40.

   - Ask students to move the minute hand and count the number of minutes until 10 o'clock and then count another 12 minutes. Have them make a note of 20 minutes plus 12 minutes on the printout.

   - Explain that they moved the hand to 10 o'clock as a way to help them count the minutes easily. When they counted 20 minutes to reach 10 o'clock and then added 12 minutes, it was easier than counting minute-by-minute.

   - How many minutes were the muffins in the oven? 32 minutes

5. Explain that students can count forward first by hours and then by minutes to get to the target time, or they can use the method of counting minutes forward to the next whole hour and then count on by hours. Either way, remind them to record the hours and minutes as they count forward.

6. Have students read Problems 3 and 4. Help them count as they move the minute hand. Help them keep track of the hours and minutes and record their answers on the printout.

   Ask: In Problem 3, how long was Kelly at the zoo? 4 hours and 25 minutes

   Ask: In Problem 4, how long was the plane in the air? 6 hours and 32 minutes

7. Have students read Problem 5. Explain that they can identify the end time when the problem gives them the start time and the elapsed time.

   - Have students set the clock to 2:10.

   - Have them move the minute hand forward 2 hours and 7 minutes. Help them count as they move the hand around the clock.

   - **Ask:** What time did the movie end? 4:17

8. Have students complete Problems 6–8 on the printout. Help them as necessary with counting the hours and minutes as they move the minute hand of the learning tool.

   Ask: In Problem 6, what time did Mr. Walters return home? 9:53

   Ask: In Problem 7, what time did Lee's karate class end? 5:10

   Ask: In Problem 8, what time did Becky finish her art project? 9:05

LEARN Across A.M. and P.M.

ONLINE
20min

Objectives

- Determine elapsed time to the nearest minute.

Students will learn how to find the elapsed time in story problems that give a start and end time for events that cross over 12:00 noon or 12:00 midnight. They will also learn how to find the end time of events when the elapsed time crosses over 12:00 noon or 12:00 midnight.

Gather the Across A.M. and P.M. printout.

DIRECTIONS FOR USING THE CLOCK LEARNING TOOL

1. Click Begin.

2. Remind students that elapsed time is the amount of time that passes between a start time and an end time. Tell students that they will learn about elapsed time that crosses from a.m. to p.m and from p.m. to a.m.

3. Give students the printout and have them read Problem 1.

   - Have students drag the minute hand around the analog clock until the time is 10:30 a.m., the starting time in Problem 1.

   - Tell students that, to find out how long Jake spends at the museum, they will need to drag the minute hand to 1:43 p.m., the ending time, and count forward while doing so.

   - Have them move the minute hand 3 full rotations and count aloud "1 hour, 2 hours, 3 hours." They should make a note on the printout that they have counted 3 hours.

   - As they drag the minute hand past 12 o'clock, have them observe that a.m. changes to p.m., the word *noon* appears, and the sun pops up.

   - Tell students that now they have to count from 1:30 p.m. to 1:43 p.m. to complete the elapsed time. Have them move the minute hand 10 minutes and then 3 minutes.

   - **Say:** 1:30 to 1:40 is 10 minutes, and 1:40 to 1:43 is 3 minutes, for 13 minutes.

- Have students make a note on the printout that they counted 13 minutes. They should see that their notes show 3 hours and 13 minutes.
- **Ask:** How long did Jake spend at the museum? 3 hours and 13 minutes

4. Have students read Problem 2 on the printout and drag the minute hand to set the time to 11:50 a.m.
   - Ask students to first drag the minute hand and count the number of minutes until noon, which is 10 minutes. They should make a note of 10 minutes on their printout.
   - Then they should drag the minute hand and count another 1 hour and 27 minutes to get to 1:27 p.m. and make a note of that time span. Then they should add 1 hour and 27 minutes to 10 minutes for a total of 1 hour and 37 minutes.
   - Explain that they can use that method of counting time before 12 o'clock and then after 12 o'clock and then adding the two times together.

5. Repeat Steps 3 and 4 to guide students to complete Problems 3 and 4 on the printout. As students move the clock hands in Problem 4, have them note that when the clock shows 12 midnight, the word *midnight* appears and the moon appears.

   Ask: How much time did Tyler spend at the zoo? 3 hours and 52 minutes

   Ask: How much time did Eddie sleep? 9 hours and 31 minutes

6. Tell students they will now find the end time of events that cross from a.m. to p.m. and from p.m. to a.m. They will be given the start time and elapsed time.

7. Have students read Problem 5 and drag the minute hand to set the clock to 11:30 a.m.
   - Have students start by moving the minute hand 7 full rotations, counting aloud by hours as they go. The clock will show 6:30 p.m.
   - Have students move the minute hand 20 minutes past 6:30 p.m.
   - **Ask:** What time does the clock show and what is the answer to Problem 5? 6:50 p.m.

8. Have students read Problems 6–8 and guide them to find the end times by using the learning tool.

   Ask: What time did Mrs. Kish finish painting the dining room? 2:43 p.m.

   Ask: What time does Tonya's dance class end? 12:20 p.m.

   Ask: What time did Monica wake up? 7:22 a.m.

| **Tips** | Allow students to try finding elapsed time across 12:00 noon and 12:00 midnight by visualizing the clock hands moving forward. Begin by giving them some short elapsed-time problems. |

TRY IT How Much Time?

Objectives

• Determine elapsed time to the nearest minute.

Students will practice determining elapsed time to the nearest minute. They also will practice finding the end time when they are given the start time and elapsed time. Have students turn to the How Much Time? activity page in their Activity Book and read the directions with them.

Students should copy the problems from the Activity Book into their Math Notebook as necessary and solve them there.

Tips Have students show the start time on a clock drawing. Then have them count forward on the model to determine the elapsed time.

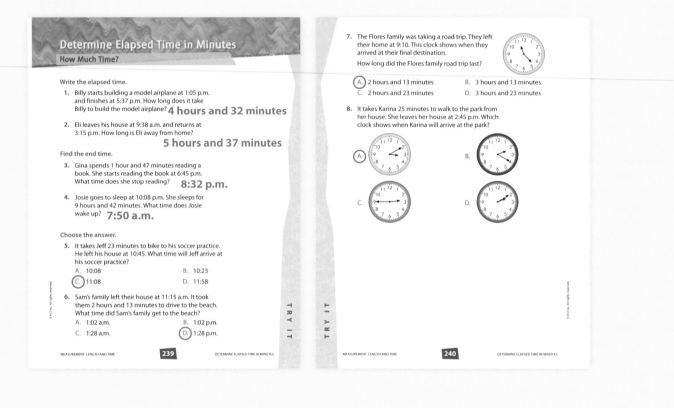

Determine Elapsed Time in Minutes
How Much Time?

Write the elapsed time.

1. Billy starts building a model airplane at 1:05 p.m. and finishes at 5:37 p.m. How long does it take Billy to build the model airplane? **4 hours and 32 minutes**

2. Eli leaves his house at 9:38 a.m. and returns at 3:15 p.m. How long is Eli away from home? **5 hours and 37 minutes**

Find the end time.

3. Gina spends 1 hour and 47 minutes reading a book. She starts reading the book at 6:45 p.m. What time does she stop reading? **8:32 p.m.**

4. Josie goes to sleep at 10:08 p.m. She sleeps for 9 hours and 42 minutes. What time does Josie wake up? **7:50 a.m.**

Choose the answer.

5. It takes Jeff 23 minutes to bike to his soccer practice. He left his house at 10:45. What time will Jeff arrive at his soccer practice?
   A. 10:08   B. 10:23
   (C.) 11:08   D. 11:58

6. Sam's family left their house at 11:15 a.m. It took them 2 hours and 13 minutes to drive to the beach. What time did Sam's family get to the beach?
   A. 1:02 a.m.   B. 1:02 p.m.
   C. 1:28 a.m.   (D.) 1:28 p.m.

7. The Flores family was taking a road trip. They left their home at 9:10. This clock shows when they arrived at their final destination. How long did the Flores family road trip last?
   (A.) 2 hours and 13 minutes   B. 3 hours and 13 minutes
   C. 2 hours and 23 minutes   D. 3 hours and 23 minutes

8. It takes Karina 25 minutes to walk to the park from her house. She leaves her house at 2:45 p.m. Which clock shows when Karina will arrive at the park?

MEASUREMENT: LENGTH AND TIME   239   DETERMINE ELAPSED TIME IN MINUTES
MEASUREMENT: LENGTH AND TIME   240   DETERMINE ELAPSED TIME IN MINUTES

Elapsed Time on a Calendar

▶ Lesson Objectives

Use a calendar to determine elapsed time.

▶ Prerequisite Skills

- Identify relationships between units of time, such as minutes in an hour, days in a month, and weeks in a year.
- Determine elapsed time in hours, such as 11:00 a.m. to 4:00 p.m.

▶ Content Background

Students will learn to use a calendar to determine elapsed time. Elapsed time on a calendar is the amount of time that passes between a start date and an end date.

Elapsed time can include elapsed hours, elapsed days, elapsed months, or other time periods. Students need to understand that when counting to determine elapsed time, they count beginning with the hour, day, or month after the starting time. For example, if students are counting how many hours there are between 2:00 p.m. and 7:00 p.m., they begin counting with 3:00—3:00, 4:00, 5:00, 6:00, 7:00—to find that there are 5 hours between 2:00 p.m. and 7:00 p.m. Similarly, if students want to know the number of months from June to September, they begin counting with July—July, August, September—to find that there are 3 months from June to September. Students should use this counting principle in any type of counting-on situation, either from a number or from another starting point such as time.

Materials to Gather

SUPPLIED

Elapsed Time Between Days activity page

Number of Days activity page

ALSO NEEDED

calendar, 12-month

ONLINE
10min

GET READY Days and Months

Objectives

Students will review units of time on a calendar. They will review the number of days in a week, the number of days in a month, and the number of months in a year.

Encourage students to find their birthday on the calendar and to look at how many days their birthday month has.

Have students read the poem aloud several times to help them commit it to memory.

- Identify relationships between units of time, such as minutes in an hour, days in a month, and weeks in a year.

LEARN Elapsed Time Within a Month

Students will determine elapsed time in days when given a start date and an end date in the same month. When students find elapsed time in days, they count the complete 24-hour time periods that have passed. They can do this in two ways:

1. Students can use their finger to hop on a calendar, beginning at the start date and hopping from day to day to count how many complete days have passed. When they count this way, they start counting on the day after the start date, because on that date the first 24-hour period has passed and 1 day of elapsed time has occurred. For example, if the start date is April 6, students point to April 6 on a calendar and move their finger to April 7 for a count of 1 day. If the end date is April 10, students would count April 7, 8, 9, and 10 to get a count of 4 days of elapsed time.

2. When the start and end dates are in the same month, students can simply subtract the start date from the end date to get the number of elapsed days. For example, if the start date is April 6 and the end date is April 10, they can subtract $10 - 6 = 4$; the number of elapsed days is 4.

Objectives

- Use a calendar to determine elapsed time.

Tips

Encourage students to solve problems both by counting on the calendar and by using subtraction.

LEARN Elapsed Time Between Days

Students will determine elapsed time in days when the start date is in one month and the end date is in the next month.

Gather the calendar. Have students turn to the Elapsed Time Between Days activity page in their Activity Book and read the directions to them.

Students should copy the problems from the Activity Book into their Math Notebook as necessary and solve them there.

1. **Say:** You know how to find the number of days that have elapsed between two dates in a single month. Now you'll learn how to find elapsed time when the start date is in one month and the end date is in the next month.

2. Have students recite the following poem. Explain that the poem will help them remember which months have 30 days.

    30 days have September, April, June, and November.

    All the rest have 31, except for February, the shortest one.

3. Read the problem in the Worked Example with students.

    Say: When a start date is in one month and the end date is in the next month, you count the elapsed time in two parts. First you count the days in the starting month. Then you add the days in the next month.

    Guide students through the two solutions. In the first solution, they count forward to find the number of days in the first month and then add the number of days in the second month. In the second solution, they subtract to find the number of days in the first month and then add the number of days in the second month. Make sure students understand both methods before continuing with the activity.

Objectives

- Use a calendar to determine elapsed time.

Tips

If students solve a problem using subtraction, have them check their answer by counting days on the calendar.

4. Have students read Problem 1. Have them find the two dates on the calendar. Point out that the dates are 2 weeks apart. Show students how to skip count by 7s as they move their finger down the calendar to the same day of the next week. Guide students to see that 2 weeks equals 14 days.

   Ask: How long will the King family be on vacation? 14 days

5. Guide students to solve Problem 2 using subtraction.

   Ask: How many days are in September? 30

   Guide students to subtract the start date—15—from 30 to get a difference of 15. Then have them add the number of days in October up to the current date—20—to get a sum of 35 days ($15 + 20 = 35$). They should determine that 35 days have passed since Ron's first football practice.

   Have students solve Problem 3 in the same way.

6. Have students solve Problems 4 and 5 in the same way, but this time challenge them to try solving the problems without the calendar. Remind students to say the poem to help them remember which months have 30 days.

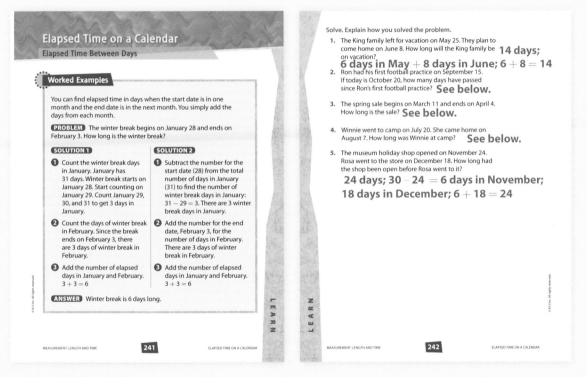

Additional Answers

2. 35 days; $30 - 15 = 15$ days in September; 20 days in October; $15 + 20 = 35$

3. 24 days; $31 - 11 = 20$ days in March; 4 days in April;
   $20 + 4 = 24$

4. 18 days; $31 - 20 = 11$ days in July; 7 days in August;
   $11 + 7 = 18$

TRY IT Number of Days

Students will practice using a calendar to find elapsed time. Remind them that finding elapsed time is done with hops on the calendar. They count beginning with the day after the starting date. Students can also subtract to calculate the elapsed time when the start and end dates are in the same month. When the start and end dates are in adjacent months, they can subtract to find the elapsed days in the start month and then add the the number from the end date. Have students turn to the Number of Days activity page in their Activity Book and read the directions with them.

Students should copy the problems from the Activity Book into their Math Notebook as necessary and solve them there.

Elapsed Time on a Calendar
Number of Days

Read the problem and answer the question.

1. The farmers' market started selling strawberries on June 12. If it is June 29, how many days have passed since the market started selling strawberries? **17 days**

2. Mrs. Lee left on April 28 for a business trip. She returned home on May 10. How long was the business trip? **12 days**

☀ APRIL ☀

Sunday	Monday	Tuesday	Wednesday	Thursday	Friday	Saturday
		1	2	3	4	5
6	7	8	9	10	11	12
13	14	15	16	17	18	19
20	21	22	23	24	25	26
27	28	29	30			

☀ MAY ☀

Sunday	Monday	Tuesday	Wednesday	Thursday	Friday	Saturday
				1	2	3
4	5	6	7	8	9	10
11	12	13	14	15	16	17
18	19	20	21	22	23	24
25	26	27	28	29	30	31

3. Winnie had her first soccer practice on August 23. The first game is September 8. How many days will pass between the first practice and the first game? **16 days**

4. A store opened on June 12. Adriana first went to the store on June 21. How long had the store been open before Adriana went to it? **9 days**

5. Maria planted some sunflower seeds on May 15. The flowers reached 2 feet tall on June 4. How long did it take the sunflowers to grow 2 feet? **20 days**

Choose the answer.

6. Jody had her first baseball practice on May 3. Today is May 19. How many days have passed since Jody's first baseball practice?
   A. 15 days   B. 16 days
   C. 21 days   D. 22 days

7. Peter finished his science project on March 15. The project was due on March 21. How early was Peter in finishing his science project?
   A. 3 days   B. 4 days
   C. 5 days   D. 6 days

8. Jeremy last went to the zoo on June 25. Today is July 13. How many days has it been since Jeremy last went to the zoo?

☀ JUNE ☀

Sunday	Monday	Tuesday	Wednesday	Thursday	Friday	Saturday
	1	2	3	4	5	6
3	4	5	6	7	8	9
10	11	12	13	14	15	16
17	18	19	20	21	22	23
24	25	26	27	28	29	30

☀ JULY ☀

Sunday	Monday	Tuesday	Wednesday	Thursday	Friday	Saturday
1	2	3	4	5	6	7
8	9	10	11	12	13	14
15	16	17	18	19	20	21
22	23	24	25	26	27	28
29	30	31				

   A. 12 days   B. 13 days
   C. 17 days   D. 18 days

TRY IT

CHECKPOINT

Students will complete an online Checkpoint. If necessary, read the directions, problems, and answer choices to students and help them with keyboard or mouse operations.

Unit Review

UNIT REVIEW Look Back	10 minutes	**ONLINE**
UNIT REVIEW Checkpoint Practice	50 minutes	**ONLINE**
⇥ **UNIT REVIEW** Prepare for the Checkpoint		

▶ Unit Objectives

This lesson reviews the following objectives:

- Identify the appropriate tools for measuring the length of an object.
- Identify the appropriate metric or English units for measuring the length of an object.
- Estimate and measure the length of an object to the nearest centimeter.
- Estimate the length of an object to the nearest $\frac{1}{2}$ inch and measure the length to the nearest $\frac{1}{4}$ inch.
- Tell time to the nearest minute.
- Determine elapsed time to the nearest minute.
- Use a calendar to determine elapsed time.

▶ Advance Preparation

In this lesson, students will have an opportunity to review previous activities in the Measurement: Length and Time unit. Look at the suggested activities in Unit Review: Prepare for the Checkpoint online and gather any needed materials.

Materials to Gather

There are no materials to gather for this lesson.

UNIT REVIEW Look Back

ONLINE **10min**

Objectives

Students will review key concepts from the unit to prepare for the Unit Checkpoint.

- Review unit objectives.

UNIT REVIEW Checkpoint Practice

ONLINE **50min**

Objectives

Students will complete an online Checkpoint Practice to prepare for the Unit Checkpoint. If necessary, read the directions, problems, and answer choices to students. Have students answer the problems on their own. Carefully review the answers with students.

- Review unit objectives.

⇥ **UNIT REVIEW** Prepare for the Checkpoint

What you do next depends on how students performed in the previous activity, Unit Review: Checkpoint Practice. If students had difficulty with any of the problems, complete the appropriate review activity listed in the table online.

Unit Checkpoint

UNIT CHECKPOINT Online	60 minutes	**ONLINE**

▶ Unit Objectives

This lesson assesses the following objectives:

- Identify the appropriate tools for measuring the length of an object.
- Identify the appropriate metric or English units for measuring the length of an object.
- Estimate and measure the length of an object to the nearest centimeter.
- Estimate the length of an object to the nearest $\frac{1}{2}$ inch and measure the length to the nearest $\frac{1}{4}$ inch.
- Tell time to the nearest minute.
- Determine elapsed time to the nearest minute.
- Use a calendar to determine elapsed time.

Materials to Gather

There are no materials to gather for this lesson.

UNIT CHECKPOINT Online

ONLINE
60min

Objectives

- Assess unit objectives.

Students will complete the Unit Checkpoint online. If necessary, read the directions, problems, and answer choices to students and help them with keyboard or mouse operations.

Measurement: Capacity and Weight

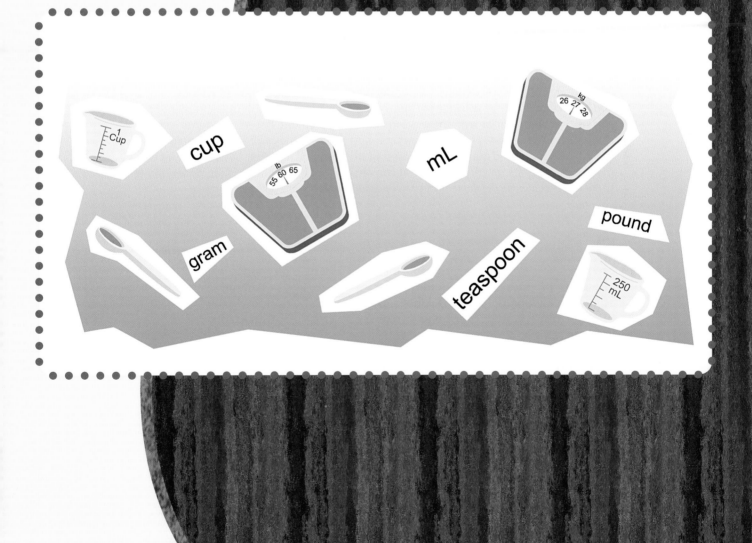

▶ Unit Objectives

- Identify the appropriate tools for measuring liquid volume.
- Identify the appropriate metric and English units for measuring liquid volume.
- Estimate and measure liquid volume to the nearest liter.
- Estimate and measure liquid volume to the nearest cup.
- Identify the appropriate tools for measuring the weight of an object.
- Identify the appropriate metric and English units for measuring the weight of an object.
- Estimate and measure the weight of an object to the nearest gram.
- Estimate and measure the weight of an object to the nearest ounce.
- Write a simple unit conversion, such as inches to feet, as an expression or an equation.
- Use a simple unit conversion, such as centimeters to meters, to solve a problem.
- Solve a unit-conversion story problem by using multiplication or division.

▶ Big Ideas

Measurement is the process of repeatedly using a unit over a quantity to determine how much you have.

▶ Unit Introduction

In this unit, students will extend their understanding of measurement of weight, mass, and liquid volume. They will identify appropriate metric and English measurement tools and will become familiar with the units in each measurement system. Students will estimate liquid measures to the nearest liter and cup, and they will estimate weight to the nearest ounce and mass to the nearest gram. They will use their understanding of measurement units to write simple unit conversions such as inches to feet, or centimeters to meters. Finally they will use unit conversions to solve story problems.

▶ Keywords

capacity
cup (c)
equivalent measures
estimate (n.)
estimate (v.)
expression
fluid ounce (fl oz)

gallon (gal)
gram (g)
kilogram (kg)
liquid volume
liter (L)
mass
milliliter (mL)

ounce (oz)
pint (pt)
pound (lb)
quart (qt)
teaspoon (t)
tablespoon (T)
weight

Capacity

Lesson Overview		
GET READY Chart Liquid Measures	5 minutes	OFFLINE
LEARN Tools and English Units	15 minutes	OFFLINE
LEARN Tools and Metric Units	20 minutes	OFFLINE
TRY IT Tools and Units to Measure Capacity	10 minutes	OFFLINE
CHECKPOINT	10 minutes	ONLINE

▶ Lesson Objectives

- Identify the appropriate tools for measuring liquid volume.
- Identify the appropriate metric and English units for measuring liquid volume.

▶ Prerequisite Skills

Measure and compare capacities by using a standard unit (for example, use a measuring cup to measure contents of a water bottle).

▶ Content Background

Students will learn which tools and units are used to measure liquid volume, or capacity. They will learn about both metric and English units.

Students will have experiences throughout their lives measuring or judging amounts of liquid volume or capacity. Such experiences might include measuring in cooking, making lemonade, drinking an adequate amount of water in a day, equally sharing a bottle of water with a friend, and deciding how much juice to buy for a large group. As adults, they might mix paints, make homemade cleaning solutions with vinegar and baking soda, and possibly mix chemicals.

Throughout this lesson, the term *capacity* will be used interchangeably with *liquid volume*. Students will use both the metric and English systems of measuring liquids. Within the metric system, students will work with milliliters (mL) and liters (L) as the units of measure. Within the English system (also known as the customary system), they will work with teaspoons (t), tablespoons (T), fluid ounces (fl oz), cups (c), pints (pt), quarts (qt), and gallons (gal) as the units of measure. Students will use a variety of measuring spoons, cups, and marked containers in their work.

▶ Advance Preparation

- For the Get Ready: Chart Liquid Measures activity, have commercial containers or packaging for liquids available from the pantry, refrigerator, or recycling bin. Bottles, cans, and jars should indicate liquid measures, including milliliters (mL), liters (L), fluid ounces (fl oz), cups (c), pints (pt), quarts (qt), and gallons (gal).

Materials to Gather

SUPPLIED

base-10 ones cube

base-10 thousands cube

Tools and Units to Measure Capacity activity page

ALSO NEEDED

household objects – labeled commercial containers for various liquids, tablespoon, teaspoon, 1-cup liquid measuring cup, 250-milliliter liquid measuring cup

containers, transparent beverage – pint, quart, gallon, half-liter, 1 liter, 2 liter

index cards – 13

marker, permanent

- For the Learn: Tools and English Units activity, copy this chart in the students' Math Notebook:

  _____ teaspoons = 1 tablespoon

  _____ tablespoons = 1 cup

  _____ cups = 1 pint

  _____ pints = 1 quart

  _____ quarts = 1 gallon

- For the Learn: Tools and English Units activity, label seven index cards with the following: **English measures, teaspoon, tablespoon, cup, pint, quart, and gallon**. Mix them up in a pile. Gather a liquid measuring cup and beverage containers in three different sizes (pint, quart, and gallon). Use the measuring cup to pour exactly 2 cups of water into the pint container. (Use a funnel if needed.) Mark the level of the liquid on the container with a permanent marker or the bottom edge of a piece of masking tape. Pour exactly 2 pints (4 cups) of water into the quart container and mark the level of the liquid on the container. Pour exactly 4 quarts into the gallon container and mark the level of the liquid on the container. Empty all containers.

- For the Learn: Tools and Metric Units activity, label six index cards with the following: **metric measures, 1 mL, 250 mL, half-liter, 1 liter, and 2 liter**. Mix them up in a pile. Gather a liquid measuring cup marked in milliliters up to 250 mL and beverage containers in three different sizes (half-liter, 1 liter, and 2 liter). Pour exactly 500 mL into the half-liter container. Mark the level of the liquid on the container with a permanent marker or the bottom edge of a piece of masking tape. Pour exactly 1,000 mL into the 1-liter container and mark the level of the liquid on the container. Pour exactly 2,000 mL into the 2-liter container and mark the level of the liquid on the container. Empty all containers.

GET READY Chart Liquid Measures

OFFLINE 5 min

Students will find labels on cans, jars, and bottles that contain liquids to see how the contents are measured. They will make a chart of their findings.

Gather the labeled commercial containers for liquids.

1. Have students make a three-column chart in their Math Notebook. The columns should be labeled **Type of liquid**, **English measure**, and **Metric measure**.

2. Have students examine the commercial containers to see how the contents are measured.

3. Direct students to list their findings on the chart, recording both the English and metric measures.

4. Mention to students that liquids are often labeled on containers in fluid ounces, but cooking requires measuring in cups. Tell them that 1 cup is 8 fluid ounces. Have students notice the abbreviations on the containers. They will learn more about the abbreviations in later lessons.

5. Summarize the activity by discussing the various English and metric units for measuring liquid volume.

Objectives

- Measure and compare capacities by using a standard unit (for example, use a measuring cup to measure contents of a water bottle).

Type of liquid	English measure	Metric measure
Can of soup: serving size	$\frac{1}{2}$ cup	120 mL
Vanilla	1 fl oz	29 mL
Milk	1 gal	3.78 L

LEARN Tools and English Units

Students will explore tools and English units for measuring liquid volume.

Gather the index cards labeled with English units; teaspoon, tablespoon, and 1-cup liquid measuring cup; pint, quart, and gallon containers. Arrange the measuring tools in order—teaspoon, tablespoon, cup, pint, quart, and gallon. Have students turn to the prepared chart in their Math Notebook.

1. Tell students they will be working with tools and measuring units in the English system. Explain that they will be filling a tool with water and pouring the water into the next measuring tool until that tool is filled.

2. Have students fill the first tool—the teaspoon—with water and pour the water into the tablespoon. Guide students to continue filling the teaspoon with water and pouring it into the tablespoon until the tablespoon is filled. Students should count as they work.

3. Have students record the number of teaspoons in the chart in their notebook.

4. As students work, have them explain their actions. For example, "I am using a measuring spoon that measures in teaspoons to fill this tablespoon."

5. Have students take the water-filled tablespoon and pour the water into the next measuring tool—the 1-cup liquid measuring cup. Students should then continue filling the tablespoon with water and pouring the water into the cup until the cup is filled.

6. Have students record the number of tablespoons in a cup and explain their actions. For example, "I am now using a measuring spoon that measures in tablespoons to fill this cup."

7. Continue with the next container, repeating Steps 2–4 until students have filled the last measuring tool—the gallon container. (Students may want to use a funnel.)

8. Once the gallon container is full, place the card saying *English measures* on the table. Have students line up the measuring tools in order from least to greatest capacity. Have students name each tool and the unit it measures. For the pint, quart, and gallon containers, the name of the tool can be *container*, or whatever the container actually is, such as a juice bottle.

9. Have students put the index card for each measuring unit next to the appropriate container.

Objectives

- Identify the appropriate tools for measuring liquid volume.
- Identify the appropriate metric and English units for measuring liquid volume.

Tips

Have students work on a surface near a sink or provide them with a large container filled with water.

_3_ teaspoons = 1 tablespoon
_16_ tablespoons = 1 cup
_2_ cups = 1 pint
_2_ pints = 1 quart
_4_ quarts = 1 gallon

LEARN Tools and Metric Units

Students will explore tools and metric units for measuring liquid volume.

Gather the base-10 cubes; index cards labeled with metric units; 250-milliliter liquid measuring cup; and half-pint, 1-liter, and 2-liter containers. Arrange the measuring tools in order—250-milliliter liquid measuring cup, half-liter container, 1-liter container, and 2-liter container.

1. Display the base-10 ones cube.

   Say: If the ones cube were hollow, it would hold exactly 1 mL of liquid. So a milliliter is not very much liquid.

2. Display the base-10 thousands cube.

   Ask: How many ones cubes are in this thousands cube? 1,000

Objectives

- Identify the appropriate tools for measuring liquid volume.
- Identify the appropriate metric and English units for measuring liquid volume.

3. Explain that if the thousands cube were hollow, it would hold 1,000 mL, which is the same as a liter.

4. Tell students that they will be working with tools and measuring units in the metric system. Explain that they will be filling a tool with water and pouring the water into the next measuring tool until that tool is filled.

5. In the Math Notebook, write the following for students to complete as they fill the containers:

    ___ mL = 1 half-liter

    ___ mL = 1 liter

    ___ mL = 2 liters

6. Have students fill the first tool—the 250-milliliter measuring cup—with water and pour the water into the half-liter container. Guide students to continue filling the cup with water and pouring it into the container until the water level reaches the mark. They should count as they work. (Students may want to use a funnel.)

7. Have students explain their actions. For example, "I am using a measuring cup that measures 250 milliliters to fill this half-liter container."

8. Guide students to calculate the number of milliliters in the half-liter container. 500 mL
   Have students record their findings in their notebook. Explain that *mL* is the abbreviation for *milliliter*.

9. Have students use the half-liter container to fill the next container—the 1-liter container.

10. Have students explain their actions and determine the number of milliliters needed to fill the 1-liter container. 1,000 mL

11. Have students compare the 1-liter capacity to the base-10 thousands cube. Remind them that if the thousands cube could be filled with water, it would hold 1,000 mL, which is the same as 1 liter.

12. Have students continue the process using the 1-liter container to fill the 2-liter container. Have students explain their actions and complete the chart indicating the number of milliliters equal to 2 liters. 2,000 mL

13. Once the 2-liter container is full, place the card saying *metric measures* on the table. Have students line up the measuring tools (including the base-10 ones cube and thousands cube) in order from least capacity to greatest. Have students name each tool and the unit it measures. The thousands cube and liter container should be together, since they have the same capacity. For the half-liter, 1-liter, and 2-liter containers, the name of the tool can be *container* or whatever the container actually is, such as a water bottle.

14. Have students put the index card for each measuring unit next to the appropriate container.

OFFLINE

10min

TRY IT Tools and Units to Measure Capacity

Students will practice identifying the appropriate tool or unit for measuring liquid volume. Have students turn to the Tools and Units to Measure Capacity activity page in their Activity Book and read the directions with them.

Students should copy the problems from the Activity Book into their Math Notebook as necessary and solve them there.

Objectives

- Identify the appropriate tools for measuring liquid volume.

- Identify the appropriate metric and English units for measuring liquid volume.

Capacity
Tools and Units to Measure Capacity

Circle the tools or units that match the description.

1. Tools that measure capacity, or liquid volume:

   thermometer   (tablespoon)   scale

   (measuring cup)   (teaspoon)   ruler

2. English units of measure and metric units of measure:

   (teaspoons   quarts   cups)   **English units**

   (tablespoons   gallons   pints)

   (milliliters   liters)   **metric units**

Choose the answer.

3. Sheela measured the amount of juice a pitcher would hold. Which unit of measure did she use?
   - A. feet
   - (B.) cups
   - C. miles
   - D. pounds

4. Manny wanted to measure the capacity of the gasoline tank in his car. Which unit would be the most appropriate for him to use?
   - (A.) liter
   - B. kilogram
   - C. kilometer
   - D. centimeter

5. Lena washed a load of clothes. How much water did the washing machine likely hold when it was full?
   - A. 30 fluid ounces
   - B. 30 cups
   - C. 30 pints
   - (D.) 30 gallons

6. How much liquid is the spoon most likely to hold?
   - A. 15 liters
   - B. 15 meters
   - C. 15 centimeters
   - (D.) 15 milliliters

7. The capacity of which container is most likely measured in gallons?

   A. teapot

   B. bowl

   C. mug

   (D.) water cooler

8. Which has a capacity of about 1 quart?

   A. mug

   (B.) pitcher

   C. toy bathtub

   D. spoon

9. Marilyn's plant needs 8 fluid ounces of water twice a week. Which is the **best** tool to use to measure the amount of water the plant needs for one week?
   - A. ruler
   - B. balance
   - C. thermometer
   - (D.) measuring cup

10. Clarissa is baking a cake. She needs to measure some milk for the batter. Which measurement tool should Clarissa use?

    (A.) measuring cup

    B. scale

    C. tape measure

    D. thermometer

11. What should a measuring cup be used to measure?
    - A. temperature
    - (B.) liquid volume
    - C. weight
    - D. height

CHECKPOINT

ONLINE 10 min

Students will complete an online Checkpoint. If necessary, read the directions, problems, and answer choices to students and help them with keyboard or mouse operations.

Objectives

- Identify the appropriate tools for measuring liquid volume.
- Identify the appropriate metric and English units for measuring liquid volume.

Measure to the Nearest Liter

Lesson Overview

Skills Update	5 minutes	ONLINE
GET READY Milliliters and Liters	5 minutes	ONLINE
LEARN Estimate and Measure in Liters	30 minutes	OFFLINE
TRY IT Identify Volume	10 minutes	OFFLINE
CHECKPOINT	10 minutes	ONLINE

▶ Lesson Objectives

Estimate and measure liquid volume to the nearest liter.

▶ Prerequisite Skills

Identify the appropriate metric and English units for measuring liquid volume.

▶ Content Background

Students will learn to estimate the capacity of various containers in liters. Students will then use a liter container to find the actual capacity of each container.

While many quantities need to be measured precisely, some can simply be estimated. Estimation is important for students, since it focuses them on which unit is being used in the measurement and helps them develop a greater feel for the size of that unit. Most students view estimating as a fun guessing game. They will learn that the more they estimate and check their estimates, the better they will become in estimating measures. Measuring precisely is a key skill as well, since not doing so can lead to undesirable results, such as a fallen cake, a salty stew, or a watery milk shake.

When finding actual measures, students need to take special care in both using and reading the measuring instrument accurately. They should understand that all measures that the average person makes are only close approximations, both because of the lack of precision of the tools used in daily life and because of human error.

Students will have experiences throughout their lives measuring or judging amounts of liquid volume, or capacity. Such experiences might include measuring in cooking, making lemonade, drinking an adequate amount of water in a day, equally sharing a bottle of water with a friend, and deciding how much juice to buy for a large group. As adults, they might mix paints, make homemade cleaning solutions with vinegar and baking soda, and possibly mix chemicals.

▶ Common Errors and Misconceptions

Students might have difficulty knowing how to read the numbers on a measurement scale. They may count the number of tick marks starting with 0 (on a ruler, or scale on the side of a volume measure, for example) rather than the units between the marks. Students may treat the 1 tick mark as the starting point instead of the 0 or place the edge of an object at the 1-inch tick mark rather than the 0 tick mark. Students might have the same problems when reading a volume measure (on a measuring jug, for example).

Materials to Gather

SUPPLIED

Identify Volume activity page

ALSO NEEDED

household objects – various containers that hold more than 1 liter, 250-milliliter liquid measuring cup

container, transparent beverage – 1 liter

index cards – 4

markers, permanent – 2 colors

tape, masking

▶ Advance Preparation

On two index cards, write the following in one color: **milliliter** and **liter**. On two index cards, write the following abbreviations in another color: **mL** and **L**. On the back of all four cards, write **Metric Capacity Units**.

Gather containers such as pitchers, buckets and plastic trash containers of varying sizes, and other containers that can hold water.

GET READY Milliliters and Liters

ONLINE 5 min

Students will be shown an object that holds liquid and will identify whether the liquid volume would be measured in milliliters or liters. Explain to students that when they measure an amount of liquid, they are measuring *liquid volume*. When they find how much liquid a container holds, they measure the liquid *capacity* of the container. They should say, "The volume of liquid is 1 liter" or "The capacity of the container is 1 liter."

Have students write the words *volume* and *capacity* in their Math Notebook.

Objectives

- Identify the appropriate metric and English units for measuring liquid volume.

LEARN Estimate and Measure in Liters

OFFLINE 30 min

Students will estimate the capacity of containers in liters. They will then use a 1-liter container to find the actual measurement of each container.

Gather the labeled index cards, markers, measuring cup, tape, and containers.

1. Lay out the index cards with the Metric Capacity Units side showing.

2. Turn over the card that says *milliliter* first, followed by the card that says *liter*. Put these cards side by side. Turn over the cards with the abbreviations and give them to students. Have students place each abbreviation card under the word they think the abbreviation matches. They should learn how to say and recognize each word and how to recognize and write each abbreviation.

3. Have students fill the measuring cup four times. Have them pour the water (a total of 1,000 mL) into a 1-liter container, such as a large water or soda bottle. Have them mark the level of the liquid on the container with a permanent marker or with the bottom edge of a piece of masking tape. Tell students their bottle now holds 1 liter. Explain that they'll be using this bottle to measure the number of liters other containers can hold.

4. Tell students they will be estimating how many liters will fill a variety of containers before actually measuring to see how close their estimates were. Let them know that the more they practice estimating, the easier it will be.

5. Have students make a three-column chart in their Math Notebook. The columns should be labeled **Container**, **My estimate**, and **Actual liters**.

Objectives

- Estimate and measure liquid volume to the nearest liter.

Tips

When students are filling the 1-liter container, make sure that the liquid is level with the line they drew or masking tape they placed.

6. Have students move from one container to the next (in any order), first recording on the chart the type of container and then making an estimate of how many liters it will hold. When measuring the capacity of cooking pots or bowls, students should pick a height near the top of the pot or bowl, mark that spot with tape, and then estimate how many liters it would take to fill it to that level. Since people usually don't fill pots to the brim when cooking, students don't need to measure to the brim. They should measure to the nearest liter.

7. Have students fill their bottle to the liter mark, and then pour the water into one of the containers. (Students may want to use the funnel.) They should count the liters as they fill the container with their liter bottle. Ask students to come up with a good way to keep track of the number of liters (such as tally marks or laying down an index card or tile for each liter they pour). They should record the actual measurement on their chart to the nearest liter. Have them repeat this process until they've measured the capacity of all the containers.

8. Have students review their estimates and measurements to see how close they were.

9. Tell students that the measures most people make are only very close approximations, both because of the lack of precision of the tools used in daily life and because of human error.

10. If there is extra time, find a container that holds more than 1 liter and is large enough to hold a base-10 thousands cube. Place that container inside an even-larger container. Remind students that a milliliter of water is the amount of water that would fit in a base-10 ones cube, and that if they could fill a thousands cube, it would be 1,000 milliliters or 1 liter. Fill the smaller container to the brim with water. Use toothpicks or other small objects to submerge the thousands cube in the water. See if the displaced water that overflows into the larger, empty container measures 1 liter. (Do not use your fingers to submerge the cube; that would displace too much water.)

OFFLINE 10 min

TRY IT Identify Volume

Objectives

- Estimate and measure liquid volume to the nearest liter.

Students will practice identifying the liquid volume of various objects. Have students turn to the Identify Volume activity page in their Activity Book and read the directions with them.

Students should copy the problems from the Activity Book into their Math Notebook as necessary and solve them there.

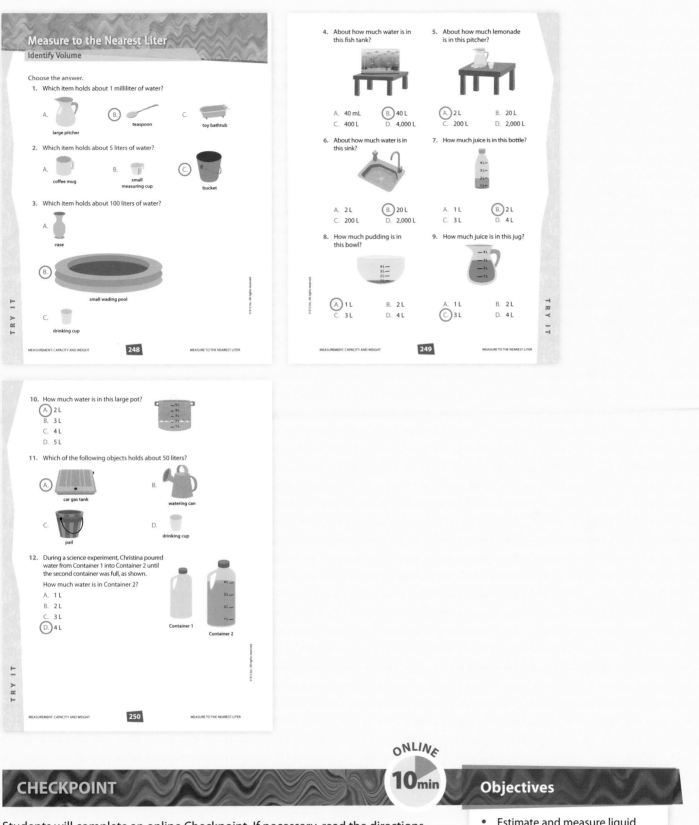

Measure to the Nearest Liter
Identify Volume

Choose the answer.

1. Which item holds about 1 milliliter of water?

   A. large pitcher B. teaspoon C. toy bathtub

2. Which item holds about 5 liters of water?

   A. coffee mug B. small measuring cup C. bucket

3. Which item holds about 100 liters of water?

   A. vase
   B. small wading pool
   C. drinking cup

4. About how much water is in this fish tank?

   A. 40 mL B. 40 L
   C. 400 L D. 4,000 L

5. About how much lemonade is in this pitcher?

   A. 2 L B. 20 L
   C. 200 L D. 2,000 L

6. About how much water is in this sink?

   A. 2 L B. 20 L
   C. 200 L D. 2,000 L

7. How much juice is in this bottle?

   A. 1 L B. 2 L
   C. 3 L D. 4 L

8. How much pudding is in this bowl?

   A. 1 L B. 2 L
   C. 3 L D. 4 L

9. How much juice is in this jug?

   A. 1 L B. 2 L
   C. 3 L D. 4 L

10. How much water is in this large pot?

    A. 2 L
    B. 3 L
    C. 4 L
    D. 5 L

11. Which of the following objects holds about 50 liters?

    A. car gas tank
    B. watering can
    C. pail
    D. drinking cup

12. During a science experiment, Christina poured water from Container 1 into Container 2 until the second container was full, as shown.

    How much water is in Container 2?
    A. 1 L
    B. 2 L
    C. 3 L
    D. 4 L

    Container 1   Container 2

ONLINE
10 min

CHECKPOINT

Students will complete an online Checkpoint. If necessary, read the directions, problems, and answer choices to students and help them with keyboard or mouse operations.

Objectives

- Estimate and measure liquid volume to the nearest liter.

English Units of Capacity

Lesson Overview

Skills Update	5 minutes	**ONLINE**
GET READY Identify English Capacity Units	5 minutes	**ONLINE**
LEARN Abbreviation Match	5 minutes	**ONLINE**
LEARN Estimate and Measure Capacity	25 minutes	**OFFLINE**
TRY IT Estimate Capacity in English Units	10 minutes	**OFFLINE**
CHECKPOINT	10 minutes	**ONLINE**

▶ Lesson Objectives

Estimate and measure liquid volume to the nearest cup.

▶ Prerequisite Skills

Identify the appropriate metric and English units for measuring liquid volume.

▶ Content Background

Students will learn to estimate and measure capacity in English units. They will fill various containers with cups of water and explore equivalent measurements of a pint, a quart, and a gallon.

While many quantities need to be measured precisely, some can simply be estimated. Estimation is important for students, since it focuses them on which unit is being used in the measurement and helps them develop a greater feel for the size of a unit. Most students view estimating as a fun guessing game. They will learn that the more they estimate and check their estimates, the better they will become at estimating measures. Measuring precisely is also a key skill, since not doing so can lead to undesirable results, such as a fallen cake, a salty stew, or a watery milkshake.

When finding actual measures, students need to take special care in both using and reading the measuring instrument accurately. They should understand that all measures that the average person makes are only close approximations, both because of the lack of precision of the tools used in daily life and because of human error.

Students will have experiences throughout their lives measuring or judging amounts of liquid volume, or capacity. Such experiences might include measuring in cooking, making lemonade, drinking an adequate amount of water in a day, equally sharing a bottle of water with a friend, and deciding how much juice to buy for a large group. As adults, they might mix paints, make homemade cleaning solutions with vinegar and baking soda, and possibly mix chemicals.

▶ Advance Preparation

Gather the containers. Suggestions include pitchers, buckets and plastic trash containers of varying sizes, and other containers that can hold water.

Materials to Gather

SUPPLIED

Estimate Capacity in English Units activity page

ALSO NEEDED

household objects – 8-ounce liquid measuring cup

transparent beverage containers – pint, quart, gallon

various containers that hold more than 1 cup

GET READY Identify English Capacity Units

Students will identify English units of measure for capacity. Remind them that the *capacity* of a container is the amount it holds, and that when they're measuring the amount of liquid in a container, they're measuring the *liquid volume*. Seven units of capacity are used in this activity: teaspoon, tablespoon, fluid ounce, cup, pint, quart, and gallon. If students mix up *ounce* with *fluid ounce*, remind them that ounces are used when measuring weight, but that fluid ounces are used to measure an amount or volume of liquid.

Objectives

- Identify the appropriate metric and English units for measuring liquid volume.

LEARN Abbreviation Match

Students will practice reading English units of capacity. Then they will match abbreviations to English capacity units. Encourage students to remember the abbreviations. Remind them that there are no periods in these abbreviations.

Students will see the following English units to measure capacity, along with their abbreviations:

- teaspoon (t)
- tablespoon (T)
- fluid ounce (fl oz)
- cup (c)
- pint (pt)
- quart (qt)
- gallon (gal)

Objectives

- Estimate and measure liquid volume to the nearest cup.

LEARN Estimate and Measure Capacity

Students will estimate and measure the capacity of various containers in English units. Gather the measuring cup; pint, quart, and gallon containers; and other containers of various sizes.

1. Show students how to fill the measuring cup to the 1-cup mark.
2. Explain to students that 1 cup is also 8 fluid ounces. Remind them that when measuring for cooking, people often measure in cups, but that food packaging often lists the liquid volume in fluid ounces. Students should be familiar with both units of measure.
3. Tell students that they'll estimate how many cups will fill different containers, and then they'll measure to see how many cups each container holds.

   Say: The more you practice estimating and measuring, the easier it will be.
4. Have students make a three-column chart in their Math Notebook. The columns should be labeled **Container**, **My estimate**, and **Actual cups**.
5. Have students choose one of the smaller containers. Guide them to write a name for the container or draw a picture of it in the first column.

   Ask: How many cups do you think will fill this container?

Objectives

- Estimate and measure liquid volume to the nearest cup.

Tips

Have students work near a sink, in a bathtub, or outdoors to control any spills. Allow them to use a funnel for the smaller containers, if you wish.

6. Have students record their estimate in the second column.

7. Have students measure how many cups the container actually holds by pouring 1 cup of water at a time into the container. (Students may want to use the funnel.) Check that they are filling the measuring cup to the 1-cup mark each time. Help them keep track of the number of cups by using tally marks or counters. Guide students to record the closest cup measure.

8. Have students compare the actual capacity to their estimate.

9. Have students repeat Steps 5–7 with each of the other containers. They may know from past experience how many cups a pint, quart, and gallon hold. When they work with each container, encourage them to remember those equivalencies.

10. Summarize by telling students that the measures most people make are only close approximations both because of the lack of precision of the tools used in daily life and because of human error.

TRY IT Estimate Capacity in English Units

OFFLINE 10 min

Students will practice estimating capacity in English units. Have students turn to the Estimate Capacity in English Units activity page in their Activity Book and read the directions with them.

Students should copy the problems from the Activity Book into their Math Notebook as necessary and solve them there.

Objectives

- Estimate and measure liquid volume to the nearest cup.

Tips

Provide cup and gallon containers for reference, if you wish.

English Units of Capacity
Estimate Capacity in English Units

Match the capacity to the container.

Container	Capacity
1.	A. less than 1 cup
2.	B. about 1 cup
3.	C. more than 1 cup

1. C; 2. A; 3. B

Container	Capacity
4.	A. about 1 gallon
5.	B. less than 1 gallon
6.	C. more than 1 gallon

4. C; 5. A; 6. B

MEASUREMENT: CAPACITY AND WEIGHT   **251**   ENGLISH UNITS OF CAPACITY

TRY IT

Choose the answer.

7. A juice box contains about how much liquid?
   A. 1 fl oz
   B. 1 gal
   C. 1 qt
   D. 1 c

8. Which object would hold about 4 cups of liquid when completely filled?
   A. baby bottle
   B. large fish tank
   C. kitchen sink
   D. pitcher

9. Which object would hold about 3 cups of liquid when completely filled?
   A. bottle of ketchup
   B. kitchen sink
   C. cooler
   D. gas tank

10. How much milk is left in this container?
    A. 4 c
    B. 8 c
    C. 12 c
    D. 16 c

11. How much pudding is in this bowl?
    A. 1 c
    B. 3 c
    C. 2 c
    D. 4 c

TRY IT

MEASUREMENT: CAPACITY AND WEIGHT   **252**   ENGLISH UNITS OF CAPACITY

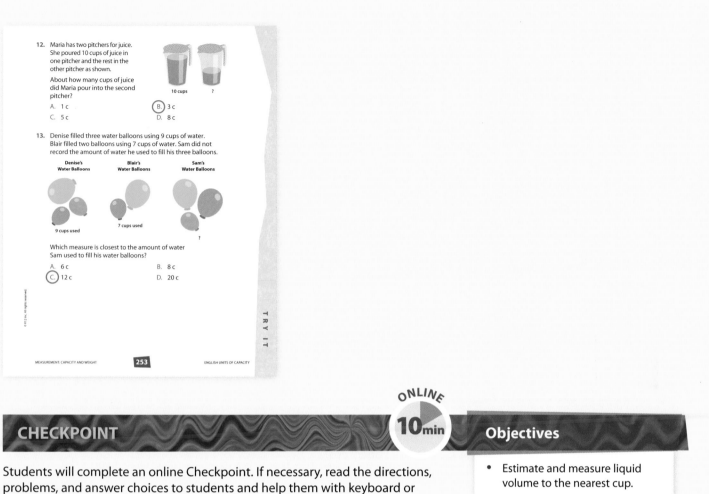

12. Maria has two pitchers for juice. She poured 10 cups of juice in one pitcher and the rest in the other pitcher as shown.

About how many cups of juice did Maria pour into the second pitcher?

10 cups   ?

A. 1 c
B. 3 c
C. 5 c
D. 8 c

13. Denise filled three water balloons using 9 cups of water. Blair filled two balloons using 7 cups of water. Sam did not record the amount of water he used to fill his three balloons.

Denise's Water Balloons

Blair's Water Balloons

Sam's Water Balloons

9 cups used

7 cups used

?

Which measure is closest to the amount of water Sam used to fill his water balloons?

A. 6 c
B. 8 c
C. 12 c
D. 20 c

T R Y   I T

ONLINE
10min

CHECKPOINT

Objectives

Students will complete an online Checkpoint. If necessary, read the directions, problems, and answer choices to students and help them with keyboard or mouse operations.

- Estimate and measure liquid volume to the nearest cup.

Measure in English and Metric Units

Lesson Overview

GET READY Heavier and Lighter	10 minutes	OFFLINE
LEARN Units to Measure Weight and Mass	20 minutes	OFFLINE
LEARN Tools to Measure Weight and Mass	10 minutes	ONLINE
TRY IT Measure Weight and Mass	10 minutes	ONLINE
CHECKPOINT	10 minutes	ONLINE

▶ Lesson Objectives

- Identify the appropriate tools for measuring the weight of an object.
- Identify the appropriate metric and English units for measuring the weight of an object.

▶ Prerequisite Skills

- Compare objects by weight (heavier and lighter).
- Use a nonstandard unit to describe the weight of an object and compare the weights of two or more objects (for example, the pencil is as heavy as 12 paper clips, and the marker is as heavy as 19 paper clips).

▶ Content Background

Students will learn the units to measure weight and mass in the English and metric systems. They will gain an understanding of ounces and pounds, and of grams and kilograms. They will also learn the different tools that can be used to measure weight and mass.

MEASUREMENT OF WEIGHT

Students will have experiences throughout their lives measuring or judging how much objects weigh. Some examples might include weighing themselves or a pet, measuring in cooking, and knowing how long to bake something if directions are given by weight. As adults, they might need to weigh items to be mailed for proper postage, decide how much produce to buy when priced by the pound, estimate how much potato salad to buy when serving a meal to a large group of people, and weigh luggage before flying.

Students will use both the metric and English systems of measuring weight. Within the metric system, they will work with grams (g) and kilograms (kg) as the units of measure. Within the English system (also known as the customary system), they will work with ounces (oz) and pounds (lb) as the units of measure. They will see a variety of types of scales used to weigh objects.

THE DIFFERENCES BETWEEN WEIGHT AND MASS

Weight is the measurement of the pull of gravity on an object, while *mass* is a measurement of the amount of matter something contains. The mass of an object doesn't change when an object's location changes. Weight, on the other hand, does change with location. For example, a baseball on the earth has one

Materials to Gather

SUPPLIED

base-10 ones cubes – 28

ALSO NEEDED

household objects – 2 objects that are about the same size but are different weights, 10 nickels, 9 quarters, 1 $1 bill, 1 banana, 1 orange, 4 sticks of butter (1 lb), 1 can of soup, 1 paper clip, 3 plastic bags (small, clear, resealable)

mass. On the moon, it has the same mass. On the earth, it has one weight; on the moon, it weighs less.

The difference between weight and mass will be introduced later in students' math education. For now, be sure students are aware that the units to measure weight include pounds and ounces, while the units to measure mass include grams and kilograms.

▶ Advance Preparation

Gather the various household items. Place the base-10 ones cubes in a plastic bag, the quarters in a second plastic bag, and the nickels in a third plastic bag.

GET READY Heavier and Lighter

OFFLINE **10** min

Students will explore weight by comparing two objects they hold in their hands. Gather the two objects that are similar in size but different in weight.

Show students the two objects. Ask them which one they think is heavier. Then have them hold the two objects, one in each hand. Have them compare the weights, saying which object is heavier and which is lighter.

Turn the activity into a game in which you look at nearby objects, pick up two objects at a time, and have students guess which one will feel heavier. Then give students the objects so they can judge the weights. Trade places with students, having them pick objects. Then make them guess and compare the objects. Look for objects in every room, such as a knickknack, shoe, couch pillow, bowl, small cooking pot, crayon, and fork. Try to select pairs of objects close in weight but different enough so that anyone holding the objects can tell which one is heavier.

Objectives

- Compare objects by weight (heavier and lighter).
- Use a nonstandard unit to describe the weight of an object and compare the weights of two or more objects (for example, the pencil is as heavy as 12 paper clips, and the marker is as heavy as 19 paper clips).

LEARN Units to Measure Weight and Mass

OFFLINE **20** min

Students will learn the metric and English units used to measure mass and weight. They will also be introduced to the weights of common objects in ounces and pounds, and the mass of objects in grams and kilograms, giving them a general frame of reference for those units of measure.

Gather the various household objects.

Explain to students that there are two systems of measurement—the metric system and the English system (sometimes called the customary system). There are different units in each system. Tell students they will explore two units of weight in the English system, the ounce and the pound.

ENGLISH UNITS

1. Show students the bag of base-10 ones cubes. Explain that all these cubes together weigh about 1 ounce.

2. Remove 5 quarters from the bag and give them to students. Explain to students that the 5 quarters also weigh about 1 ounce. Students may compare the ones cubes and the quarters to see that they have about the same weight.

Objectives

- Identify the appropriate tools for measuring the weight of an object.
- Identify the appropriate metric and English units for measuring the weight of an object.

Tips

Make a two-column chart. Label the columns English units and metric units. Write ounce and pound under the column head for the English units. Write gram and kilogram under the column head for the metric units.

3. Explain to students that it is helpful to use various objects in their environment as found measures, or known amounts, when weighing other objects. Now that they know what an ounce feels like, they can look for other objects that can be weighed in ounces. Have students identify one more object that weighs about 1 ounce.

4. Have students work with the following objects to identify found measures. They should have the 5 quarters handy.

   • Give students a stick of butter to hold. Ask them if they think the stick of butter weighs more or less than 1 ounce. more
     Tell students that the stick of butter (if packaged 4 to a pound) weighs 4 ounces.

   • Give students an average-sized orange and ask them to compare its weight to the quarters and the butter. The orange weighs more than the quarters and the butter. Tell students that the orange weighs about 12 ounces.

   • Give students a can of soup and explain that it weighs more than the other objects they've looked at so far. Tell them that the can weighs about 13 ounces. Explain that 16 ounces equals 1 pound and that the can of soup is close to 1 pound.

5. Show students 1 pound of butter. Tell them it weighs 16 ounces, or 1 pound. Allow them to hold the butter and compare its weight to the lighter objects (orange, can of soup).

6. Allow students to identify a variety of objects in their environment that weigh about 1 pound.

METRIC UNITS

7. Tell students that now they will explore two units in the metric system, the gram and the kilogram. Explain that in the metric system, when measuring in grams and kilograms, they say they're measuring the *mass* of an object.

8. Give students a single base-10 ones cube, a small paper clip, and a $1 bill. Tell them that the mass of each object is about 1 gram. Allow them to pick up each object and compare the masses. Students should notice that the masses are similar. Have them identify other objects that have a mass of about 1 gram.

9. Have students work with the following objects to identify found measures:

   • Give students a nickel. Tell them that the mass of a nickel is about 5 grams. Discuss with students that the mass of 1 nickel is the same as the mass of 5 base-10 ones cubes or 5 small paper clips.

   • Give students the bag of 9 quarters. Explain that the mass of these quarters is about 50 grams. For comparison, tell them that this is 10 times more than the mass of one nickel. Students would need 10 nickels to equal 50 grams.

   • Give students a banana. Explain that the mass of a banana is about 170 grams.

   • Give students the can of soup. Discuss that in the metric system, the mass of the can is about 350 grams.

10. Tell students that 1,000 grams equals 1 kilogram. Ask them to find objects labeled in grams that add up to 1,000 grams. Place these objects together to help students understand the measure of 1 kilogram.

11. Ask students to identify other objects in their environment that have a mass of about 1 kilogram.

LEARN Tools to Measure Weight and Mass

Objectives

- Identify the appropriate tools for measuring the weight of an object.
- Identify the appropriate metric and English units for measuring the weight of an object.

Students will learn about various tools to measure weight and mass. They will see a variety of scales and balances, and they'll learn which units correspond to the different tools.

After students have studied the scales, take them to the local grocery or hardware store. Allow them to identify the different scales used in the stores. Have them weigh fruits and vegetables at the grocery store and compare the weight of different-sized boxes of nails at the hardware store. Some hardware stores sell nails by the pound and have a scale that students can see. Have students note whether the scales weigh in English or metric units or both.

TRY IT Measure Weight and Mass

Objectives

- Identify the appropriate tools for measuring the weight of an object.
- Identify the appropriate metric and English units for measuring the weight of an object.

Students will complete an online Try It. If necessary, read the directions, problems, and answer choices to students and help them with keyboard or mouse operations.

CHECKPOINT

Objectives

- Identify the appropriate tools for measuring the weight of an object.
- Identify the appropriate metric and English units for measuring the weight of an object.

Students will complete an online Checkpoint. If necessary, read the directions, problems, and answer choices to students and help them with keyboard or mouse operations.

Measure in Grams

▶ Lesson Objectives

Estimate and measure the weight of a given object to the nearest gram.

▶ Prerequisite Skills

Identify the appropriate metric and English units for measuring the weight of an object.

▶ Content Background

Students will learn to measure and estimate the mass of an object to the nearest gram. In this lesson, they will use the metric system of measuring weight. Within the metric system, they will work with grams (g) and kilograms (kg) as the units of measure.

Students will have experiences throughout their lives measuring or judging how much objects weigh. Some examples include weighing themselves or a pet, measuring in cooking, and knowing how long to bake something by its weight. As adults, they might need to weigh items to be mailed for proper postage, decide how much produce to buy when priced by the pound, estimate how much potato salad to buy when serving a meal to a large group of people, and weigh luggage before flying.

Weight is the measurement of the pull of gravity on an object, while *mass* is a measurement of the amount of matter something contains. The mass of an object doesn't change when an object's location changes. Weight, on the other hand, does change with location. For example, a baseball on the earth has one mass. On the moon, it has the same mass. On the earth, it has one weight; on the moon, it weighs less.

The difference between weight and mass will be introduced later in students' math education. For now, be sure students are aware that the units to measure weight include pounds and ounces, while the units to measure mass include grams and kilograms.

Materials to Gather

SUPPLIED

base-10 ones cubes – 50

Metric Units of Mass activity page

ALSO NEEDED

balance supplies – 2 paper clips, 2 rubber bands, pointed-end safety scissors, wooden skewer or other thin stick about 9 inches long, masking tape, dental floss or sturdy lightweight string, 2 small identical containers (transparent or translucent, such as clear plastic cups), 2 medium identical containers (such as disposable plastic containers for leftovers)

household objects – 5 nickels, 9 quarters, 1 $1 bill, 4 sticks of butter (1 lb), 1 can of soup (350 g), 1 cup of yogurt, deck of cards, cell phone, roll of coins

index cards – 10 (4 labeled)

markers, permanent – 2 colors

While many quantities need to be measured precisely, some can simply be estimated. Estimation is important for students, since it focuses them on which unit is being used in the measurement and helps them develop a greater feel for the size of that unit. Most students view estimating as a fun guessing game. They will learn that the more they estimate and check their estimates, the better they will become at estimating measures. Measuring precisely is also a key skill, since not doing so can lead to undesirable results, such as a fallen cake, a salty stew, or a watery milkshake.

When finding actual measures, students need to take special care in both using and reading the measuring instrument accurately.

▶ Advance Preparation

- For the Learn: Gram and Kilogram activity, on two index cards, write the following in one color: **gram** and **kilogram**. On two index cards, write the following abbreviations in another color: **g** and **kg**. On the back of all four cards, write **Metric Units of Mass**.

- For the Learn: Use a Balance activity and the Learn: Compare Masses activity, make a hanging balance. Test the balance to make sure it works.

PREPARE THE CUPS

An asterisk * marks steps that students might help with.

*1. Place a thick rubber band around the rim of each of 2 identical, lightweight, transparent or translucent cups.

*2. Cut 2 equal lengths of string about 18 inches long.

*3. For each cup, tie each end of a string to the rubber band, with the ends of the string on opposite sides of the cup rim.

*4. Attach a paper clip to the middle of each string as a loop from which the cup will hang.

PREPARE THE BALANCE BEAM

5. Gather a wooden chopstick, bamboo skewer, or other thin stick. If the stick has pointed ends, remove the sharp points.

6. Make grooves on the stick where strings will be secured. Mark the center of the stick, and make a groove with the blade of a pair of scissors. Measure one-half inch from each end of the stick, and make a groove in each place.

7. Cut a string about 12 inches long. Tie a loop at one end. Tie the other end to the middle of the stick at the groove. The groove should be deep enough to hold the string in place, but you may use tape to secure the string if necessary.

8. Hang both cups by their paper clips over the grooves at each end of the beam. You may tape the paper clips to the beam.

HANG AND TEST

9. Hang the balance so the cups are just a few inches above a flat surface. The balance is sensitive. Only a few grams difference in the cups can tip it and tangle the strings. A surface below the balance helps prevent that problem.

You may hang the balance from a ruler on a table with heavy objects on one end of the ruler. The other end of the ruler would stick out from the edge of the table. A chair under the balance can provide a flat surface so that the balance won't tilt too much when objects are placed in the cups.

10. If the balance beam (the stick) is horizontal, then the cups are balanced. If the balance beam isn't horizontal, check that the paper clips and center string haven't moved. If they are in place, then add some tape to the bottom of the lighter cup until the stick is horizontal.

11. Put a base-10 ones cube (a centimeter cube) in each cup and look at the balance beam to make sure it's balanced. Adjust as necessary.

12. Decide where you will hang the balance when you do the lesson: a table, chair, open cupboard doorknob above a counter, or even a low tree branch with a chair or table under it. If no surface underneath is available, be sure a helper holds the cups while you place objects in them.

▶ Safety

Make sure students handle the scissors carefully and be sure to store them in a safe place.

Handle the materials carefully when constructing the balance and be sure to store them in a safe place.

GET READY How Much Does It Weigh?

ONLINE **5 min**

Students will identify the most appropriate weight for a given object or group of objects. The activity reinforces students' grasp of various units of measure.

Objectives

- Identify the appropriate metric and English units for measuring the weight of an object.

LEARN Gram and Kilogram

OFFLINE **5 min**

Students will learn the abbreviations for the metric units of mass—gram and kilogram. Gather the labeled index cards, one base-10 ones cube, and $1 bill.

1. Tell students that they will measure the mass of objects using metric units.

2. Tell students that they will focus on two metric units for mass—grams and kilograms. Explain that a gram is a small unit of measure. A $1 bill and a base-10 ones cube each have a mass of about 1 gram. Let students hold a base-10 ones cube and a $1 bill so that they get a sense of what 1 gram feels like. Also explain that a kilogram is 1,000 grams. Tell students that 1,000 ones cubes, 1,000 $1 bills, and 9 sticks of butter each have a mass of about 1 kilogram.

3. Lay out the index cards with the Metric Units of Mass side showing. Turn them over. Put the spelled-out units next to each other and give students the abbreviation cards. Have students place each abbreviation card under the word they think the abbreviation matches.

4. Discuss the words and abbreviations. By the end of the activity, students should be able to say and recognize all the words and abbreviations.

Objectives

- Estimate and measure the weight of an object to the nearest gram.

Tips

Have students locate the weight on labels of packaged food in their kitchen. Have them note that the labels show the weight in both metric and English units.

LEARN Use a Balance

Objectives

- Estimate and measure the weight of an object to the nearest gram.

Students will measure objects to the nearest gram.

Gather the hanging balance, base-10 cubes, blank index cards, nickels, quarters, $1 bill, and other small objects to weigh.

Tips Have students choose a card. If the card shows an abbreviation, have them say the unit it represents. If the card shows a word, have them write the abbreviation.

1. Set up the hanging balance. Explain to students that they will be using a homemade balance, and explain how it works.

2. Set out the objects to weigh and an index card for each.

3. Explain that the base-10 ones cube has a mass of about 1 gram and that students can use ones cubes to compare masses.

4. Have students place a ones cube in each cup to test the balance. Then have them balance a ones cube with a $1 bill.

5. Have students find the mass of a nickel in grams. close to 5 g

    Ask: if a nickel is 5 grams, does that mean a penny is 1 gram? No, but it sounds logical. You can't mix up units of measure for mass and money.

6. Ask students to pick an object and use the ones cubes to find its mass. They may also use nickels as 5-gram weights to counterbalance their objects. Have them write the object's name on the card and put the mass in grams in the upper right corner using the abbreviation *g* for grams. Repeat with one other object.

7. Have students look over all the objects and try to arrange them in order from the one they think has the least mass to the one with the greatest. Have them include objects they've already compared.

8. As students guess and weigh each object, have them write its name in the center of the card and the mass in the upper right corner.

9. As students get more information about the mass of different objects, encourage them to rearrange the objects they ordered from least to greatest.

10. As students get comfortable, have them estimate the mass of an object before they compare it and put their guess in the lower left corner of the card.

11. If students don't have enough cubes as counterweights, encourage them to use heavier objects whose mass they know. For instance, they can use 9 quarters to represent 50 grams.

12. When students have found the mass of all the objects, have them pick five of the most memorable objects to record in their Math Notebook. Have them record each object's name, the estimate, and the actual mass.

OFFLINE **10** min

- Estimate and measure the weight of an object to the nearest gram.

Students will use a balance to weigh heavier objects to the nearest gram and explore objects that have a mass of about a kilogram.

Gather the hanging balance; base-10 cubes; blank index cards; nickels; quarters; butter; and other objects to weigh, such as a cup of yogurt, can of soup, deck of cards, cell phone, and roll of coins.

1. Show students the hanging balance. Review how to use it. Explain that the thin balance beam is perfect for measuring items in grams but is too thin to compare full kilograms. Remind students that 1 kilogram is the same as 1,000 grams. Tell students that they can compare 500-gram masses with the balance if they use bigger containers. Have students replace the small containers with larger containers by carefully removing the rubber bands and placing them around larger containers. Check that the balance is level. If necessary, add extra strings to keep the container from tipping when objects are placed in it.

2. Set out the various larger household objects and an index card for each item. Explain that a stick of butter has a mass of about 113 grams, 4 sticks of butter have a mass of about 450 grams, and 9 quarters plus 4 sticks of butter have a mass of about 500 grams. Tell students that they can use these known masses and the base-10 ones cubes to compare masses and find the mass of a larger object in grams.

3. Have students place a can of soup in one container of the balance and sticks of butter and ones cubes in the opposite container until the balance is level.

   Ask: How many sticks of butter and ones cubes are in the container that is opposite the container holding the can of soup? about 3 sticks of butter and 10 ones cubes

   Ask: So what is the weight of a can of soup in grams? close to 350 g

4. Ask students to pick an object and use the sticks of butter, can of soup, quarters, or base-10 ones cubes to estimate its mass to the nearest gram. They may also use nickels as 5-gram weights to counterbalance the objects. Have students write the object's name on an index card and put the mass in grams in the upper right corner using the abbreviation *g* for grams.

5. Repeat Step 4 for another object.

6. Have students explore what 1 kilogram feels like by combining objects to find a total mass of around 1,000 grams. An example might include a can of soup, cup of yogurt, and 4 sticks of butter.

7. Have students look for objects that have the mass labeled, such as a bag of nuts, candle, or jar of baby food. Challenge them to find items of different masses and use the balance to compare the masses of known and unknown objects. Have them write sentences describing the masses by using the words *more* and *less* and then estimate each mass. A cell phone weighs less than a stick of butter. The estimated mass of the cell phone is about 90 grams.

   As students get more experience weighing objects and estimating masses, they will refine their intuitive sense of relative masses of objects.

TRY IT Metric Units of Mass

Objectives

- Estimate and measure the weight of an object to the nearest gram.

Students will practice judging the mass of objects in grams. Have students turn to the Metric Units of Mass activity page in their Activity Book and read the directions with them.

Students should copy the problems from the Activity Book into their Math Notebook as necessary and solve them there.

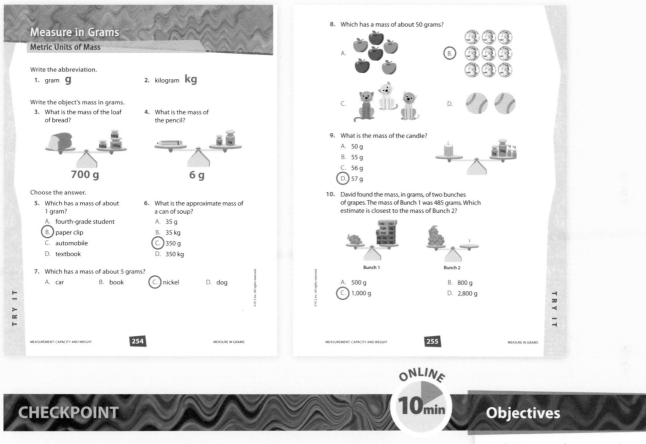

CHECKPOINT

Objectives

- Estimate and measure the weight of an object to the nearest gram.

Students will complete an online Checkpoint. If necessary, read the directions, problems, and answer choices to students and help them with keyboard or mouse operations.

Measure Weight in Ounces and Pounds

Lesson Overview

Skills Update	5 minutes	ONLINE
GET READY Match Scales to Objects	5 minutes	ONLINE
LEARN Identify Ounces and Pounds	5 minutes	ONLINE
LEARN Compare Weights with a Balance	25 minutes	OFFLINE
TRY IT Estimate and Measure Weight	10 minutes	OFFLINE
CHECKPOINT	10 minutes	ONLINE

▶ Lesson Objectives

Estimate and measure the weight of an object to the nearest ounce.

▶ Prerequisite Skills

- Identify the appropriate tools for measuring the weight of an object.
- Identify the appropriate metric and English units for measuring the weight of an object.

▶ Content Background

Students will learn to estimate and measure the weight of objects to the nearest ounce. They will also explore measuring objects in pounds.

ESTIMATION AND PRECISE MEASUREMENT

While many quantities need to be measured precisely, some can simply be estimated. Estimation is important for students, since it focuses them on which unit is being used in the measurement and helps them develop a greater feel for the size of that unit. Most students view estimating as a fun guessing game. They will learn that the more they estimate and check their estimates, the better they will become at estimating measures. Measuring precisely is also a key skill, since not doing so can lead to undesirable results, such as a fallen cake, a salty stew, or a watery milkshake.

When finding actual measures, students need to take special care in both using and reading the measuring instrument accurately. They should understand that all measures that the average person makes are only close approximations, both because of the lack of precision of the tools used in daily life and because of human error.

THE DIFFERENCES BETWEEN WEIGHT AND MASS

Weight is the measurement of the pull of gravity on an object, while *mass* is a measurement of the amount of matter something contains. The mass of an object doesn't change when an object's location changes. Weight, on the other hand, does change with location. For example, a baseball on the earth has one mass. On the moon, it has the same mass. On the earth, it has one weight; on the moon, it weighs less.

Materials to Gather

SUPPLIED

base-10 ones cubes – 28

Estimate and Measure Weight activity page

ALSO NEEDED

hanging balance from Measure in Grams lesson

balance supplies –2 rubber bands (large, thick), pointed-end safety scissors, 3 wooden skewer or other thin sticks about 9 inches long, masking tape, dental floss or sturdy lightweight string, 2 medium identical containers (such as disposable plastic containers for leftovers)

household objects – 10 quarters, 4 small objects that weight about 1 ounce (such as small nail clippers, large binder clip, glue stick, and small nail clippers), 4–6 objects that weigh about 1 pound (such as keys, marbles, canned goods, and boxed foods), plastic bag (small, clear, resealable)

index cards – 6

The difference between weight and mass will be introduced later in students' math education. For now, be sure students are aware that the units to measure weight include pounds and ounces, while the units to measure mass include grams and kilograms.

▶ Advance Preparation

For the Learn: Compare Weights with a Balance activity, gather various household objects and the hanging balance from the Measure in Grams lesson. If you do not have the hanging balance, refer to the Measure in Grams lesson in the Lesson Guide for instructions on how to create it. Modify the hanging balance.

1. Tape three wooden skewers or other thin sticks together to make a heavier balance beam. (If the sticks have pointed ends, remove the sharp points.) Replace the single-stick beam with this one.

2. If the containers are not large enough to hold a pound of butter or a few pieces of fruit, replace them with larger ones. To do so, remove the rubber bands from previous containers and carefully place them around the upper lip of the larger containers. It's helpful if the containers have a lip so that the rubber bands don't pull off with heavier weights.

The new version should look similar to the illustration. Be sure each paper clip sits in a groove that is either cut in the sticks (with scissors) or made by wrapping tape around the stick on either side of the paper clip.

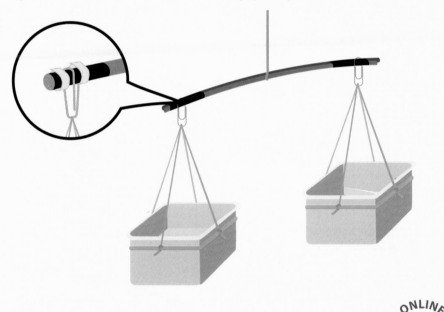

ONLINE 5min

GET READY Match Scales to Objects

Students will match each object with the correct type of scale used to measure the weight of the object. When students complete the matching, they will learn about a type of large scale.

Objectives

- Identify the appropriate tools for measuring the weight of an object.

LEARN Identify Ounces and Pounds

Objectives

- Estimate and measure the weight of an object to the nearest ounce.

Students will learn that ounces and pounds are two English units for measuring weight. They will see common items that weigh 1 ounce and that weigh 1 pound. They will learn why *pound* is abbreviated as *lb* and why *ounce* is abbreviated as *oz*. They also will match each abbreviation to the correct word.

LEARN Compare Weights with a Balance

Objectives

- Estimate and measure the weight of an object to the nearest ounce.

Students will compare the weights of different objects to known weights. They will record the weight of each object in ounces or pounds.

Gather the hanging balance, quarters, base-10 ones cubes, index cards, sticks of butter, and household objects.

1. Set up the hanging balance from a table, chair, plant hook, open cupboard door, coat rack, or any place it can hang freely. Try to hang the balance no more than a few inches above a flat surface. That way, when it's unbalanced, the heavier container will touch the surface rather than tilt the beam too far and cause the strings to tangle. Explain to students how the balance works.

2. Set out the household objects and an index card for each.

3. Explain that 5 quarters or 28 base-10 ones cubes weigh about 1 ounce and that the quarters (or ones cubes) can be used to compare weights of different objects.

4. Have students place 5 quarters in each container to test the balance. Explain that when the balance beam is horizontal, the balance is level. If it isn't level, check that the paper clips holding the containers are in the correct position and that the string holding the balance beam is still in the groove. If it still doesn't balance, add tape to the bottom of the lighter container until it is balanced. This small adjustment should not greatly affect the performance of the balance. Then have students test the balance again with 5 quarters in one container and 28 ones cubes in the other.

5. Tell students to remove the quarters and ones cubes from the containers.

   - Explain that a stick of butter weighs 4 ounces. Have them label an index card stick of butter and write 4 oz in the upper right corner.

   - Have students place 5 quarters in one container and a stick of butter in the other. Then have them place small objects in the container with the quarters until the two sides balance.

   - Have students remove the small objects from the container and place them in a plastic bag labeled 3 oz.

   Students now have the following weights:

   - 1 oz: 5 quarters or 28 ones cubes
   - 2 oz: 10 quarters
   - 3 oz: bag of small objects
   - 4 oz: stick of butter

Tips

Put the 28 base-10 ones cubes in a lightweight sandwich bag to make a 1-ounce weight.

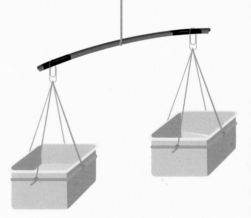

6. Ask students to pick an object from those gathered and use their homemade weights to find its weight. They may also use multiple sticks of butter to counterbalance their object. (Each stick is a 4-ounce weight.) Have students write the object name on an index card and record the weight in ounces in the upper right corner, using the abbreviation *oz* for *ounces*. Repeat this step with one other object.

7. Tell students to look over all the objects gathered and try to arrange them by weight from the least to the greatest. Have students include the objects they already weighed in the lineup.

8. Have students check the order of their objects by weighing the objects one at a time.

   - Have them create index cards for each object that doesn't have one yet. Have them write the name of the object in the center of the card.

   - Before they weigh each object, have them estimate the weight in ounces and write their guess in the lower left corner of the corresponding card.

   - After they weigh each object, have them write the actual weight in ounces in the upper right corner of its card.

   - As students get more information about the weight of different objects, encourage them to rearrange the objects in their least-to-greatest line. If they are trying to find the weight of something heavy, encourage them to use heavier objects for which they know the weight. For instance, they can use a banana (about 6 ounces), can of soup (about 13 ounces), or other homemade weights.

9. Have students feel the weight of 4 sticks of butter. Explain that this is what 1 pound feels like. Have students put the pound of butter in one container. Have them choose other items that they think might weigh about a pound, such as a number of potatoes, pieces of fruit, vegetables, or other objects. Have them balance the objects with the pound of butter to find out whether the objects weigh more or less than a pound.

10. When students have a good sense of a pound and have weighed all the objects from Step 8, have them choose five of the most memorable objects to record in their Math Notebook. Have them write down each object's name, the estimate, and the actual weight.

OFFLINE

10 min

TRY IT Estimate and Measure Weight

Objectives

- Estimate and measure the weight of an object to the nearest ounce.

Students will practice comparing the weights of objects in ounces. Have students turn to the Estimate and Measure Weight activity page in their Activity Book and read the directions with them.

Students should copy the problems from the Activity Book into their Math Notebook as necessary and solve them there. In Problems 2–4, assist students in reading the marks on the scale shown in the problem. Explain to students that by looking at the labeled marks on a scale, they can determine the value of the unlabeled marks.

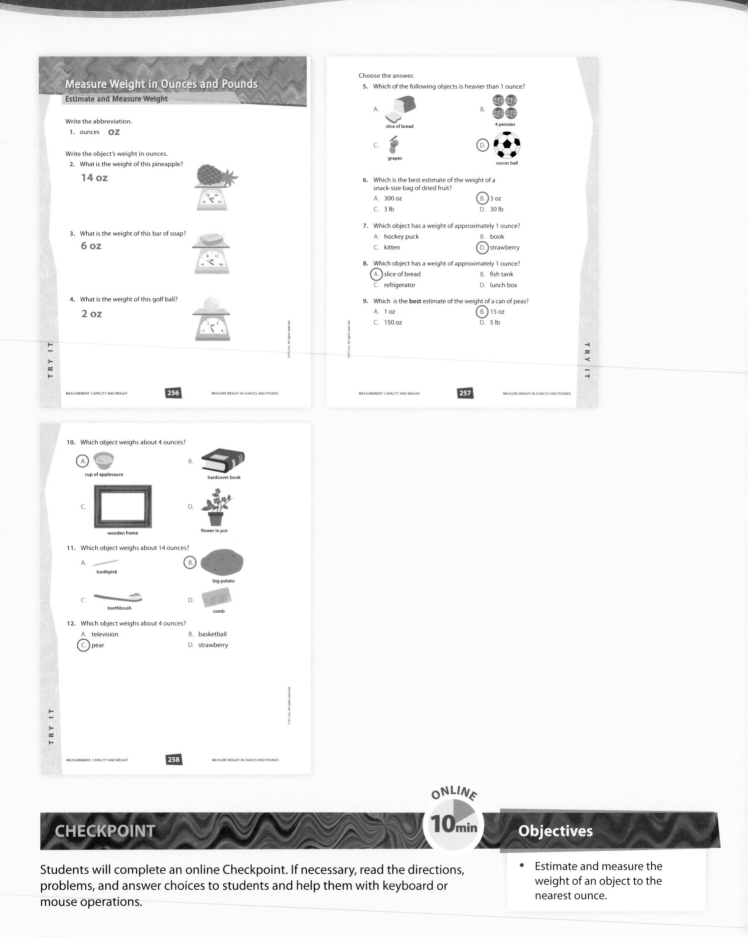

Measure Weight in Ounces and Pounds
Estimate and Measure Weight

Write the abbreviation.

1. ounces **OZ**

Write the object's weight in ounces.

2. What is the weight of this pineapple?

   14 oz

3. What is the weight of this bar of soap?

   6 oz

4. What is the weight of this golf ball?

   2 oz

TRY IT

Choose the answer.

5. Which of the following objects is heavier than 1 ounce?

   A. slice of bread

   B. 4 pennies

   C. grapes

   (D.) soccer ball

6. Which is the best estimate of the weight of a snack-size bag of dried fruit?
   A. 300 oz
   (B.) 3 oz
   C. 3 lb
   D. 30 lb

7. Which object has a weight of approximately 1 ounce?
   A. hockey puck
   B. book
   C. kitten
   (D.) strawberry

8. Which object has a weight of approximately 1 ounce?
   (A.) slice of bread
   B. fish tank
   C. refrigerator
   D. lunch box

9. Which is the **best** estimate of the weight of a can of peas?
   A. 1 oz
   (B.) 15 oz
   C. 150 oz
   D. 5 lb

TRY IT

---

10. Which object weighs about 4 ounces?

    (A.) cup of applesauce

    B. hardcover book

    C. wooden frame

    D. flower in pot

11. Which object weighs about 14 ounces?

    A. toothpick

    (B.) big potato

    C. toothbrush

    D. comb

12. Which object weighs about 4 ounces?
    A. television
    B. basketball
    (C.) pear
    D. strawberry

TRY IT

ONLINE
10 min

CHECKPOINT

Students will complete an online Checkpoint. If necessary, read the directions, problems, and answer choices to students and help them with keyboard or mouse operations.

Objectives

- Estimate and measure the weight of an object to the nearest ounce.

Unit Conversions

Lesson Overview

GET READY Time Relationships	5 minutes	ONLINE
LEARN Measurement Match	15 minutes	ONLINE
LEARN Convert Units of Measure	25 minutes	OFFLINE
TRY IT Write the Conversion	10 minutes	OFFLINE
CHECKPOINT	5 minutes	ONLINE

▶ Lesson Objectives

Write a simple unit conversion, such as inches to feet, as an expression or an equation.

▶ Prerequisite Skills

- Identify relationships between units of time, such as minutes in an hour, days in a month, weeks in a year.
- Use a mathematical expression to represent a relationship between quantities.

▶ Content Background

In this lesson, students will learn how to convert one measurement unit to another. They will write expressions to represent conversions. For example, since there are 12 inches in a foot, the number of inches in 5 feet is represented by the expression 5×12.

Expressions can be numbers only, or symbols and numbers together, that represent a value. Expressions do not include $<$, $>$, and $=$ symbols. Number sentences, on the other hand, compare quantities using $<$, $>$, and $=$ symbols. When a number sentence has an equals symbol, it can be called an equation. An equation shows that two values are equal. Since equations are one kind of number sentence, continue to use the term *number sentence* with students rather than *equation*.

Students will use number sentences to represent unit conversions (for example, 12 inches $=$ 1 foot). They will also work on memorizing common unit conversions. In everyday life, students will have many opportunities to convert one measurement unit to another. They may need to convert inches to feet for one purpose, or feet to inches for another. They also may need to convert grams to kilograms, cups to ounces, quarters to dollars, minutes to hours, or even dozens to individual items. To be smart consumers, students will benefit from memorizing many of the common conversions they see in this lesson.

Materials to Gather

SUPPLIED

Measurement Conversion Chart (printout)

Convert Units of Measure activity page

Write the Conversion activity page

▶ Common Errors and Misconceptions

Students might incorrectly reason that when a greater number of units is given, they need to divide to convert the units, and when a lesser number of units is given, they need to multiply. Students also might think they need to divide if the given number of units is a multiple of the conversion unit. For example, in the problem 144 feet = ? inches, students might automatically divide 144 by 12 because 144 is a multiple of 12, rather than realize that they are converting a larger unit to a smaller unit, so they have to multiply.

▶ Advance Preparation

Print the Measurement Conversion Chart.

GET READY Time Relationships

ONLINE **5**min

Students will answer questions about units of time. They'll also write number sentences to show the relationship between units. Learning to write these relationships as number sentences is the first step in being able to convert one unit to another.

Objectives

- Identify relationships between units of time, such as minutes in an hour, days in a month, weeks in a year.
- Use a mathematical expression to represent a relationship between quantities.

LEARN Measurement Match

ONLINE **15**min

Students will learn about unit conversions. They'll also practice matching smaller and larger units of measure.
  Gather the Measurement Conversion Chart.

Objectives

- Write a simple unit conversion, such as inches to feet, as an expression or an equation.

1. Have students look over the measurement conversions on the chart. Ask them to point out any conversions that are familiar. Discuss any conversions that are new to students or that they do not understand.

2. Have students go through the online screens that show unit conversions. Encourage them to find each one on the Measurement Conversion Chart. Then have them match the smaller units to the larger ones as directed.

LEARN Convert Units of Measure

OFFLINE **25**min

Students will write unit conversions as expressions and number sentences. Gather the Measurement Conversion Chart. Have students turn to the Convert Units of Measure activity page in their Activity Book and read the directions with them.

  Students should copy the problems from the Activity Book into their Math Notebook as necessary and solve them there.

Objectives

- Write a simple unit conversion, such as inches to feet, as an expression or an equation.

1. Review the Measurement Conversion Chart with students. Explain that people use these unit conversions to change, or convert, measurements from one unit to another. For instance, have students find the conversion

 484 MEASUREMENT: CAPACITY AND WEIGHT

12 inches = 1 foot. Explain that they can find the number of inches in 2 feet by using the expression 2 × 12. Remind students that expressions represent quantities. Expressions can have numbers and symbols, but they do not include the comparison symbols <, >, or =.

Say: When you solve the conversion, write a number sentence to show equal values. The number sentence 2 × 12 = 24 is used to show that 2 feet = 24 inches.

Remind students that number sentences do include the comparison symbols <, >, or =.

Say: Notice that when you changed from a larger unit (feet) to a smaller unit (inches), you multiplied. If the problem was to find how many feet are in 24 inches, you would be changing 24 inches (smaller units) into feet (larger units) and you would divide.

2. Read the first Worked Example with students. Have them explain in their own words why they need to multiply, not divide, to solve this problem. **Sample explanation:** I'm changing feet to inches. Since there are 12 inches in each foot, I will multiply by 5 to find how many inches are in 5 feet. When I'm changing larger units to smaller units, I need to multiply.

3. Repeat Step 2 for the second Worked Example. Note that this example requires changing smaller units to larger units; therefore, students will divide.

4. Guide students through Problem 1. Prompt them with questions such as:
   - What are the two measures in the problem? ounces and pounds
   - What do you need to find to solve the problem? how many ounces are in 7 pounds
   - What conversion number sentence compares the two measures? 16 ounces = 1 pound
   - Are you changing larger units to smaller units, or smaller units to larger ones? larger units to smaller ones
   - Will you multiply or divide? multiply
   - What expression will you write to convert the units? 7 × 16
   - What number sentence could you write to convert the units? 7 × 16 = 112

5. Have students complete Problems 2–5. Encourage them to refer to the Worked Examples for the steps to follow. Students may use abbreviations when writing their conversion number sentences.

Tips

Show items to help students visualize the conversions, such as a 1-foot ruler marked in inches, a carton of 1 dozen eggs, and a measuring cup marked in fluid ounces.

Convert Units of Measure

Worked Examples

You can write an expression and a number sentence to convert one unit of measure to another.

PROBLEM 1 Write an expression and a number sentence to show how many inches there are in 5 feet.

SOLUTION

❶ Look for the two measures in the problem. The measures are inches and feet.

❷ Identify what you need to find to solve the problem. You need to find the number of inches in 5 feet.

❸ Write the conversion number sentence that compares the two measures. The number sentence 12 inches = 1 foot compares the measures.

❹ Identify which unit of measure you have. Is it the larger unit or the smaller unit? You have 5 feet and you want to know how many inches that is. You're changing from larger units (feet) to smaller units (inches).

❺ Decide whether you will multiply or divide. Multiply if you're changing larger units to smaller units. You will have more of the smaller units. Multiply the number of units you're converting (5) by the number of smaller units (12) in the conversion number sentence.

Multiply. You have 5 feet, and you know there are 12 inches in each foot. So multiply 5 × 12 to find the total number of inches.

L E A R N

---

❻ Write the expression and number sentence.
Expression: 5 × 12
Number sentence: 5 × 12 = ?

ANSWER 5 × 12 = 60
There are 60 inches in 5 feet.

PROBLEM 2 Write an expression and a number sentence to show how many yards equal 12 feet.

SOLUTION

❶ Look for the two measures in the problem. The measures are feet and yards.

❷ Identify what you need to find to solve the problem. You need to find the number of yards in 12 feet.

❸ Write the conversion number sentence that compares the two measures. The number sentence 3 feet = 1 yard compares the measures.

❹ Identify which unit of measure you have. Is it the larger unit or the smaller unit? You have 12 feet, and you want to know how many yards that is. You're changing from smaller units (feet) to larger units (yards).

❺ Decide if you will multiply or divide. Divide if you're changing smaller units to larger units. You will have fewer of the larger units. Divide the number of units you're converting (12) by the number of smaller units (3) in the conversion number sentence.

Divide. You have 12 feet, and you know that 3 feet equal 1 yard. So divide 12 ÷ 3 to find the number of yards.

L E A R N

---

❻ Write the expression and number sentence.
Expression: 12 ÷ 3
Number sentence: 12 ÷ 3 = ?

ANSWER 12 ÷ 3 = 4
4 yards equal 12 feet.

Write the expression.

1. Write an expression to show how many ounces are in 7 pounds. (16 ounces = 1 pound) **7 × 16**

2. Write an expression to show how many items are in 3 dozen. (12 items = 1 dozen) **3 × 12**

Write the number sentence.

3. Write a number sentence to show how many quarts are in 16 pints. (2 pints = 1 quart) **16 ÷ 2 = ?**

4. Write a number sentence to show how many minutes are in 5 hours. (60 minutes = 1 hour) **5 × 60 = ?**

5. Write a number sentence to show how many dollars are equal to 24 quarters. (4 quarters = 1 dollar)
   24 ÷ 4 = ?

L E A R N

TRY IT Write the Conversion

- Write a simple unit conversion, such as inches to feet, as an expression or an equation.

Students will practice writing simple unit conversions as an expression or a number sentence. Have students turn to the Write the Conversion activity page in their Activity Book and read the directions with them.

Students should copy the problems from the Activity Book into their Math Notebook as necessary.

Unit Conversions
Write the Conversion

Write the measurement conversion. Use the conversion to solve the problem.

1. How many weeks are in 1 year?
1 year = 52 weeks

2. How many quarters are in $5?
$1 = 4 quarters; There are 20 quarters in $5.

3. Curtis bought 36 eggs. How many dozen eggs did he buy?
12 items = 1 dozen; Curtis bought 3 dozen eggs.

Choose the answer.

4. Which expression shows how many inches are in 6 feet? (12 in. = 1 ft)
   (A) 6 × 12
   B. 12 ÷ 6

5. Which number sentence shows how many quarts are in 10 pints? (2 pt = 1 qt)
   A. 10 × 2 = ?
   (B.) 10 ÷ 2 = ?

6. Sally is 3 feet tall. Which number sentence could be used to find how tall Sally is in inches? (12 in. = 1 ft)
   (A) 3 × 12 = ?
   B. 3 + 12 = ?
   C. 10 − 3 = ?
   D. 3 × 10 = ?

7. A desk is 2 meters wide. Which number sentence could be used to figure out how wide the desk is in centimeters? (100 cm = 1 m)
   A. 2 + 2 = ?
   (B.) 2 × 100 = ?
   C. 100 + 2 = ?
   D. 100 − 2 = ?

8. Ken is serving juice at his party. Each juice bottle contains 2 liters of juice. Which number sentence will tell how many milliliters of juice are in each bottle? (1,000 mL = 1 L)
   (A) 2 × 1,000 = ?
   B. 1,000 ÷ 2 = ?
   C. 2 × 100 = ?
   D. 100 ÷ 2 = ?

MEASUREMENT: CAPACITY AND WEIGHT · 262 · UNIT CONVERSIONS

9. Mindy needed 8 cups of strawberries. Which number sentence could be used to figure out how many pints of strawberries Mindy should buy? (2 c = 1 pt)
   A. 8 + 2 = ?
   (B.) 8 ÷ 2 = ?
   C. 8 − 2 = ?
   D. 8 × 2 = ?

10. Susie filled up her car with 48 quarts of gas. Which number sentence could be used to figure out how many gallons of gas Susie put into her car? (4 qt = 1 gal)
    A. 48 × 4 = ?
    (B.) 48 ÷ 4 = ?
    C. 48 + 4 = ?
    D. 48 − 4 = ?

11. A bag of sugar has a mass of 5 kilograms. Which expression could be used to figure out the mass of the sugar in grams? (1,000 g = 1 kg)
    (A) 5 × 1,000
    B. 1,000 ÷ 5
    C. 5 × 100
    D. 100 ÷ 5

12. The baker said the bread would stay fresh for 7 days. Which number sentence could be used to figure out how many hours that is? (24 hours = 1 day)
    A. 24 − 7 = ?
    B. 24 ÷ 7 = ?
    C. 24 + 7 = ?
    (D.) 7 × 24 = ?

13. In 2 years Andrew will take a trip around the world. Which number sentence could be used to figure out how many months will pass before Andrew takes his trip? (12 months = 1 year)
    (A.) 12 × 2 = ?
    B. 12 ÷ 2 = ?
    C. 12 + 2 = ?
    D. 12 − 2 = ?

14. A jar contained $8 in dimes. Which number sentence could be used to figure out how many dimes are in the jar? (10 dimes = $1)
    A. 10 + 8 = ?
    B. 10 ÷ 8 = ?
    (C.) 10 × 8 = ?
    D. 10 − 8 = ?

MEASUREMENT: CAPACITY AND WEIGHT · 263 · UNIT CONVERSIONS

CHECKPOINT

- Write a simple unit conversion, such as inches to feet, as an expression or an equation.

Students will complete an online Checkpoint. If necessary, read the directions, problems, and answer choices to students and help them with keyboard or mouse operations.

Measurement Conversions (A)

Lesson Overview		
GET READY Conversion Match-Up	10 minutes	**ONLINE**
LEARN Multiply or Divide to Convert	15 minutes	**ONLINE**
LEARN Conversion Stories	20 minutes	**OFFLINE**
TRY IT Convert and Solve	15 minutes	**OFFLINE**

▶ Lesson Objectives

- Use a simple unit conversion, such as centimeters to meters, to solve a problem.
- Solve a unit-conversion story problem by using multiplication or division.

▶ Prerequisite Skills

Write a simple unit conversion, such as inches to feet, as an expression or an equation.

▶ Content Background

In this lesson, students will learn to use a simple unit conversion, such as centimeters to meters, to solve a problem. They will also learn to use multiplication or division to solve unit-conversion story problems.

Knowing when to multiply or divide is a key skill students need when converting measurements. They will continue to practice and memorize measurement conversions. They will apply these skills and use multiplication and division to solve story problems involving measurement conversions. Students may need to convert inches to feet, grams to kilograms, cups to ounces, quarters to dollars, minutes to hours, or dozens to individual items. They will learn tips to determine whether to multiply or divide to solve the measurement conversion problems.

▶ Common Errors and Misconceptions

Students might incorrectly reason that when a greater number of units is given, they need to divide to convert the units, and when a lesser number of units is given, they need to multiply. Students also might think they need to divide if the given number of units is a multiple of the conversion unit. For example, in the problem 144 feet = ? inches, students might automatically divide 144 by 12 because 144 is a multiple of 12, rather than realize that they are converting a larger unit to a smaller unit, so they have to multiply.

▶ Advance Preparation

Print the Measurement Conversion Chart.

Materials to Gather

SUPPLIED

Measurement Conversion Chart (printout)

Conversion Stories activity page

Convert and Solve activity page

GET READY Conversion Match-Up

ONLINE 10 min

Students will practice matching up the parts of conversion sentences.

Gather the Measurement Conversion Chart. Review the conversions with students before doing the online activity.

Objectives

- Write a simple unit conversion, such as inches to feet, as an expression or an equation.

LEARN Multiply or Divide to Convert

ONLINE 15 min

Students will identify whether they need to multiply or divide to convert units. Remind students that when changing from a larger unit such as feet to a smaller unit such as inches, they can think: 1 foot = 12 inches, so 2 feet would be 2 × 12 inches. They will soon become accustomed to the idea that when converting from larger units to smaller units, they multiply. And they will know that when going from larger units to smaller units, they divide.

Gather the Measurement Conversion Chart. Allow students to refer to the chart as needed while they complete the online activity.

Objectives

- Use a simple unit conversion, such as centimeters to meters, to solve a problem.
- Solve a unit-conversion story problem by using multiplication or division.

LEARN Conversion Stories

OFFLINE 20 min

Students will use multiplication or division to solve unit-conversion story problems. Encourage them to use any strategy they are comfortable with to solve problems. For example, at times using repeated subtraction to solve division problems will be easier for students. Their understanding will increase as they apply their own techniques. Gather the Measurement Conversion Chart. Have students turn to the Conversion Stories activity page in their Activity Book and read the directions with them.

Students should copy the problems from the Activity Book into their Math Notebook as necessary and solve them there.

Objectives

- Use a simple unit conversion, such as centimeters to meters, to solve a problem.
- Solve a unit-conversion story problem by using multiplication or division.

1. Review with students what a number sentence is and how number sentences are used in measurement conversions.

   Say: A number sentence compares quantities using <, >, or =. When you say 12 inches = 1 foot, you are using a number sentence to show two equal values. To convert 2 feet into inches, you would write the number sentence 2 × 12 = ? and then find the answer.

2. Read the first Worked Example with students. Have them find the conversion 60 seconds = 1 minute on the Measurement Conversion Chart.

3. Have students explain in their own words why they need to multiply, not divide, to solve this problem. **Sample explanation:** Since there are 60 seconds in 1 minute, there would be 2 × 60 seconds in 2 minutes. When I'm changing larger units to smaller units, I need to multiply.

4. Read the second Worked Example with students. Point out that this story problem is a 2-step problem. First subtract to find the number of quarters remaining. Then divide the remaining quarters by 4 to convert them to dollars.

5. Have students explain in their own words why they need to divide, not multiply, to solve this problem. **Sample explanation:** I'm changing quarters to dollars. Dollars are the larger units. When I'm changing smaller units to larger units, I need to divide.

6. Guide students through Problem 1. Prompt them with questions such as:

   • What are the two measures in the problem? feet and yards

   • What do you need to find to solve the problem? how many yards of ribbon Rosa has

   • What conversion number sentence compares the two measures? 3 feet = 1 yard

   • Are you changing larger units to smaller units, or smaller units to larger ones? smaller units to larger ones

   • Will you multiply or divide? divide

   • What number sentence will you write to convert the units? 12 ÷ 3 = 4

7. Have students complete Problems 2–4. Encourage them to refer to the Worked Examples for the steps to follow. Students should use the Measurement Conversion Chart to find the conversions they need. Encourage them to use abbreviations for units of measure whenever possible. (**Note:** Problems 3 and 4 are two-step story problems. If needed, help students identify the steps and the operations to complete them.)

Measurement Conversions (A)

Conversion Stories

Worked Examples

You can multiply or divide to solve a unit-conversion story problem.

PROBLEM 1 Ron set the microwave for 2 minutes. How many seconds are in 2 minutes?

SOLUTION

❶ Look for the two measures in the problem. The measures are minutes and seconds.

❷ Identify what you need to find to solve the problem. You need to find the number of seconds in 2 minutes.

❸ Write the conversion number sentence that compares the two measures. The number sentence 60 seconds = 1 minute compares the measures.

❹ Identify which unit of measure you have. Is it the larger unit or the smaller unit? You have 2 minutes and you want to know how many seconds that is. You're changing from larger units (minutes) to smaller units (seconds).

❺ Decide whether you will multiply or divide. You have 2 minutes, and you know that there are 60 seconds in each minute. Multiply if you're changing larger units to smaller units.

Multiply 2 × 60 to find the total number of seconds.

L E A R N

---

❻ Write the number sentence to convert the minutes to seconds.

Number sentence: 2 × 60 = ?

ANSWER 2 × 60 = 120
There are 120 seconds in 2 minutes.

PROBLEM 2 Mrs. Murphy had 64 quarters. She threw 12 quarters into a fountain. How many dollars does Mrs. Murphy have left in quarters?

SOLUTION

❶ Look for the two measures in the problem. The measures are quarters and dollars.

❷ Identify what you need to find to solve the problem. You need to find how many dollars Mrs. Murphy has left in quarters. But first you need to find out how many quarters Mrs. Murphy had after she threw 12 quarters into the fountain. Subtract the number of quarters Mrs. Murphy threw into the fountain (12) from the number of quarters she started with (64).

64 − 12 = 52

Mrs. Murphy has 52 quarters.

❸ Write the conversion number sentence that compares the two measures. The number sentence 4 quarters = 1 dollar compares the measures

❹ Identify which unit of measure you have. Is it the larger unit or the smaller unit? You have 52 quarters and you want to know how many dollars that is. You're changing from smaller units (quarters) to larger units (dollars).

L E A R N

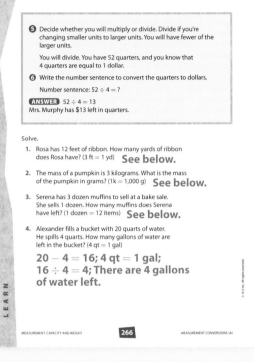

Inside the image:

5 Decide whether you will multiply or divide. Divide if you're changing smaller units to larger units. You will have fewer of the larger units.

You will divide. You have 52 quarters, and you know that 4 quarters are equal to 1 dollar.

6 Write the number sentence to convert the quarters to dollars.

Number sentence: 52 ÷ 4 = ?

ANSWER 52 ÷ 4 = 13
Mrs. Murphy has $13 left in quarters.

Solve.

1. Rosa has 12 feet of ribbon. How many yards of ribbon does Rosa have? (3 ft = 1 yd) **See below.**

2. The mass of a pumpkin is 3 kilograms. What is the mass of the pumpkin in grams? (1k = 1,000 g) **See below.**

3. Serena has 3 dozen muffins to sell at a bake sale. She sells 1 dozen. How many muffins does Serena have left? (1 dozen = 12 items) **See below.**

4. Alexander fills a bucket with 20 quarts of water. He spills 4 quarts. How many gallons of water are left in the bucket? (4 qt = 1 gal)

**20 − 4 = 16; 4 qt = 1 gal;
16 ÷ 4 = 4; There are 4 gallons
of water left.**

MEASUREMENT: CAPACITY AND WEIGHT   266   MEASUREMENT CONVERSIONS (A)

Additional Answers

1. 3 ft = 1 yd; 12 ÷ 3 = 4; Rosa has 4 yards of ribbon.

2. 1,000 g = 1 kg; 3 × 1,000 = 3,000; The mass is 3,000 grams.

3. 3 − 1 = 2; 12 items = 1 dozen; 2 × 12 = 24; Serena has 24 muffins.

TRY IT Convert and Solve

OFFLINE **15 min**

Objectives

Students will practice using multiplication and division to solve unit-conversion problems. Have students turn to the Convert and Solve activity page in their Activity Book and read the directions with them.

Students should copy the problems from the Activity Book into their Math Notebook as necessary and solve them there.

- Use a simple unit conversion, such as centimeters to meters, to solve a problem.

- Solve a unit-conversion story problem by using multiplication or division.

Tips   Encourage students to use repeated addition if they are having difficulty multiplying and to use repeated subtraction if they are having difficulty dividing.

Solve.

1. 10 dimes equal 1 dollar. How many dimes equal 6 dollars?

   $6 \times 10 = 60;$
   60 dimes equal 6 dollars.

2. There are 2 pints in 1 quart. How many quarts equal 14 pints?

   $14 \div 2 = 7 \text{ quarts};$
   7 quarts equal 14 pints.

3. Cole's cat Bix is 3 years old. He wants to figure out Bix's age in months. There are 12 months in a year.

   How many months are in 3 years?

   3×12
   $(\text{or } 12 + 12 + 12) = 36;$
   There are 36 months in 3 years.

4. Katrina has 4 liters of juice to serve at her party. Her mom brings home another liter of juice.

   How many milliliters of juice does Katrina have altogether? (1,000 mL = 1 L)

   $4 + 1 = 5;$
   $5 \times 1{,}000 = 5{,}000;$
   Katrina has 5,000 milliliters.

5. Jackson has 600 centimeters of rope. He uses 100 centimeters of rope as a lasso.

   How many meters of rope does he have left? (100 cm = 1 m)

   $600 - 100 = 500;$
   $500 \div 100 = 5;$
   Jackson has 5 meters of rope left.

6. Beth bought 3 dozen eggs. How many eggs did she buy? (12 items = 1 dozen)

   $3 \times 12 = 36;$
   Beth bought 36 eggs.

7. Tiffany biked 2 km. How many meters did she bike? (1,000 m = 1 km)

   $2 \times 1{,}000 = 2{,}000;$
   Tiffany biked 2,000 meters.

8. 4 hours is equivalent to how many minutes? (60 minutes = 1 hour)

   $4 \times 60 = 240;$
   4 hours is equivalent to 240 minutes.

9. How many quarts are in 24 pints? (2 pints = 1 quart)

   $24 \div 2 = 12;$ **There are 12 quarts in 24 pints.**

Choose the answer.

10. How many quarters are equal to 4 dollars?
    (4 quarters = $1)

    A. 1   B. 4

    C. 16   D. 20

11. Jan is riding her bike 9 kilometers to her grandmother's house. She has biked 2 kilometers already.

    How many more meters does Jan have to bike?
    (1,000 m = 1 km)

    A. 70 m   B. 700 m

    C. 7,000 m   D. 70,000 m

12. Jorge found two jars filled with pennies. One jar held $2 and the other jar held $3.

    How many pennies did Jorge find? (100 pennies = $1)

    A. 5   B. 20

    C. 500   D. 1,000

13. Della has 3 pounds of apples for a fruit salad. Each apple weighs about 6 ounces. Della knows there are 16 ounces in a pound.

    How many apples does Della have for the fruit salad?

    A. 2   **B. 8**

    C. 24   D. 48

TRY IT

Measurement Conversions (B)

Lesson Overview

Skills Update	5 minutes	**ONLINE**
GET READY Match Measurements	5 minutes	**ONLINE**
LEARN Conversion Story Problems	10 minutes	**ONLINE**
LEARN Solve and Convert Answers	20 minutes	**OFFLINE**
TRY IT Measurement Problems	10 minutes	**OFFLINE**
CHECKPOINT	10 minutes	**ONLINE**

▶ Lesson Objectives

- Use a simple unit conversion, such as centimeters to meters, to solve a problem.
- Solve a unit-conversion story problem by using multiplication or division.

▶ Prerequisite Skills

Write a simple unit conversion, such as inches to feet, as an expression or an equation.

▶ Content Background

Students will continue to use a simple unit conversion, such as centimeters to meters, to solve a problem. They will also use multiplication or division to solve unit-conversion story problems.

Knowing when to multiply or divide is a key skill students need when converting measurements. They will continue to practice and memorize measurement conversions. They will apply these skills and use multiplication and division to solve story problems involving measurement conversions. They may need to convert inches to feet, grams to kilograms, cups to ounces, quarters to dollars, minutes to hours, or dozens to individual items. They will learn tips to determine whether to multiply or divide to solve the measurement-conversion problems.

▶ Common Errors and Misconceptions

Students might incorrectly reason that when a greater number of units is given, they need to divide to convert the units, and when a lesser number of units is given, they need to multiply. Students also might think they need to divide if the given number of units is a multiple of the conversion unit. For example, in the problem 144 feet = ? inches, students might automatically divide 144 by 12 because 144 is a multiple of 12, rather than realize that they are converting a larger unit to a smaller unit, so they have to multiply.

▶ Advance Preparation

Print the Measurement Conversion Chart.

Materials to Gather

SUPPLIED

Measurement Conversion Chart (printout)

Solve and Convert Answers activity page

Measurement Problems activity page

GET READY Match Measurements

Students will match measurements that show equal amounts, such as 12 inches and 1 foot. Gather the Measurement Conversion Chart. Students may use the chart during this activity. However, the goal is to help students begin to memorize the equivalencies.

Objectives

- Write a simple unit conversion, such as inches to feet, as an expression or an equation.

Tips

Have students repeat this activity several times to help them memorize equivalent measures.

LEARN Conversion Story Problems

Students will identify the correct number sentence to solve a measurement-conversion story problem.

Gather the Measurement Conversion Chart. Students may refer to the chart as needed.

Objectives

- Use a simple unit conversion, such as centimeters to meters, to solve a problem.
- Solve a unit-conversion story problem by using multiplication or division.

LEARN Solve and Convert Answers

Students will solve measurement story problems and then use multiplication or division to convert the units in the solution. Gather the Measurement Conversion Chart. Have students turn to the Solve and Convert Answers activity page in their Activity Book and read the directions with them.

Students should copy the problems from the Activity Book into their Math Notebook as necessary and solve them there.

1. Read the first Worked Example with students.
2. **Ask:** What number sentence shows how many muffins Mrs. Ford baked altogether? $24 + 12 = 36$
3. Go through each step of the Worked Example, helping students identify the measures, decide whether to multiply or divide, and write the number sentence that will solve the problem.
4. Read the second Worked Example with students. Point out that this story problem is a 2-step problem. Help students understand that since they're changing the larger unit of time (hours) to a smaller unit of time (minutes), they will multiply.
5. Use the Worked Examples to help students complete Problems 1–4. Students may use the Measurement Conversion Chart as needed. Encourage them to use abbreviations for units of measure whenever possible. (**Note:** These problems are 2-step story problems. If needed, help students identify the steps and the operations to complete them.)

Objectives

- Use a simple unit conversion, such as centimeters to meters, to solve a problem.
- Solve a unit-conversion story problem by using multiplication or division.

Tips

Encourage students to become familiar with all the units on the Measurement Conversion Chart.

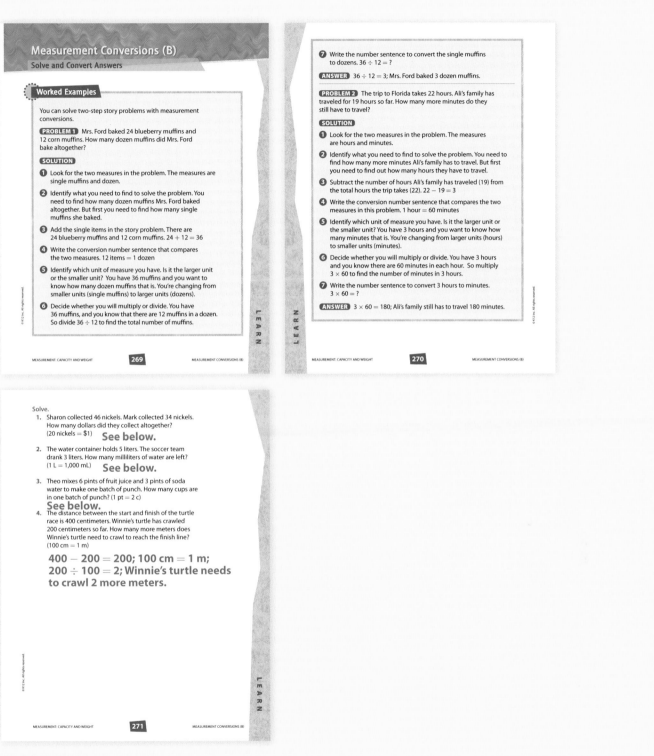

Measurement Conversions (B)
Solve and Convert Answers

Worked Examples

You can solve two-step story problems with measurement conversions.

PROBLEM 1 Mrs. Ford baked 24 blueberry muffins and 12 corn muffins. How many dozen muffins did Mrs. Ford bake altogether?

SOLUTION

❶ Look for the two measures in the problem. The measures are single muffins and dozen.

❷ Identify what you need to find to solve the problem. You need to find how many dozen muffins Mrs. Ford baked altogether. But first you need to find how many single muffins she baked.

❸ Add the single items in the story problem. There are 24 blueberry muffins and 12 corn muffins. $24 + 12 = 36$

❹ Write the conversion number sentence that compares the two measures. 12 items = 1 dozen

❺ Identify which unit of measure you have. Is it the larger unit or the smaller unit? You have 36 muffins and you want to know how many dozen muffins that is. You're changing from smaller units (single muffins) to larger units (dozens).

❻ Decide whether you will multiply or divide. You have 36 muffins, and you know that there are 12 muffins in a dozen. So divide $36 \div 12$ to find the total number of muffins.

---

❼ Write the number sentence to convert the single muffins to dozens. $36 \div 12 = ?$

ANSWER $36 \div 12 = 3$; Mrs. Ford baked 3 dozen muffins.

PROBLEM 2 The trip to Florida takes 22 hours. Ali's family has traveled for 19 hours so far. How many more minutes do they still have to travel?

SOLUTION

❶ Look for the two measures in the problem. The measures are hours and minutes.

❷ Identify what you need to find to solve the problem. You need to find how many more minutes Ali's family has to travel. But first you need to find out how many hours they have to travel.

❸ Subtract the number of hours Ali's family has traveled (19) from the total hours the trip takes (22). $22 - 19 = 3$

❹ Write the conversion number sentence that compares the two measures in this problem. 1 hour = 60 minutes

❺ Identify which unit of measure you have. Is it the larger unit or the smaller unit? You have 3 hours and you want to know how many minutes that is. You're changing from larger units (hours) to smaller units (minutes).

❻ Decide whether you will multiply or divide. You have 3 hours and you know there are 60 minutes in each hour. So multiply 3×60 to find the number of minutes in 3 hours.

❼ Write the number sentence to convert 3 hours to minutes. $3 \times 60 = ?$

ANSWER $3 \times 60 = 180$; Ali's family still has to travel 180 minutes.

Solve.

1. Sharon collected 46 nickels. Mark collected 34 nickels. How many dollars did they collect altogether? (20 nickels = $1) **See below.**

2. The water container holds 5 liters. The soccer team drank 3 liters. How many milliliters of water are left? (1 L = 1,000 mL) **See below.**

3. Theo mixes 6 pints of fruit juice and 3 pints of soda water to make one batch of punch. How many cups are in one batch of punch? (1 pt = 2 c) **See below.**

4. The distance between the start and finish of the turtle race is 400 centimeters. Winnie's turtle has crawled 200 centimeters so far. How many more meters does Winnie's turtle need to crawl to reach the finish line? (100 cm = 1 m)

   $400 - 200 = 200$; 100 cm = 1 m; $200 \div 100 = 2$; Winnie's turtle needs to crawl 2 more meters.

Additional Answers

1. $46 + 34 = 80$; 20 nickels = $1; $80 \div 20 = 4$; They collected $4.

2. $5 - 3 = 2$; 1 L = 1,000 mL; $2 \times 1,000 = 2,000$; There are 2,000 milliliters of water left.

3. $6 + 3 = 9$; 1 pt = 2 c; $9 \times 2 = 18$; There are 18 cups in one batch of punch.

TRY IT Measurement Problems

Objectives

- Use a simple unit conversion, such as centimeters to meters, to solve a problem.
- Solve a unit-conversion story problem by using multiplication or division.

Students will practice using multiplication and division to solve unit-conversion story problems. Have students turn to the Measurement Problems activity page in their Activity Book and read the directions with them.

Students should copy the problems from the Activity Book into their Math Notebook as necessary and solve them there. Have students use whatever strategies they are most comfortable with to figure out the conversions. For instance in Problem 1, when finding out how many days are in 72 hours, some students will find it easier to subtract 24 hours repeatedly to get the solution. Using these strategies assures that students understand what they're doing rather than following a rote method.

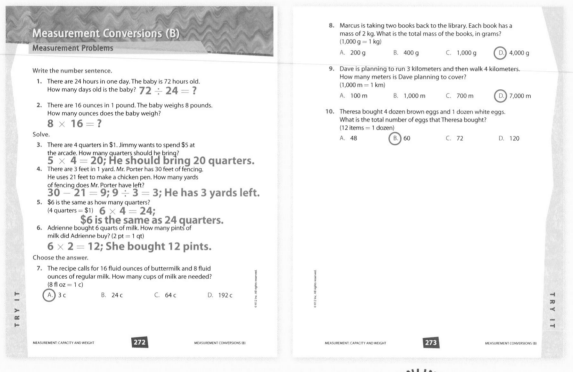

Measurement Conversions (B)
Measurement Problems

Write the number sentence.

1. There are 24 hours in one day. The baby is 72 hours old. How many days old is the baby? **72 ÷ 24 = ?**

2. There are 16 ounces in 1 pound. The baby weighs 8 pounds. How many ounces does the baby weigh?
8 × 16 = ?

Solve.

3. There are 4 quarters in $1. Jimmy wants to spend $5 at the arcade. How many quarters should he bring?
5 × 4 = 20; He should bring 20 quarters.

4. There are 3 feet in 1 yard. Mr. Porter has 30 feet of fencing. He uses 21 feet to make a chicken pen. How many yards of fencing does Mr. Porter have left?
30 − 21 = 9; 9 ÷ 3 = 3; He has 3 yards left.

5. $6 is the same as how many quarters?
(4 quarters = $1) **6 × 4 = 24;**
$6 is the same as 24 quarters.

6. Adrienne bought 6 quarts of milk. How many pints of milk did Adrienne buy? (2 pt = 1 qt)
6 × 2 = 12; She bought 12 pints.

Choose the answer.

7. The recipe calls for 16 fluid ounces of buttermilk and 8 fluid ounces of regular milk. How many cups of milk are needed?
(8 fl oz = 1 c)
(A.) 3 c   B. 24 c   C. 64 c   D. 192 c

8. Marcus is taking two books back to the library. Each book has a mass of 2 kg. What is the total mass of the books, in grams?
(1,000 g = 1 kg)
A. 200 g   B. 400 g   C. 1,000 g   (D.) 4,000 g

9. Dave is planning to run 3 kilometers and then walk 4 kilometers. How many meters is Dave planning to cover?
(1,000 m = 1 km)
A. 100 m   B. 1,000 m   C. 700 m   (D.) 7,000 m

10. Theresa bought 4 dozen brown eggs and 1 dozen white eggs. What is the total number of eggs that Theresa bought?
(12 items = 1 dozen)
A. 48   (B.) 60   C. 72   D. 120

CHECKPOINT

Objectives

- Solve a unit-conversion story problem by using multiplication or division.
- Use a simple unit conversion, such as centimeters to meters, to solve a problem.

Students will complete an online Checkpoint. If necessary, read the directions, problems, and answer choices to students and help them with keyboard or mouse operations.

Tips Suggest that students record the different units and the basic conversion in each problem before they solve the problem.

Unit Review

UNIT REVIEW Look Back	10 minutes	**ONLINE**
UNIT REVIEW Checkpoint Practice	50 minutes	**ONLINE**
⤷ **UNIT REVIEW** Prepare for the Checkpoint		

▶ Unit Objectives

This lesson reviews the following objectives:

- Identify the appropriate tools for measuring liquid volume.
- Identify the appropriate metric and English units for measuring liquid volume.
- Estimate and measure liquid volume to the nearest liter.
- Estimate and measure liquid volume to the nearest cup.
- Identify the appropriate tools for measuring the weight of an object.
- Identify the appropriate metric and English units for measuring the weight of an object.
- Estimate and measure the weight of an object to the nearest gram.
- Estimate and measure the weight of an object to the nearest ounce.
- Write a simple unit conversion, such as inches to feet, as an expression or an equation.
- Use a simple unit conversion, such as centimeters to meters, to solve a problem.
- Solve a unit-conversion story problem by using multiplication or division.

▶ Advance Preparation

In this lesson, students will have an opportunity to review previous activities in the Measurement: Capacity and Weight unit. Look at the suggested activities in Unit Review: Prepare for the Checkpoint online and gather any needed materials.

Materials to Gather

There are no materials to gather for this lesson.

UNIT REVIEW Look Back

ONLINE
10min

Objectives

- Review unit objectives.

Students will review key concepts from the unit to prepare for the Unit Checkpoint.

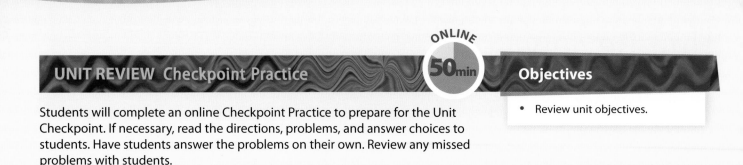

UNIT REVIEW Checkpoint Practice

ONLINE
50min

Objectives

- Review unit objectives.

Students will complete an online Checkpoint Practice to prepare for the Unit Checkpoint. If necessary, read the directions, problems, and answer choices to students. Have students answer the problems on their own. Review any missed problems with students.

➔ **UNIT REVIEW** Prepare for the Checkpoint

What you do next depends on how students performed in the previous activity, Unit Review: Checkpoint Practice. If students had difficulty with any of the problems, complete the appropriate review activity listed in the table online.

Unit Checkpoint

UNIT CHECKPOINT Online

60 minutes | **ONLINE**

▶ Unit Objectives

This lesson assesses the following objectives:

- Identify the appropriate tools for measuring liquid volume.
- Identify the appropriate metric and English units for measuring liquid volume.
- Estimate and measure liquid volume to the nearest liter.
- Estimate and measure liquid volume to the nearest cup.
- Identify the appropriate tools for measuring the weight of an object.
- Identify the appropriate metric and English units for measuring the weight of an object.
- Estimate and measure the weight of an object to the nearest gram.
- Estimate and measure the weight of an object to the nearest ounce.
- Write a simple unit conversion, such as inches to feet, as an expression or an equation.
- Use a simple unit conversion, such as centimeters to meters, to solve a problem.
- Solve a unit-conversion story problem by using multiplication or division.

Materials to Gather

There are no materials to gather for this lesson.

UNIT CHECKPOINT Online

ONLINE 60min

Objectives

- Assess unit objectives.

Students will complete the Unit Checkpoint online. If necessary, read the directions, problems, and answer choices to students and help them with keyboard or mouse operations.

Mathematical Reasoning

▶ Unit Objectives

- Analyze a story problem by identifying the question, recognizing relevant information, and developing a solution strategy.

- Demonstrate when and how to break a multistep story problem into simpler steps.

- Use estimation to predict a solution to a story problem and to determine whether calculations are reasonable.

- Apply strategies and results from a simpler story problem to either a more complex problem or to a similar problem.

- Explain mathematical reasoning in a story problem by using words, numbers, symbols, charts, graphs, tables, diagrams, or models.

- Express the solution to a story problem clearly and logically with appropriate mathematical notation, terms, and accurate language.

- Determine the answer to a story problem to a specific degree of accuracy, such as hundredths.

- Explain the advantages of exact answers and approximate answers to story problems.

- Check the accuracy of a calculation in a story problem.

▶ Big Ideas

- The use of letters, numbers, and mathematical symbols makes possible the translation of complex situations or long word statements into concise mathematical sentences or expressions.

- Estimation is a useful tool in problem solving.

▶ Unit Introduction

In this unit, students will develop strategies to solve story problems by identifying the question they must answer; determining when and how to break a multistep problem into simpler parts; and using words, numbers, graphs, tables, and models to explain their problem-solving reasoning about problem situations. They will learn the importance of estimating to verify the reasonableness of answers. They will find that some story problems require an exact answer while others may need only an approximate solution. As students learn to analyze problems, they will use a variety of strategies to solve story problems, explain the advantage of using a particular strategy for a given problem, compute answers to a given degree of accuracy, check the accuracy of their answer, and be able to explain their reasoning by following a 4-step problem-solving plan: (1) understand the problem; (2) devise a plan; (3) carry out the plan; and (4) look back.

▶ Keywords

approximate (v.)	expression	reasoning
degree of accuracy	reasonableness	strategy
estimate (n.)		

Analyze Story Problems (A)

Lesson Overview

Skills Update	5 minutes	**ONLINE**
GET READY The Yo-Yo Train	5 minutes	**ONLINE**
LEARN Identify Needed Facts	15 minutes	**ONLINE**
LEARN Necessary Information	10 minutes	**ONLINE**
LEARN Sort Problem Facts	10 minutes	**ONLINE**
TRY IT Needed and Unneeded Facts	15 minutes	**ONLINE**

▶ Lesson Objectives

Analyze a story problem by identifying the question, recognizing relevant information, and developing a solution strategy.

▶ Prerequisite Skills

Determine whether addition, subtraction, multiplication, or division is the appropriate operation to use to solve a story problem and solve the problem.

▶ Content Background

Students will learn to identify the question in a story problem. They will also learn to identify the information they need and the information they don't need to solve a problem.

Solving a story problem is a strategic process; it is often not a straightforward one. The following 4-step problem-solving method was developed by George Pólya, and it is an effective way to solve a variety of story problems: (1) understand the problem; (2) devise a plan; (3) carry out the plan; and (4) look back.

If students have difficulty with the first step of this process—understand the problem—it will interfere with their ability to solve the problem. The secret to success is in students' ability to carefully read the problem, reword the problem, analyze the question, and find relationships among the given pieces of information. Once students complete these steps, they can recognize relevant and irrelevant information and gain the confidence to proceed to the second step—devise a plan. They devise their plan by deciding on an effective strategy for solving the problem.

In this lesson, students will focus on the first step of Pólya's problem-solving plan. They will focus on identifying the question and the relevant and irrelevant information. Students should realize that there is often more than one way to solve a problem and more than one strategy they can use. By using many different strategies, they learn to be flexible in their problem solving and learn that some strategies are more efficient than others.

Materials to Gather

There are no materials to gather for this lesson.

GET READY The Yo-Yo Train

Students will solve a multistep story problem about a yo-yo train. The problem involves adding and subtracting distances.

1. Read the online problem with students. Discuss strategies to solve the problem.
2. Guide students to solve the problem and explain their steps. They might mentally add and subtract, add and subtract on paper, or sketch a number line to help them keep track of the forward and backward distances.

    Ask: What information in the problem is not needed? the statement that the train stopped for 30 minutes

3. Have students type their answer and check it.

- Determine whether addition, subtraction, multiplication, or division is the appropriate operation to use to solve a story problem and solve the problem.

LEARN Identify Needed Facts

Students will identify the question in a given story problem, the facts they need to solve the problem, and the facts they do not need. Explain to students that when they are figuring out problems in everyday life, they can follow these same steps. They should consider all the information, then decide what information they need and what they do not need to solve the problem.

- Analyze a story problem by identifying the question, recognizing relevant information, and developing a solution strategy.

LEARN Necessary Information

Students will identify the necessary and unnecessary information in a story problem. They will also identify additional information needed to solve a problem. The focus is on understanding the problem and deciding what information they need. Have students ask themselves, "Do I understand all the words in the problem?"

Discuss the meaning of any unknown words in the story problem. As students do the activity, ask them the following questions:

- What is the question I have to answer?
- What information in the problem is needed to answer the question?
- What information in the problem is not needed?

Explain that information that is needed is the *necessary* information. The information that is not needed is the *unnecessary* information. In some cases there may also be missing information. Students should get into the habit of asking themselves what (if any) information is not given in the problem, but is needed to answer the question. Explain to students that when they are figuring out problems in everyday life, they can follow these same steps. They should consider all the information, then decide what information they need and what they do not need to solve the problem.

- Analyze a story problem by identifying the question, recognizing relevant information, and developing a solution strategy.

LEARN Sort Problem Facts

Objectives

Students will identify which given facts are needed and which are not needed to solve different story problem questions.

- Analyze a story problem by identifying the question, recognizing relevant information, and developing a solution strategy.

TRY IT Needed and Unneeded Facts

Objectives

Students will complete an online Try It. If necessary, read the directions, problems, and answer choices to students and help them with keyboard or mouse operations.

- Analyze a story problem by identifying the question, recognizing relevant information, and developing a solution strategy.

Analyze Story Problems (B)

Lesson Overview

LEARN Problem-Solving Plan	15 minutes	ONLINE
LEARN Plan a Solution Strategy	30 minutes	OFFLINE
TRY IT Understand and Plan	15 minutes	OFFLINE

▶ Lesson Objectives

Analyze a story problem by identifying the question, recognizing relevant information, and developing a solution strategy.

▶ Prerequisite Skills

Determine whether addition, subtraction, multiplication, or division is the appropriate operation to use to solve a story problem and solve the problem.

▶ Content Background

Solving a story problem is a strategic process; it is often not a straightforward one. The following 4-step problem-solving method was developed by George Pólya, and it is an effective way to solve a variety of story problems: (1) understand the problem; (2) devise a plan; (3) carry out the plan; and (4) look back.

If students have difficulty with the first step of this process—understand the problem—it will interfere with their ability to solve the problem. The secret to success is in students' ability to carefully read the problem, reword the problem, analyze the question, and find relationships among the given pieces of information. Once students complete these steps, they can recognize relevant and irrelevant information and gain the confidence to proceed to the second step—devise a plan. They devise their plan by deciding on an effective strategy for solving the problem.

Students should realize that there is often more than one way to solve a problem and more than one strategy they can use. By using many different strategies, they learn to be flexible in their problem solving and learn that some strategies are more efficient than others.

▶ Advance Preparation

Print the Problem-Solving Plan.

Materials to Gather

SUPPLIED

Problem-Solving Plan (printout)

Plan a Solution Strategy activity page

Understand and Plan activity page

LEARN Problem-Solving Plan

ONLINE 15 min

Students will become familiar with Pólya's 4-step problem-solving plan, review the steps to understanding the problem, and learn about devising a plan. Devising a plan involves picking a strategy that makes the problem easier to solve.

Objectives

- Analyze a story problem by identifying the question, recognizing relevant information, and developing a solution strategy.

LEARN Plan a Solution Strategy

Objectives

- Analyze a story problem by identifying the question, recognizing relevant information, and developing a solution strategy.

Students will read a story problem and identify the question, the facts they need, and the facts they do not need. They'll develop a plan to solve it. Students will not be expected to solve the problem yet; instead, they will focus on the first two steps of the problem-solving plan. Gather the Problem-Solving Plan. Have students turn to the Plan a Solution Strategy activity page in their Activity Book and read the directions with them.

Students should copy the problems from the Activity Book to their Math Notebook as necessary and solve them there.

1. Give students the Problem-Solving Plan. Tell them that in this activity, they'll be focusing on the first two steps of the plan.

2. Read the story problem in the Worked Example with students.

   Say: The first step in solving the problem is to understand it. Read the problem again and look for any words you do not understand.

   Explain that the word *block* has several meanings. Make sure students know that the block in this problem is a city block from one corner to the next. Also make sure they know what it means to say that Joanna rode "3 times as many blocks."

3. Read the solution and answer with students. Make sure they understand why they don't need to know how far Joanna lives from her friend to solve this story problem.

4. Point out that this particular problem contains several smaller problems. (First students need to find how far Joanna rode the second day. Then students need to find out how far she rode in all.) Explain that many problems are made up of several smaller problems. Remind students that they have done multistep problems of this type in the past. Tell them that now they're learning to analyze multistep problems so they'll have more strategies to use in the future.

5. Have students look at the first step on the Problem-Solving Plan. Point out that they've completed this step for the problem in the Worked Example. Tell them that now they can devise a plan to solve the problem, which is the second step of the problem-solving plan.

6. Tell students that making a table can be a good way to organize information. Mention that there are different ways to show information in a table, and that any way that organizes the information clearly is okay. Point out that the Worked Example shows two different ways to organize the information.

   Say: Another person might not use a table. That person might go straight to a number sentence and write $14 + 3 \times 14 = ?$ In this case, without a table to separate the parts of the problem, the person would need to use the rules for the order of operations. He or she would do the multiplication first and then do the addition.

7. Have students look at the second step on the Problem-Solving Plan. Point out the two strategies you've just discussed (make a table, chart, or graph; and translate into a number sentence).

8. Have students read Problem 1 and complete the table. Guide them to complete the problem.

9. Have students read Problem 2 and complete the table. Have them complete the problem. Students may refer to the Problem-Solving Plan for ideas on strategies they can use. If they cannot choose a strategy, suggest they use the "draw a picture or diagram" strategy and the "translate into a number sentence" strategy.

Analyze Story Problems (B)
Plan a Solution Strategy

Worked Examples

You can analyze a story problem and devise a plan to solve it.

PROBLEM Joanna lives 4 blocks from her friend's house. On the day she visited her friend, she rode her bike 14 blocks. The next day, she rode 3 times as many blocks. How many blocks did Joanna ride in all?

SOLUTION

① Understand the problem. **The question:** How many blocks did Joanna ride in all? **Facts you need:** Joanna rode her bike 14 blocks the first day. She rode 3 times that many blocks the second day. **Facts you do NOT need:** Joanna lives 4 blocks from her friend's house.

② Decide on a strategy.
  • Make a table.
  • Write a number sentence.

③ Make a plan (see Answer).

ANSWER The plan to solve the problem is
Step 1: Make a table showing the number of blocks Joanna rode each day.
Step 2: Add the number of blocks.
Step 3: Solve. $14 + 42 = ?$ or $14 + 14 + 14 + 14 = ?$

Blocks Joanna Rode			Blocks Joanna Rode	
	First day	Second day	First day	Second day
	14	3×14	14	$14 + 14 + 14$
Daily Total	14	42	$14 + 14 + 14 + 14 = ?$	
	$14 + 42 = ?$			

Complete the table. Describe the plan to solve the problem.

1. Chuck puts 6 baseball cards on each page of an album. He puts cards on 57 pages and has 3 cards left over. Each card is more than 2 years old.
   How many baseball cards does Chuck have?

   Understand the Problem

The question	See below.
Facts I need	See below.
Facts I do NOT need	See below.

   Devise a Plan
   Multiply the number of cards per page (6) by ___?___ .
   Then add ___?___ .
   Write a number sentence.
   ## See below.

2. The books on sale cost $45 for 5. The CDs on sale cost $5.75 each. Hayley buys 1 book and she has a coupon for $2.50 off.
   How much does Hayley pay for the book?

   Understand the Problem

The question	See below.
Facts I need	See below.
Facts I do NOT need	See below.

   Devise a Plan   See below.
   Draw a picture. Divide $45 by ___?___ to get the price of 1 book.
   Take the price of 1 book and subtract ___?___ for the coupon.
   Write a number sentence.

Additional Answers

1. **Question:** How many baseball cards does Chuck have?
   Facts I need: the number of cards on each page (6)
   the number of pages (57)
   the number of cards left over (3)

   Facts I do NOT need: The cards are 2 years old.
   Sample plan: Multiply the number of cards per page (6) by the number of pages (57). Then add the leftover cards (3). Write a number sentence.

2. **Question:** How much does Hayley pay for the book?
   Facts I need: Books on sale cost $45 for 5.
   Hayley buys 1 book.
   She has a coupon for $2.50 off.
   Facts I do NOT need: CDs on sale cost $5.75 each.
   Sample plan: Draw a picture. Divide $45 by 5 to get the price of 1 book. Take the price of 1 book and subtract $2.50 for the coupon. Write a number sentence.

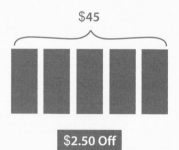

$45

$2.50 Off

TRY IT Understand and Plan

Objectives

Students will practice devising a plan for solving a problem by deciding which strategy makes it easier to solve. Have students turn to the Understand and Plan activity page in their Activity Book and read the directions with them.

Students should copy the problems from the Activity Book into their Math Notebook as necessary and solve them there.

- Analyze a story problem by identifying the question, recognizing relevant information, and developing a solution strategy.

Analyze Story Problems (B)
Understand and Plan

Explain the steps needed to solve the problem.

1. The candle store sold 169 candles on Monday and 198 candles on Tuesday. Each candle cost $3.

   How many more candles did the store sell on Tuesday than on Monday? **See below.**

Choose the answer.

2. Which question is being asked in this problem?

   Jim bought 4 pounds of apples and 6 pounds of oranges.
   Jim bought how many more pounds of oranges than apples?

   A. What is the difference between the weight of apples Jim bought and the weight of oranges he bought?

   B. How many pounds of apples did Jim buy?

   C. How many pounds of apples and oranges combined did Jim buy?

3. Johnny is building a scratching post for his cats. He needs a piece of wood $1\frac{1}{2}$ feet long for the base and a piece of wood twice that length for the post. There are 4 pieces of carpeting on the post.

   How long a piece of wood does Johnny need to buy? Choose the correct calculation.

   A. $1\frac{1}{2} + 2$

   B. $1\frac{1}{2} + 4$

   C. $1\frac{1}{2} + 1\frac{1}{2} + 1\frac{1}{2}$

   D. $1\frac{1}{2} + 2 + 4$

MATHEMATICAL REASONING   276   ANALYZE STORY PROBLEMS (B)

---

4. Which information is necessary to solve this problem?

   There were 58 blackbirds and 6 sparrows sitting in a tree. At 12:30 p.m., 26 more blackbirds landed on the tree, and 12 blackbirds flew away.

   How many blackbirds were left on the tree?

   A. 58 blackbirds, 26 blackbirds, 12 blackbirds

   B. 58 blackbirds, 26 blackbirds, 6 sparrows, 12 blackbirds

   C. 58 blackbirds, 12:30 p.m., 12 blackbirds

5. Which option shows steps that could be used to solve this problem?

   Joanne drove 126 miles the first day. She drove twice as far the second day.

   How far did Joanne drive in two days?

   A. Add 126 and 126 and then multiply by 2.

   B. Add 126 and 126 and then divide by 2.

   C. Multiply 126 by 2 and then add 126.

6. Which **two** options show steps that could be used to solve this problem?

   Olivia has two soup mixes in her cupboard. One mix makes 18 ounces of soup and one mix makes 24 ounces of soup. Each bowl holds 6 ounces of soup.

   How many bowls of soup can Olivia make?

   A. **Step 1:** Divide 18 by 6.
      Step 2: Divide 24 by 6.
      Step 3: Add the two quotients.

   B. **Step 1:** Add 18 and 24.
      Step 2: Divide the sum by 6.

   C. **Step 1:** Divide 18 by 6.
      Step 2: Divide 24 by 6.
      Step 3: Subtract the two quotients.

MATHEMATICAL REASONING   277   ANALYZE STORY PROBLEMS (B)

---

7. Which **two** options show steps that could be used to solve this problem?

   Tickets to a concert cost $25 for adults and $13 for children.

   How much would tickets cost for 3 adults and 3 children?

   A. **Step 1:** Subtract $13 from $25.
      Step 2: Multiply the answer by 3.

   B. **Step 1:** Multiply $25 by 3.
      Step 2: Multiply $13 by 3.
      Step 3: Add the two products.

   C. **Step 1:** Add $25 and $13.
      Step 2: Multiply the answer by 3.

MATHEMATICAL REASONING   278   ANALYZE STORY PROBLEMS (B)

Additional Answers

1. **Example:** Subtract the number of candles sold on Monday from the number of candles sold on Tuesday.

Analyze Story Problems (C)

Lesson Overview

GET READY Wildlife Count	5 minutes	OFFLINE
LEARN Bakery Stories	15 minutes	OFFLINE
LEARN Amusement Park Fun	20 minutes	OFFLINE
TRY IT What Are the Steps?	10 minutes	OFFLINE
CHECKPOINT	10 minutes	ONLINE

▶ Lesson Objectives

Analyze a story problem by identifying the question, recognizing relevant information, and developing a solution strategy.

▶ Prerequisite Skills

Determine whether addition, subtraction, multiplication, or division is the appropriate operation to use to solve a story problem and solve the problem.

▶ Content Background

Students will use the first two steps of the 4-step problem-solving plan to analyze story problems and create solution strategies. They will learn to identify the question in a story problem. They'll also learn to identify the information they need and the information they do not need to solve the problem.

Solving a story problem is a strategic process; it is often not a straightforward one. The following 4-step problem-solving method was developed by George Pólya, and it is an effective way to solve a variety of story problems: (1) understand the problem; (2) devise a plan; (3) carry out the plan; and (4) look back.

If students have difficulty with the first step of this process—understand the problem—it can interfere with their ability to solve the problem. The secret to success is in students' ability to carefully read the problem, reword the problem, analyze the question, and find relationships among the given pieces of information. Once students complete these steps, they can recognize relevant and irrelevant information and gain the confidence to proceed to the second step— devise a plan. They devise their plan by deciding on an effective strategy for solving the problem.

In this lesson, students will continue to focus on the first step of Pólya's problem-solving plan. They will focus on identifying the question and the relevant and irrelevant information. Students should realize that there is often more than one way to solve a problem and more than one strategy they can use. By using many different strategies, they learn to be flexible in their problem solving and learn that some strategies are more efficient than others.

Materials to Gather

SUPPLIED

Problem-Solving Plan (printout)
Amusement Park Fun activity page
What Are the Steps? activity page

Advance Preparation

- Print the Problem-Solving Plan. Save it for use throughout the lesson.
- For the Learn: Bakery Stories activity, write the following two problems:

  Problem 1: The baker used 25 cups of white flour, 2 cups of whole wheat flour, and 7 cups of sugar each day. How much flour did the baker use in 5 days?

  Problem 2: The baker sold 50 boxes of cookies and 20 pies on Saturday. She sold 30 boxes of cookies on Sunday. If the baker sold each box of cookies for $8, how much money did she earn selling cookies on Saturday and Sunday?

GET READY Wildlife Count

OFFLINE 5 min

Students will use what they know about the problem-solving plan to solve a unique story problem that requires common knowledge about animals to get all the needed information.

Gather the Problem-Solving Plan.

1. Give students the Problem-Solving Plan. Review the first two steps of the plan with them.

2. Present the following problem to students:
   - The wildlife count showed that there were 1,000 deer, 500 birds, and 50 snakes. How many feet were there?

3. Have students follow the problem-solving plan to explain what they understand about the problem, which information they need, and which information they do not need. Students should also recognize that they need to know that deer have 4 feet, birds have 2 feet, and snakes have no feet. needed: the number of deer and the number of birds; not needed: the number of snakes

4. Have students share their their plan to solve the problem and the order in which they would complete the steps. Answers may include multiplying 4 times 1,000, multiplying 2 times 500, and adding the two products.
   $4 \times 1,000 = 4,000$
   $2 \times 500 = 1,000$
   $4,000 + 1,000 = 5,000$
   There are 5,000 feet in the wildlife count.

Objectives

- Determine whether addition, subtraction, multiplication, or division is the appropriate operation to use to solve a story problem and solve the problem.

LEARN Bakery Stories

OFFLINE 15 min

Students will explain the first two steps for solving a multistep story problem.
Gather the Problem-Solving Plan and the two problems you wrote.

1. Have students read the first story problem. Refer to the Problem-Solving Plan and have students ask themselves the questions listed in the first step.

Objectives

- Analyze a story problem by identifying the question, recognizing relevant information, and developing a solution strategy.

2. Have students ask themselves the following questions to check their understanding of the problem:
   - **What question do I need to answer?** How much flour did the baker use in 5 days?
   - **What facts do I need?** The baker used 25 cups of white flour and 2 cups of whole wheat flour each day.
   - **What facts do I not need?** The baker used 7 cups of sugar each day.

3. Tell students that once they understand the problem, they need to devise a plan to solve it. Refer to the second step of the Problem-Solving Plan. Have students ask themselves the following questions:
   - What are some strategies I've used before that might be good for this problem?
   - Is this a multistep problem?
   - Is there a picture or diagram I could draw?
   - Can I model the problem with objects?
   - What steps will I use to solve the problem?

4. Have students explain the strategies they will use and the steps to solving the problem.

5. Point out that some students might solve the problem by multiplying 5×25, multiplying 5×2, and then adding the products.

   Point out that other students might solve the problem by adding $25 + 2$ and then multiplying 5×27.

   Ask students which way is easier for them and have them explain why, which will give insights into how they problem solve.

6. Have students read the second story problem and ask themselves the questions listed in the first step of the Problem-Solving Plan.

7. Have students ask themselves the following questions to check their understanding of the problem:
   - **What question do I need to answer?** How much money did the baker earn selling cookies on Saturday and Sunday?
   - **What facts do I need?** The baker sold 50 boxes of cookies on Saturday. She sold 30 boxes of cookies on Sunday. The baker sold each box of cookies for $8.
   - **What facts do I not need?** She sold 20 pies on Saturday.

8. Remind students that once they understand the problem, they need to devise a plan to solve it. Refer to the second step of the Problem-Solving Plan. Have students ask themselves the the questions in Step 3 above.

9. Have students explain the strategies they will use and the steps to solving the problem.

10. Point out that some students might solve the problem by multiplying $\$8 \times 50$, multiplying $\$8 \times 30$, and then adding the products. Explain that others might add all the cookies together, $50 + 30$, and then multiply, $\$8 \times 80$. Discuss with students which method they think is easier.

LEARN Amusement Park Fun

Students will analyze a story problem and devise a plan to solve it. Gather the Problem-Solving Plan. Have students turn to the Amusement Park Fun activity page in their Activity Book and read the directions with them.

Students should copy the problems from the Activity Book into their Math Notebook as necessary and solve them there.

1. Read the Worked Example with students. Point out that the solution shows two different strategies that can be used to answer the question. Tell students that they may use any strategy that helps them solve a problem.

2. Read Problem 1 with students. Refer to the Problem-Solving Plan and have students ask themselves the questions listed in the first step.

3. Have students complete the chart to check their understanding of the question and separate the facts into those needed and those not needed.

4. Guide students to devise a plan to solve the problem. Refer to the second step in the Problem-Solving Plan. Have students ask themselves the following questions:

   - What are some strategies I've used before that might be good for this problem?
   - Is this a multistep problem?
   - Is there a picture or diagram I could draw?
   - Can I model the problem with objects?
   - What steps will I use to solve the problem?

5. Have students record their plan to solve the problem.

6. Repeat Steps 1–5 above for Problems 2–5.

Objectives

- Analyze a story problem by identifying the question, recognizing relevant information, and developing a solution strategy.

Tips

Encourage students to use a variety of strategies to solve the problems.

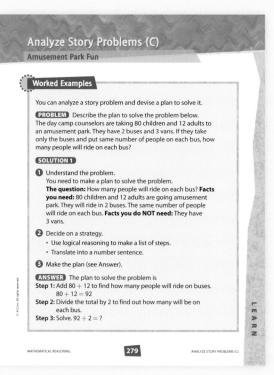

Analyze Story Problems (C)
Amusement Park Fun

Worked Examples

You can analyze a story problem and devise a plan to solve it.

PROBLEM Describe the plan to solve the problem below. The day camp counselors are taking 80 children and 12 adults to an amusement park. They have 2 buses and 3 vans. If they take only the buses and put same number of people on each bus, how many people will ride on each bus?

SOLUTION 1

1. Understand the problem.
   You need to make a plan to solve the problem.
   The question: How many people will ride on each bus? **Facts you need:** 80 children and 12 adults are going amusement park. They will ride in 2 buses. The same number of people will ride on each bus. **Facts you do NOT need:** They have 3 vans.

2. Decide on a strategy.
   - Use logical reasoning to make a list of steps.
   - Translate into a number sentence.

3. Make the plan (see Answer).

ANSWER The plan to solve the problem is
Step 1: Add 80 + 12 to find how many people will ride on buses.
80 + 12 = 92
Step 2: Divide the total by 2 to find out how many will be on each bus.
Step 3: Solve. 92 ÷ 2 = ?

MATHEMATICAL REASONING   279   ANALYZE STORY PROBLEMS (C)

SOLUTION 2

1 Understand the problem (see Solution 1).

2 Decide on a strategy.
  • Make tally charts.

3 Make the plan (see Answer).

ANSWER The plan to solve the problem is

Step 1: Make two tally charts, one for each bus.

Step 2: Make a tally mark for each child and each adult so that there are the same number of tally marks in each chart.

Step 3: Count the tally marks in one chart.

Bus 1	Bus 2

Complete the table. Describe the plan to solve the problem.

1. The campers plan to leave camp at 9:00 a.m. and return at 5:00 p.m. The puppet show is at 2:00 p.m. The drive to and from the amusement park is about 30 minutes each way.

   How much time will the campers have at the park?

Understand the Problem		
The question	Facts I need	Facts I do NOT need
See below.	See below.	See below.

Devise a Plan
What strategy will you use?
What steps will you follow?

Accept any reasonable answer. See below.

2. There are 80 campers and 10 counselors. Two counselors are assigned to each group. There are 100 bottles of water. If each group has the same number of campers, how many campers are in each group?

Understand the Problem		
The question	Facts I need	Facts I do NOT need
See below.	See below.	See below.

Devise a Plan
What strategy will you use?
What steps will you follow?

Accept any reasonable answer. See below.

3. The camp counselors bought 80 child tickets, 12 adult tickets, and 10 tote bags. The child tickets were $9 each, and the adult tickets were $5 each.

   How much did the camp counselors spend on tickets?

Understand the Problem		
The question	Facts I need	Facts I do NOT need
See below.	See below.	See below.

Devise a Plan
What strategy will you use?
What steps will you follow?

Accept any reasonable answer. See below.

Additional Answers

1.

Understand the Problem		
The question	Facts I need	Facts I do NOT need
How much time will the campers have at the park?	The campers plan to leave camp at 9:00 a.m. and return at 5:00 p.m. The drive to and from the amusement park is about 30 minutes each way.	The puppet show is at 2:00 p.m.

Example:

Step 1: Find how many hours there are between 9:00 a.m. and 5:00 p.m.

Step 2: Subtract 30 minutes twice to take away the time spent driving.

2.

Understand the Problem		
The question	Facts I need	Facts I do NOT need
How many campers are in each group?	There are 80 campers and 10 counselors. Two counselors are assigned to each group.	There are 100 bottles of water.

Example:

Step 1: Divide 10 by 2 to find how many groups.

Step 2: Divide 80 by the quotient to find how many campers are in each group.

3.

Understand the Problem		
The question	Facts I need	Facts I do NOT need
How much did the camp counselors spend on tickets?	The camp counselors bought 80 child tickets and 12 adult tickets. The child tickets were $9 each, and the adult tickets were $5 each.	They bought 10 tote bags.

Example:

Step 1: Multiply $9 × 80 to get the cost of the child tickets.

Step 2: Multiply $5 × 12 to find the cost of the adult tickets.

Step 3: Add the products.

4. Counselor Tim spent $20 on 4 patches and $5.50 on snacks. Each patch cost the same amount of money.

How much did each patch cost?

Understand the Problem		
The question	Facts I need	Facts I do NOT need
See below.	See below.	See below.

Devise a Plan
What strategy will you use?
What steps will you follow? **Accept any reasonable answer.**
See below.

5. The bus drivers drove $20\frac{1}{2}$ miles to the amusement park. They parked for 6 hours. They drove an additional $2\frac{1}{2}$ miles when they had to take a detour on the way home.

How many miles did the bus drivers drive on the way home?

Understand the Problem		
The question	Facts I need	Facts I do NOT need
See below.	See below.	See below.

Devise a Plan
What strategy will you use?
What steps will you follow? **Accept any reasonable answer.**

See below.

4.

Understand the Problem		
The question	Facts I need	Facts I do NOT need
How much did each patch cost?	Counselor Tim spent $20 on 4 patches.	Counselor Tim spent $5.50 on snacks.

Example: Divide $20 by 4 to find how much each patch costs.

5.

Understand the Problem		
The question	Facts I need	Facts I do NOT need
How many miles did the bus drivers drive on the way home?	The bus drivers drove $20\frac{1}{2}$ miles to the amusement park. They drove an additional $2\frac{1}{2}$ miles when they had to take a detour on the way home.	They parked for 6 hours.

Example: Add $20\frac{1}{2} + 2\frac{1}{2}$ to find the total number of miles driven on the way home.

OFFLINE
10 min

TRY IT What Are the Steps?

Students will practice analyzing a story problem and making a plan to solve the problem. Have students turn to the What Are the Steps? activity page in their Activity Book and read the directions with them.

Students should copy the problems from the Activity Book into their Math Notebook as necessary and solve them there.

Objectives

- Analyze a story problem by identifying the question, recognizing relevant information, and developing a solution strategy.

Tips   Allow students to refer to the Problem-Solving Plan if needed.

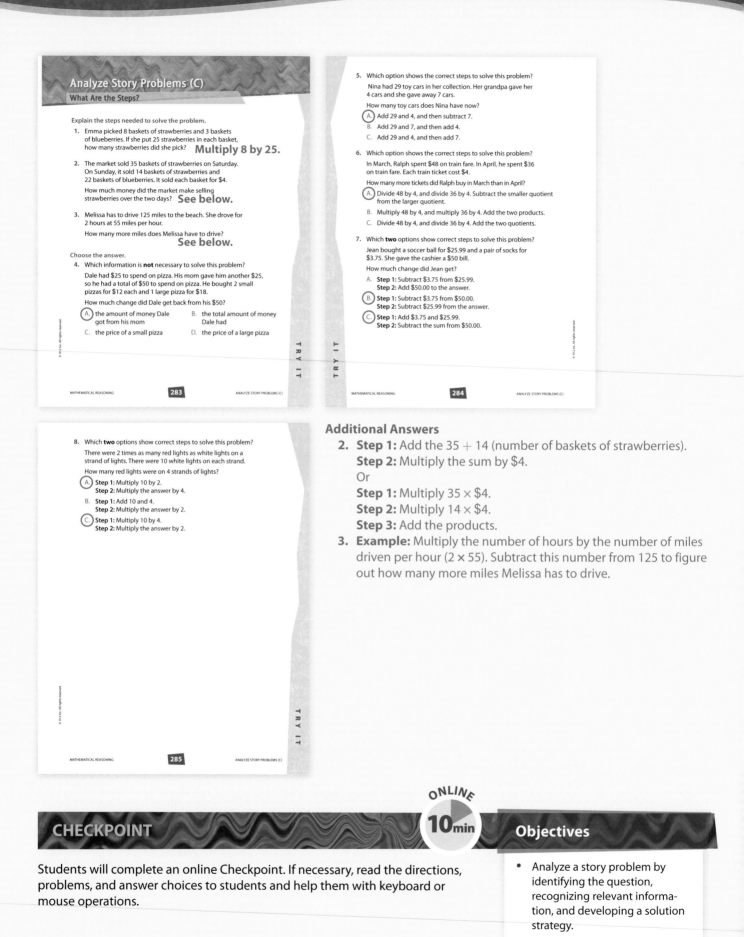

Analyze Story Problems (C)
What Are the Steps?

Explain the steps needed to solve the problem.

1. Emma picked 8 baskets of strawberries and 3 baskets of blueberries. If she put 25 strawberries in each basket, how many strawberries did she pick? **Multiply 8 by 25.**

2. The market sold 35 baskets of strawberries on Saturday. On Sunday, it sold 14 baskets of strawberries and 22 baskets of blueberries. It sold each basket for $4.

   How much money did the market make selling strawberries over the two days? **See below.**

3. Melissa has to drive 125 miles to the beach. She drove for 2 hours at 55 miles per hour.

   How many more miles does Melissa have to drive? **See below.**

Choose the answer.

4. Which information is **not** necessary to solve this problem?

   Dale had $25 to spend on pizza. His mom gave him another $25, so he had a total of $50 to spend on pizza. He bought 2 small pizzas for $12 each and 1 large pizza for $18.

   How much change did Dale get back from his $50?

   A. the amount of money Dale got from his mom
   B. the total amount of money Dale had
   C. the price of a small pizza
   D. the price of a large pizza

TRY IT

---

5. Which option shows the correct steps to solve this problem?

   Nina had 29 toy cars in her collection. Her grandpa gave her 4 cars and she gave away 7 cars.

   How many toy cars does Nina have now?

   A. Add 29 and 4, and then subtract 7.
   B. Add 29 and 7, and then add 4.
   C. Add 29 and 4, and then add 7.

6. Which option shows the correct steps to solve this problem?

   In March, Ralph spent $48 on train fare. In April, he spent $36 on train fare. Each train ticket cost $4.

   How many more tickets did Ralph buy in March than in April?

   A. Divide 48 by 4, and divide 36 by 4. Subtract the smaller quotient from the larger quotient.
   B. Multiply 48 by 4, and multiply 36 by 4. Add the two products.
   C. Divide 48 by 4, and divide 36 by 4. Add the two quotients.

7. Which **two** options show correct steps to solve this problem?

   Jean bought a soccer ball for $25.99 and a pair of socks for $3.75. She gave the cashier a $50 bill.

   How much change did Jean get?

   A. Step 1: Subtract $3.75 from $25.99.
      Step 2: Add $50.00 to the answer.
   B. Step 1: Subtract $3.75 from $50.00.
      Step 2: Subtract $25.99 from the answer.
   C. Step 1: Add $3.75 and $25.99.
      Step 2: Subtract the sum from $50.00.

TRY IT

---

8. Which **two** options show correct steps to solve this problem?

   There were 2 times as many red lights as white lights on a strand of lights. There were 10 white lights on each strand.

   How many red lights were on 4 strands of lights?

   A. Step 1: Multiply 10 by 2.
      Step 2: Multiply the answer by 4.
   B. Step 1: Add 10 and 4.
      Step 2: Multiply the answer by 2.
   C. Step 1: Multiply 10 by 4.
      Step 2: Multiply the answer by 2.

TRY IT

Additional Answers

2. **Step 1:** Add the 35 + 14 (number of baskets of strawberries).
   Step 2: Multiply the sum by $4.
   Or
   Step 1: Multiply 35 × $4.
   Step 2: Multiply 14 × $4.
   Step 3: Add the products.

3. **Example:** Multiply the number of hours by the number of miles driven per hour (2 × 55). Subtract this number from 125 to figure out how many more miles Melissa has to drive.

CHECKPOINT

ONLINE **10** min

Students will complete an online Checkpoint. If necessary, read the directions, problems, and answer choices to students and help them with keyboard or mouse operations.

Objectives

- Analyze a story problem by identifying the question, recognizing relevant information, and developing a solution strategy.

Understand Multistep Problems

▶ Lesson Objectives

Demonstrate when and how to break a multistep story problem into simpler steps.

▶ Prerequisite Skills

Determine whether addition, subtraction, multiplication, or division is the appropriate operation to use to solve a story problem and solve the problem.

▶ Content Background

In this lesson, students will learn to solve multistep problems by making a plan and breaking the problem into simpler steps.

Solving a story problem is a strategic process; it is often not a straightforward one. The following 4-step problem-solving method was developed by George Pólya, and it is an effective way to solve a variety of story problems: (1) understand the problem; (2) devise a plan; (3) carry out the plan; and (4) look back.

Although students use many problem-solving strategies—including invented strategies of their own—one strategy they can use when solving a multistep problem is to break the problem into simpler parts. Solving smaller problems can help students feel more confident when solving more complex problems. In this lesson, students will focus on when and how to break apart a story problem into simpler parts.

▶ Advance Preparation

Print the Problem-Solving Plan.

Materials to Gather

SUPPLIED

Problem-Solving Plan (printout)

Make a Plan activity page

Stepping Through Multistep Problems activity page

GET READY Choose the Operation

ONLINE 5min

Students will read a story problem and decide whether addition, subtraction, multiplication, or division should be used to solve the problem.

Objectives

- Determine whether addition, subtraction, multiplication, or division is the appropriate operation to use to solve a story problem and solve the problem.

LEARN Organize Information in a Problem

Students will use a problem-solving plan to solve a multistep problem. They will break the multistep problem into simpler problems. The strategy they will use will be to make a table to organize the information. The table will help students do each part of the problem.

- Demonstrate when and how to break a multistep story problem into simpler steps.

LEARN Make a Plan

Students will learn to break multistep problems into simpler problems. For this activity, they should focus on the steps to solve the problems. They do not need to get final answers but should record the steps they would use to get an answer. Gather the Problem-Solving Plan. Have students turn to the Make a Plan activity page in their Activity Book and read the directions with them.

   Students should copy the problems from the Activity Book into their Math Notebook as necessary and solve them there.

- Demonstrate when and how to break a multistep story problem into simpler steps.

Tips

Note that students should be expected only to make a plan. They do not need to solve the problem.

1. Give students the Problem-Solving Plan. Review the first two steps of the plan with students.

2. Tell students that when devising a plan to solve the problem, they should ask themselves questions like these:
   - Is this a multistep problem?
   - What are some strategies I've used before that might be good for this problem?
   - Is there a picture or diagram I could draw?
   - Can I model the problem with objects?
   - What steps will I use to solve the problem?

3. Read the Worked Example with students. Point out that this problem is a multistep problem. Remind students that they should break multistep problems into simpler parts to solve them.

   Ask: Suppose Jaime's mother had only a $20 bill and she asked for change. What new step would be needed to find out how much change she received? I would need to subtract the total cost of food from $20.

4. Have students read Problem 1. Have them go through the problem and explain the steps to solve the problem. Students should recognize that they must first find how far the family bicycled and then add the distance the family traveled by train.

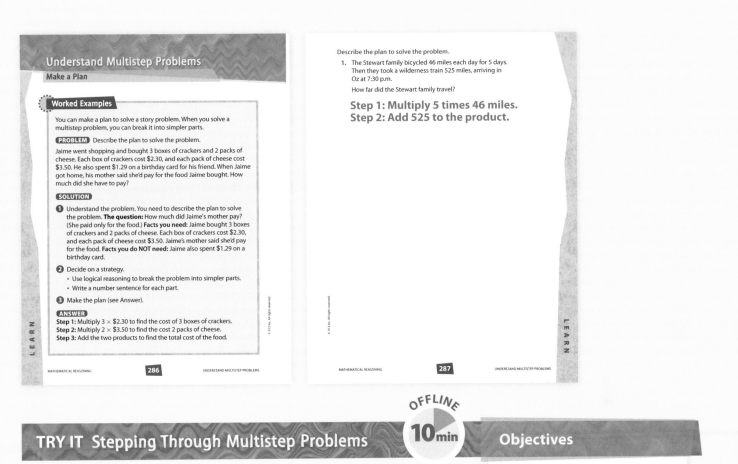

Understand Multistep Problems
Make a Plan

Worked Examples

You can make a plan to solve a story problem. When you solve a multistep problem, you can break it into simpler parts.

PROBLEM Describe the plan to solve the problem.

Jaime went shopping and bought 3 boxes of crackers and 2 packs of cheese. Each box of crackers cost $2.30, and each pack of cheese cost $3.50. He also spent $1.29 on a birthday card for his friend. When Jaime got home, his mother said she'd pay for the food Jaime bought. How much did she have to pay?

SOLUTION

❶ Understand the problem. You need to describe the plan to solve the problem. **The question:** How much did Jaime's mother pay? (She paid only for the food.) **Facts you need:** Jaime bought 3 boxes of crackers and 2 packs of cheese. Each box of crackers cost $2.30, and each pack of cheese cost $3.50. Jaime's mother said she'd pay for the food. **Facts you do NOT need:** Jaime also spent $1.29 on a birthday card.

❷ Decide on a strategy.
  • Use logical reasoning to break the problem into simpler parts.
  • Write a number sentence for each part.

❸ Make the plan (see Answer).

ANSWER

Step 1: Multiply 3 × $2.30 to find the cost of 3 boxes of crackers.
Step 2: Multiply 2 × $3.50 to find the cost 2 packs of cheese.
Step 3: Add the two products to find the total cost of the food.

Describe the plan to solve the problem.

1. The Stewart family bicycled 46 miles each day for 5 days. Then they took a wilderness train 525 miles, arriving in Oz at 7:30 p.m.

   How far did the Stewart family travel?

   Step 1: Multiply 5 times 46 miles.
   Step 2: Add 525 to the product.

TRY IT Stepping Through Multistep Problems

OFFLINE **10 min**

Objectives

Students will practice identifying the steps needed to solve a multistep problem. Have students turn to the Stepping Through Multistep Problems activity page in their Activity Book and read the directions with them.

Students should copy the problems from the Activity Book into their Math Notebook as necessary and solve them there.

• Demonstrate when and how to break a multistep story problem into simpler steps.

Understand Multistep Problems
Stepping Through Multistep Problems

Explain the steps needed to solve the problem.

1. Serena went swimming 5 days in a row. On the first 3 days, she swam for 45 minutes each day. On days 4 and 5, she swam for 60 minutes each day. How many total minutes did Serena spend swimming during those 5 days? **See below.**

Choose the answer.

2. Which option describes the calculations that could be used to solve this problem?

   Word puzzle books are on sale at 6 for $3. Pencils are on sale for $1.50 a box. Alexander bought 12 word puzzle books and a box of pencils. How much did Alexander spend?

   A. Find the cost of 12 word puzzle books. Subtract the price of 1 box of pencils.

   B. Find the cost of 6 word puzzle books. Add this to the price of 1 box of pencils.

   C. Find the cost of 12 word puzzle books. Add this to the price of 1 box of pencils.

3. Which option describes the simpler problems that could be used to solve this problem?

   David has 25 boys and 20 girls in his sports camp. All campers will be going on a boat trip. Each boat can hold 5 people. How many boats does David need altogether?

   A. Add the number of boys and the number of girls at the camp. Divide this number by the number of people who can fit in a boat.

   B. Multiply the number of boys and the number of girls at the camp. Subtract the number of boats.

   C. Add the number of boys and the number of girls at the camp. Multiply this number by the number of people who can fit in a boat.

4. Which option describes the calculations that could be used to solve this problem?

   The Hudson family drove 124 miles each day for 3 days. They then flew 1,254 miles. How far did the Hudson family travel?

   A. Divide 124 by 3. Then add 1,254.

   B. Multiply 124 by 3. Then add 1,254.

   C. Multiply 124 by 3. Then subtract that product from 1,254.

5. Which option describes the calculations that could be used to solve this problem?

   Janine rode 34 miles on her bike the first day of her trip. On the second day, she rode twice as far. How far did Janine ride in two days?

   A. Add 34 and 2. Then add 2 to the sum.

   B. Multiply 34 by 2. Then add 34.

   C. Divide 34 by 2. Then add 2.

6. Which option describes the calculations that could be used to solve this problem?

   Noah earned $320 one week and $264 the following week. He makes $8 an hour. How many hours did Noah work in two weeks?

   A. Divide $320 by $8. Then add $264.

   B. Divide $320 by 8. Divide $264 by 8. Multiply the two quotients.

   C. Divide $320 by 8. Divide $264 by 8. Add the two quotients.

7. Which **two** options show the correct steps to solve this problem?

   Richard bought 5 mystery books and 3 sports books. Each book cost $4. How much money did Richard spend?

   A. Multiply 5×3. Then add $4 to the product.

   B. Add 5 and 3. Then multiply the total by $4.

   C. Multiply $5 \times \$4$. Then multiply $3 \times \$4$. Then add the 2 products together.

Additional Answers

1. **Example:** Multiply 3×45. Multiply 2×60. Add the products.

CHECKPOINT

ONLINE 10 min

Students will complete an online Checkpoint. If necessary, read the directions, problems, and answer choices to students and help them with keyboard or mouse operations.

Objectives

- Demonstrate when and how to break a multistep story problem into simpler steps.

Estimate to Predict Solutions

Lesson Overview

Skills Update	5 minutes	ONLINE
GET READY Choose the Operation	5 minutes	ONLINE
LEARN Estimate Sums and Differences	15 minutes	ONLINE
LEARN Estimate Products and Quotients	15 minutes	ONLINE
TRY IT Estimation and Story Problems	10 minutes	ONLINE
CHECKPOINT	10 minutes	ONLINE

▶ **Lesson Objectives**

Use estimation to predict a solution to a story problem and to determine whether calculations are reasonable.

▶ **Prerequisite Skills**

Determine whether addition, subtraction, multiplication, or division is the appropriate operation to use to solve a story problem and solve the problem.

▶ **Content Background**

Students will learn to estimate the answer to a story problem and use estimation to determine whether the calculations used to solve a problem are reasonable. They will make decisions about when to estimate. They'll make an estimate to predict the solution to a story problem, compare their prediction against the final answer, and verify that the answer is reasonable.

In math problems, an *estimate* is an approximate amount. When students estimate, they find "about how many." Words such as *about, near, a little more than, a little less than, approximately,* and *almost* before a number signal that the number is an estimate, a more convenient number that's close to the exact number. An estimate, or an approximate calculation, is sufficient and appropriate in many everyday situations. However, an estimate would not be best when paying a bill. So in some situations, estimation is inappropriate. Yet in everyday life an overestimate, or an approximation that is obviously greater than the exact number, is often desirable. For example, a customer wants to buy two items. The item are priced at $55.48 and $44.95. If the customer rounded each number to the nearest dollar, he would get $55 and $45, respectively. The sum of $55 and $45 is $100. But if the customer brought only $100 to the store, he would not have enough money, because the exact cost is $100.43. In this case, an overestimate would be better.

When students estimate, they round numbers to make it easy to get a quick estimate. When they learn to round numbers, they use *boundary numbers,* which are the numbers less than and greater than the target number that they're rounding. For example, to round the target number 845 to the nearest hundred, the boundary numbers are 800 and 900. Students decide whether 845 is closer to 800 or to 900. The answer is that 845 rounded to the nearest hundred is 800. The selection of boundary numbers depends on whether the problem asks for rounding to the nearest ten, hundred, or thousand. Then students identify the boundary number that is closest to the target number.

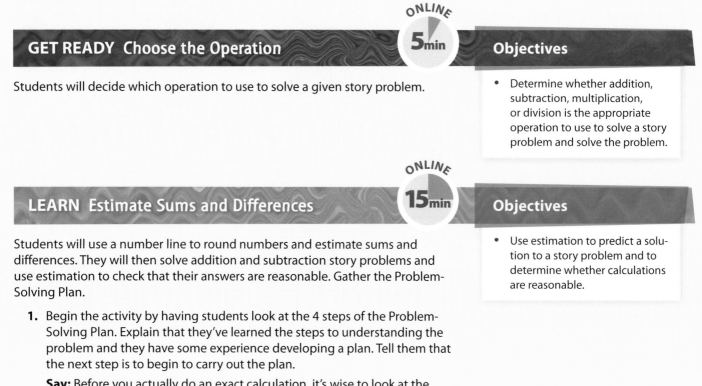

When rounding numbers to make estimates, students usually round to the highest place value, or to a place value that makes the calculation the easiest. Rounding and estimation are two skills that are very useful in everyday situations.

Students will continue to use the 4-step problem-solving plan developed by George Pólya. It is an effective way to solve a variety of story problems. The four steps include (1) understand the problem; (2) devise a plan; (3) carry out the plan; and (4) look back.

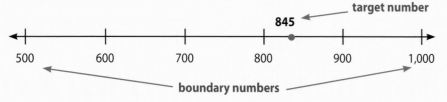 Advance Preparation

Print the Problem-Solving Plan. Save it for use throughout the lesson.

GET READY Choose the Operation

ONLINE
5min

Objectives

Students will decide which operation to use to solve a given story problem.

- Determine whether addition, subtraction, multiplication, or division is the appropriate operation to use to solve a story problem and solve the problem.

LEARN Estimate Sums and Differences

ONLINE
15min

Objectives

Students will use a number line to round numbers and estimate sums and differences. They will then solve addition and subtraction story problems and use estimation to check that their answers are reasonable. Gather the Problem-Solving Plan.

- Use estimation to predict a solution to a story problem and to determine whether calculations are reasonable.

1. Begin the activity by having students look at the 4 steps of the Problem-Solving Plan. Explain that they've learned the steps to understanding the problem and they have some experience developing a plan. Tell them that the next step is to begin to carry out the plan.

   Say: Before you actually do an exact calculation, it's wise to look at the problem and get an estimate of the answer so that later you can check to see if your answer is reasonable. You can use "friendly numbers" to make the problems easier. For example, if you are adding 320 to another number, you could use the friendly number 300 as an estimate.

2. Tell students that they can use different estimation strategies to predict an approximate answer and check the reasonableness of answers. Explain that an answer is reasonable if the estimate or approximate answer is close to the exact answer.

LEARN Estimate Products and Quotients

ONLINE 15min

Students will review patterns of multiplying and dividing by 10 as a strategy to help them estimate the answers to multiplication and division story problems. They will also solve multiplication and division story problems using the 4-step problem-solving plan. And they'll estimate to check that their answers are reasonable.

Gather the Problem-Solving Plan.

Tips Note that students may find that a multiplication facts chart will help them decide how best to round dividends in the division problems.

Objectives

- Use estimation to predict a solution to a story problem and to determine whether calculations are reasonable.

TRY IT Estimation and Story Problems

ONLINE 10min

Students will complete an online Try It. If necessary, read the directions, problems, and answer choices to students and help them with keyboard or mouse operations.

Tips Review how to round numbers to the greatest place value to estimate sums, differences, and products and how to round using basic facts to estimate quotients.

Objectives

- Use estimation to predict a solution to a story problem and to determine whether calculations are reasonable.

CHECKPOINT

ONLINE 10min

Students will complete an online Checkpoint. If necessary, read the directions, problems, and answer choices to students and help them with keyboard or mouse operations.

Objectives

- Use estimation to predict a solution to a story problem and to determine whether calculations are reasonable.

Strategies to Solve Complex Problems

Lesson Overview

GET READY Break Down Complex Problems	5 minutes	ONLINE
LEARN Problem-Solving Strategies	15 minutes	OFFLINE
LEARN Learn More Strategies	15 minutes	OFFLINE
TRY IT Strategy Practice	15 minutes	OFFLINE
CHECKPOINT	10 minutes	ONLINE

▶ Lesson Objectives

Apply strategies and results from a simpler story problem to either a more complex problem or to a similar problem.

▶ Prerequisite Skills

- Demonstrate an understanding of connections between similar addition or subtraction computation problems, involving sums and minuends up through 1,000.
- Analyze a story problem by identifying the question, recognizing relevant information, and developing a solution strategy.
- Demonstrate when and how to break a multistep story problem into simpler steps.

▶ Content Background

Students will learn to apply strategies or results from a simpler problem to a more complex problem.

Effective problem solvers use certain strategies over and over to solve different problems. In order for students to do this, they need to recognize similarities between problems. One problem-solving strategy they can employ is to use a simpler problem to solve a more complex problem. When using this strategy, students begin to see that instead of treating each problem as a new experience, they can apply successful strategies used in solving simple problems to solve more complex problems. More complex problems can include problems with greater numbers, problems with fractions and decimals, and multistep problems.

The following 4-step problem-solving plan was developed by George Pólya, and it is an effective way to solve a variety of story problems: (1) understand the problem; (2) devise a plan; (3) carry out the plan; and (4) look back. As students work on simple and complex problems, they should follow this plan. It is in the "devise a plan" step that students will decide if they can use a simpler problem to solve a more complex one.

▶ Advance Preparation

Print the Problem-Solving Plan. Save it for use throughout the lesson.

Materials to Gather

SUPPLIED

blocks – K (10 green)

Problem-Solving Plan (printout)

Problem-Solving Strategies activity page

Learn More Strategies activity page

Strategy Practice activity page

GET READY Break Down Complex Problems

Objectives

- Demonstrate an understanding of connections between similar addition or subtraction computation problems, involving sums and minuends up through 1,000.
- Analyze a story problem by identifying the question, recognizing relevant information, and developing a solution strategy.
- Demonstrate when and how to break a multistep story problem into simpler steps.

Students will read questions related to a story problem and decide if they would need to break the problem down into simpler steps to solve it.

LEARN Problem-Solving Strategies

Objectives

- Apply strategies and results from a simpler story problem to either a more complex problem or to a similar problem.

Students will use the draw-a-sketch strategy and the guess-and-test strategy to understand and solve problems. They will will use charts and tables to organize the information. Gather the Problem-Solving Plan. Have students turn to the Problem-Solving Strategies activity page in their Activity Book and read the directions with them.

Students should copy the problems from the Activity Book into their Math Notebook as necessary and solve them there.

1. Tell students that they will use the draw-a-sketch strategy and the guess-and-test strategy to understand and solve story problems.

2. Review the Problem-Solving Plan with students. Emphasize the second step, "devise a plan," and draw students' attention to the list of possible problem-solving strategies.

3. Read the first Worked Example with students. Go over each part of the Problem-Solving Plan as you go through the problem. When students are ready to calculate 8×14, ask them to make an estimate. They can think of it as 8×15 and calculate 8×10 plus 8×5 and add $80 + 40 = 120$ to get an estimate. Be sure students understand and can verify the answer.

4. Have students look at Problem 1. Discuss how this problem is similar to the Worked Example. Ask students how many beads are in each pattern. 4 red, 5 clear, and 4 black for a total of 13 beads in each pattern

    Ask: How many clear beads are in each pattern? 5

    Ask: How many copies of the pattern will it take to use 15 clear beads? 3

    Ask: How many beads will be in 1 necklace? $3 \times 13 = 39$ beads in 1 necklace

    Ask: How can you find out how many beads are in 4 necklaces? multiply 4×39

    Ask: How could you estimate your answer? multiply 4×40 to get an estimate of 160

5. Read the second Worked Example with students. This problem employs the guess-and-test strategy, using a table to keep track of the guesses. Discuss the benefits of using the table to organize the information generated with the guess-and-test strategy.

6. Have students do Problem 2, following the steps in the Worked Example. In this problem the numbers are greater, so students may start with guesses that are multiples of 10. They may guess 10 for the number of tulips, and find that it's too low. They may jump to 20 and find that it's too high. A guess of 15 will work.

Have students do the "look back" step to make sure they answered the question asked in the problem and did their calculations correctly.

Remind students that they are getting experience with a wide range of strategies that will help them be better problem solvers.

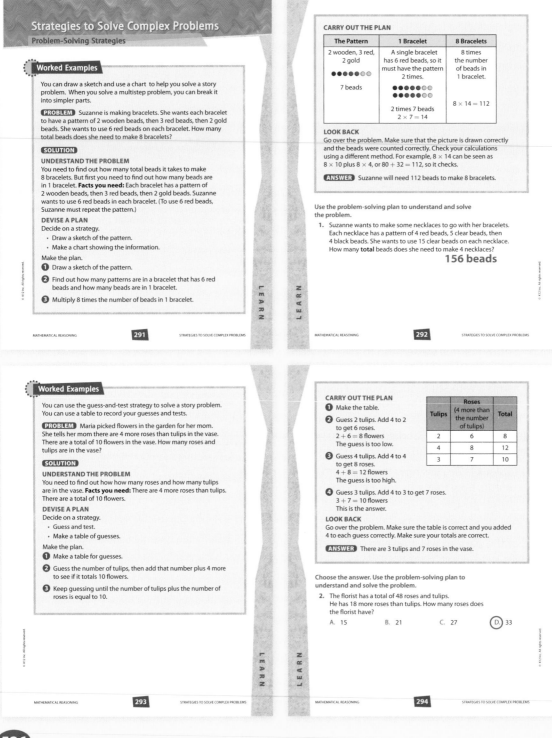

LEARN Learn More Strategies

Objectives

- Apply strategies and results from a simpler story problem to either a more complex problem or to a similar problem.

Students will use tables and models to understand and solve story problems. They will use the results from a simpler problem-solving activity to solve a more complex problem. Gather the K blocks and the Problem-Solving Plan. Have students turn to the Learn More Strategies activity page in their Activity Book and read the directions with them.

Students should copy the problems from the Activity Book into their Math Notebook as necessary and solve them there.

1. Read the first Worked Example with students. Use the Problem-Solving Plan to guide students through the problem. Emphasize the benefit of using a table to organize the information in the problem. Discuss how students can use the answer from the first part of the problem to answer the second question.

2. Have students complete Problem 1 on their own.

3. Read the second Worked Example with students. Explain that the problem in this Worked Example is a complex problem, but if it is broken down into smaller, simpler problems, it becomes easier to solve.

4. Have students solve Problem 2 on their own.

5. Discuss with students that these were difficult problems but that by making a plan and using several strategies, the problems were much easier to solve.

Strategies to Solve Complex Problems
Learn More Strategies

Worked Examples

You can find a pattern in a table to solve a story problem.

PROBLEM Marcus volunteers 9 hours every 2 weeks at the library. He made the following table to figure out how many hours he will volunteer in 8 weeks. How long will it take Marcus to volunteer 63 hours?

Week	Hours Volunteered
2	9
4	18
6	27
8	36

SOLUTION

UNDERSTAND THE PROBLEM
You need to find out how long it will take Marcus to volunteer 63 hours.
Facts you need: Marcus volunteers 9 hours every 2 weeks.

DEVISE A PLAN
Decide on strategies.
- Make a table.
- Look for a pattern.

Make the plan.
❶ Make a table.
❷ Find the pattern in Marcus's table.

❸ Extend the pattern until the number of hours volunteered is 63.

CARRY OUT THE PLAN
Make a table. The Week column increases by 2 with each row. The Hours Volunteered column increases by 9 with each row.

Week	Hours volunteered
2	9
4	18
6	27
8	36
10	45
12	54
(14)	63

LOOK BACK
Go over the problem. Make sure you answered the question asked. Make sure the table is correct and you added 9 to each row correctly. Check your answer. Notice that 63 is in the 7th row and that 7×9 is 63, so it checks.

ANSWER It will take Marcus 14 weeks to volunteer 63 hours.

Use the problem-solving plan to understand and solve the problem.

1. Marcus volunteers 9 hours every 2 weeks at the library. How long will it take Marcus to volunteer 90 hours? **20 weeks**

Worked Examples

You can solve some story problems by solving simpler problems using a table. You can look for a pattern in that table and then use the pattern to solve the more complex problem.

PROBLEM What is the distance around 50 triangular animal pens when they are set next to each other as shown? Each side = 1 unit, and all sides are the same length.

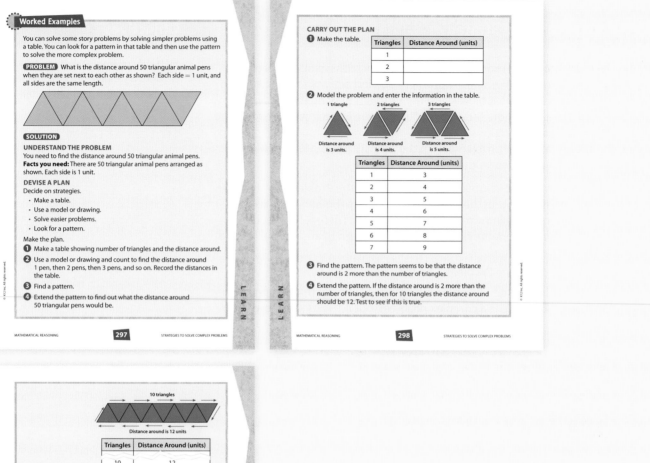

SOLUTION

UNDERSTAND THE PROBLEM
You need to find the distance around 50 triangular animal pens.
Facts you need: There are 50 triangular animal pens arranged as shown. Each side is 1 unit.

DEVISE A PLAN
Decide on strategies.
- Make a table.
- Use a model or drawing.
- Solve easier problems.
- Look for a pattern.

Make the plan.
❶ Make a table showing number of triangles and the distance around.
❷ Use a model or drawing and count to find the distance around 1 pen, then 2 pens, then 3 pens, and so on. Record the distances in the table.
❸ Find a pattern.
❹ Extend the pattern to find out what the distance around 50 triangular pens would be.

CARRY OUT THE PLAN

❶ Make the table.

Triangles	Distance Around (units)
1	
2	
3	

❷ Model the problem and enter the information in the table.

1 triangle — Distance around is 3 units.
2 triangles — Distance around is 4 units.
3 triangles — Distance around is 5 units.

Triangles	Distance Around (units)
1	3
2	4
3	5
4	6
5	7
6	8
7	9

❸ Find the pattern. The pattern seems to be that the distance around is 2 more than the number of triangles.

❹ Extend the pattern. If the distance around is 2 more than the number of triangles, then for 10 triangles the distance around should be 12. Test to see if this is true.

---

10 triangles — Distance around is 12 units

Triangles	Distance Around (units)
10	12

The pattern works.
For 50 triangles, the distance around would be 50 + 2 = 52.

Triangles	Distance Around (units)
50	52

LOOK BACK
Go over the problem. Make sure you answered the question asked. Make sure the table is correct. Look for another way to explain it. Notice that with 10 triangles, there are 5 sides that make the distance along the top of the figure and 5 that make the distance along the bottom. So there are 5 + 5 sides on the top and bottom and 2 end sides that make the total distance of 12 units around the animal pens. If there were 50 triangles, there would be 25 + 25 sides on the top and bottom and 2 end sides, for a total of 52 units around the pens.

ANSWER The distance around 50 animal pens, arranged as shown, is 52 units.

Use the problem-solving plan to understand and solve the problem.

2. What is the distance around 100 triangular animal pens when they are set next to each other as shown? Each side = 1 unit, and all sides are the same length.

102 units

TRY IT Strategy Practice

Students will practice using a variety of strategies to solve complex story problems. Gather the Problem-Solving Plan. Have students turn to the Strategy Practice activity page in their Activity Book and read the directions with them.

Students should copy the problems from the Activity Book into their Math Notebook as necessary and solve them there.

- Apply strategies and results from a simpler story problem to either a more complex problem or to a similar problem.

Tips   Allow students to refer to the Problem-Solving Plan if needed.

Strategies to Solve Complex Problems
Strategy Practice

Use the problem-solving plan to understand and solve the problem.

1. Darlene wanted to make necklaces by using this pattern:

   She wanted to use 8 dotted beads for each necklace. Darlene drew a diagram to figure out the total number of beads she needed for 1 necklace.

   How many beads would Darlene need to make 9 necklaces? **144**

2. Colette's mom asked her to figure out how many oranges were in the fridge. Her mom said there were 2 more oranges than apples. The fridge had a total of 8 pieces of fruit.

   - First Colette guessed 4 oranges. Since there were 2 more oranges than apples, there would be 2 apples and a total of 6 pieces of fruit. Her guess was too low.
   - Next Colette guessed 6 oranges. That meant 4 apples and a total of 10 pieces of fruit, which was too high.
   - Then Colette guessed 5 oranges. That meant there would be 3 apples and a total of 8 pieces of fruit. Right!

   Colette then solved this math problem: Jason wants to buy a total of 56 apples and oranges. He wants 14 more oranges than apples.

   How many oranges should Jason buy? **35**

Choose the answer.

3. Sean earns $15 every 2 weeks babysitting. He wants to know how much he will earn in 6 weeks.

   Sean made this table.

Week	Total Amount Earned
2	$15
4	$30
6	$45

   How long will it take Sean to earn $135?

   A. 7 weeks   B. 9 weeks
   C. 15 weeks   (D.) 18 weeks

4. Julio has 4 boxes of pencils and 2 boxes of crayons. Each box of pencils has 4 pencils, and each box of crayons has 6 crayons. Julio wants to know how many pencils and crayons he has altogether.

   He multiplied 4×4 to calculate that he had 16 pencils. Then he multiplied 2×6 to calculate that he had 12 crayons. He added the products to figure out that he had 28 crayons and pencils altogether.

   Julio got some more pencils and crayons. Now he has 6 boxes of pencils and 8 boxes of crayons.

   How many crayons and pencils does Julio have altogether?

   A. 24   B. 36   C. 48   (D.) 72

TRY IT

CHECKPOINT

Students will complete an online Checkpoint. If necessary, read the directions, problems, and answer choices to students and help them with keyboard or mouse operations.

- Apply strategies and results from a simpler story problem to either a more complex problem or to a similar problem.

Story Problem Reasoning (A)

Lesson Overview

LEARN Three Strategies	20 minutes	ONLINE
LEARN Work Backward	20 minutes	ONLINE
TRY IT Story Problem Practice	20 minutes	OFFLINE

▶ Lesson Objectives

Explain mathematical reasoning in a story problem by using words, numbers, symbols, charts, graphs, tables, diagrams, or models.

▶ Prerequisite Skills

- Justify the procedures selected for addition or subtraction problem-solving situations with sums or minuends up through 1,000.
- Apply strategies and results from a simpler story problem to either a more complex problem or to a similar problem.

▶ Content Background

Students will use different representations to solve story problems and explain their reasoning. They might use diagrams, drawings, or number lines as they work backward or guess and test.

Having students solve a variety of story problems will help them gain confidence so they can solve problems efficiently using a variety of representations. The different representations include, but are not limited to, words, numbers, symbols, charts, graphs, tables, diagrams, and models. One of the most important skills students need to learn is how to explain and justify which strategies are most efficient for them and why. Math helps students learn how to verbalize and write their reasons for making the choices they have made. A strategy that is efficient for one student may not be efficient for another. Encourage students to invent mathematically valid strategies that work best for them in solving new problems.

The following 4-step problem-solving plan was developed by George Pólya, and it is an effective way to solve a variety of story problems: (1) understand the problem; (2) devise a plan; (3) carry out the plan; and (4) look back. The goal of this lesson is to help students become flexible in their thinking, increase their ability to choose a strategy, organize the information in a problem, make a plan, carry out the plan, and look back and be confident in their answer. The only way to know if students have achieved this goal is if they become expert explainers. Effective problem solvers are able to explain what they do during each step.

▶ Advance Preparation

Print the Problem-Solving Plan. Save it for use throughout the lesson.

Materials to Gather

SUPPLIED

Problem-Solving Plan (printout)

Story Problem Practice activity page

LEARN Three Strategies

ONLINE 20min

Students will see that there is often more than one way to solve a story problem, using different strategies. The focus of the activity is more on how students explain their strategies than on the final answer itself.

When students are asked to choose a strategy and work the problem using that strategy, have them write the solution in their Math Notebook. Then have them explain their work to you in terms of the problem-solving plan before moving on. Gather the Problem-Solving Plan.

Objectives

- Explain mathematical reasoning in a story problem by using words, numbers, symbols, charts, graphs, tables, diagrams, or models.

LEARN Work Backward

ONLINE 20min

Students will work with problems that are most easily solved by working backward. They'll see that using a diagram often helps with this type of problem, as well.

Again, students' explanations are the focus of this activity, even more so than the final answer to the problems. Gather the Problem-Solving Plan. Have students explain the working of the problems to you in terms of this plan.

Objectives

- Explain mathematical reasoning in a story problem by using words, numbers, symbols, charts, graphs, tables, diagrams, or models.

TRY IT Story Problem Practice

OFFLINE 20min

Students will practice using different representations to explain their solutions to story problems. Remind them that they may use tables, drawings, time lines, and any other representations that help them solve the problems. Have students turn to the Story Problem Practice activity page in their Activity Book and read the directions with them.

Students should copy the problems from the Activity Book into their Math Notebook as necessary and solve them there.

Objectives

- Explain mathematical reasoning in a story problem by using words, numbers, symbols, charts, graphs, tables, diagrams, or models.

Tips Allow students to use the Problem-Solving Plan to guide them in solving the story problems.

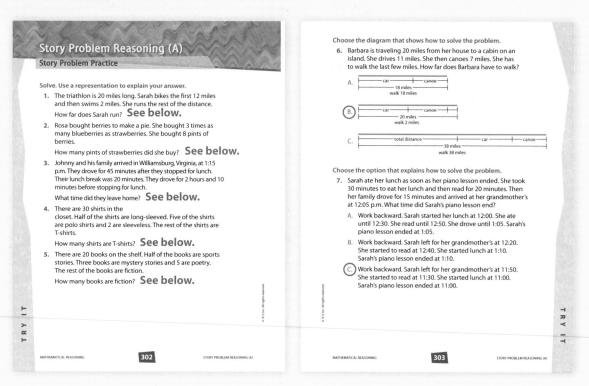

Additional Answers

1. 6 miles; Accept any reasonable answer that shows students explaining their solution.

2. 2 pints; Accept any reasonable answer that shows students explaining their solution.

3. 10:00 a.m.; Accept any reasonable answer that shows students explaining their solution.

4. 8 T-shirts; Accept any reasonable answer that shows students explaining their solution.

5. 2 fiction books; Accept any reasonable answer that shows students explaining their solution.

Story Problem Reasoning (B)

▶ Lesson Objectives

Explain mathematical reasoning in a story problem by using words, numbers, symbols, charts, graphs, tables, diagrams, or models.

▶ Prerequisite Skills

- Justify the procedures selected for addition or subtraction problem-solving situations with sums or minuends up through 1,000.

- Apply strategies and results from a simpler story problem to either a more complex problem or to a similar problem.

▶ Content Background

Students will continue to use different representations to solve story problems and explain their reasoning. They will learn about using a Venn diagram and a double bar graph. Venn diagrams provide a way to see overlapping groups of objects. Double bar graphs provide a way to compare the data of two groups by having two bars side by side.

Having students solve a variety of story problems will help them gain confidence so they can solve problems efficiently using a variety of representations. The different representations include, but are not limited to, words, numbers, symbols, charts, graphs, tables, diagrams, and models. One of the most important skills to learn is how to explain and justify which strategies are most efficient and why. Math helps students learn how to verbalize and write their reasons for making the choices they have made. A strategy that is efficient for one student may not be for another. Encourage students to invent mathematically valid strategies that work best for them in solving new problems.

The following 4-step problem-solving plan was developed by George Pólya, and it is an effective way to solve a variety of story problems: (1) understand the problem; (2) devise a plan; (3) carry out the plan; and (4) look back. The goal of this lesson is to continue to help students become flexible in their thinking, increase their ability to choose a strategy, organize the information in a problem, make a plan, carry out the plan, and look back and be confident in their answer. The only way to know if students have achieved this goal is to see if they've become expert explainers. Effective problem solvers are able to explain what they do during each step.

▶ Advance Preparation

Print the Problem-Solving Plan. Save it for use throughout this lesson.

Materials to Gather

SUPPLIED

Problem-Solving Plan (printout)
Double Bar Graphs activity page
Graphs and Diagrams activity page

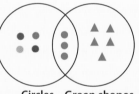

Circles   Green shapes

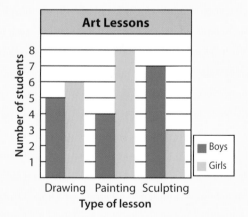

LEARN Venn Diagrams

ONLINE 25min

Students will use Venn diagrams to sort objects and solve story problems.

Objectives

- Explain mathematical reasoning in a story problem by using words, numbers, symbols, charts, graphs, tables, diagrams, or models.

LEARN Double Bar Graphs

OFFLINE 15min

Students will use double bar graphs to solve story problems. Have them turn to the Double Bar Graphs activity page in their Activity Book.

Students should copy the problems from the Activity Book into their Math Notebook as necessary and solve them there.

Objectives

- Explain mathematical reasoning in a story problem by using words, numbers, symbols, charts, graphs, tables, diagrams, or models.

1. Look at the double bar graph in the Worked Example. Before reading the problem, introduce students to the double bar graph. Point out the title, labels, scale, key, and bars on the double bar graph. Explain to students that the scale on bar graphs doesn't always label every number. On this bar graph, the scale is numbered only with even numbers.

   Say: A double bar graph is used to show data for two groups of people, such as adults and children or boys and girls, or other types of groups.

2. Discuss with students how the double bar graph in the Worked Example is different from other bar graphs they have seen. The discussion should include the fact that the ticket sales for adults and children are shown with different-colored bars that are right next to each other. Also, there is a key to tell what each color represents.

3. Ask the following questions to help students read the data on the graph. Have students explain how they found the answer to each question.

   - How many adult tickets were sold on Friday? 25
   - How many child tickets were sold on Friday? 20
   - On Friday, were there more adult tickets or child tickets sold? adult
   - For which day were the most tickets sold? Saturday

4. Go over the Worked Example with students. Help them see how the problem-solving plan can be used to solve this type of problem.

5. Have students try Problems 1 and 2 on their own. In Problem 2, guide students to see that they need to look at the blue bars representing the boys who played basketball and soccer.

534 MATHEMATICAL REASONING

Story Problem Reasoning (B)
Double Bar Graphs

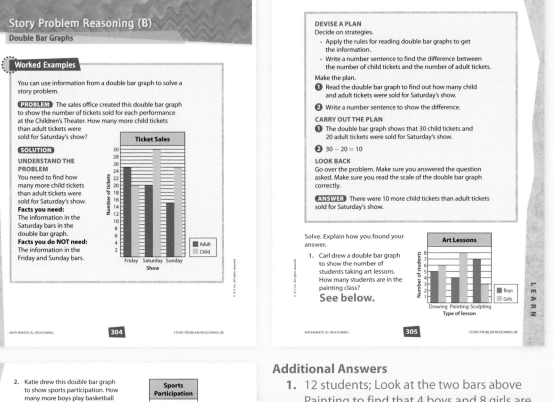

Worked Examples

You can use information from a double bar graph to solve a story problem.

PROBLEM The sales office created this double bar graph to show the number of tickets sold for each performance at the Children's Theater. How many more child tickets than adult tickets were sold for Saturday's show?

SOLUTION

UNDERSTAND THE PROBLEM
You need to find how many more child tickets than adult tickets were sold for Saturday's show.
Facts you need:
The information in the Saturday bars in the double bar graph.
Facts you do NOT need:
The information in the Friday and Sunday bars.

Ticket Sales

DEVISE A PLAN
Decide on strategies.
- Apply the rules for reading double bar graphs to get the information.
- Write a number sentence to find the difference between the number of child tickets and the number of adult tickets.

Make the plan.
① Read the double bar graph to find out how many child and adult tickets were sold for Saturday's show.
② Write a number sentence to show the difference.

CARRY OUT THE PLAN
① The double bar graph shows that 30 child tickets and 20 adult tickets were sold for Saturday's show.
② $30 - 20 = 10$

LOOK BACK
Go over the problem. Make sure you answered the question asked. Make sure you read the scale of the double bar graph correctly.

ANSWER There were 10 more child tickets than adult tickets sold for Saturday's show.

Solve. Explain how you found your answer.

1. Carl drew a double bar graph to show the number of students taking art lessons. How many students are in the painting class.
See below.

Art Lessons

2. Katie drew this double bar graph to show sports participation. How many more boys play basketball than soccer?
See right.

Sports Participation

Additional Answers

1. 12 students; Look at the two bars above Painting to find that 4 boys and 8 girls are in the painting class. Add the two amounts to find that 12 students in all are in the painting class. ($4 + 8 = 12$)

2. Four more boys play basketball than soccer. Look at the blue bars to find that 23 boys play basketball and 19 boys play soccer. Find the difference between the two amounts to find that 4 more boys play basketball than soccer. ($23 - 19 = 4$)

TRY IT Graphs and Diagrams

OFFLINE
20min

Objectives

- Explain mathematical reasoning in a story problem by using words, numbers, symbols, charts, graphs, tables, diagrams, or models.

Students will practice using Venn diagrams and double bar graphs to solve story problems, and will explain their reasoning. Gather the Problem-Solving Plan. Have students turn to the Graphs and Diagrams activity page in their Activity Book and read the directions with them. They may also need some help with terms used in the graphs, such as *multicolored* in Problem 7.

Students should copy the problems from the Activity Book into their Math Notebook as necessary and solve them there.

Tips Allow students to use the Problem-Solving Plan to guide them in solving the story problems.

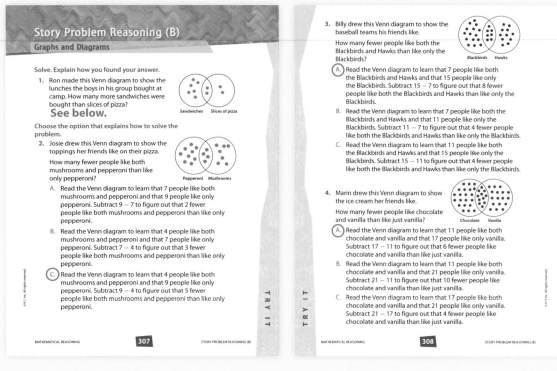

Additional Answers

1. 4; Count the dots in the Sandwiches circle (8) and the dots in the Slices-of-pizza circle (4). Find the difference (4) by subtracting 8 − 4. Or since the 2 dots in the middle are the same for both, subtract the number in the Slices-of-pizza-only section (2) from the number in the Sandwiches-only section (6) to get a difference of 4.

5. Callie drew this Venn diagram to show the subjects her friends like.

How many more people like math and science than like just science?

Math   Science

A. Read the Venn diagram to learn that 24 people like both math and science and that 17 like just science. Subtract 24 − 17 to figure out that 7 more people like math and science than like just science.

B. Read the Venn diagram to learn that 24 people like both math and science and that 19 like just science. Subtract 24 − 19 to figure out that 5 more people like math and science than like just science.

C. Read the Venn diagram to learn that 19 people like both math and science and that 17 like just science. Subtract 19 − 17 to figure out that 2 more people like math and science than like just science.

6. Robyn drew this double bar graph to show the number of children who took music lessons.

How many children took guitar lessons?

Music Lessons

Number of students

Piano   Guitar
Instrument

■ Boys
■ Girls

A. Read the graph to learn that 8 boys took guitar lessons and that 9 girls took guitar lessons. Add 8 + 9 to figure out that 17 children took guitar lessons.

B. Read the graph to learn that 7 boys took guitar lessons and that 3 girls took guitar lessons. Add 7 + 3 to figure out that 10 children took guitar lessons.

C. Read the graph to learn that 8 boys took guitar lessons and that 7 girls took guitar lessons. Add 8 + 7 to figure out that 15 children took guitar lessons.

7. Jackson drew this double bar graph to show the number of animals in the shelter.

How many animals were multicolored?

Shelter Animals

Number of animals

Solid   Multicolored
Color

■ Dogs
■ Cats

A. Read the graph to learn that 2 dogs are multicolored and 8 cats are multicolored. Add 2 + 8 to figure out that 10 animals in the shelter are multicolored.

B. Read the graph to learn that 8 dogs are multicolored and 7 cats are multicolored. Add 8 + 7 to figure out that 15 animals in the shelter are multicolored.

C. Read the graph to learn that 2 dogs are multicolored and 9 cats are multicolored. Add 2 + 9 to figure out that 11 animals in the shelter are multicolored.

8. Tara drew this double bar graph to show the number of fabric patterns.

How many patterns are blue?

Fabric Patterns

Number of patterns

Blue   Red
Pattern

■ Checkered
■ Striped

A. Read the graph to learn that 4 checkered patterns are blue and 9 striped patterns are blue. Add 4 + 9 to figure out that 13 of the patterns are blue.

B. Read the graph to learn that 4 checkered patterns are blue and 8 striped patterns are blue. Add 4 + 8 to figure out that 12 of the patterns are blue.

C. Read the graph to learn that 5 checkered patterns are blue and 9 striped patterns are blue. Add 5 + 9 to figure out that 14 of the patterns are blue.

TRY IT

TRY IT

Story Problem Reasoning (C)

Lesson Overview

GET READY 100 Rhombuses	5 minutes	ONLINE
LEARN Numbers and Tables	20 minutes	OFFLINE
TRY IT Justify Solutions	25 minutes	OFFLINE
CHECKPOINT	10 minutes	ONLINE

▶ Lesson Objectives

Explain mathematical reasoning in a story problem by using words, numbers, symbols, charts, graphs, tables, diagrams, or models.

▶ Prerequisite Skills

- Justify the procedures selected for addition or subtraction problem-solving situations with sums or minuends up through 1,000.
- Apply strategies and results from a simpler story problem to either a more complex problem or to a similar problem.

▶ Content Background

Students will continue to use different representations to solve story problems and explain their reasoning. Specifically they will use tables and the work backward strategy.

Having students solve a variety of story problems will help them gain confidence so that they can solve problems efficiently using a variety of representations. The different representations include, but are not limited to, words, numbers, symbols, charts, graphs, tables, and diagrams or models. One of the most importan t skills for students to learn is how to explain and justify which strategies are most efficient for them and why. Math helps students learn how to verbalize and write their reasons for making the choices they have made. A strategy that is efficient for one student may not be efficient for another. Encourage students to invent mathematically valid strategies that work best for them in solving new problems.

The following 4-step problem-solving plan was developed by George Pólya, and it is an effective way to solve a variety of story problems: (1) understand the problem; (2) devise a plan; (3) carry out the plan; and (4) look back. The goal of this lesson is to help students become flexible in their thinking, increase their ability to choose a strategy, organize the information in a problem, make a plan, carry out the plan, and look back and be confident in their answer. The only way to know if students have achieved this goal is if they become expert explainers. Effective problem solvers are able to explain what they do during each step.

Materials to Gather

SUPPLIED
Problem-Solving Plan (printout)
Justify Solutions activity page

▶ Advance Preparation

- Print the Problem-Solving Plan. Save it for use throughout this lesson.
- For the Learn: Numbers and Tables activity, copy the following two problems into the students' Math Notebook, one problem per page:

  Problem 1: Ron said, "I am thinking of a secret number. Add 7 to this number. Multiply the sum by 3. The answer is 183." What is Ron's secret number?

  Problem 2: Serena's swim team hires 3 coaches for every 22 swimmers. This season, the team hired 12 coaches. How many swimmers are on the team?

GET READY 100 Rhombuses

ONLINE 5 min

In this activity, students will use the pattern in a simpler problem to solve a more difficult problem. The problem involves using small rhombus shapes to make a big rhombus shape. Remind students that a rhombus is a 4-sided shape whose sides are equal in length.

Tips If students have difficulty understanding the problem, have them model the pictures with rhombuses (L blocks).

Objectives

- Apply strategies and results from a simpler story problem to either a more complex problem or to a similar problem.

LEARN Numbers and Tables

OFFLINE 20 min

Students will use a table and the work backward strategy to solve story problems and explain their solutions.

Gather the Problem-Solving Plan. Have students turn to the two problems you copied in their Math Notebook.

PROBLEM 1

1. Tell students they will continue to solve problems using the Problem-Solving Plan. Have students read the first problem that you wrote in their Math Notebook:

   - Ron said, "I am thinking of a secret number. Add 7 to this number. Multiply the sum by 3. The answer is 183." What is Ron's secret number?

   Work through the following steps together, and refer to the Problem-Solving Plan to make sure students understand the problem.

2. Have students ask themselves the following questions as they work through the first two steps of the plan:

   - What operations can I use to solve the problem?
   - How did I solve problems like this in the past?

3. If students are having difficulty, mention that since they know the final number in the problem, the work backward strategy would be one good choice.

Objectives

- Explain mathematical reasoning in a story problem by using words, numbers, symbols, charts, graphs, tables, diagrams, or models.

Tips

Allow students to use counters or base-10 blocks to help them calculate the numbers in the table.

Explain that students can start with the fact that 3 times *the secret number plus 7* is 183. They don't know what *the secret number plus 7* is, but they do know that when they multiply it by 3, they get 183. Start on the right side of the page under the problem in the Math Notebook, and write the following number sentence. Be sure that the box is large enough to write a solution in it. Ask students if they can figure out what number goes in the box. They need to find what number times 3 equals 183.

$$\boxed{\text{secret number}} \times 3 = 183$$

Using the inverse of multiplication, students can solve $183 \div 3$ to find that the number in the box would be 61. Have students write 61 in the box.

4. If students can complete the problem at this point, have them share and carry out their plan. Encourage students to explain which steps they are following and which math skills they are using.

   If students are still having difficulty, explain that Ron's *secret number plus 7* is 61. Now, under the completed number sentence, write this number sentence:

$$\boxed{\boxed{\text{secret number}} + 7} = 61, \text{ so } \_\_ + 7 = 61$$

   Now students only have to figure out what number plus 7 equals 61.

   This time, using the inverse of addition, students can solve $61 - 7 = ?$ to get 54 as Ron's secret number.

   Work with students until they get an answer. If their answer isn't correct, don't mention it; let them go through the steps to discover what is wrong.

5. Have students look at their answer and ask themselves the following questions:

   • Did I answer the question?

   • Does my answer make sense when I reread the problem?

   • If I start with my answer, add 7, and then multiply by 3, do I get 183?

PROBLEM 2

6. Have students read the second problem you wrote in their Math Notebook:

   Serena's swim team hires 3 coaches for every 22 swimmers. This season, the team hired 12 coaches. How many swimmers are on the team?

   Ask students to explain the problem in their own words and explain a strategy for solving it. Have them describe the steps of their plan before solving it.

7. If students have difficulty, mention that when they're given one amount, such as 3 coaches for every 22 players, a table can be a useful strategy. Show students how to make a table like the one here.

Coaches				
Swimmers				

8. Discuss the quantities given in the problem, and show students how to use those quantities to complete the table.

   Say: You know that for every 3 coaches, there are 22 swimmers.

9. Write the numbers *3* and *22* in the second column. Then guide students through completing the table with the following questions:

Coaches	3			
Swimmers	22			

   • If there are 3 more coaches, how many how many coaches will there be? 6
   • If there are 6 coaches, how many swimmers will there be? 44
   • If there is another set of coaches, how many coaches will there be? 9
   • If there are 9 coaches, how many swimmers will there be? 66
   • If there is another set of coaches, how many coaches will there be? 12
   • How many swimmers will there be for 12 coaches? 88

Coaches	3	6	9	12
Swimmers	22	44	66	88

10. Have students look at the answer and compare it to the question in the problem to see if it makes sense.

Tips If students suggest simply multiplying 4 by 22 to get the answer, have them fully explain why that would work. Then have them look at the table as an alternate strategy.

OFFLINE
25min

TRY IT Justify Solutions

Students will practice using different representations to explain their solutions to story problems. Have students turn to the Justify Solutions activity page in their Activity Book and read the directions with them.

   Students should copy the problems from the Activity Book into their Math Notebook as necessary and solve them there.

Tips Allow students to use the Problem-Solving Plan to guide them in solving the story problems.

Objectives

• Explain mathematical reasoning in a story problem by using words, numbers, symbols, charts, graphs, tables, diagrams, or models.

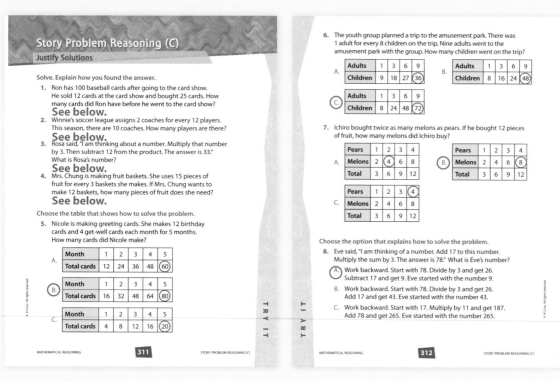

Solve. Explain how you found the answer.

1. Ron has 100 baseball cards after going to the card show. He sold 12 cards at the card show and bought 25 cards. How many cards did Ron have before he went to the card show?
See below.

2. Winnie's soccer league assigns 2 coaches for every 12 players. This season, there are 10 coaches. How many players are there?
See below.

3. Rosa said, "I am thinking about a number. Multiply that number by 3. Then subtract 12 from the product. The answer is 33." What is Rosa's number?
See below.

4. Mrs. Chung is making fruit baskets. She uses 15 pieces of fruit for every 3 baskets she makes. If Mrs. Chung wants to make 12 baskets, how many pieces of fruit does she need?
See below.

Choose the table that shows how to solve the problem.

5. Nicole is making greeting cards. She makes 12 birthday cards and 4 get-well cards each month for 5 months. How many cards did Nicole make?

A.

Month	1	2	3	4	5
Total cards	12	24	36	48	(60)

B.

Month	1	2	3	4	5
Total cards	16	32	48	64	(80)

C.

Month	1	2	3	4	5
Total cards	4	8	12	16	(20)

6. The youth group planned a trip to the amusement park. There was 1 adult for every 8 children on the trip. Nine adults went to the amusement park with the group. How many children went on the trip?

A.

Adults	1	3	6	9
Children	9	18	27	(36)

B.

Adults	1	3	6	9
Children	8	16	24	(48)

C.

Adults	1	3	6	9
Children	8	24	48	(72)

7. Ichiro bought twice as many melons as pears. If he bought 12 pieces of fruit, how many melons did Ichiro buy?

A.

Pears	1	2	3	4
Melons	2	(4)	6	8
Total	3	6	9	12

B.

Pears	1	2	3	4
Melons	2	4	6	(8)
Total	3	6	9	12

C.

Pears	1	2	3	(4)
Melons	2	4	6	8
Total	3	6	9	12

Choose the option that explains how to solve the problem.

8. Eve said, "I am thinking of a number. Add 17 to this number. Multiply the sum by 3. The answer is 78." What is Eve's number?

A. Work backward. Start with 78. Divide by 3 and get 26. Subtract 17 and get 9. Eve started with the number 9.

B. Work backward. Start with 78. Divide by 3 and get 26. Add 17 and get 43. Eve started with the number 43.

C. Work backward. Start with 17. Multiply by 11 and get 187. Add 78 and get 265. Eve started with the number 265.

T R Y   I T

Additional Answers

1. 87; Accept any reasonable explanation. Students may use the work backward strategy and explain that before Ron bought the 25 cards, he had $100 - 25$ or 75 cards. And before he sold the 12 cards, he had $75 + 12$ or 87 cards.

2. 60; Accept any reasonable explanation. Students may explain that they used a table like the following:

Coaches	2	4	6	8	10
Players	12	24	36	48	60

3. 15; Accept any reasonable explanation. Students may explain that they used the work backward strategy and opposite operations to find that $33 + 12 = 45$; $45 \div 3 = 15$.

4. 60; Accept any reasonable explanation. Students may explain that they used a table like the following:

Baskets	3	6	9	12
Fruit	15	30	45	60

CHECKPOINT

ONLINE
10 min

Students will complete an online Checkpoint. If necessary, read the directions, questions, and answer choices to students and help them with keyboard or mouse operations.

Objectives

- Explain mathematical reasoning in a story problem by using words, numbers, symbols, charts, graphs, tables, diagrams, or models.

Explain Solutions to Problems

Lesson Overview		
GET READY Organize the Shapes	10 minutes	OFFLINE
LEARN Explain the Steps	15 minutes	OFFLINE
LEARN Show Multistep Solutions	15 minutes	OFFLINE
TRY IT Express Solutions Clearly	10 minutes	OFFLINE
CHECKPOINT	10 minutes	ONLINE

▶ Lesson Objectives

Express the solution to a story problem clearly and logically with appropriate mathematical notation, terms, and accurate language.

▶ Prerequisite Skills

Explain mathematical reasoning in a story problem by using words, numbers, symbols, charts, graphs, tables, diagrams, or models.

▶ Content Background

Students will solve problems and clearly explain the steps they took, using words, number sentences, and proper mathematical language. They will focus on the "look back" step of the problem-solving plan.

Because every story problem is different, students must be able to clearly and logically express how they solve each problem and give their solution. The goal is to help students become flexible in their thinking, increase their ability to choose a strategy, organize the information in a problem, make a plan, carry out the plan, look back, and be confident in their answer. To measure these goals, students must become expert explainers. Being able to explain problem-solving processes is a key skill in problem solving. The role of the learning coach is critical, not for showing students how to do problems, but for guiding students to ask themselves questions that will lead them to solving the problem in a way that makes sense. Students should ask: "Is my strategy working? Is there another strategy that would be better? Am I on the right path? Is this really going to answer the question? Is there another way to see this?"

In the "look back" step of the problem-solving plan, students should be able to explain their solution and to see if there's a different way to look at the problem that leads to the same solution. The goal of the "look back" step is for students to have complete confidence in their answer and to feel as though they have moved further toward mastering the strategy.

The following 4-step problem-solving plan was developed by George Pólya, and it is an effective way to solve a variety of story problems: (1) understand the problem; (2) devise a plan; (3) carry out the plan; and (4) look back.

▶ Advance Preparation

- Print the Problem-Solving Plan. Save it for use throughout the lesson.
- For the Get Ready: Organize the Shapes activity, gather the blocks and place them in a container. Do not mention to students how many blocks of each type are in the container.

Materials to Gather

SUPPLIED

blocks – A, B, C, D, J (1 red, 1 green, 1 blue of each)

blocks – K (3)

Problem-Solving Plan (printout)

Explain the Steps activity page

Show Multistep Solutions activity page

Express Solutions Clearly activity page

ALSO NEEDED

container

- For the Get Ready: Organize the Shapes activity, draw a three-circle Venn diagram labeled as shown. Make it big enough so that several blocks can fit in each section. Place labels as shown near the edge of the circles.

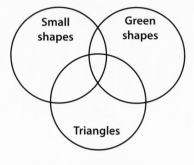

OFFLINE 10min

GET READY Organize the Shapes

Objectives

- Explain mathematical reasoning in a story problem by using words, numbers, symbols, charts, graphs, tables, diagrams, or models.

Students will use a Venn diagram to organize shapes.

Gather the Venn diagram you drew and the container you filled with blocks (A, B, C, D, and J: 1 red, 1 green, 1 blue of each; K: 3).

1. Explain to students what a Venn diagram is.

   Say: A Venn diagram is a drawing with overlapping circles. It is a useful tool for sorting.

2. Show students the Venn diagram with the three labeled circles. Read the following problem to students:

   - William has a basket of shapes in 3 colors. He wants to organize the shapes by placing them into the sections of the Venn diagram.

3. Give students the container of blocks. Have them put the blocks in the appropriate sections of the Venn diagram. Have them explain what each section of the Venn diagram means (small shapes, green shapes, triangles, small green shapes, small triangles, green triangles, small green triangles).

4. After students have placed the blocks, ask:

   - How many small shapes are there? 9 (3 triangles, 3 circles, and 3 rectangles)
   - How many green shapes are there? 8 (3 small triangles, 1 large triangle, 1 small circle, 1 large circle, 1 small rectangle, and 1 large rectangle)
   - How many triangles are there? 6 (3 small triangles, 3 large triangles)
   - What do the shapes that are not small, or green, or triangles have in common? They are all big.
   - How many big shapes are there? 9 (3 triangles, 3 circles, and 3 rectangles)
   - How many shape pieces are there in all? 18 (9 large and 9 small)
   - Is the sum of the small shapes, the green shapes, the triangles, and the big shapes the same as the number of shapes in all? Why or why not? No, because some of the shapes are counted more than once, because they're in more than one circle.

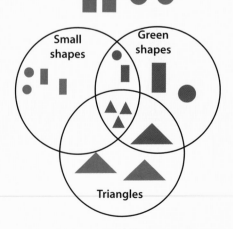

LEARN Explain the Steps

Objectives

- Express the solution to a story problem clearly and logically with appropriate mathematical notation, terms, and accurate language.

Students will solve problems using the problem-solving plan. They will focus on explaining their solution. Gather the Problem-Solving Plan. Have students turn to the Explain the Steps activity page in their Activity Book and read the directions with them.

Students should copy the problems from the Activity Book into their Math Notebook as necessary and solve them there.

1. Tell students that in this lesson they will focus on the "look back" step of the problem-solving plan. Emphasize the importance of being able to explain story-problem solutions in a clear and organized way.

2. Read the Worked Example with students. Make sure they understand how the answer was reached. Point out how each number appears in only one section of the diagram.

3. Ask students to read Problem 1. Have them solve the problem and explain their answer by using words, numbers, and a Venn diagram. Guide students through the steps of the problem-solving plan as was done in the Worked Example. When students are ready to choose a strategy, some may make a list of the numbers from 1 to 30 and circle all the even multiples of 5. Others might write down the multiples of 5 and then circle the even multiples of 5. All students should plan to make a Venn diagram to show the solution that way as well.

As students carry out their plan, help them put labels on their Venn diagram and sort the numbers into the proper place in the diagram.

In the "look back" step, have students say what the three numbers in the overlapping section have in common. Students may notice that the three numbers are all multiples of 10, but they may not realize that this is the same as being multiples of 2 and 5.

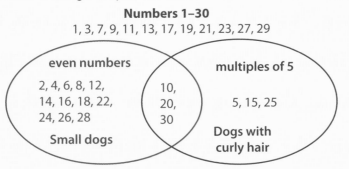

Numbers 1–30
1, 3, 7, 9, 11, 13, 17, 19, 21, 23, 27, 29

even numbers

2, 4, 6, 8, 12,
14, 16, 18, 22,
24, 26, 28

10,
20,
30

multiples of 5

5, 15, 25

Small dogs

Dogs with curly hair

Encourage students to view the Venn diagram as one way to find the solution. Stress the importance of students being able to explain their method and to clearly represent the answer.

Explain Solutions to Problems
Explain the Steps

Worked Examples

You can use a Venn diagram to solve and explain the solution to a story problem.

PROBLEM This weekend, Nick's baseball team gets their uniforms. The coach has asked the players to pick a two-digit number between 1 and 100 to go on their uniform. Nick wants his number to be a multiple of 5 and a multiple of 6. What numbers could be on Nick's uniform?

SOLUTION

UNDERSTAND THE PROBLEM
You need to find what numbers could be on Nick's uniform. You need to find two-digit numbers that are multiples of 5 and multiples of 6. **Facts you need:** The numbers are two-digit numbers. The numbers must be multiples of 5 and multiples of 6. **Facts you do NOT need:** The numbers are between 1 and 100. (All two-digit numbers are between 1 and 100.)

DEVISE A PLAN
Decide on a strategy.
- Draw a diagram.
- Make an organized list.

Make the plan

❶ Draw a Venn diagram with two overlapping circles. Label one circle "Multiples of 5," and label the other circle "Multiples of 6."

❷ Count by 5s to 100. Using a pencil, write the multiples of 5 in the circle labeled for 5s. Then count by 6s to 100. Write the multiples of 6 in the 6s circle. Find the numbers that are multiples of both 5 and 6. Write them in the overlapping section. Make sure that each number is only on the chart 1 time.

❸ Make a list of the numbers that are multiples of both 5 and 6. (the numbers in the overlapping section).

CARRY OUT THE PLAN

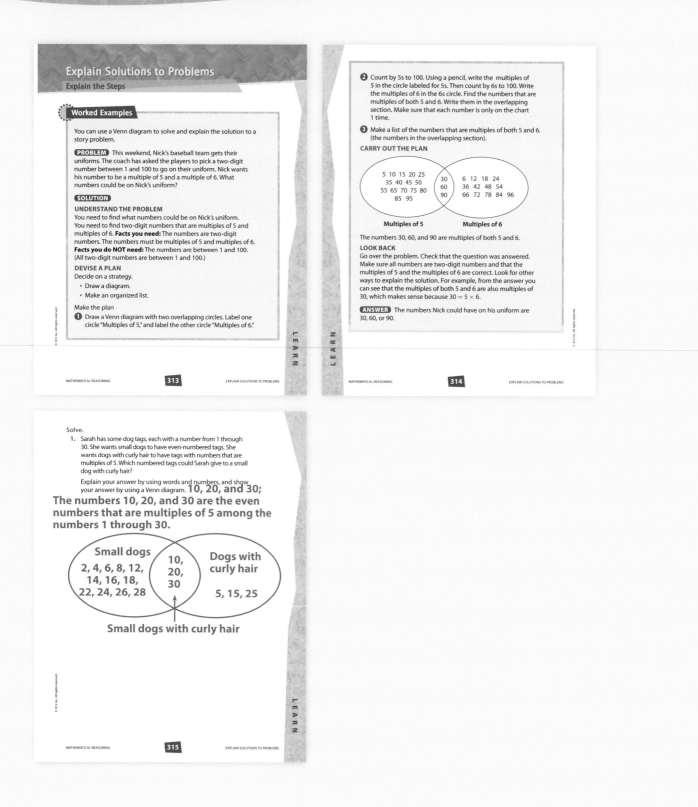

| Multiples of 5 | | Multiples of 6 |

5 10 15 20 25 35 40 45 50 55 65 70 75 80 85 95 — 30 60 90 — 6 12 18 24 36 42 48 54 66 72 78 84 96

The numbers 30, 60, and 90 are multiples of both 5 and 6.

LOOK BACK
Go over the problem. Check that the question was answered. Make sure all numbers are two-digit numbers and that the multiples of 5 and the multiples of 6 are correct. Look for other ways to explain the solution. For example, from the answer you can see that the multiples of both 5 and 6 are also multiples of 30, which makes sense because $30 = 5 \times 6$.

ANSWER The numbers Nick could have on his uniform are 30, 60, or 90.

Solve.

1. Sarah has some dog tags, each with a number from 1 through 30. She wants small dogs to have even-numbered tags. She wants dogs with curly hair to have tags with numbers that are multiples of 5. Which numbered tags could Sarah give to a small dog with curly hair?

Explain your answer by using words and numbers, and show your answer by using a Venn diagram. **10, 20, and 30;**

The numbers 10, 20, and 30 are the even numbers that are multiples of 5 among the numbers 1 through 30.

Small dogs 2, 4, 6, 8, 12, 14, 16, 18, 22, 24, 26, 28 — 10, 20, 30 — **Dogs with curly hair** 5, 15, 25

Small dogs with curly hair

LEARN Show Multistep Solutions

Objectives

Students will use the 4-step problem-solving plan to solve story problems and focus on explaining the solution by using words, numbers, pictures, charts, or objects. Gather the Problem-Solving Plan. Have students turn to the Show Multistep Solutions activity page in their Activity Book and read the directions with them.

Students should copy the problems from the Activity Book into their Math Notebook as necessary and solve them there.

- Express the solution to a story problem clearly and logically with appropriate mathematical notation, terms, and accurate language.

1. Direct students' attention to the Worked Example. Go through each step with them. When students start to carry out the plan, encourage them to explain their thinking and represent it with words, numbers, pictures, charts, and objects.

2. Have students go through similar steps for Problem 1. Guide them to see that they need to find the following: the number of each type of coin, the value of each type of coin, and the total value of all the coins. Have students choose a strategy, but if they have difficulty, suggest that they try a table as shown on the activity page.

- The number of dimes: $16 \times 2 = 32$
- The number of nickels: $20 \div 2 = 10$
- The value of the quarters: 4 quarters in \$1; 16 quarters = \$4.00
- The value of the dimes: 10¢ $\times$ 32 = 320¢ = \$3.20
- The value of the nickels: 5¢ $\times$ 10 = 50¢ = \$0.50
- The value of the pennies: 1¢ $\times$ 20 = 20¢ = \$0.20
- Total value of coins: \$4.00 + \$3.20 + \$0.50 + \$0.20 = \$7.90

Explain Solutions to Problems
Show Multistep Solutions

Worked Examples

You can use a table to solve a story problem and help explain the solution.

PROBLEM Roger received 5 silver dollars for his birthday. When he opened his coin box, he saw that he had twice as many quarters as he had silver dollars. When he put the quarters and silver dollars together, how much money did he have?

SOLUTION

UNDERSTAND THE PROBLEM
You need to find how much money Roger has.
Facts you need: Roger has 5 silver dollars. He has twice as many quarters as silver dollars.

DEVISE A PLAN
Decide on a strategy.
- Make a table.
- Write a number sentence to find the total value.

Make the plan.
❶ Make a table showing how many of each type of coin Roger has.

❷ Find the value of all the coins of the same type (the total value of the quarters and the total value of the silver dollars).

❸ Write a number sentence to add the total value of all the coins.

CARRY OUT THE PLAN
❶ There are twice as many quarters as silver dollars, and there are 5 silver dollars, so there must be 10 quarters.

	Silver Dollars	Quarters
Number	5	10

$5 \times \$1 = \$5$ $10 \times 25¢ = 250¢$ or \$2.50

❷ $\$5 + \$2.50 = \$7.50$

LOOK BACK
Go over the problem. Check that the question was answered. Make sure the table is correct, that you got the right number of quarters, and that you calculated the values correctly.

ANSWER Roger has \$7.50.

Solve.

1. Wendy sorts and counts the coins in her piggy bank. She has 16 quarters. She has twice as many dimes as quarters. She has 20 pennies. She has half as many nickels as pennies. Does Wendy have enough money to buy a toy that costs \$7.82? How do you know?

	Quarters	Dimes	Pennies	Nickels
Number	16	32	20	10

Yes; Wendy has \$7.90, and \$7.90 is more than \$7.82.

TRY IT Express Solutions Clearly

Objectives

Students will practice using the problem-solving plan to solve story problems. The main goal is to have them clearly express solutions. Have students turn to the Express Solutions Clearly activity page in their Activity Book and read the directions with them.

Students should copy the problems from the Activity Book into their Math Notebook as necessary and solve them there.

- Express the solution to a story problem clearly and logically with appropriate mathematical notation, terms, and accurate language.

Tips   Allow students to refer to the Problem-Solving Plan if needed.

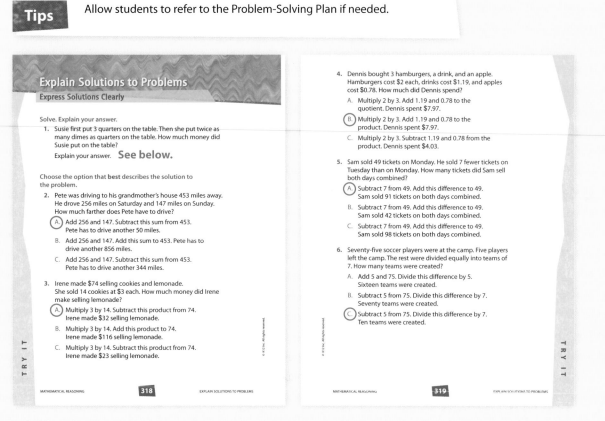

Explain Solutions to Problems
Express Solutions Clearly

Solve. Explain your answer.
1. Susie first put 3 quarters on the table. Then she put twice as many dimes as quarters on the table. How much money did Susie put on the table?
   Explain your answer.   **See below.**

Choose the option that **best** describes the solution to the problem.

2. Pete was driving to his grandmother's house 453 miles away. He drove 256 miles on Saturday and 147 miles on Sunday. How much farther does Pete have to drive?
   - A. Add 256 and 147. Subtract this sum from 453. Pete has to drive another 50 miles.
   - B. Add 256 and 147. Add this sum to 453. Pete has to drive another 856 miles.
   - C. Add 256 and 147. Subtract this sum from 453. Pete has to drive another 344 miles.

3. Irene made $74 selling cookies and lemonade. She sold 14 cookies at $3 each. How much money did Irene make selling lemonade?
   - A. Multiply 3 by 14. Subtract this product from 74. Irene made $32 selling lemonade.
   - B. Multiply 3 by 14. Add this product to 74. Irene made $116 selling lemonade.
   - C. Multiply 3 by 14. Subtract this product from 74. Irene made $23 selling lemonade.

4. Dennis bought 3 hamburgers, a drink, and an apple. Hamburgers cost $2 each, drinks cost $1.19, and apples cost $0.78. How much did Dennis spend?
   - A. Multiply 2 by 3. Add 1.19 and 0.78 to the quotient. Dennis spent $7.97.
   - B. Multiply 2 by 3. Add 1.19 and 0.78 to the product. Dennis spent $7.97.
   - C. Multiply 2 by 3. Subtract 1.19 and 0.78 from the product. Dennis spent $4.03.

5. Sam sold 49 tickets on Monday. He sold 7 fewer tickets on Tuesday than on Monday. How many tickets did Sam sell both days combined?
   - A. Subtract 7 from 49. Add this difference to 49. Sam sold 91 tickets on both days combined.
   - B. Subtract 7 from 49. Add this difference to 49. Sam sold 42 tickets on both days combined.
   - C. Subtract 7 from 49. Add this difference to 49. Sam sold 98 tickets on both days combined.

6. Seventy-five soccer players were at the camp. Five players left the camp. The rest were divided equally into teams of 7. How many teams were created?
   - A. Add 5 and 75. Divide this difference by 5. Sixteen teams were created.
   - B. Subtract 5 from 75. Divide this difference by 7. Seventy teams were created.
   - C. Subtract 5 from 75. Divide this difference by 7. Ten teams were created.

MATHEMATICAL REASONING   **318**   EXPLAIN SOLUTIONS TO PROBLEMS

MATHEMATICAL REASONING   **319**   EXPLAIN SOLUTIONS TO PROBLEMS

Additional Answers
1. **Sample answer:** Susie put 3 quarters on the table. Twice as many dimes as quarters means that Susie put 6 dimes on the table.

   1 quarter: 25¢
   3 quarters: 25¢ × 3 = 75¢

   1 dime: 10¢
   6 dimes: 10¢ × 6 = 60¢

   Susie has 75¢ + 60¢.
   Susie has 135¢ or $1.35.

CHECKPOINT

Objectives

Students will complete an online Checkpoint. If necessary, read the directions, problems, and answer choices to students and help them with keyboard or mouse operations.

- Express the solution to a story problem clearly and logically with appropriate mathematical notation, terms, and accurate language.

Exact and Approximate Solutions

Lesson Overview

Skills Update	5 minutes	ONLINE
GET READY Estimate Solutions	5 minutes	ONLINE
LEARN Exact or Approximate	15 minutes	ONLINE
LEARN Rounded Answers	15 minutes	OFFLINE
TRY IT Accurate Solutions	10 minutes	OFFLINE
CHECKPOINT	10 minutes	ONLINE

▶ Lesson Objectives

- Determine the answer to a story problem to a specific degree of accuracy, such as hundredths.
- Explain the advantages of exact answers and approximate answers to story problems.

▶ Prerequisite Skills

- Round numbers through 10,000.
- Use estimation to predict a solution to a story problem and to determine whether calculations are reasonable.
- Explain mathematical reasoning in a story problem by using words, numbers, symbols, charts, graphs, tables, diagrams, or models.

▶ Content Background

Students will learn to determine an answer in a problem situation to a specific degree of accuracy, and they will explain the advantages of an exact answer in some situations and an approximate answer in other situations.

Finding an answer to a specific degree of accuracy is not the same as estimating. When estimating, students round the numbers in a problem to make the problem easier to solve. When finding an answer to a specific degree of accuracy, they round only the answer to make it easier to remember or to work with.

An estimate, or an approximate calculation, is sufficient and appropriate in many situations. Students should understand that in math problems "an estimate" is a mathematical term that means "about how many" and that different everyday situations require different degrees of accuracy. Yet, in some situations, estimation is inappropriate. For example, a pharmacist should not estimate when filling a prescription. Students will learn to base their choice of an appropriate estimation strategy on the context of each story problem.

The following 4-step problem-solving method was developed by George Pólya, and it is an effective way to solve a variety of story problems: (1) understand the problem; (2) devise a plan; (3) carry out the plan; and (4) look back.

Materials to Gather

SUPPLIED
Rounded Answers activity page
Accurate Solutions activity page

GET READY Estimate Solutions

Students will estimate the solution to a story problem and will find out if their estimate was reasonable or unreasonable.

Tips   Allow students to use a number line to help with estimates.

LEARN Exact or Approximate

Students will decide if a situation gives an exact amount or an approximate amount. Also, they will round whole numbers and money amounts. Discuss with students the idea that in some situations they need to know an exact amount, such as how much flour to put in a cake, or what time the train leaves. At other times an approximate amount is fine, such as when they want to know about how much something costs, or around what time someone will be home.

LEARN Rounded Answers

Students will learn to round an answer in a story-problem situation. They'll also learn to explain the advantages of an exact answer in some situations and an approximate answer in other situations. Have students turn to the Rounded Answers activity page in their Activity Book and read the directions with them.

   Students should copy the problems from the Activity Book into their Math Notebook as necessary and solve them there.

1. Explain to students when they would use an exact answer in some situations and an estimate in others.

   Say: One way to estimate the answer to a story problem is to round the numbers before calculating. This makes the calculation easier. At other times you may want to calculate an exact answer but then round it to a friendly number that's easier to remember. Sometimes a problem only asks for an answer to a certain degree of accuracy, such as to the nearest ten, hundred, thousand, or the nearest dollar.

2. Go through the Worked Example with students.

3. Have students read Problem 1. Guide students to solve the problem and find an exact answer. Then tell students that they should round the answer to the nearest thousand.

   Ask: The exact answer is 9,935. How do you know which thousand to round to? I look at the digit in the hundreds place and see that it is a 9, so I know the nearest thousand is 10,000 rather than 9,000.

Objectives

- Round numbers through 10,000.
- Use estimation to predict a solution to a story problem and to determine whether calculations are reasonable.
- Explain mathematical reasoning in a story problem by using words, numbers, symbols, charts, graphs, tables, diagrams, or models.

Objectives

- Determine the answer to a story problem to a specific degree of accuracy, such as hundredths.
- Explain the advantages of exact answers and approximate answers to story problems.

Objectives

- Determine the answer to a story problem to a specific degree of accuracy, such as hundredths.
- Explain the advantages of exact answers and approximate answers to story problems.

4. Have students solve Problem 2 on their own. Offer guidance as needed.

   Say: Sometimes there are advantages to having an exact answer, and sometimes it's more convenient to round the number to a specific degree of accuracy.

5. Have students read Problem 3. Explain that students do not need to calculate or round answers for this problem. Discuss with students that an estimate, or approximate answer, is appropriate when deciding if there is enough money, but an exact amount is needed when paying a bill.

6. Discuss Problems 4 and 5 with students. Have students answer the questions on their own.

Tips

For Problems 1–3, remind students to calculate exact answers and then round the answers.

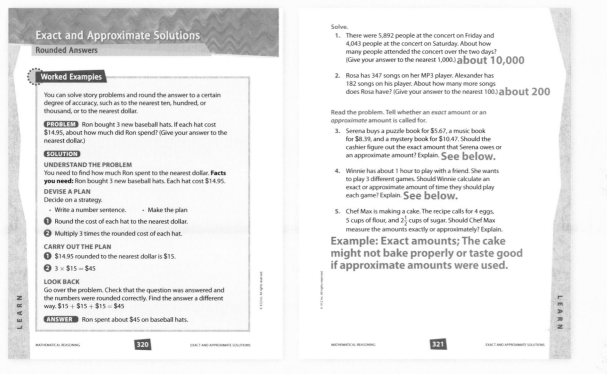

Additional Answers

3. **Example:** Exact amount; Serena doesn't want to overpay and the store doesn't want Serena to underpay.

4. **Example:** Approximate amount; She can use an approximate amount of time because an exact amount of time is not necessary.

TRY IT Accurate Solutions

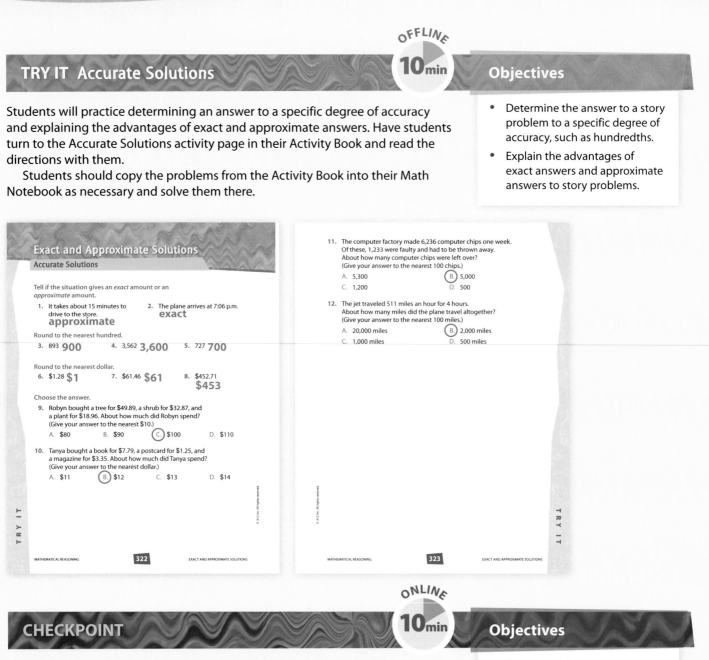

OFFLINE

10 min

Objectives

- Determine the answer to a story problem to a specific degree of accuracy, such as hundredths.
- Explain the advantages of exact answers and approximate answers to story problems.

Students will practice determining an answer to a specific degree of accuracy and explaining the advantages of exact and approximate answers. Have students turn to the Accurate Solutions activity page in their Activity Book and read the directions with them.

Students should copy the problems from the Activity Book into their Math Notebook as necessary and solve them there.

Exact and Approximate Solutions

Accurate Solutions

Tell if the situation gives an *exact* amount or an *approximate* amount.

1. It takes about 15 minutes to drive to the store.
    approximate

2. The plane arrives at 7:06 p.m.
    exact

Round to the nearest hundred.

3. 893 **900**   4. 3,562 **3,600**   5. 727 **700**

Round to the nearest dollar.

6. $1.28 **$1**   7. $61.46 **$61**   8. $452.71 **$453**

Choose the answer.

9. Robyn bought a tree for $49.89, a shrub for $32.87, and a plant for $18.96. About how much did Robyn spend? (Give your answer to the nearest $10.)
    A. $80   B. $90   C. $100   D. $110

10. Tanya bought a book for $7.79, a postcard for $1.25, and a magazine for $3.35. About how much did Tanya spend? (Give your answer to the nearest dollar.)
    A. $11   B. $12   C. $13   D. $14

11. The computer factory made 6,236 computer chips one week. Of these, 1,233 were faulty and had to be thrown away. About how many computer chips were left over? (Give your answer to the nearest 100 chips.)
    A. 5,300   B. 5,000
    C. 1,200   D. 500

12. The jet traveled 511 miles an hour for 4 hours. About how many miles did the plane travel altogether? (Give your answer to the nearest 100 miles.)
    A. 20,000 miles   B. 2,000 miles
    C. 1,000 miles   D. 500 miles

TRY IT

MATHEMATICAL REASONING   **322**   EXACT AND APPROXIMATE SOLUTIONS

MATHEMATICAL REASONING   **323**   EXACT AND APPROXIMATE SOLUTIONS

CHECKPOINT

ONLINE

10 min

Objectives

- Determine the answer to a story problem to a specific degree of accuracy, such as hundredths.
- Explain the advantages of exact answers and approximate answers to story problems.

Students will complete an online Checkpoint. If necessary, read the directions, problems, and answer choices to students and help them with keyboard or mouse operations.

Check Accuracy of a Solution

Lesson Overview

GET READY Check Calculations	10 minutes	OFFLINE
LEARN Solve and Check	30 minutes	OFFLINE
TRY IT Look Back and Check	10 minutes	OFFLINE
CHECKPOINT	10 minutes	ONLINE

▶ Lesson Objectives

Check the accuracy of a calculation in a story problem.

▶ Prerequisite Skills

Check the accuracy of calculations from the context of addition or subtraction problem-solving situations with sums and minuends up through 1,000 with regrouping.

▶ Content Background

In this lesson, students will check answers to story problems and analyze the calculations for accuracy. This lesson focuses on the "look back" step of the 4-step problem-solving plan.

The following 4-step problem-solving plan was developed by George Pólya, and it is an effective way to solve a variety of story problems: (1) understand the problem; (2) devise a plan; (3) carry out the plan; and (4) look back. As students solve story problems using the problem-solving plan, an important aspect of the "look back" step is checking the accuracy of the work.

Students know that the opposite of addition is subtraction and the opposite of multiplication is division. The term used to describe these opposite pairs of operations is *inverse operations*. Students can check their calculations using inverse operations. For example, when they see $300 + 400 = 700$, they can subtract $700 - 400 = 300$ to check that the answer is correct. When they see $900 - 600 = 300$, they can check the calculation by adding $300 + 600 = 900$. The same principle applies with multiplication and division. If $600 \times 3 = 1,800$, then $1,800 \div 3 = 600$; and if $800 \div 4 = 200$, then $200 \times 4 = 800$. Students can use this and other invented strategies to check that their calculations are accurate.

▶ Advance Preparation

- For the Get Ready: Check Calculations activity, write the following two story problems on index cards, one per card:

  Problem 1: Ron solved this problem: The auditorium can seat 452 people. There are 370 people sitting in the auditorium. How many seats are empty? Ron's answer: 182 seats

  Problem 2: Winnie solved this problem: Tonya and her friends collected 356 cans to take to the recycling center. Mike and his friends collected 372 cans. How many cans did they collect altogether? Winnie's answer: 728 cans

- Print the Problem-Solving Plan. Save it for use throughout the lesson.

SUPPLIED

Problem-Solving Plan (printout)

Solve and Check activity page

Look Back and Check activity page

ALSO NEEDED

index cards – 2

GET READY Check Calculations

Students will use inverse operations to check the answers to story problems. Gather the index cards on which you have written the story problems.

- Check the accuracy of calculations from the context of addition or subtraction problem-solving situations with sums and minuends up through 1,000 with regrouping.

1. Have students read the first story problem and Ron's answer.

2. Have students write the subtraction problem vertically with Ron's answer shown. Have students check the answer by using the inverse operation, addition.

   Ask: What numbers will you add together to check Ron's answer? 370 and 182 Have students write the addition problem vertically and find the sum.

3. Guide students to see that the sum does not match the total number of seats in the auditorium; therefore, Ron made an error in his calculation. Ask students to explain what Ron did wrong and give the correct answer. When he subtracted, he regrouped but forgot to cross out the 4 in the hundreds place; correct answer: 82 seats.

4. Have students read the second story problem and Winnie's answer.

5. Have students write down the addition problem vertically with Winnie's answer shown. Tell students to use an inverse operation to check Winnie's answer.

   Ask: Which inverse operation will you use to check the answer? subtraction

6. Have students write the subtraction problem vertically and find the difference.

   Ask: Is Winnie's answer correct? How do you know? Yes; the difference matches the other addend.

Ron's work   **Check**

$$
\begin{array}{r} 552 \\ -370 \\ \hline 182 \end{array}
\qquad
\begin{array}{r} 182 \\ +370 \\ \hline 552 \end{array}
$$

Ron is incorrect.

The correct solution is:

$$
\begin{array}{r} 452 \\ -370 \\ \hline 82 \end{array}
\qquad
\begin{array}{r} 82 \\ +370 \\ \hline 452 \end{array}
$$

Winnie's work   **Check**

$$
\begin{array}{r} 356 \\ +372 \\ \hline 728 \end{array}
\qquad
\begin{array}{r} 728 \\ -372 \\ \hline 356 \end{array}
$$

LEARN Solve and Check

Students will solve problems using the 4-step problem-solving plan with a focus on the "look back" step. They will estimate answers, do calculations, and check accuracy to verify their answers. Gather the Problem-Solving Plan. Have students turn to the Solve and Check activity page in their Activity Book and read the directions with them.

   Students should copy the problems from the Activity Book into their Math Notebook as necessary and solve them there.

- Check the accuracy of a calculation in a story problem.

1. Have students look at the Problem-Solving Plan. Review the steps of the plan. Tell students that in this lesson they will focus on the "look back" step of the plan. Discuss how students will check their answer using estimation and inverse operations.

2. Have students read the Worked Example. Guide them through each step of the plan to solve the problem. Ask these questions as students work through each step:

Understand the problem.

- Do you understand the problem?
- What are you asked to find?
- Can you sketch or model the problem?
- What information do you have? What do you need? What do you not need?

Devise a plan.

- What strategy can you use?
- How many steps do you need?
- Which operations do you need?

Carry out the plan.

- How can you show your work?

3. Point to the "look back" step. Have students estimate the difference and the quotient in whatever way they find easiest. For instance, instead of subtracting 27 from 4,290, they might subtract 30 to get 4,260. Next they would divide 4,260 by 3. To make the division easy, they might make 4,260 simply 4,200. Remember, when students estimate division problems, they should round the dividend (the number being divided) to a number that divides evenly. Finally students would divide 4,200 by 3 to get an estimate of 1,400. Ask students to compare the estimate to the actual answer, tell if the answer is reasonable or not, and explain why or why not. Yes, the answer is reasonable; the actual answer is close to the estimate.

Say: The answer is close to the estimate, so it is reasonable. However, it is important to check to make sure the calculation is accurate. You can use inverse operations to check answers.

Ask: What inverse operation do you use to check division? multiplication

Ask: What inverse operation do you use to check subtraction? addition

4. Have students use inverse operations to check the calculations. Explain that the calculation is correct if the final answer matches the original amount of 4,290 books. Ask students these final questions to complete the example problem and check understanding:

- Did you answer exactly what the question asked?
- How do you decide if the answer makes sense?
- How did you use inverse operations to check the calculation?
- Have you forgotten anything?

5. Have students read Problem 1 and use the Problem-Solving Plan as they work through the problem. Have them concentrate on the "look back" step when they verify their answers. Use the questions in Steps 2 and 4 to guide students through the plan. Encourage students to use both estimation and inverse operations to check their work.

6. Repeat Step 5 for Problem 2.

7. Have students read Problems 3–6 on the activity page. Explain that they need to check the work for each problem and explain whether it is correct or incorrect. Students may estimate, use inverse operations, or invent a method to check the calculations. Emphasize that students need to be able to explain how they checked the answers and determine the error if there is one.

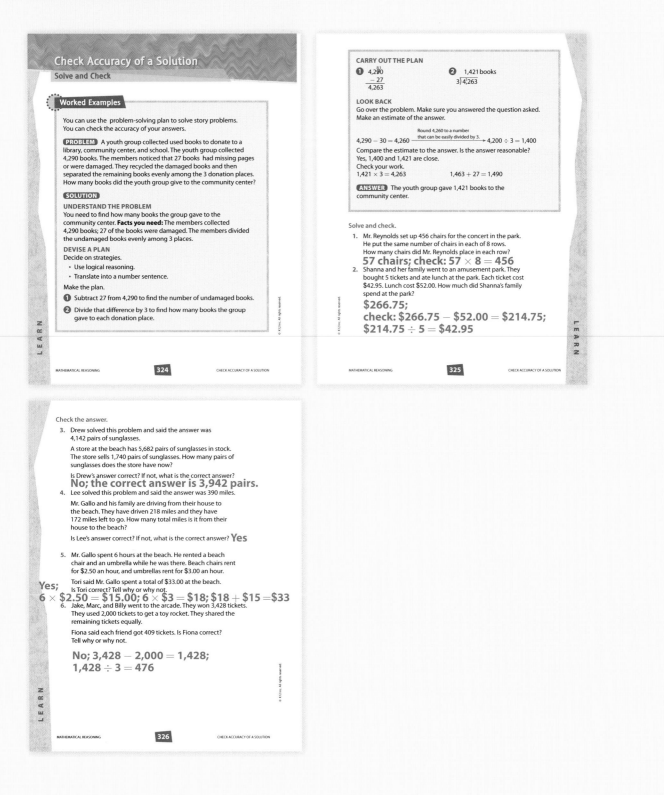

Check Accuracy of a Solution
Solve and Check

Worked Examples

You can use the problem-solving plan to solve story problems. You can check the accuracy of your answers.

PROBLEM A youth group collected used books to donate to a library, community center, and school. The youth group collected 4,290 books. The members noticed that 27 books had missing pages or were damaged. They recycled the damaged books and then separated the remaining books evenly among the 3 donation places. How many books did the youth group give to the community center?

SOLUTION

UNDERSTAND THE PROBLEM
You need to find how many books the group gave to the community center. **Facts you need:** The members collected 4,290 books; 27 of the books were damaged. The members divided the undamaged books evenly among 3 places.

DEVISE A PLAN
Decide on strategies.
- Use logical reasoning.
- Translate into a number sentence.

Make the plan.

❶ Subtract 27 from 4,290 to find the number of undamaged books.

❷ Divide that difference by 3 to find how many books the group gave to each donation place.

CARRY OUT THE PLAN

❶
$$4,2\overset{8}{9}0$$
$$-\ 27$$
$$4,263$$

❷ 1,421 books
$$3\overline{)4,263}$$

LOOK BACK
Go over the problem. Make sure you answered the question asked. Make an estimate of the answer.

$4,290 - 30 = 4,260$ → [Round 4,260 to a number that can be easily divided by 3.] → $4,200 \div 3 = 1,400$

Compare the estimate to the answer. Is the answer reasonable? Yes, 1,400 and 1,421 are close.
Check your work.
$1,421 \times 3 = 4,263$ $1,463 + 27 = 1,490$

ANSWER The youth group gave 1,421 books to the community center.

Solve and check.

1. Mr. Reynolds set up 456 chairs for the concert in the park. He put the same number of chairs in each of 8 rows. How many chairs did Mr. Reynolds place in each row?
   57 chairs; check: $57 \times 8 = 456$

2. Shanna and her family went to an amusement park. They bought 5 tickets and ate lunch at the park. Each ticket cost $42.95. Lunch cost $52.00. How much did Shanna's family spend at the park?
   $266.75;
   check: $266.75 - $52.00 = $214.75;
   $214.75 \div 5 = $42.95

Check the answer.

3. Drew solved this problem and said the answer was 4,142 pairs of sunglasses.

   A store at the beach has 5,682 pairs of sunglasses in stock. The store sells 1,740 pairs of sunglasses. How many pairs of sunglasses does the store have now?

   Is Drew's answer correct? If not, what is the correct answer?
   No; the correct answer is 3,942 pairs.

4. Lee solved this problem and said the answer was 390 miles.

   Mr. Gallo and his family are driving from their house to the beach. They have driven 218 miles and they have 172 miles left to go. How many total miles is it from their house to the beach?

   Is Lee's answer correct? If not, what is the correct answer? **Yes**

5. Mr. Gallo spent 6 hours at the beach. He rented a beach chair and an umbrella while he was there. Beach chairs rent for $2.50 an hour, and umbrellas rent for $3.00 an hour.

   Tori said Mr. Gallo spent a total of $33.00 at the beach. Is Tori correct? Tell why or why not.
   Yes;
   $6 \times $2.50 = $15.00; 6 \times $3 = $18; $18 + $15 = 33

6. Jake, Marc, and Billy went to the arcade. They won 3,428 tickets. They used 2,000 tickets to get a toy rocket. They shared the remaining tickets equally.

   Fiona said each friend got 409 tickets. Is Fiona correct? Tell why or why not.

   No; $3,428 - 2,000 = 1,428$;
   $1,428 \div 3 = 476$

TRY IT Look Back and Check

Objectives

- Check the accuracy of a calculation in a story problem.

Students will practice checking the solution to story problems. Have students turn to the Look Back and Check activity page in their Activity Book and read the directions with them.

Students should copy the problems from the Activity Book into their Math Notebook as necessary and solve them there.

Check Accuracy of a Solution
Look Back and Check

Solve.

1. A restaurant has 52 tables that each seat 4 people and 14 tables that each seat 8 people. Two hundred eighty-five people are sitting in the restaurant.

   Eric said there are 35 empty seats in the restaurant. Is Eric correct? Explain. **Yes; 52 × 4 = 208; 14 × 8 = 112; 208 + 112 = 320; 320 − 285 = 35**

Choose the answer.

2. The sports club bought 8 new baseball bats for $320.

   Valerie said that each baseball bat cost $40. Which calculation can be used to check Valerie's answer?

   A. 40 × 8
   Valerie is not correct.

   B. 40 ÷ 320
   Valerie is not correct.

   C. 40 ÷ 8
   Valerie is not correct.

   D. 40 × 8 ⃝
   Valerie is correct.

3. Candy had two coffee containers. One had 22 ounces of coffee and one had 34 ounces of coffee.

   Gino said Candy had a total of 12 ounces of coffee. Which statement is true?

   A. Gino is correct.

   B. ⃝ Gino is not correct. Candy has a total of 56 ounces of coffee.

   C. Gino is not correct. Candy has a total of 112 ounces of coffee.

   D. Gino is not correct. Candy has a total of 748 ounces of coffee.

MATHEMATICAL REASONING   **327**   CHECK ACCURACY OF A SOLUTION

T R Y   I T

T R Y   I T

4. The animal park had 765 butterflies. It released 433 of the butterflies into the wild.

   Nina said that the animal park now has 332 butterflies. Which statement is true?

   A. ⃝ Nina is correct.

   B. Nina is not correct. The park has 1,198 butterflies.

   C. Nina is not correct. The park has 1,100 butterflies.

   D. Nina is not correct. The park has 432 butterflies.

5. Lauren solved this problem and said the answer was 6.

   Yael made 24 ounces of pudding. She put the same amount of pudding into 6 cups. How much pudding was in each cup?

   Is Lauren's answer correct? If not, what is the correct answer?

   No; the correct answer is 4 ounces.

MATHEMATICAL REASONING   **328**   CHECK ACCURACY OF A SOLUTION

CHECKPOINT

Objectives

- Check the accuracy of a calculation in a story problem.

Students will complete an online Checkpoint. If necessary, read the directions, problems, and answer choices to students and help them with keyboard or mouse operations.

Unit Review

Lesson Overview

UNIT REVIEW Look Back	10 minutes	ONLINE
UNIT REVIEW Checkpoint Practice	50 minutes	ONLINE
▶ **UNIT REVIEW** Prepare for the Checkpoint		

▶ Unit Objectives

This lesson reviews the following objectives:

- Analyze a story problem by identifying the question, recognizing relevant information, and developing a solution strategy.

- Demonstrate when and how to break a multistep story problem into simpler steps.

- Use estimation to predict a solution to a story problem and to determine whether calculations are reasonable.

- Apply strategies and results from a simpler story problem to either a more complex problem or to a similar problem.

- Explain mathematical reasoning in a story problem by using words, numbers, symbols, charts, graphs, tables, diagrams, or models.

- Express the solution to a story problem clearly and logically with appropriate mathematical notation, terms, and accurate language.

- Determine the answer to a story problem to a specific degree of accuracy, such as hundredths.

- Explain the advantages of exact answers and approximate answers to story problems.

- Check the accuracy of a calculation in a story problem.

Materials to Gather

There are no materials to gather for this lesson.

▶ Advance Preparation

In this lesson, students will have an opportunity to review previous activities in the Mathematical Reasoning unit. Look at the suggested activities in Unit Review: Prepare for the Checkpoint online and gather any needed materials.

UNIT REVIEW Look Back

ONLINE 10 min

Students will review key concepts from the unit to prepare for the Unit Checkpoint.

Objectives

- Review unit objectives.

Students will complete an online Checkpoint Practice to prepare for the Unit Checkpoint. If necessary, read the directions, problems, and answer choices to students. Have students answer the problems on their own. Review any missed problems with students.

⮕ **UNIT REVIEW** Prepare for the Checkpoint

What you do next depends on how students performed in the previous activity, Unit Review: Checkpoint Practice. If students had difficulty with any of the problems, complete the appropriate review activity listed in the table online.

Unit Checkpoint

UNIT CHECKPOINT Online	60 minutes	**ONLINE**

▶ Unit Objectives

This lesson assesses the following objectives:

- Analyze a story problem by identifying the question, recognizing relevant information, and developing a solution strategy.

- Demonstrate when and how to break a multistep story problem into simpler steps.

- Use estimation to predict a solution to a story problem and to determine whether calculations are reasonable.

- Apply strategies and results from a simpler story problem to either a more complex problem or to a similar problem.

- Explain mathematical reasoning in a story problem by using words, numbers, symbols, charts, graphs, tables, diagrams, or models.

- Express the solution to a story problem clearly and logically with appropriate mathematical notation, terms, and accurate language.

- Determine the answer to a story problem to a specific degree of accuracy, such as hundredths.

- Explain the advantages of exact answers and approximate answers to story problems.

- Check the accuracy of a calculation in a story problem.

Materials to Gather

There are no materials to gather for this lesson.

UNIT CHECKPOINT Online

ONLINE
60min

Objectives

- Assess unit objectives.

Students will complete the Unit Checkpoint online. If necessary, read the directions, problems, and answer choices to students and help them with keyboard or mouse operations.

Perimeter, Area, and Volume

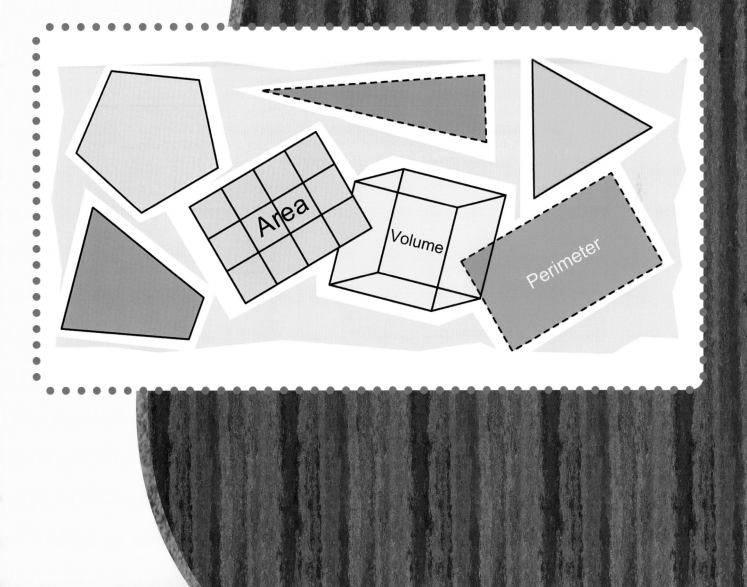

▶ Unit Objectives

- Determine the perimeter of a polygon with whole-number side lengths.
- Use multiplication or division to solve a story problem involving rectangular area.
- Estimate or determine the number of squares required to cover the area of a solid figure.
- Estimate or determine the number of cubes required to fill a solid figure.

▶ Big Ideas

- Geometric figures can be described and classified by the shapes of their faces and by how many faces, sides, edges, or vertices they have.
- Every geometric figure has several useful aspects that can be measured, calculated, or approximated. Area is a measure of how much material is needed to cover a plane figure.

▶ Unit Introduction

In this unit, students will learn about perimeter, area, and volume. They will learn that *perimeter* is the measure of the distance around an object, and that perimeter is measured in centimeters, inches, or in other units of length. They will find the perimeter of polygons with whole-number side lengths. Students will then learn that *area* is the measure of the space inside two-dimensional figures, and that area is measured in square units. They will use multiplication or division to solve story problems involving rectangular area. They will use their understanding of area to determine the number of squares required to cover cubes and other rectangular solids. Students will then look at *volume* and learn that volume is measured in cubic units. They will estimate and determine the number of cubes required to fill a solid rectangular figure. Students will **not** use formulas to find perimeter, area, or volume, but will focus on developing an understanding and use that understanding to find these measures by their own methods.

▶ Keywords

area	cubic unit	side
cubic centimeter	grid	square unit
cubic foot	line segment	volume
cubic inch	perimeter	

Find the Perimeter of Objects

Lesson Overview

GET READY Draw and Name Polygons	10 minutes	OFFLINE
LEARN Identify Perimeter	10 minutes	OFFLINE
LEARN Measure Perimeter	20 minutes	OFFLINE
TRY IT Perimeter of Polygons	10 minutes	OFFLINE
CHECKPOINT	10 minutes	ONLINE

▶ Lesson Objectives

Determine the perimeter of a polygon with whole-number side lengths.

▶ Prerequisite Skills

Identify, describe, and classify a polygon according to the number of its sides.

▶ Content Background

Students will learn that the distance around an object or a shape is called the *perimeter*. They'll learn that perimeter is measured in centimeters, inches, or other units of length.

The side lengths of a shape must be known if the perimeter is to be determined. Often the side lengths of the shape can be found by using the properties of the shape. For example, rectangles have opposite sides that are equal, so the perimeter can be found when only one length and one width are known. Students can apply their knowledge of properties of shapes to find the perimeter of more complex figures. They will not use a particular rule or formula to find perimeter. Instead, they will use their understanding of perimeter to determine that they can find the distance around an object by adding the side lengths of a given shape.

Materials to Gather

SUPPLIED

blocks – K, L, M, N (3 of each); E (8)

Isometric Dot Paper (printout) – several copies

Centimeter Grid Paper (printout)

Measure Perimeter activity page

Perimeter of Polygons activity page

ALSO NEEDED

ruler, dual-scale

household objects – string (4 ft)

index card

pipe cleaner or long twist tie

crayons or markers, coloring – 2

scissors, adult

▶ Advance Preparation

- Print the Centimeter Grid Paper and several copies of the Isometric Dot Paper.
- For the Learn: Measure Perimeter activity, students will need shapes that have been drawn on the dot paper. They may use the shapes from the Get Ready, or you may draw the following shapes in advance:

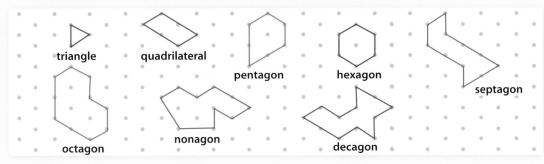

triangle quadrilateral pentagon hexagon septagon octagon nonagon decagon

GET READY Draw and Name Polygons

OFFLINE
10 min

Objectives

- Identify, describe, and classify a polygon according to the number of its sides.

Students will draw polygons and name figures with 3 to 10 sides.

Gather the Isometric Dot Paper.

Have students use the dot paper to draw and label the polygons below. Encourage them to draw shapes in such a way that they always draw a line through one of the nearest dots, as shown in the sample below. This will make it easy to reuse the shapes in the Learn: Measure Perimeter activity.

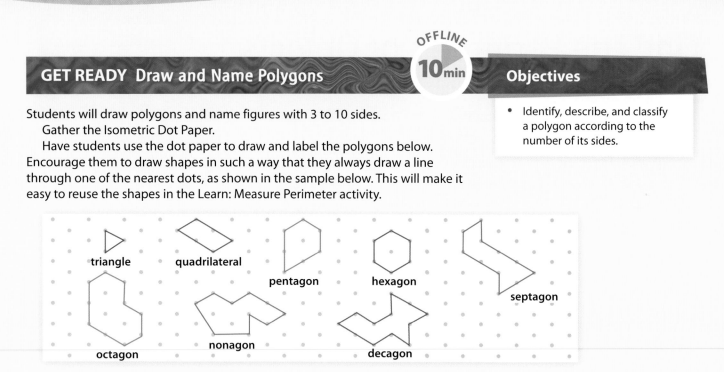

Polygons with lines like those shown in red in the following picture cannot be reused. However, if students want to draw these sorts of lines, they can draw new shapes in the perimeter activity.

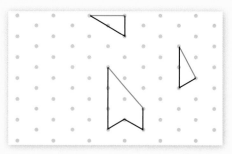

LEARN Identify Perimeter

OFFLINE
10 min

Objectives

- Determine the perimeter of a polygon with whole-number side lengths.

Students will learn about perimeter by measuring around the outside of a shape or an object.

Gather the blocks, ruler, string, index card, markers or crayons, scissors, and pipe cleaner or twist tie.

1. Tell students that in everyday life, there are times when they'll need to know the distance around a shape or an object. For example, they might need to know the distance that joggers run around a track, the length of a fence around a garden, or how long the wood is around the sides of a sandbox. The distance around a shape or an object is called the *perimeter*.

2. Write the word *perimeter* on an index card and draw arrows around the edge as shown here.

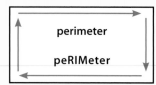

3. Have students trace around the edge of the card with their finger to show the perimeter. Tell students that they can remember it because the word *rim* is part of the word *perimeter*. Students can think of perimeter as the distance around the rim of an object.

4. Have students run their finger around the perimeter of a table. Have them point out the perimeter of the room they're in.

5. Explain to students that perimeter is a measurement of the distance around a shape or an object. Tell them that perimeter can be measured in inches, feet, yards, and even miles.

6. Give students a K block (small green triangle). Have them use a ruler to measure one side in inches. Bend a pipe cleaner or twist tie tightly around the perimeter of the triangle. Cut it at the end of the third side. Straighten it out and measure it (3 inches). Have students trace the K block, write "1 inch" next to each side, and write "perimeter = 3 inches" under the picture.

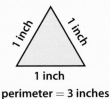

perimeter = 3 inches

7. Pick up the other blocks.

   Ask: If the length of one side of the green triangle is 1 inch, how long is the length of one side of each of the other blocks in this group?

   Students should determine that all block pieces have 1-inch side lengths, except for one side of the trapezoid. They can find the perimeter of each block by counting the side lengths in inches. Have them find the length of the longest side of the trapezoid by using the edge of one of the other pieces. Have them trace each shape, label the lengths of the sides, and write "perimeter = $\underline{?}$ inches" below the shape. (In place of the question mark, students should write the measurement.)

8. Have students estimate and then determine the perimeter of the L block (blue rhombus), the N block (yellow hexagon), and the M block (red trapezoid). Have them record the perimeter under each of their tracings. L block: 4 in.; N block: 6 in.; M block: 5 in.

9. Have students put together two green triangles to form a rhombus. Explain that when two triangles are put together, one side of each is now on the inside, so the outside edges form a rhombus. The new rhombus has the same perimeter as the rhombus block.

10. Show students that the perimeter of a group of blocks can vary, depending on how the blocks are arranged. First have students use four E blocks (squares) to make a 2 by 2 square, and have them find the perimeter. 8 inches Then give them four more squares and ask them to make a shape with a different perimeter.

    Ask: Why do the two arrangements of four squares have different perimeters? When more sides are on the inside of the design, there are fewer sides around the outside, so the perimeter is less.

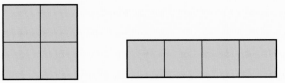

perimeter = 8 inches   **perimeter = 10 inches**

11. Have students use any 10 blocks to create a design. Have them estimate the perimeter of the design and then find the exact perimeter. Emphasize that since perimeter is a distance, it needs to be measured with a unit of measure. Have them write the perimeter of their design. Then have them use the same 10 blocks to create a new design with a different perimeter. Have students estimate the perimeter and then find the exact perimeter.

12. Have students look at a piece of notebook paper. Have them hold up the string and show how much of it they think would equal the perimeter of the paper. Have students mark the distance on the string and estimate the length to that mark in inches. Then have them use the string to go around the perimeter of the paper. Mark the actual perimeter on the string in a different color. (Note that measuring with string is always an approximation because string stretches and measuring is often not exact.) Have students use what they know about notebook paper to calculate the exact perimeter. $8\frac{1}{2} + 11 + 8\frac{1}{2} + 11 = 39$ inches

Have students compare their estimate to the exact length.

LEARN Measure Perimeter

Students will measure the perimeter of different shapes. Gather the Centimeter Grid Paper and the shapes drawn on dot paper. Have students turn to the Measure Perimeter activity page in their Activity Book and read the directions with them.

Students should copy the problems from the Activity Book into their Math Notebook as necessary and solve them there.

1. Show students the Centimeter Grid Paper. Explain that each square on the paper is 1 cm on each side. Tell students that they can draw shapes on the grid paper and know the exact perimeter as long as they stay on the lines. Point out that a diagonal line drawn between corners of any square would not be 1 cm. Have students draw three different rectangles on the centimeter grid paper and determine the perimeter of each. Be sure students do not use diagonal lines to make the rectangles.

2. Have students describe how they found the perimeter of each rectangle. Encourage them to share any shortcuts they may have discovered for finding the perimeter.

3. Have students draw a rectangle that is 15 centimeters long and 3 centimeters wide. Ask them how they would find the perimeter of this rectangle. Students should understand that they do not have to count each side length because they know that opposite sides of rectangles are equal. Therefore, they can think $15 + 15 + 3 + 3$.

4. Have students make several interesting geometric shapes on the grid paper. Make sure each shape has only square corners. Have students find the perimeter of each shape.

Objectives

- Determine the perimeter of a polygon with whole-number side lengths.

Tips

Remind students not to draw diagonal lines on the Centimeter Grid Paper. The length of a diagonal line is greater than 1 unit.

5. Have students look at the prepared shapes on the dot paper. Have them hold the paper horizontally. Tell them that the dots are spaced in such a way that some are closer together than others. Point to a diagonal or vertical row of dots. Tell students that the distance between two adjacent dots in any of these rows is 1 unit. Next point to a horizontal row of dots. Tell students that these dots are more than 1 unit apart.

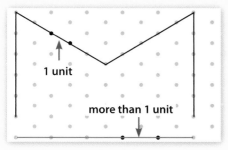

6. Have students find the perimeter of any shapes on the dot paper with sides that only pass through dots that are 1 unit apart. Explain that if a shape has lines connecting dots that are farther apart than 1 unit, they can't be sure of the perimeter. (In the illustration below, the perimeter of the shapes with red lines is unknown.) Have students write the measurement below each shape as $P = ?$ (In place of the question mark, students should write the measurement.) Tell students that the abbreviation for *perimeter* is an uppercase *P*.

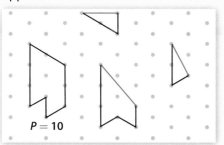

7. Focus students' attention on the Measure Perimeter activity page. Go over the Worked Example. Make sure students understand both ways of finding the perimeter. They can add all the sides, or if there are several sides that are equal length, they can multiply to find the total for those sides.

8. Have students look at Problems 1–4. Guide them through each problem. Encourage them to explain what they know about each shape before they find the perimeter. For example, when students are finding the perimeter of the square, remind them that a square has 4 equal sides, so if they know the length of one side, they know the length of the other 3 sides. When finding the perimeter of a rectangle, remind students that opposite sides are equal. Tell them that the tick marks (short lines) on the sides of the triangle in Problem 3 and the pentagon in Problem 4 show that those sides have equal lengths.

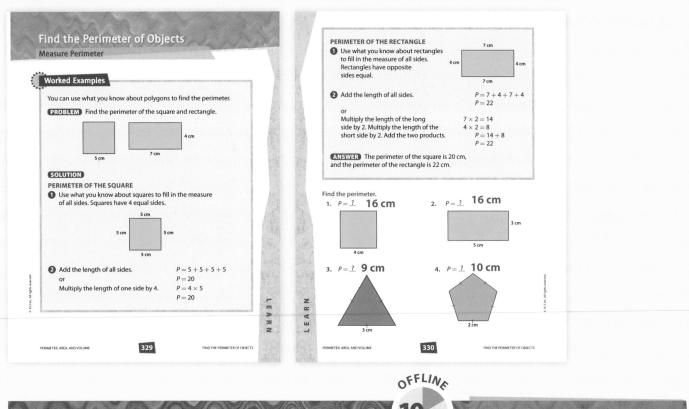

TRY IT Perimeter of Polygons

OFFLINE 10 min

Objectives

- Determine the perimeter of a polygon with whole-number side lengths.

Students will practice finding the perimeter of different shapes and objects. Have students turn to the Perimeter of Polygons activity page in their Activity Book and read the directions with them.

Students should copy the problems from the Activity Book into their Math Notebook as necessary and solve them there.

Remind students that perimeter is the distance around the outside of a shape or object. Also point out that tick marks on the sides of a shape indicate that those sides are the same length. In Problem 9, help students see that they can determine the lengths of the unmarked sides by looking at the lengths on the sides opposite them.

Tips

If students have difficulty with Problems 4 and 9, have them draw the figures on grid paper.

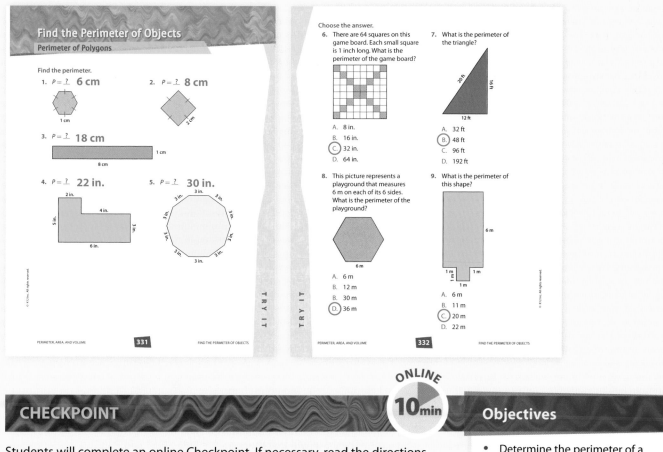

Find the Perimeter of Objects
Perimeter of Polygons

Find the perimeter.

1. $P = \underline{?}$ **6 cm**

2. $P = \underline{?}$ **8 cm**

3. $P = \underline{?}$ **18 cm**

4. $P = \underline{?}$ **22 in.**

5. $P = \underline{?}$ **30 in.**

PERIMETER, AREA, AND VOLUME **331** FIND THE PERIMETER OF OBJECTS

TRY IT

Choose the answer.

6. There are 64 squares on this game board. Each small square is 1 inch long. What is the perimeter of the game board?

   A. 8 in.
   B. 16 in.
   C. 32 in.
   D. 64 in.

7. What is the perimeter of the triangle?

   A. 32 ft
   B. 48 ft
   C. 96 ft
   D. 192 ft

8. This picture represents a playground that measures 6 m on each of its 6 sides. What is the perimeter of the playground?

   A. 6 m
   B. 12 m
   B. 30 m
   D. 36 m

9. What is the perimeter of this shape?

   A. 6 m
   B. 11 m
   C. 20 m
   D. 22 m

TRY IT

PERIMETER, AREA, AND VOLUME **332** FIND THE PERIMETER OF OBJECTS

ONLINE 10 min

CHECKPOINT

Students will complete an online Checkpoint. If necessary, read the directions, problems, and answer choices to students and help them with keyboard or mouse operations.

Objectives

- Determine the perimeter of a polygon with whole-number side lengths.

Rectangular Area

▶ Lesson Objectives

Use multiplication or division to solve a story problem involving rectangular area.

▶ Prerequisite Skills

- Use an area model to explain multiplication.
- Use objects or sketches to solve a division problem.

▶ Content Background

Students will learn that area is the measure of the space inside two-dimensional figures. They'll learn that area is measured in square units. They will will use multiplication or division to solve story problems involving rectangular area.

Students will explore the area of rectangular shapes. They will see that the units of measure used to determine the length of a side of a rectangle can be used to create square units. They will also see that the area of a rectangle can be described by counting the square units. After counting units, students should recognize that it's easier to count the number of rows and the number of squares in each row and multiply those values. Students will not use a particular rule or formula to find area. Instead they will use their mathematical understanding to create their own strategy. Be sure they understand that area is measured in square units. Students need to understand that saying "the rectangle has an area of 20" has no meaning unless the units are identified, such as 20 square miles, 20 square inches, or 20 of another square unit.

▶ Common Errors and Misconceptions

- Students might think of all measurements as length. For example, they might perceive area as a distance—something that they can measure with a ruler. Consequently, they often measure the perimeter (the path around the figure).
- Students might believe that it doesn't matter if units are all identical. They may believe that if they can fill a region (such as a box) with units of measure (such as beans), it doesn't matter if some of the units of measure (beans) are of a different size. They will simply count the number of objects contained within the region (box).
- Students might believe that although the units of measure should be identical, it doesn't matter if they do not completely cover a region.

Materials to Gather

SUPPLIED

blocks – E (all)

Inch Grid Paper (printout)

Grid-Paper Story Problems activity page

Area Story Problems activity page

ALSO NEEDED

index card – 3 by 5 in.

▶ Advance Preparation
- Print the Inch Grid Paper.
- For the Get Ready: Perimeter and the Area Model activity, gather a 3 by 5 in. index card. The size is important because the card will be covered by an exact number of blocks.

GET READY Perimeter and the Area Model

OFFLINE 10 min

Students will review the concept of area that they learned with the area model of multiplication and will identify the difference between area and perimeter.
Gather the index card and the blocks.

1. Tell students that they have determined the perimeter of an object and now they are going to study area.

2. Give students the index card. Ask them to trace the perimeter of the card with their finger. They should run their finger around the rim of the card. Remind students that *perimeter* has the word *rim* in it.

3. Explain that the space on the surface of the card is called the *area*. Have students flatten their hand and rub it over the surface of the card. Have them write "area" on the card and then lightly shade the card with a pencil.

4. Have students look at a table and identify its perimeter by tracing their finger around the edge. Have them rub their hands across the surface of the table to identify the area.

5. Choose another flat surface that has a different area from the table. Have students use their finger to go around the perimeter of the second surface and use their hands to go over the area. Ask them which surface has a greater area and how they know. Students will probably say that there is more space on one surface than the other.

6. Remind students that they measure perimeter in straight units, called *linear units*. Tell them that inches and feet are examples of linear units. Explain that they need a way to measure area so they can describe the flat surface of an object.

   Say: You can't measure area in inches or units because that will only tell how long or wide something is. Instead, you need to use *square units* to measure area.

7. Have students use their square blocks to completely cover the index card. Guide students to fit the square blocks against each other so no part of the index card is showing.

   Ask: How many square blocks does it take to cover the index card?
   15 square blocks

8. Have students look at the square blocks covering the card. Ask them to explain what multiplication sentence is shown by the square blocks.
   Students should recognize that the square blocks show 3 rows of 5 or $3 \times 5 = 15$ (or 5 rows of 3 or $5 \times 3 = 15$).

   Say: Since each square block has a length and width of 1 inch, you say that each square is 1 square inch. You can use square inches as a unit of measure and say that the area of the card is 15 square inches. You can write 15 sq in. as an abbreviation.

   Have students write 15 square inches on one side of the card and 15 sq in. on the other.

Objectives

- Use an area model to explain multiplication.

Tips

Write the two multiplication sentences and have students explain how each matches the arrangement of squares covering the index card.

LEARN Geoboard Shapes and Area

Objectives

- Use multiplication or division to solve a story problem involving rectangular area.

Students will use the Geoboard Learning Tool to explore the area of rectangular shapes. They will recognize that area is measured in square units. They'll also explore the perimeter of rectangular shapes.

DIRECTIONS FOR USING THE GEOBOARD LEARNING TOOL

1. Click Lesson Mode. If necessary, click Menu and Help to review the instructions for the learning tool.

2. Have students use the Geoboard to create the smallest possible square, as shown here. Ask them to identify the perimeter of the square. 4 units

   Explain that area is a measure of the number of square units inside a shape or an object. Point out that the rubber band surrounds one square, so the area of the square is 1 square unit. Explain that on the Geoboard, the rubber bands show the perimeter and the squares inside show the area.

Tips

If students have difficulty working with the Geoboard Learning Tool, have them draw the shapes on grid paper, shading squares as they count to find the area.

Say: This square has a perimeter of 4 units and an area of 1 square unit.

3. Explain to students that for this activity, they will be working with shapes that have only lines that go up and down or sideways (vertical or horizontal lines). They will not create shapes with diagonal lines. Ask students to make a rectangle with an area of 3 square units. Guide them to use additional rubber bands to outline each square and show that the area is exactly 3 square units.

4. Have students make rectangular shapes with the following areas:
   - 8 square units
   - 12 square units

   Students should outline the square units in each figure and count to find the area.

5. Have students make larger rectangular shapes with the following areas:
   - 15 square units
   - 18 square units

   This time, encourage students to outline groups of squares, such as rows or columns. For example, they might show an area of 18 as a 3 by 6 rectangle. They could then use additional rubber bands to show 3 rows of 6, proving that there are 18 square units in the shape.

6. Have students explain the area and perimeter of one of their shapes. Encourage them to use their finger to go around the perimeter and their hand to move over the surface to show area.

7. Present the following story problem:
   - Winnie has 18 tiles. Show two different shapes that Winnie can make with the 18 tiles.

   Have students find both the area and perimeter of each shape. Help them recognize that 18 tiles will always have an area of 18, but the perimeter can change, depending on how the tiles are arranged.

8. Have students create a complex shape. Guide them to use only vertical and horizontal lines, not diagonal lines. Tell students that their shape is the floor plan of a room that needs to be tiled. Have them use additional rubber bands to break the shape into rectangles to find the area. Students may shade areas by clicking a rubber band and then clicking a color.

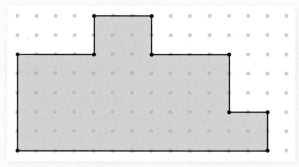

Encourage students to share any shortcuts they may have discovered for finding area. Students should begin to realize that they can count the number of squares in a row and then multiply by the number of rows to more quickly find the area of a rectangular section of a shape.

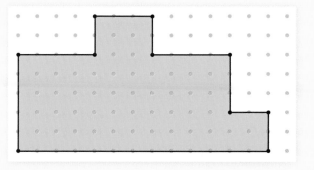

9. Have students follow these steps to check the area and perimeter they recorded:

- Click the rubber band that goes entirely around the figure.
- Click the yellow ruler button to see the lengths of the sides.
- Add all the lengths.
- Click Show Info to confirm their calculations and get more information on the shape.

10. Click Hide Info and turn off the yellow ruler. Have students find the area and perimeter of the entire Geoboard. Discuss with students how they might use shortcuts of repeated addition or multiplication to find the area. Have them count or calculate first and then check, using the Show Info button.

11. Have students use the Geoboard to solve the following problem:

- Alexander has some big tiles to make a giant game board. He has 63 tiles, and he wants his game board to be a rectangle that is 9 tiles wide. How long can he make his board? 7 tiles long

Ask students how they found their answer. Some will have counted by 9s, extending their rectangle until it had 63 squares. Some will have thought, "9 times what number equals 63?" or "63 divided by 9 equals what number?" Both of these methods work, but as the numbers in problems become greater, it is important for students to understand that they can divide the area by one dimension to get the other dimension.

12. Have students solve the following problem and explain how they found their answer:

- Serena has 45 squares of carpet for the hallway of a dollhouse. If she places the squares 3 across, how many squares long will the carpeting be?
  15 squares long

LEARN Grid-Paper Story Problems

OFFLINE
10min

Objectives

- Use multiplication or division to solve a story problem involving rectangular area.

Students will use multiplication or division to solve story problems involving rectangular area. Gather the Inch Grid Paper and the blocks. Have students turn to the Grid-Paper Story Problems activity page in their Activity Book and read the directions with them.

Students should copy the problems from the Activity Book into their Math Notebook as necessary and solve them there.

Tips

By default, many printers scale documents to fit to a printable area. Be sure to turn off page scaling so that documents print at 100% of their intended size.

1. Direct students' attention to the Worked Example. Go through each step together.

2. Have students read the story problem for Problems 1–3. Explain that each square on the grid represents 1 foot by 1 foot, which is 1 square foot.

3. Have students answer Problems 1 and 2. Point out the length and width labels next to the grid. Students can confirm the dimensions by counting the number of squares. Remind them that the grid is similar to an area model used for multiplication.

4. Discuss how finding the area of the tree house floor will help students determine how many square feet of carpet Megan needs. Have students describe different ways they might find the area. Guide them to use multiplication to find the area of the rectangle. Tell them that they should express their answer in square feet because area is measured in square units.

5. Have students read the story problem for Problems 4 and 5. Ask them how they can solve the problem. Guide them to see that finding the area of the tray will tell them how many tiles are needed because each tile is 1 square inch.

6. Talk with students about how the grid can be divided into more than one rectangle. Have them use the given dimensions to find the area of the different rectangles. Encourage them to divide the grid in whatever way they find easiest. Then guide them to add the areas to determine the total area of the tray. Tell students that no matter how the area was divided into rectangles, the total area will always be 54 square inches. Have students answer Problems 4 and 5.

7. Have students read Problem 6. Compare this problem to the Worked Example. Tell students that they need to find the area of the couch shown by the shaded L shape. Guide them to divide the L shape into two different rectangles, find the area of each rectangle, and then find the total area.

8. Have students read Problem 7. Have them use the grid paper and the square blocks to solve this problem. Guide them to choose 32 squares and arrange 4 in a row on the grid paper. Students can place the remaining squares in rows of 4 to determine how many concrete tiles in length the walkway will be.

9. Discuss with students how they can solve Problem 7 using division. Guide them to see that 32 divided by 4 equals 8.

10. Have students solve Problem 8 using division. They can use the squares to check their answer.

Rectangular Area
Grid-Paper Story Problems

Worked Examples

You can find the area of a shape by finding the length and width and finding how many square units fit inside the shape.

PROBLEM Charles is putting a vegetable garden in his yard. The picture shows where he plans to put his garden. What is the area of the garden?

10 yd

garden

10 yd

SOLUTION

① Count the squares along the long side of the garden to find that the width of the garden is 4 yards.

② Count the squares along the short side of the garden to find that the length of the garden is 3 yards.

③ Use the length and the width to know that the garden covers 3 rows of 4 square yards, or $3 \times 4 = 12$.

ANSWER The area of the garden is 12 square yards.

Use this story problem to solve Problems 1–3.

Megan wants to carpet the floor of her tree house. The size of the floor is shown in the grid.

5 ft

length

7 ft

width

1. How many feet wide is the floor? **5 ft**
2. How many feet long is the floor? **7 ft**
3. How many square feet of carpet will Megan need? **35 sq ft**

Use this story problem to solve Problems 4 and 5.

Mrs. Parker wants to cover a tray with tiles. The tiles are each 1 inch square. The grid below shows the size of the tray.

3 in.

4 in.

4. What is the area of each of the different rectangles?
Sample answer: 42 sq in.; 12 sq in.
5. How many tiles will Mrs. Parker need? **54**

Solve.

6. This picture shows where the couch is in Johnny's living room.

What is the area of the couch?
24 sq ft

15 ft

couch

10 ft

7. Patrick has 32 concrete blocks to make a walkway. If he makes the walkway 4 blocks wide, how long can he make the walkway? **8 blocks long**

8. Quinn has 27 tiles to use on the wall behind her sink. She wants to put 9 tiles in each row. How many rows of tiles can she make? **3**

TRY IT Area Story Problems

Students will practice using multiplication or division to solve story problems involving rectangular area. Have students turn to the Area Story Problems activity page in their Activity Book and read the directions with them.

Students should copy the problems from the Activity Book into their Math Notebook as necessary and solve them there.

Tips Allow students to use grid paper and squares to solve Problems 5, 7, and 8.

- Use multiplication or division to solve a story problem involving rectangular area.

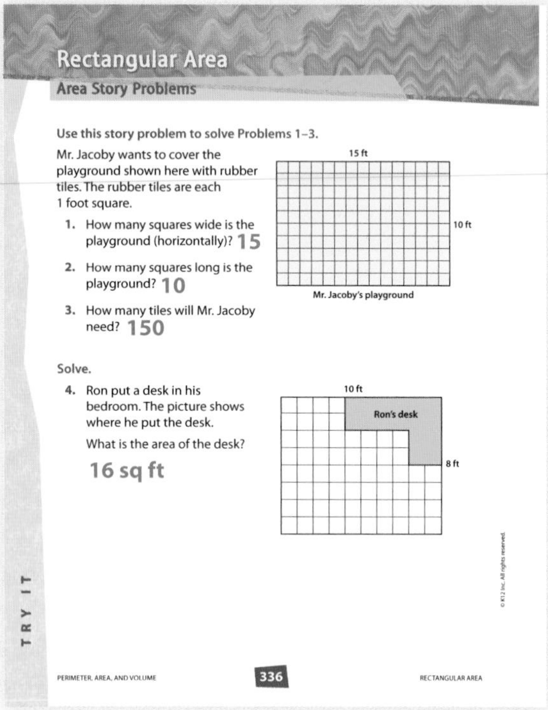

Rectangular Area
Area Story Problems

Use this story problem to solve Problems 1–3.

Mr. Jacoby wants to cover the playground shown here with rubber tiles. The rubber tiles are each 1 foot square.

15 ft
10 ft
Mr. Jacoby's playground

1. How many squares wide is the playground (horizontally)? **15**

2. How many squares long is the playground? **10**

3. How many tiles will Mr. Jacoby need? **150**

Solve.

4. Ron put a desk in his bedroom. The picture shows where he put the desk.
   What is the area of the desk?
   16 sq ft

10 ft
Ron's desk
8 ft

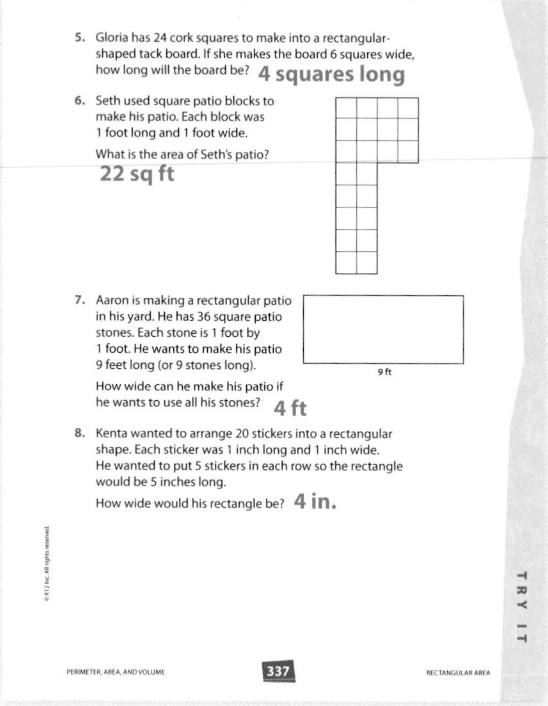

5. Gloria has 24 cork squares to make into a rectangular-shaped tack board. If she makes the board 6 squares wide, how long will the board be? **4 squares long**

6. Seth used square patio blocks to make his patio. Each block was 1 foot long and 1 foot wide.
   What is the area of Seth's patio?
   22 sq ft

7. Aaron is making a rectangular patio in his yard. He has 36 square patio stones. Each stone is 1 foot by 1 foot. He wants to make his patio 9 feet long (or 9 stones long).
   How wide can he make his patio if he wants to use all his stones? **4 ft**
   9 ft

8. Kenta wanted to arrange 20 stickers into a rectangular shape. Each sticker was 1 inch long and 1 inch wide. He wanted to put 5 stickers in each row so the rectangle would be 5 inches long.
   How wide would his rectangle be? **4 in.**

9. Yolanda wanted to arrange 45 stickers into a rectangular shape. Each sticker was 1 inch long and 1 inch wide. She wanted to put 5 stickers in each row so the rectangle would be 5 inches long.

How wide would her rectangle be? **9 in.**

Choose the answer.

10. Judy visited a flower garden.

What is the area of the flower garden?

A. 4 sq ft
B. 8 sq ft
C. 16 sq ft
D. 60 sq ft

10 ft

flower garden   6 ft

11. These figures all have a perimeter of 16 inches. Which one has an area of 16 square inches?

A.

B.

C.

D.

TRY IT

CHECKPOINT

ONLINE
10min

Students will complete an online Checkpoint. If necessary, read the directions, problems, and answer choices to students and help them with keyboard or mouse operations.

Objectives

- Use multiplication or division to solve a story problem involving rectangular area.

How Many Squares Does It Take?

Lesson Overview

Skills Update	5 minutes	ONLINE
GET READY Wall Area	5 minutes	ONLINE
LEARN Area and Solid Figures	15 minutes	OFFLINE
LEARN Surface Area from Pictures	15 minutes	ONLINE
TRY IT Cover the Solid	10 minutes	OFFLINE
CHECKPOINT	10 minutes	ONLINE

▶ Lesson Objectives

Estimate or determine the number of squares required to cover the area of a solid figure.

▶ Prerequisite Skills

Use multiplication or division to solve a story problem involving rectangular area.

▶ Content Background

Students will learn how to find the number of squares required to cover the area of the faces of a solid figure.

Avoid using the word *sides* with students when referring to the faces of a solid.

Students know how to find a rectangular area and will now explore the area of the faces of cubes and other rectangular solids. First students will estimate the number of squares needed to cover these solid figures, and then they will determine the exact measurement. Mathematicians call this measure *surface area*, but at this level students will think about the more concrete idea of covering the outside of an object with squares. Students will use square units of measure such as square inches, square centimeters, or other square units. At times when the squares are not a standard unit length, they will learn to simply call the units *square units*. As long as students show which square unit they are using to measure, they can find the surface area. They will also learn to write the standard notation of square units as u^2. At this level, students will not be taught why this notation is used, but they will understand it as a shortcut to writing square units.

▶ Common Errors and Misconceptions

- Students might think of all measurements as length. For example, they might perceive area as a distance—something that they can measure with a ruler. Consequently, they often measure the perimeter (the path around the figure).

- Students might believe that it doesn't matter if units are all identical. They may believe that if they can fill a region (such as a box) with units of measure (such as beans), it doesn't matter if some of the units of measure (beans) are of a different size. They will simply count the number of objects contained within the region (box).

Materials to Gather

SUPPLIED

base-10 blocks

blocks – P, Q (1 of each)

Quarter-Inch Grid Paper (printout)

Centimeter Grid Paper (printout)

Cover the Solid activity page

ALSO NEEDED

tape, clear – $\frac{3}{4}$ in. wide

scissors, adult

- Students might believe that although the units of measure should be identical, it doesn't matter if they do not completely cover a region.

▶ Advance Preparation

- Print the Quarter-Inch Grid Paper and Centimeter Grid Paper.
- Use base-10 ones cubes and tape to make three 3 by 3 arrangements of ones cubes that stay together. Place a piece of tape down with the sticky side up, and place a ones cube in the center of the tape. Notice that the tape is wide enough to place cubes on either side of the first cube such that all three will stick to the tape even though they're each held by just a small amount of tape. Lay down a new piece of tape right next to the first one, and make another line of three cubes. Repeat this step so that you have a 3 by 3 arrangement of cubes. Trim any tape that extends beyond the edge of the cubes. Make two more sets, and then stack the three sets into a 3 by 3 by 3 cube.

▶ Safety

Supervise students when they are working with the geometric solid blocks. These blocks have sharp corners.

GET READY Wall Area

ONLINE
5 min

Students will use multiplication or division to solve a story problem involving rectangular area.

Objectives

- Use multiplication or division to solve a story problem involving rectangular area.

LEARN Area and Solid Figures

OFFLINE
15 min

Students will learn to estimate and determine the number of squares required to cover the area of cubes and other rectangular solids.

Gather the P and Q blocks, the base-10 blocks, the 3 by 3 by 3 cube you assembled out of base-10 ones cubes, and the Centimeter Grid Paper and Quarter-Inch Grid Paper.

1. Tell students that they will learn to find how many square units it takes to cover a solid figure.

   Say: You've learned to find the area of rectangular shapes. Now you'll use this information to find the number of square units it takes to cover rectangular solids. You can think of this as finding the area of paper you'd need to cover a box without any overlapping.

Objectives

- Estimate or determine the number of squares required to cover the area of a solid figure.

2. Give students the P block (cube) and the Q block (rectangular prism). Ask students to describe each block by saying the number of faces and the shape of each face. The cube has 6 faces and each face is a square. The rectangular prism has 6 faces. Two of the faces are long, thin rectangles; 2 are long, wide rectangles; and there are 2 smaller rectangular faces.

   Ask: How are the two solids alike? How are they different? Both are rectangular prisms with 6 faces, 12 edges, and 8 vertices. The cube is a special type of rectangular prism because all 6 faces are squares.

3. Hold up a thousands cube. Have students say what shape it is and tell how many faces it has. cube, 6 faces

   Show the Centimeter Grid Paper. Ask students to estimate how many squares on the Centimeter Grid Paper it would take to cover the thousands cube. Guide students to estimate, without calculating, by asking these questions:

   • Would it take a thousand squares to cover the thousands cube?

   • Would it take less than a thousand? More than a thousand?

   Have students look at the cube. Point out that each square has an area of 1 square centimeter.

   Ask: How many centimeter squares are there on one face? 100

   Ask: How many centimeter squares would it take to cover all 6 faces? 600

   Write "600 square cm" and "600 cm²." Point to cm².

   Say: You measured the area in centimeter squares. So you say there are 600 square centimeters. You can write *square cm* or use a shortcut to record the units. You can place a little 2 in the corner above the unit centimeters. This is a way to record square units.

4. Show students the 3 by 3 by 3 cube made from the ones cubes. Have them estimate how many centimeter squares it would take to cover the entire cube. Ask them not to calculate, just to make an estimate. If students hesitate, guide them by asking: Is the number greater than 10? Greater than 20? Greater than 30? Greater than 50?

   Have students examine the cube more closely.

   Ask: How many centimeter squares would it take to cover one face of the cube? 9

   Ask: How many faces does the cube have? 6

   Ask: How many centimeter squares would it take to cover the entire cube? $6 \times 9 = 54$

   Compare the actual area of 54 square centimeters to the estimate by students.

5. Give students the P block and the Quarter-Inch Grid Paper. Explain that they will find how many squares it takes to cover the cube. Have them first estimate how many squares will cover the cube. Explain that each square on the paper can be considered 1 square unit.

6. Have students trace a face of the cube on the grid paper. Be sure they align the cube so that it matches up with a vertical line and a horizontal line on the grid paper. Tell them to count the number of squares it takes to cover one face of the cube. 36

   Ask: How can you calculate how many squares it takes to cover the entire cube? Why? Multiply 6×36. There are 6 faces of the cube. Each face has the same area.

   Have students record the total area of the faces of the cube. 216 square units or 216 u²

7. Review what students learned in this activity.

Say: You've found the number of squares it takes to cover all the faces of the cube. This is the same as finding the area of the surface of the block. Mathematicians call this measurement the *surface area*.

Explain that when measuring area, it is important to record the size of the squares used because the squares are the unit of measure. Point out that students used square centimeters to measure the base-10 cube and small squares or square units to measure the other cube (P block).

Say: The surface area of the base-10 cube is 600 square centimeters. The surface area of the P-block cube is 216 square units—where each unit is one of the smaller squares.

Show the shortcut to write each measurement: 600 cm^2 and 216 u^2.

8. Repeat Step 5 using the Q-block rectangular prism. Ask students if they think the rectangular prism will have a greater or lesser surface area than the cube.

9. Repeat Step 6 for the Q-block rectangular prism. Guide students to see that the faces of the rectangular prism are three different sizes. They will need to trace each face, then add the different areas to find the total number of square units.

Two of the rectangles are 4 units by 12 units. These have an area of 48 u^2 + 48 u^2 = 96 u^2.

Two of the rectangles are 6 units by 12 units. These have an area of 72 u^2 + 72 u^2 = 144 u^2.

Two of the rectangles are 4 units by 6 units. These have an area of 24 u^2 + 24 u^2 = 48 u^2.

The total area of the faces is 96 u^2 + 144 u^2 + 48 u^2 = 288 u^2.

10. Have students compare the surface area of the P-block cube to that of the Q-block rectangular prism. Point out that both areas are in the same-sized square units, and therefore students can compare them. Ask students whether the cube or the rectangular prism has the greater surface area.
rectangular prism

LEARN Surface Area from Pictures

ONLINE
15 min

Objectives

Students will use pictures and their knowledge of cubes and prisms to find the surface area of solid figures.

- Estimate or determine the number of squares required to cover the area of a solid figure.

DIRECTIONS FOR USING THE SURFACE AREA LAB LEARNING TOOL

1. Click Explore.

Say: Look at the cube.

Ask: What are the length, width, and height of the cube? 1 cm

Ask: How many faces does the cube have? 6

Ask: How many square centimeters would it take to cover the cube? 6 cm^2

Remind students that the little 2 tells them that the units are square units, rather than just a centimeter of length. Also remind them that the number of square units it takes to cover the whole surface of the cube is called the *surface area*.

2. Click Show Net in the lower-left corner.

   Say: This shows what the paper would look like if you covered the cube. Lime green shows the top and bottom, light green shows the front and back, and dark green shows the faces on the left and right.

   Click Hide Net.

3. Move the slider for height up to 10. Have the students explain why the surface area is 42 cm². Four faces have a surface area of 10 cm², so that's 40. The top and bottom each have an area of 1 cm². That makes 42 cm².

   Click Show Net and have the students confirm with the net that the surface area is 42.

   Click Hide Net.

   Move the slider for height back to 1.

4. Repeat Step 3 with the width and length sliders to help students see that even though the shape is shown differently, it still has a surface area of 42 cm².

5. Move all sliders back to 1.

   Say: Let's look at the surface area of cubes.

   Ask: What do you know about cubes? All faces are square, and they all have the same area.

   Ask: How many faces does a cube have? 6

   Explain that since all faces of a cube have the same area, they can multiply the area of one face by 6 to get the total surface area. Students saw this with the single cube.

   Move all sliders to 10 to show that this also applies to larger cubes.

   Click Show Net to confirm that there are 6 faces with 100 units on each face, making a total surface area of 600 cm².

6. Have students make a cube with length, width, and height equal to 2.

   Ask: What is the area of each face? 4 cm²

   Ask: How would you find the surface area of the entire cube? multiply 4 × 6 to get 24 cm²

7. Repeat Step 6 with cubes that have side length of 3 through 9. Students don't need to do the calculations, just say what they would be.

   Say: The side lengths of a cube are all the same. Let's see how to find the surface area of a figure when the side lengths are all different.

8. Have students make a shape with a length of 5, a width of 3, and a height of 2.

   Remind students that this shape is called a rectangular prism.

   Ask: How many faces does this figure have? 6

   Ask: Which faces are the same? the top and bottom, the front and back, and the left and right

   Ask: What is the surface area of the top? 5 × 3 = 15

   Ask: What is the surface area of the front? 3 × 2 = 6

   Ask: What is the surface area of the face on the right? 2 × 5 = 10

   Ask: How would you find the total surface area? Add 15 + 15 for the top and bottom, add 6 + 6 for the front and back, and add 10 + 10 for the left and right faces. 15 + 15 + 6 + 6 + 10 + 10 = 62

   Click Show Net so students can match their calculation to the picture.

Tips

Allow students to use Centimeter Grid Paper to sketch each face or base-10 ones cubes to model each solid.

9. Have student find the surface area of another rectangular prism of their choice that has no two dimensions the same.

10. Finally have students make a rectangular prism with length and width the same but height different. Guide students to notice that when two dimensions are the same, two surface areas are squares and the other four surfaces have the same area. Click Show Net to confirm this. To show that this is always the case, have students change which two dimensions are the same.

11. As time permits, click Menu and then click Find the Surface Area to do some challenge problems.

TRY IT Cover the Solid

Objectives

- Estimate or determine the number of squares required to cover the area of a solid figure.

Students will practice estimating and determining the number of squares needed to cover the area of cubes and other rectangular solids. Have students turn to the Cover the Solid activity page in their Activity Book and read the directions with them.

Students should copy the problems from the Activity Book into their Math Notebook as necessary and solve them there.

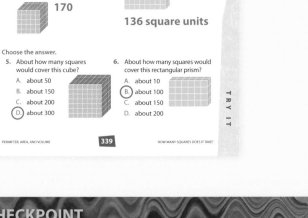

How Many Squares Does It Take?
Cover the Solid

Solve.
1. Connor wants to completely cover this rectangular prism using square tiles.
   How many square tiles does Connor need?   58

2. Josh wants to completely cover this rectangular prism using square tiles.
   How many square tiles does Josh need?   92

3. Clancy wants to completely cover this cube using square tiles.
   How many square tiles does Clancy need?   170

4. Find the number of square units it takes to cover this solid.
   136 square units

Choose the answer.
5. About how many squares would cover this cube?
   A. about 50
   B. about 150
   C. about 200
   D. about 300

6. About how many squares would cover this rectangular prism?
   A. about 10
   B. about 100
   C. about 150
   D. about 200

PERIMETER, AREA, AND VOLUME   **339**   HOW MANY SQUARES DOES IT TAKE?

TRY IT

CHECKPOINT

Objectives

- Estimate or determine the number of squares required to cover the area of a solid figure.

Students will complete an online Checkpoint. If necessary, read the directions, problems, and answer choices to students and help them with keyboard or mouse operations.

How Many Cubes Does It Take?

Lesson Overview

LEARN Use Blocks to Model Volume	20 minutes	OFFLINE
LEARN Strategies to Find Volume	15 minutes	ONLINE
TRY IT Measure Volume	15 minutes	OFFLINE
CHECKPOINT	10 minutes	ONLINE

▶ Lesson Objectives

Estimate or determine the number of cubes required to fill a solid figure.

▶ Prerequisite Skills

Use a nonstandard unit to compare the volumes of two or more objects.

▶ Content Background

Students will learn about the volume of rectangular solids by finding how many cubes are needed to fill a solid figure.

Volume is measured in cubic units (cubic centimeters, cubic inches, or just cubic units when the cubes are not a standard measure). Students will not use a rule or formula to find the volume of objects, but will be encouraged to count cubes or find their own strategy to determine volume.

Students may recognize that when finding the volume of rectangular solids, they can find the number of cubes on the bottom layer and then repeatedly add that amount for each layer. They will learn that they can use multiplication instead of repeated addition.

Students will explore solids in which not every cube is visible and will use their knowledge of three-dimensional shapes to figure out how many cubes will fill the solid. They will label volume with cubic centimeters or cubic units. Students will also learn to write the standard notation of cubic units as u^3. At this level, students will not be taught why this notation is used but will understand it as a shortcut to writing cubic units.

▶ Common Errors and Misconceptions

- Students might think of all measurements as length. For example, they might perceive area as a distance—something that they can measure with a ruler. Consequently, they often measure the perimeter (the path around the figure).

- Students might believe that it doesn't matter if units are all identical. They may believe that if they can fill a region (such as a box) with units of measure (such as beans), it doesn't matter if some of the units of measure (beans) are of a different size. They will simply count the number of objects contained within the region (box).

Materials to Gather

SUPPLIED

base-10 blocks

blocks – 0 (12 each of three colors)

Measure Volume activity page

ALSO NEEDED

tape, clear – $\frac{3}{4}$ in. wide

scissors, adult

▶ Advance Preparation

Use base-10 ones cubes and tape to make three 3 by 3 arrangements of ones cubes that stay together. Place a piece of tape down with the sticky side up and place a ones cube in the center of the tape. Notice that the tape is wide enough to place cubes on either side of the first cube such that all three will stick to the tape even though they're each held by just a small amount of tape. Lay down a new piece of tape right next to the first one and make another line of three cubes. Repeat this step so that you have a 3 by 3 arrangement of cubes. Trim any tape that extends beyond the edge of the cubes. Make two more sets, and then stack the three sets into a 3 by 3 by 3 cube.

LEARN Use Blocks to Model Volume

OFFLINE 20 min

Objectives

- Estimate or determine the number of cubes required to fill a solid figure.

Students will learn how to find the volume of an object by finding how many cubes it takes to fill an object. They will model volume with base-10 blocks and cubes.

Gather the blocks, the base-10 ones cubes, and the 3 by 3 by 3 cube you made.

1. Tell students they have learned that perimeter, or the distance around the outside of an object, is measured in centimeters (cm), inches (in.), or other units of length (u). They have also learned that the area of a rectangular shape is measured in square units (u²).

2. Tell students they will explore how many cubes it takes to fill rectangular prisms. Show students the 3 by 3 by 3 cube made from the ones cubes. Have students estimate how many small ones cubes make up the larger cube. Try to get students to estimate without calculating. If they hesitate, ask if they think the number is greater than 10? Greater than 20?

3. Have students separate the three layers and count each layer to figure out how many small cubes make up the larger cube. Since each layer has 9 cubes, there are 27, or 3 × 9, cubes in the three layers.

4. Have students put the layers back together to make the larger cube.

5. Explain to students that they have measured the volume of water by using cups and gallons, and milliliters and liters. When they measure the volume of solid figures, they measure the volume in cubic units. Show students the base-10 ones cube and explain that it has a volume of 1 cubic centimeter. Show students the 3 by 3 by 3 cube and explain that it has a volume of 27 cubic centimeters because it takes 27 one-centimeter cubes to fill the larger cube. Model how to write the volume in three ways: 27 cubic centimeters; 27 cubic cm; 27 cm³. Explain to students that they use a small 3 to indicate cubic units.

6. Take one layer off the cube.

   Ask: How many cubes make up this shape? 18

   Explain that the volume of the shape is 18 cm³. Have students say the volume to be sure they are expressing the units correctly.

7. Put the three layers side by side into one long, flat prism that is 3 by 9 by 1.

   Ask: What is the volume of this prism? 27 cm³

   Have students make a tower with the three layers that is 3 by 3 by 3.

   Ask: What is the volume of this tower? 27 cm³

8. Show students a base-10 hundreds flat.

   Ask: How many ones cubes make up the hundreds flat? 100

   Ask: What is the volume of the hundreds flat? 100 cubic centimeters or 100 cm³

9. Have students look at the base-10 thousands cube. Have them use the hundreds flats to show how many small ones cubes it would take to fill the thousands cube. Students should stack 10 hundreds flats to show that there are 10 hundred or 1,000 ones cubes in one thousands cube.

10. Use 6 tens rods to make a rectangular prism by laying 3 tens rods next to each other and then putting 3 more on top to make a 3 by 10 by 2 prism. Have students find the volume in cubic centimeters. Explain to students that when the blocks are stacked, they may not be able to see all the centimeter cubes. However, they can use what they know about solids to determine how many cubes are in each layer and the entire solid.

11. Explain to students that units can be any size, as long as they identify what units they are using. For example, they can make shapes with cubes (O blocks) and since cubes are not a standard measure, they will call it 1 cubic unit, or 1 unit³, or simply 1 u³.

12. Have students snap together a row of 4 cubes, all the same color.

    Ask: What is the volume of the shape? 4 u³

    Have students make two more rows the same length and the same color. Put the three rows together to make a flat rectangular solid that is 3 by 4 by 1.

    Ask: What is the volume of the shape? 12 u³

    This shape will become one layer of a new solid. Make two more layers like the first layer. Each layer should be a different color. Put all the layers together to form a solid figure.

    Ask: What is the volume of this solid? 36 u³

    Ask: What multiplication sentence did you use to find the answer?
    3 × 12 = 36

LEARN Strategies to Find Volume

ONLINE 15 min

Students will use different strategies to estimate and determine the number of cubes needed to fill a rectangular solid.

Objectives

- Estimate or determine the number of cubes required to fill a solid figure.

DIRECTIONS FOR USING THE VOLUME LAB LEARNING TOOL

1. Click Explore.

   Say: Look at the single cube. This is 1 cubic centimeter. Abbreviate it by writing cm³. (Point to the 1 cm³.) You have seen that volume is the number of cubes that fill a space. You will use this tool to make rectangular prisms and see the volume. The volume of this cube is 1 cubic centimeter.

2. Use the sliders to make a prism that has length 4, width 5, and height 1.

   Ask: How many cubes make up this prism? 20

   Ask: What multiplication problem is shown by this shape? 4 × 5 or 5 × 4

Ask: If you added a second layer, how many cubes would there be? 40

Have the students move the slider for height to 2.

Ask: If you keep adding layers, how many more cubes will you add with each layer? 20

Have students change the height to 3, then 4, and then 5. Have them count by 20s with each layer to state the volume. Continue to 10, where the volume will be 200.

Have students check Expand to see all the layers.

Uncheck Expand to have the layers go back to a solid prism.

3. Have students make prisms of their choice and explain how to find the volume. Encourage them to look for shortcuts. For example, if a prism has dimensions of 3, 4, and 5, students could look at the top layer and say the each layer has 12 cubes and there are 5 layers, so the volume is $5 \times 12 = 60$ cm^3. But they might also notice that the front layer has 20 cubes and there are 3 layers going toward the back, so the volume is $3 \times 20 = 60$ cm^3. Either way you get the same answer, but the calculation is easier the second way.

4. When students confidently understand volume, click Menu and click Find the Volume to try some challenge problems.

TRY IT Measure Volume

OFFLINE
15 min

Objectives

Students will practice finding the volume of objects. Have them turn to the Measure Volume activity page in their Activity Book and read the directions with them.

Students should copy the problems from the Activity Book into their Math Notebook as necessary and solve them there.

- Estimate or determine the number of cubes required to fill a solid figure.

How Many Cubes Does It Take?
Measure Volume

Find the volume.

1. 16 u^3

2. 72 u^3

Solve.

3. Jack stacked these cubes. How many cubes did he use? 14

4. Look at how Allison stacked her cubes. How many cubes did she use? 36

Choose the answer.

5. The picture at right shows 1 cube. John used the cubes to build the shape below. How many cubes are in the shape John built?
   A. 24
   B. 20
   C. 14
   D. 12

6. The picture at right shows 1 cube. Laura built the wall with the cubes. How many cubes did Laura use to build the wall?
   A. 7
   B. 14
   C. 21
   D. 28

7. Marcus is using blocks to make a cube. If each cube is solid and has no holes, how many blocks did Marcus use?
   A. 16
   B. 48
   C. 64
   D. 96

8. What is the volume in cubic centimeters of the figure shown at right?
   A. 15 cm^3
   B. 21 cm^3
   C. 35 cm^3
   D. 105 cm^3

   = 1 cubic centimeter

9. Matilda is filling a box with 1-inch sugar cubes. She filled the bottom with one layer as shown in the picture at right.
   When she completely fills the box, how many sugar cubes will be in the box?
   A. 12
   B. 19
   C. 84
   D. 133

TRY IT

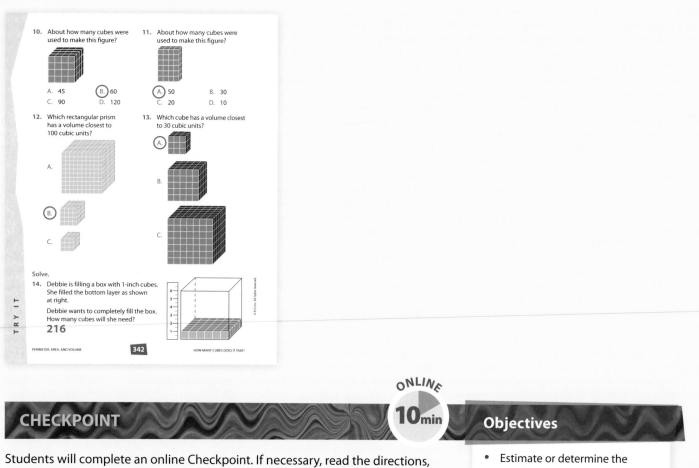

10. About how many cubes were used to make this figure?

A. 45   (B.) 60
C. 90   D. 120

11. About how many cubes were used to make this figure?

(A.) 50   B. 30
C. 20   D. 10

12. Which rectangular prism has a volume closest to 100 cubic units?

A.

(B.)

C.

13. Which cube has a volume closest to 30 cubic units?

(A.)

B.

C.

Solve.

14. Debbie is filling a box with 1-inch cubes. She filled the bottom layer as shown at right.

Debbie wants to completely fill the box. How many cubes will she need?

216

TRY IT

CHECKPOINT

ONLINE 10 min

Students will complete an online Checkpoint. If necessary, read the directions, questions, and answer choices to students and help them with keyboard or mouse operations.

Objectives

- Estimate or determine the number of cubes required to fill a solid figure.

Unit Review

UNIT REVIEW Look Back	10 minutes	ONLINE
UNIT REVIEW Checkpoint Practice	50 minutes	ONLINE
⇶ UNIT REVIEW Prepare for the Checkpoint		

▶ Unit Objectives

This lesson reviews the following objectives:

- Determine the perimeter of a polygon with whole-number side lengths.
- Use multiplication or division to solve a story problem involving rectangular area.
- Estimate or determine the number of squares required to cover the area of a solid figure.
- Estimate or determine the number of cubes required to fill a solid figure.

▶ Advance Preparation

In this lesson, students will have an opportunity to review previous activities in the Perimeter, Area, and Volume unit. Look at the suggested activities in Unit Review: Prepare for the Checkpoint online and gather any needed materials.

Materials to Gather

There are no materials to gather for this lesson.

UNIT REVIEW Look Back   **10**min   **Objectives**

Students will review key concepts from the unit to prepare for the Unit Checkpoint.

- Review unit objectives.

UNIT REVIEW Checkpoint Practice   **50**min   **Objectives**

Students will complete an online Checkpoint Practice to prepare for the Unit Checkpoint. If necessary, read the directions, problems, and answer choices to students. Have students answer the problems on their own. Review any missed problems with students.

- Review unit objectives.

⇶ UNIT REVIEW Prepare for the Checkpoint

What you do next depends on how students performed in the previous activity, Unit Review: Checkpoint Practice. If students had difficulty with any of the problems, complete the appropriate review activity listed in the table online.

Unit Checkpoint

| **UNIT CHECKPOINT** Online | 60 minutes | **ONLINE** |

▶ Unit Objectives

This lesson assesses the following objectives:

- Determine the perimeter of a polygon with whole-number side lengths.
- Use multiplication or division to solve a story problem involving rectangular area.
- Estimate or determine the number of squares required to cover the area of a solid figure.
- Estimate or determine the number of cubes required to fill a solid figure.

Materials to Gather

There are no materials to gather for this lesson.

UNIT CHECKPOINT Online

ONLINE 60min

Students will complete the Unit Checkpoint online. If necessary, read the directions, problems, and answer choices to students and help them with keyboard or mouse operations.

Objectives

- Assess unit objectives.

Semester Review

Lesson Overview

SEMESTER REVIEW Look Back	10 minutes	**ONLINE**
SEMESTER REVIEW Checkpoint Practice	50 minutes	**ONLINE**
▶▶ **SEMESTER REVIEW** Prepare for the Checkpoint		

▶ Semester Objectives

This lesson reviews the following objectives:

- Use the order of operations to evaluate an expression.
- Determine whether addition, subtraction, multiplication, or division is the appropriate operation to use to solve a story problem and solve the problem.
- Solve a story problem involving two or more operations.
- Identify, describe, and classify a polygon according to the number of its sides.
- Identify and describe common solid geometric figures.
- Identify decimal place values through thousandths.
- Solve a story problem involving multiplication or division of money amounts in decimal notation.
- Explain that a fraction can be used to represent part of a set, the relationship of a part to a whole, and a rational number on the number line.
- Compare and order unit fractions, such as $\frac{1}{4}$, and fractions with like denominators, such as $\frac{2}{5}$ and $\frac{4}{5}$, by using objects or sketches.
- Explain that a simple fraction and a decimal amount can represent the same quantity.
- Identify whether specific events are certain, likely, unlikely, or impossible.
- Summarize and display the results of a probability experiment in a clear and organized way.
- Estimate and measure the length of an object to the nearest centimeter.
- Estimate the length of an object to the nearest $\frac{1}{2}$ inch and measure the length to the nearest $\frac{1}{4}$ inch.
- Determine elapsed time to the nearest minute.
- Write a simple unit conversion, such as inches to feet, as an expression or an equation.
- Analyze a story problem by identifying the question, recognizing relevant information, and developing a solution strategy.
- Use estimation to predict a solution to a story problem and to determine whether calculations are reasonable.
- Explain mathematical reasoning in a story problem by using words, numbers, symbols, charts, graphs, tables, diagrams, or models.
- Determine the perimeter of a polygon with whole-number side lengths.

Materials to Gather

There are no materials to gather for this lesson.

- Use multiplication or division to solve a story problem involving rectangular area.
- Estimate or determine the number of squares required to cover the area of a solid figure.
- Estimate or determine the number of cubes required to fill a solid figure.
- Identify attributes of isosceles, equilateral, and right triangles.
- Identify attributes of parallelograms, rectangles, and squares.
- Solve a story problem involving addition or subtraction of money amounts in decimal notation.
- Solve and simplify an addition or subtraction problem involving fractions with like denominators.
- Tell time to the nearest minute.
- Use a simple unit conversion, such as centimeters to meters, to solve a problem.

▶ Advance Preparation

In this lesson, students will have an opportunity to review previous activities from the semester. Look at the suggested activities in Semester Review: Prepare for the Checkpoint online and be prepared to gather any needed materials.

SEMESTER REVIEW Look Back

ONLINE
10min

Objectives

- Review semester objectives.

As students prepare to complete the semester, they should refresh their knowledge of the math they have learned thus far. You may notice that some of the objectives in the Semester Review are not necessarily included in the Semester Checkpoint. Some of these concepts are particularly important to review in order to be successful with the upcoming topics students will encounter, and others contribute to a greater understanding of the concepts that are being assessed. Therefore, a complete review of the objectives in this lesson is recommended.

To review, students will play a Super Genius game. If students answer a problem incorrectly, the correct answer will display. Be sure to help students understand why the answer is correct before students move on to the next problem. If they miss several problems, have students play the game again.

SEMESTER REVIEW Checkpoint Practice

ONLINE
50min

Objectives

- Review semester objectives.

Students will complete an online Checkpoint Practice to prepare for the Semester Checkpoint. If necessary, read the directions, questions, and answer choices to students. Have students answer the problems on their own. Review any missed problems with students.

➲ SEMESTER REVIEW Prepare for the Checkpoint

What you do next depends on how students performed in the previous activity, Semester Review: Checkpoint Practice. If students had difficulty with any of the problems, complete the appropriate review activity listed in the table online.

Because there are many concepts to review, consider using the Your Choice day to continue preparing for the Semester Checkpoint.

Semester Checkpoint

SEMESTER CHECKPOINT Online   60 minutes · **ONLINE**

▶ Semester Objectives

This lesson assesses the following objectives:

- Use the order of operations to evaluate an expression.
- Determine whether addition, subtraction, multiplication, or division is the appropriate operation to use to solve a story problem and solve the problem.
- Solve a story problem involving two or more operations.
- Identify, describe, and classify a polygon according to the number of its sides.
- Identify and describe common solid geometric figures.
- Solve a story problem involving multiplication or division of money amounts in decimal notation.
- Explain that a fraction can be used to represent part of a set, the relationship of a part to a whole, and a rational number on the number line.
- Compare and order unit fractions, such as $\frac{1}{4}$, and fractions with like denominators, such as $\frac{2}{5}$ and $\frac{4}{5}$, by using objects or sketches.
- Identify whether specific events are certain, likely, unlikely, or impossible.
- Summarize and display the results of a probability experiment in a clear and organized way.
- Estimate and measure the length of an object to the nearest centimeter.
- Estimate the length of an object to the nearest $\frac{1}{2}$ inch and measure the length to the nearest $\frac{1}{4}$ inch.
- Write a simple unit conversion, such as inches to feet, as an expression or an equation.
- Analyze a story problem by identifying the question, recognizing relevant information, and developing a solution strategy.
- Use estimation to predict a solution to a story problem and to determine whether calculations are reasonable.
- Explain mathematical reasoning in a story problem by using words, numbers, symbols, charts, graphs, tables, diagrams, or models.
- Determine the perimeter of a polygon with whole-number side lengths.
- Use multiplication or division to solve a story problem involving rectangular area.
- Estimate or determine the number of squares required to cover the area of a solid figure.
- Identify attributes of isosceles, equilateral, and right triangles.
- Identify attributes of parallelograms, rectangles, and squares.
- Solve a story problem involving addition or subtraction of money amounts in decimal notation.

Materials to Gather

There are no materials to gather for this lesson.

- Solve and simplify an addition or subtraction problem involving fractions with like denominators.
- Tell time to the nearest minute.
- Use a simple unit conversion, such as centimeters to meters, to solve a problem.

SEMESTER CHECKPOINT Online

ONLINE
60min

Objectives

- Assess semester objectives.

Students will complete the Semester Checkpoint online. If necessary, read the directions, problems, and answer choices to students and help them with keyboard or mouse operations.

Glossary

addend — one of the two or more numbers that are added to find a sum

algorithm — a step-by-step way to solve a problem

angle — a figure formed by two rays that share the same endpoint; the rays are called the sides of the angle

angle measure — the measure of degrees that one ray rotates from the other in an angle

approximate (v.) — to estimate an amount or total; to give an approximation or say that an amount is approximately some value

area — the amount of space on a flat surface, most often measured in square units

area model — a model for multiplication that shows the product of two factors as the total number of squares on a rectangular grid; one factor is the number of rows and the other factor is the number of columns

array — a pattern of objects or numbers placed in a rectangular formation of rows and columns

associative property — a rule that says no matter how you group three numbers to add them two at a time (or three numbers to multiply), the answer will not change

associative property of multiplication — a rule that says no matter how you group factors to multiply, the product will not change

attributes — characteristics of an object, such as number of sides or types of angles

base of a figure — the bottom face of a solid figure

boundary number — the upper or lower limit that is used to round a number to a given place value

capacity — a measure indicating an amount a container can hold

centimeter (cm) — a metric unit used to measure length; 1 centimeter $= \frac{1}{100}$ of a meter

commutative property — a rule that says no matter what order you use to add two numbers (or multiply two numbers), the answer will not change

commutative property of multiplication — a rule that says no matter what order you use to multiply two factors, the product will not change

compare — to determine whether a number is less than, greater than, or equal to another number

cone — a solid figure with a circular base and a curved surface that forms a point, or vertex, at the top

cube — a solid figure with 6 square faces, 8 vertices, and 12 edges

cubic centimeter — a cube that is 1 cm on each side; a measure of volume

cubic foot — a cube that is 1 ft on each side; a measure of volume

cubic inch — a cube that is 1 in. on each side; a measure of volume

cubic unit — a cube that is 1 unit on each side; a measure of volume

cup (c) — the English, or customary, unit for measuring capacity that equals 8 fl oz

cylinder — a solid figure with 2 circular faces that are the same size and have a curved surface between them

decimal — a number written with a decimal point; sometimes called a decimal fraction

decimal notation — a way of writing numbers or money amounts using a decimal point and place values that follow

decimal place value — one of the place values that follow the decimal point in a number, such as tenths or thousandths

decimal point — the point in a decimal number that separates a whole number from the decimal (or fraction) part

degree — a unit used to measure angles

degree of accuracy — the place value that is to be used to report an answer, such as in tens or hundredths

denominator — the number in a fraction that is below the fraction bar

difference — the answer to a subtraction problem

digit — any one of the numerals 0, 1, 2, 3, 4, 5, 6, 7, 8, or 9

divide — to share equally or group an amount into equal parts

dividend — the number to be divided; the dividend divided by the divisor equals the quotient

division — an operation to share equally or group an amount into equal parts

division by 1 — the process of dividing a number by 1; the quotient equals the original number

division symbol (÷) — the symbol that signals division, which is the process of sharing equally or grouping an amount into equal parts

divisor — the number that divides the dividend; the dividend divided by the divisor equals the quotient

edge — a line segment or curve where two surfaces of a solid figure meet

elapsed time — the amount of time between a beginning time and an ending time

English system of measurement — a system of measurement using such units as inches, feet, and miles for length; quarts and gallons for capacity; and ounces and pounds for weight; this system is sometimes referred to as the customary system

equal groups — a type of multiplication or division problem that includes groups that each have the same amount or value

equal measures — a type of multiplication or division problem that uses the same measurement, such as centimeters, over and over

equal sharing — a type of division problem that shares among equal groups or creates equal groups; same as equal groups

equals symbol (=) — a symbol between two values that says the values show exactly the same amount

equilateral — having equal sides, such as an equilateral triangle or equilateral pentagon

equilateral triangle — a triangle that has all sides equal in length

equivalent fractions — fractions that name the same amount, such as $\frac{1}{2}$ and $\frac{3}{6}$

equivalent measures — measures that are equal, such as 12 in. and 1 ft

estimate (n.) — a very good guess or rough calculation of an answer when the exact answer is not necessary

estimate (v.) — to make a very good guess or rough calculation of an answer when the exact answer is not necessary

even number — any whole number that has 0, 2, 4, 6, or 8 in the ones place

expanded form — a way to write a number that shows the place value of each of its digits; for example, $543 = 500 + 40 + 3$, or 5 hundreds + 4 tens + 3 ones

expression — one or more numbers and symbols that show a certain value, such as $2 + 3$, or $3 \times ?$, or $10 - 4 + 1$

face — a flat surface of a solid figure

factor — one of two or more numbers that are multiplied

fluid ounce (fl oz) — the English, or customary, unit for measuring capacity that equals $\frac{1}{8}$ of a c

foot (ft) — the English, or customary, unit for measuring length that equals 12 in.

fraction — a number that shows part of a set, a point on a number line, a part of a whole, a quotient, or a ratio

fraction bar — the line between the numerator and denominator of a fraction that can be read as "divided by"

fractions with like denominators — fractions that have the same denominator

fractions with unlike denominators — fractions that have different denominators

function — a rule that changes an input number to an output number; for example, the rule "add 3" would change an input of 5 into an output of 8

gallon (gal) — the English, or customary, unit for measuring capacity that equals 128 fl oz or 4 qt

gram (g) — the basic metric unit of mass

greater-than symbol (>) — a symbol that shows that one amount is greater than another

grid — an arrangement of squares in rows and columns

hundredths — the place value immediately to the right of the tenths place; 10 thousandths = 1 hundredth and 10 hundredths = 1 tenth

identity property of multiplication — a rule that says that the product of a number and 1 is always the original number

improper fraction — a fraction whose numerator is greater than or equal to its denominator

inch (in.) — the basic English, or customary, unit for measuring length

intersecting lines — lines that cross at one point

inverse operations — opposite operations that undo each other; subtraction and addition are inverse operations; division and multiplication are inverse operations

inverse relationship — the relationship between operations that reverse or undo each other; addition and subtraction have an inverse relationship; multiplication and division have an inverse relationship

isosceles triangle — a triangle that has at least 2 sides equal in length; an equilateral triangle is a special type of isosceles triangle

kilogram (kg) — the metric unit for measuring mass that equals 1,000 g

kilometer (km) — the metric unit for measuring distance that equals 1,000 m

less-than symbol (<) — a symbol that shows that one amount is less than another

line — a straight path of points that goes on forever in both directions

line segment — a straight path of points that has endpoints at both ends; also called a segment

linear pattern — a pattern of numbers in which the value of the next number goes up or down by adding or subtracting the same amount each time, such as 3, 6, 9, 12, … or 10, 8, 6, 4, …

liquid volume — the amount of liquid a container will hold; the measure of liquid capacity

liter (L) — the basic metric unit for measuring capacity

mass — the amount of matter in an object; the amount of mass remains the same no matter where the object is, but the weight of an object can change depending on the pull of gravity on the object

measurement — the use of units to find out a size or quantity

meter (m) — the basic metric unit for measuring length

metric system of measurement — a measurement system with units based on powers of 10

mile (mi) — the English, or customary, unit for measuring distance that equals 5,280 ft milliliter (mL) — the metric unit for measuring capacity that equals $\frac{1}{1,000}$ L

mixed number — a whole number and a proper fraction that show a single amount

multiple — the product of a given number and any whole number

multiplication — an operation that is a shortcut for adding the same number over and over a certain number of times

multiplication fact family — a set of four related multiplication and division facts that use the same set of three numbers

multiplication facts — the set of multiplication problems with factors of 1 through 10; these problems should be memorized for easy computation

multiplication symbol (×) — a symbol indicating that factors will be multiplied, as in $4 \times 3 = 12$

multiply — to use the shortcut for adding the same number over and over a certain number of times

number sentence — a math sentence that shows that two expressions are less than, greater than, or equal to one another

numerator — the number in a fraction that is above the fraction bar

odd number — any whole number that has 1, 3, 5, 7, or 9 in the ones place

operation — the process of addition, subtraction, multiplication, or division; more operations will be taught later in math

order of operations — a set of rules that tells the correct order to use to solve a problem that has more than one operation

ounce (oz) — the basic English, or customary, unit for measuring weight as $\frac{1}{16}$ of a lb, and capacity as $\frac{1}{8}$ of a c

outcomes — the results that are possible in a probability experiment

parallel — lying in the same flat surface but not intersecting

parallel lines — lines in the same flat surface that never intersect

parallelogram — a quadrilateral with two pairs of parallel sides

partial product — the product of each place value when a multidigit factor is multiplied by a single-digit or multidigit factor; the sum of the partial products is the final product for the problem

perimeter — the distance around the edge of a shape

pint (pt) — the English, or customary, unit for measuring capacity that equals 16 fl oz or 2 c

place value — the value of a digit depending on its position, or place, in a number

place-value chart — a chart that shows the value of each digit in a number

place-value mat — a mat with columns showing place values (ones, tens…); used with corresponding base-10 blocks

place-value period — a grouping of three digits separated by commas in numbers greater than 999; for example, the number 234,567 has two place-value periods shown

plane figure — a flat shape with only two dimensions: length and width

polygon — a plane shape made of 3 or more straight sides that separate the inside of the shape from the outside

pound (lb) — the English, or customary, unit for measuring weight that equals 16 oz

predict an outcome — to observe a pattern of events to help determine future events

prism — a solid figure that has two congruent, polygon-shaped bases, and other faces that are all rectangles probability — the branch of math that measures the chances of events happening

product — the answer to a multiplication problem

quadrilateral — a polygon with 4 sides

quart (qt) — the English, or customary, unit for measuring capacity that equals 32 fl oz or 2 pt

quotient — the answer to a division problem; the dividend divided by the divisor equals the quotient

ray — a straight path of points that has an endpoint at one end and goes on forever from that endpoint

reasonableness — the sense that an answer is correct, given the facts

reasoning — the series of thoughts and steps used to understand a problem, create a plan of solution, solve a problem, and accurately explain the results

rectangle — a parallelogram with four 90° angles; a square is a special type of rectangle

rectangular prism — a solid figure with 6 faces that are rectangles

rectangular pyramid — a solid figure with a rectangle for a base and triangular side faces that meet in a point, or vertex

regrouping — to rename numbers from one place value to another, such as 1 ten and 3 ones = 13 ones

remainder — the amount left over after dividing evenly

repeated addition — to add the same addend over and over again

repeated subtraction — a method of dividing by repeatedly subtracting the divisor from the dividend until a value less than the divisor remains

right angle — an angle that measures exactly 90°

rotate — to turn a certain number of degrees

round (v.) — to change a number to the nearest place value asked in a problem; for example, rounding 532 to the nearest ten would be 530

scalene triangle — a 3-sided polygon with no sides equal in length

side — one of the line segments of a polygon

side of a polygon — one of the line segments that are the boundaries of a polygon

simplify — to create a value that is equal to another value but more simple to understand; for example, when you simplify 2 × 5, you get 10

skip count — to count by a number other than 1

solid figure — a figure with three dimensions: length, width, and height or depth

sphere — a solid figure that is perfectly round, like a ball

square — a parallelogram that has all sides equal in length and four 90° angles

square unit — a square with sides of a particular side length, such as a square meter, used to measure area

standard form — the usual way of writing a number by using digits

standard unit — a unit that is typically used in measurement, such as inches, centimeters, or kilograms

strategy — a technique used to solve a problem, such as working backward or drawing a diagram

sum — the answer to an addition problem

tablespoon (T) — the English, or customary, unit for measuring capacity that equals 3 t, $\frac{1}{2}$ fl oz, or $\frac{1}{16}$ c

teaspoon (t) — the English, or customary, unit for measuring capacity that equals $\frac{1}{3}$ T, $\frac{1}{6}$ fl oz, or $\frac{1}{48}$ c

tenths — the place value immediately to the right of the ones place after the decimal; 10 hundredths = 1 tenth and 10 tenths = 1

thousandths — the place value immediately to the right of the hundredths place after the decimal; 10 thousandths = 1 hundredth

triangular prism — a solid figure with a pair of identical parallel triangular bases joined by rectangular faces

triangular pyramid — a solid figure with a triangle for a base and triangular side faces that meet in a point, or vertex

vertex (plural: vertices) — the common endpoint of the two rays or segments that form an angle less than 180°; the vertex of a 180° angle is any point along the line

volume — the amount of space taken up by a three-dimensional object; measured in cubic units

weight — the measure of how heavy an object is, such as 10 lb

whole numbers — zero and the counting numbers (0, 1, 2, 3, 4, 5, 6, and so on)

yard (yd) — the English, or customary, unit for measuring length that equals 36 in. or 3 ft

zero property of multiplication — a rule that says that the product of a number and zero is always zero